Authors' Prof

Dr George Joseph started his research career at the Tata Institute of Fundamental Research (TIFR), Mumbai. He has been at the Space Applications Centre (SAC), Ahmedabad since 1973 where he was instrumental in developing a variety of electro-optical sensors for earth observation which were the first of their kind in India. He served SAC in various capacities including as its director from 1994–1998 and has made substantial contributions toward the realisation of various remote-sensing-related activities for shaping the long-term remote sensing programme of ISRO. He has served in a number of national and international committees/organisations—President of Technical Commission-1 of the International Society for Photogrammetry and Remote Sensing (ISPRS) during 1996–2000, Director of the Centre for Space Science and Technology Education in Asia and the Pacific (CSSTE–AP) affiliated to the United Nations during 2006–2009, to name a few.

He is a Fellow of a number of national academies and professional bodies and is a recipient of several awards, including the Padma Bhushan in 1999 for his outstanding contributions to remote sensing in India. (http://www.profgeorgej.com/)

Dr Jeganathan Chockalingam has been working in the field of geo-spatial Science and Technology since 1993, and possesses extensive teaching and research experience. He started his scientific career at the Regional Remote Sensing Service Centre (RRSSC, ISRO-Dehradun: 1993–1996), then worked at the Indian Institute of Remote Sensing (IIRS, Department of Space, Dehradun: 1996–2008) followed by the University of Southampton, United Kingdom (2008–2011). He has participated and contributed in the development of various RS–GIS educational programs at IIRS. He has also contributed significantly in many National Mission Projects (involving RS–GIS) of ISRO and developed many software packages (SPLAM, STAMP, ADAMS for ISRO, ICIMOD and IWMI, to mention a few). Since 2011, he has been Professor in the Department of Remote Sensing, Birla Institute of Technology, Mesra, Ranchi, India. His main research interests include geoinformatics, geostatistics, space–time dynamics of vegetation, natural resources monitoring and modelling, spatial decision modelling and downscaling.

He is the recipient of the Indian National Geospatial Award (2015) and Klaas Jan Beek Award (2003).

Authors' Profiles

Dr George Joseph started his research career at the Tata Institute of Fundamental Research (TIFR), Mumbai. He has been at the Space Applications Centre (SAC), Ahmedabad since 1973 where he was instrumental in developing a variety of electro-optical sensors for earth observation which were the first of their kind in India. He served SAC in various capacities including as its director from 1994 1998 and has made substantial contributions toward the realisation of various remote-sensing-related activities for shaping the long-term remote sensing programme of ISRO. He has served in a number of national and international committees organisations—President of Technical Commission I of the International Society for Photogrammetry and Remote Sensing (ISPRS) during 1996–2000, Director of the Centre for Space Science and Technology Education in Asia and the Pacific (CSSTE–AP) affiliated to the United Nations during 2006–2009 to name a few.

He is a fellow of a number of national academies and professional bodies and is a recipient of several awards including the Padma Bhushan in 1999 for his outstanding contributions to remote sensing in India (http://www.profgeorge.com/).

Dr Jeganathan Chockalingam has been working in the field of geo-spatial Science and Technology since 1993, and possesses extensive teaching and research experience. He started his scientific career at the Regional Remote Sensing Service Centre (RRSSC, ISRO-Dehradun; 1993–1996), then worked at the Indian Institute of Remote Sensing (IIRS, Department of Space, Dehradun; 1996–2008) followed by the University of Southampton, United Kingdom (2008–2011). He has participated and contributed in the development of various RS-GIS educational programs at IIRS. He has also contributed significantly to many National Mission Projects (involving RS-GIS) of ISRO) and developed many software packages (STIAM, STAMI, ADAMS for ISRO, ICIMOD and IWMI to mention a few). Since 2011, he has been Professor in the Department of Remote Sensing, Birla Institute of Technology, Mesra, Ranchi, India. His main research interests include geoinformatic, geostatistics, space-time dynamics of vegetation, natural resources monitoring and modelling, spatial decision modelling, and flow routing.

He is the recipient of the Indian National Geospatial Award (2013) and Klaas Jan Beek Award (2005).

FUNDAMENTALS OF
Remote Sensing
THIRD EDITION

George Joseph

Former Director, Space Applications Centre

ISRO, Ahmedabad

and

C Jeganathan

Professor, Department of Remote Sensing

BIT, Mesra

Universities Press

FUNDAMENTALS OF REMOTE SENSING
Third Edition

Universities Press (India) Private Limited

Registered Office
3-6-747/1/A & 3-6-754/1. Himayatnagar, Hyderabad 500 029 (Telangana), India
e-mail: info@universitiespress.com; *www.universitiespress.com*

Distributed by
Orient Blackswan Private Limited

Registered Office
3-6-752, Himayatnagar, Hyderabad 500 029 (Telangana), India

Other Offices
Bengaluru / Bhopal / Bhubaneshwar / Chennai / Guwahati / Hyderabad /
Jaipur / Kolkata / Lucknow / Mumbai / New Delhi / Noida / Patna / Vijayawada

© Universities Press (India) Private Limited 2018
First published 2003
Second Edition 2005
Reprinted 2007, 2008, 2009, 2011, 2013, 2016
Third Edition 2018

ISBN: 978-93-86235-46-6

Cover and book design
© Universities Press (India) Private Limited 2018

Typest in Minion Pro 11/13 by
Bookcraft Publishing Services (I) Pvt Ltd, Chennai

Printed at
Sriram Printing Press, Chennai 600116

Published by
Universities Press (India) Private Limited
3-6-747/1/A & 3-6-754/1, Himayatnagar,
Hyderabad 500 029, Telangana, India

501406

16112017

Foreword

The science of remote sensing has emerged as one of the most fascinating subjects over the past three decades. Earth observation from space through various remote sensing instruments has provided a vantage means of monitoring land surface dynamics, natural resources management, and the overall state of the environment itself. With the increasing concern for the earth's habitability due to the increasing anthropogenic interference with the natural systems, the emphasis on the study of earth system processes has also assumed greater importance. Deriving information about geophysical parameters from the satellite observed reflected or emitted radiation field with appropriate modelling and alogrithm development has indeed been a matter of great scientific importance. Advances in optics, devices, signal processing and materials have enabled a quantum jump in imaging and non-imaging sensor systems, providing information about the earth system, hitherto considered not possible, from satellites. Remote sensing science, thus, has been marked by significant progress in recent decades, spurred further by the advances in enabling tools such as the Geographical Information System, advanced image processing techniques, the Global Positioning System, as well as powerful computing systems. These rapid developments have pushed earth observation research and development to the forefront of scientific endeavour, challenging in the process, the traditional approaches followed in diverse fields such as meteorology, oceanography, hydrology and geology to name only a few. In the course of this progress, a multitude of new techniques and concepts have been evolved, making it imperative for the professionals in the field to understand and absorb these for their effective functioning.

Obviously, the emergence of such a broad, interdisciplinary field of study calls for a complete understanding of the spectrum of systems involved. With this in mind, it is strongly felt that there is a compelling need to provide students and other professionals, with a basic understanding of remote sensing science, technology and applications in a simplified manner. I am glad that Dr George Joseph, who has more than three decades of direct involvement with remote sensing in the country, has taken keen interest in bringing out a reader-friendly book on the subject.

I am sure that this book, striking a good balance between the wide coverage and depth required at undergraduate and postgraduate levels will serve the needs of many universities offering courses in remote sensing and allied fields. I also fervently hope that the timely publication of this book covering all the relevant disciplines of remote sensing will provide a glimpse of the amazing achievements in this ever-galloping field. This book stands further testimony to the dedication and commitment of Dr George Joseph in spreading the information on the advances in remote sensing technology and applications for which he is well-known in this country.

Dr K Kasturirangan
Chairman
Indian Space Research Organisation
March, 2003
Bangalore

Preface to the Third Edition

Since the launch of the Second Edition of this popular book in 2005, there has been steady increase in the technology and applications of remote sensing; nevertheless, many of the fundamentals have substantially remained the same. Therefore, the content of the book is still very relevant since the objective of the book is to present the basic science, principles and concepts covering various aspects of remote sensing from data collection to end utilisation. This new edition presents material that has retained value since those early days, along with additional information to keep the readers informed of the emerging trends in the subject. Though the book is not specifically designed with any syllabus in mind, the content covers much more than required for an undergraduate course. It is gratifying to note that the book has been recommended as one of the textbooks in many universities in India. The contents are organised such that each successive chapter takes the reader to the next level to logically understand the subject.

The motivation to write the Third Edition comes from the feedback received from a number of users of the book, to add some topics that are not covered in the earlier edition. Therefore we have updated all chapters except chapters 2, 3, and 4 which primarily deal with the basic physics of the subject. In Chapter 6 newer developments in sensor technology have been added. In Chapter 7, a new topic – GPR – which has many applications in civil engineering and mine detection has been added. Newer application potential is added to Chapter 11, which includes, among others, desertification and archaeology. The other chapters have also been expanded with newer information that was not addressed earlier, which will further broaden the understanding of the subject.

This edition has a co-author—Prof. C Jeganathan, whose vast experience in research and teaching of remote sensing brings 'new blood' to the book. However, we have retained the style and format of the earlier edition where the thrust of the presentation is to present basic concepts in an easily comprehensible manner for students and practitioners from different disciplines.

One of the authors (GJ) is grateful to Mr A S Kiran Kumar, the present chairman of ISRO, for giving him an honorary position in ISRO, without which he could not have accomplished this task. He is thankful to Mr Tapan Misra the present director of Space Applications Centre (SAC) who extended the necessary facilities in the course of preparation for this edition.

We are grateful to a number of individuals who helped in various ways to complete this edition: Dr Ajai, Dr M B Rajani, Prof. P S Roy, Ankur Garg, S Manthira Moorthi, Smt. G Uma Devi, K L N Sastry, Dr A S Rajawat and Dr S S Ray are some of the scientists who provided inputs for some of the sections. Additions to the Third Edition were reviewed by a number of experts including Dr Senthil Kumar, Director IIRS, Prof. A Jayaraman, Director NARL, Dr R Chandrakanth, Head, Image Processing Division, ADRIN, Dr R P Singh, S A C, Abhineet Shyam , Dr V S Rathore, BIT, Mr Saptarshi Mondal, BIT and others. Ashish Soni helped in making some of the line drawings. We thankfully acknowledge their valuable contributions.

Any omissions in mentioning contributions to this endeavour are not intentional but inadvertent. Our special thanks to Ashok Gehlot for the secretarial assistance and for the cover design.

I (GJ) would like to thank Mr Madhu Reddy, Universities Press Pvt Ltd, for having published the First Edition of this book in 2003 and his persuasion to upgrade the content which resulted in the Second Edition of the book in 2005 and this Third Edition. We also extend our thanks to the editor Dr Gita S Dattatri, whose excellent editing has given the content of the book a new look.

Our families need special appreciation for their patient understanding and support during the preparation of this edition.

George Joseph
Former Director, Space Applications Centre
ISRO, Ahmedabad
(http://www.profgeorgej.com/)

C Jeganathan
Professor, Department of Remote Sensing
BIT, Mesra

Preface to the Second Edition

It is gratifying to note that the book *Fundamentals of Remote Sensing* has been well accepted by professionals, students and teaching faculty. I have also received a number of comments and suggestions on the First Edition. I have tried to incorporate some of them in the Second Edition.

Major additions are in Chapter 11, dealing with the applications of remote sensing. Four more themes have been added. Some basic concepts of advanced classification techniques have been added in Chapter 10. The latest advancement in the IRS series has also been discussed. In order to benefit those who are approaching the subject for the first time, a list of acronyms and abbreviations has been added.

I am grateful to many of my colleagues in ISRO/DOS for helping me with these additional material for the second edition, especially, Dr (Mrs) Anjali Bahuguna and Dr SR Nayak (coastal management), Dr RM Dwivedi (marine fisheries), Dr AV Kulkarni (snow and glacier studies), Dr JK Garg (wetland), Dr B Karthikeyan, Dr A Senthilkumar and Dr R Krishnan for the advanced classification system. I also thankfully acknowledge the pains taken by Dr Ajai and Dr SR Nayak for critically going through the manuscript. However, the list is not complete. I thankfully acknowledge the secretarial assistance of Shri A V Rajesh and for generating all the line drawings on the computer.

The field of remote sensing is diverse, dynamic and evolving. It is not possible to cover exhaustively in one book all the topics presented here. I have made my best effort to bring out the fundamental concepts, covering all areas of remote sensing in a manner which can be understood by those who are beginning to learn the subject. Please continue to send me your feedback (*josephgeor@yahoo.com*).

George Joseph

Preface to the First Edition

Since the launch of LANDSAT 1, there has been a rapid growth in the science, technology and applications of remote sensing. In order to keep up with the requirement of increased trained manpower in this specialised area, a number of universities and colleges have introduced remote sensing as a separate postgraduate course or as an optional subject. Remote sensing technology and application requires scientists/engineers to cut across various disciplines. This book is an attempt to present the fundamental concepts covering various stages of remote sensing from data collection to end utilisation, which could be appreciated by the reader irrespective of the discipline from which he/she has graduated. I have tried to explain the physical principles on which remote sensing is based, without getting into complicated mathematics. The thrust is to make the concepts clear, in as simple and comprehensive a manner as possible. The book is an outcome of my numerous lectures over the past three decades, at various training programmes conducted in India. It is primarily written for those students who would like to get a basic understanding of remote sensing, with which they can pursue further in-depth studies.

The material is organised into eleven chapters. Chapter 1 presents in a nutshell what remote sensing is and sets the tone for further reading. Chapter 1 is expected to give the reader an 'end-to-end' idea of remote sensing. It also gives a historic perspective and the current status of remote sensing. Chapter 2 explains the properties of electromagnetic radiation of relevance to remote sensing. Since data collection in remote sensing is primarily a measurement of radiance, the third chapter gives an account of radiometry. The fourth chapter presents the physical process leading to various signatures based on which targets are identified. Chapters 5, 6 and 7 deal with sensors used for collection of remote sensing data. Chapter 8 highlights the capabilities and limitations of various platforms to carry the remote sensing sensors. Chapter 9 discusses the process involved in generating data products, which is used for data analysis. Chapter 11 is devoted to the application potential of remote sensing and the role of Geographical Information System (GIS) in decision-making. At the end of each chapter, a reference to further reading material including relevant websites is provided. The five appendices complement and supplement the information provided in the main text. A large number of references to original work are given for those interested in further studies.

Some of the details are given in boxes, which could be omitted on first reading without loss of continuity, but could be of use for further in-depth study. Since this book is written for beginners, for easy reading I have deliberately repeated certain statements/concepts in subsequent chapters.

I hope those interested in pursuing studies in remote sensing will find this book useful in understanding the basic concepts. I solicit comments and suggestions from the readers (*josephgeor@yahoo.com*).

Information taken from other sources has been fully acknowledged and all efforts have been made to obtain permission from authors and publishers. If any information has been used without permission from proper authorities, the lapse, which is not intentional is regretted, and shall be corrected as soon as it is brought to the notice of the author and publisher.

I am grateful to a number of my colleagues in the Indian Space Research Organisation and the Department of Space for meticulously going through the manuscript and giving valuable suggestions. I am particularly grateful to Dr J V Thomas of the Earth Observation Programme Office, Bangalore, who has critically gone through the drafts of all the chapters and given very useful comments. The secretarial assistance provided by Shri M N Narayanan during the initial phase and later by Shri A V Rajesh is gratefully acknowledged. Shri Rajesh needs to be complemented for generating most of the line drawings on the computer and for preparing the manuscript with dedication. Finally, it is a pleasure for me to acknowledge the sustained encouragement I received from my wife Mercy for completing this book.

George Joseph

Contents

Foreword   *v*

Preface to the Third Edition   *vii*

Preface to the Second Edition   *ix*

Preface to the First Edition   *xi*

1. Introduction   **1**

   1.1   Sun and Atmosphere   2

   1.2   Concept of Signatures   3

        1.2.1   Multi-Spectral Concept   4

   1.3   Remote Sensing System   6

        1.3.1   Remote Sensors   6

        1.3.2   Platforms   8

        1.3.3   Data Products Generation   9

        1.3.4   Data Analysis   10

        1.3.5   End Utilisation   11

   1.4   Why Observe Earth from Space?   11

   1.5   Remote Sensing—A Historic Perspective   13

   1.6   Indian Remote Sensing Programme   16

   1.7   The Earth Observation Evolution—The Paradigm Shift   21

   1.8   Legal and Ethical Aspects   24

2. Electromagnetic Radiation   **27**

   2.1   Velocity of EM Radiation   29

   2.2   Polarisation   30

   2.3   Coherent Radiation   31

   2.4   Propagation of EM Waves from One Medium to Another   34

        2.4.1   Fresnel Relation for Reflection and Transmission   35

        2.4.2   Some More Wave Properties of EM Radiation   37

   2.5   Attenuation   37

        2.5.1   Absorption   38

        2.5.2   Scattering   38

   2.6   Quantum Nature of EM Radiation   39

   2.7   Thermal Radiation   40

        2.7.1   Emissivity   42

   2.8   Source of EM Radiation for Remote Sensing   45

3. Fundamentals of Radiometry   **47**

   3.1   Measurement Geometry—Concept of the Solid Angle   47

	3.2	Radiometric Quantities	49
	3.3	Surface Characteristics for Radiometric Measurements	53
	3.4	Observation Geometry in Remote Sensing	55
	3.5	Radiometric Measurement	58
	3.6	Scene Reflectance Measurement	60

4. Physical Basis of Signatures   **64**
	4.1	Signature in the Reflective OIR Region	65
		4.1.1 Vegetation	65
		4.1.2 Soil	77
		4.1.3 Water Bodies/Ocean	86
		4.1.4 Snow	94
	4.2	Thermal Infrared (TIR)	100
	4.3	Microwave Region	103
		4.3.1 Microwave Emission	104
		4.3.2 Microwave Scattering	111

5. Remote Sensors—An Overview   **129**
	5.1	Classification of Remote Sensors	129
	5.2	Selection of Sensor Parameters	129
	5.3	Spatial Resolution	130
	5.4	Spectral Resolution	138
		5.4.1 Location of Spectral Bands	141
	5.5	Radiometric Resolution	142
		5.5.1 Radiometric Quality	142
	5.6	Temporal Resolution	144
	5.7	Performance Specification	145

6. Optical–Infrared Sensors   **146**
	6.1	Quality of Image in Optical Systems	146
	6.2	Imaging Mode	153
	6.3	Photographic Camera	154
		6.3.1 Photographic Films	157
		6.3.2 Characterising Film	160
		6.3.3 Distortions in Photographs	162
	6.4	Television Cameras	164
	6.5	Opto-mechanical Scanners	166
		6.5.1 Scanning Systems	169
		6.5.2 Collecting Optics	171
		6.5.3 Spectral Dispersion System	172
		6.5.4 Detectors	174
	6.6	Opto-mechanical Scanners Operated from Satellites	182
		6.6.1 LANDSAT Multi-Spectral Sensors	182
		6.6.2 Opto-Mechanical Scanner from Geo-Stationary Orbit	186

	6.7	Pushbroom Cameras	188
	6.7.1	Principle of Operation of Pushbroom Camera	189
	6.7.2	Linear Array for Pushbroom Scanning	190
	6.7.3	Collecting Optics	195
	6.7.4	Pushbroom Cameras Operated from Satellite	196
	6.7.5	High Spatial Resolution Imaging Systems	208
	6.8	Hyper-spectral Imager	214
	6.8.1	The Scanner Approach	215
	6.8.2	Pushbroom Approach	217
	6.8.3	Wedge Imaging Spectrometer	217
	6.9	Hybrid Scanners	218
	6.10	Measuring the Third Dimension	219
	6.11	Image Quality Aspects	223
	6.11.1	Radiometric Considerations	223
	6.11.2	Geometric Quality	224
	6.12	On-Orbit Performance Evaluation	225

7. Microwave Sensors   **227**

	7.1	Antenna	228
	7.1.1	Paraboloid Antenna	230
	7.1.2	Horn Antenna	230
	7.1.3	Slotted Antenna	231
	7.1.4	Phased Arrays	232
	7.2	Passive Microwave Sensors	233
	7.2.1	Principle of Microwave Radiometry	234
	7.2.2	Radiometer Performance Parameters	235
	7.2.3	Total Power Radiometer	237
	7.2.4	Dicke Radiometer	238
	7.2.5	Satellite-Borne Microwave Radiometers	239
	7.2.6	Pushbroom and Synthetic Aperture Radiometer	242
	7.3	Active Microwave Sensors	243
	7.3.1	Altimeters	245
	7.4	Side Looking Radar	249
	7.4.1	Real Aperture Radar	249
	7.4.2	Synthetic Aperture Radar	254
	7.4.3	Image Quality in Radar Imagery	262
	7.4.4	Spaceborne SAR Systems	265
	7.5	Scatterometer	270
	7.6.	Ground Penetrating Radar	275
	7.6.1	GPR Instrument	276
	7.6.2	GPR Operation	278
	7.6.3	Performance Criteria	281

8. Platforms   **284**

| | 8.1 | Principles of Satellite Motion | 285 |

8.2	Locating a Satellite in Space	287
8.3	Types of Orbit	290
	8.3.1 Geosynchronous and Geostationary Orbits	291
	8.3.2 Sunsynchronous Orbit	292
	8.3.3 Viewing Geometry from Orbit	294
8.4	Orbital Perturbations	297
8.5	The Spacecraft	297
8.6	Global Navigation Satellite System (GNSS)	301

9. Data Reception and Data Products — **307**

9.1	Data Formats	307
9.2	Ground Segment Organisation	309
	9.2.1 Remote Sensing Satellite Data Reception Station at NRSC	311
9.3	Data Pre-Processing	312
	9.3.1 Sources of Errors in Received Data	312
	9.3.2 Georeferencing	317
9.4	Referencing Scheme	321
9.5	Data Product Generation	322
	9.5.1 Product Options	326
	9.5.2 Product Request	327
9.6	Data Products Output Medium	327
	9.6.1 Photoproduct	327
	9.6.2 Digital Products	329
9.7	Special Processing	334
	9.7.1 Contrast Enhancement	334
	9.7.2 Enhancement by Colour Coding	337
	9.7.3 Spatial Filtering	338
	9.7.4 Image Transforms	341
	9.7.5 Image Fusion	343

10. Data Analysis — **356**

10.1	Visual Image Analysis	356
10.2	Digital Classification	365
	10.2.1 Optimum Band Selection for Digital Classification	366
	10.2.2 Data Registration	369
	10.2.3 Classification Techniques	372
	10.2.4 Output Stage	389
10.3	Classification Accuracy	389

11. Applications of Remote Sensing for Earth Resources Management — **395**

11.1	Agriculture	396
	11.1.1 Crop Production Forecasting	396
	11.1.2 Multiple In-Season Crop Production Forecast	402
	11.1.3 Precision Farming	403
	11.1.4 Agricultural Drought Assessment	404

11.2	Forestry Application	406
	11.2.1 Type and Density Mapping	407
	11.2.2 Forest Cover Change	410
	11.2.3 Forest Status in India	410
11.3	Land Cover/Land Use Mapping	411
	11.3.1 Wastelands	412
	11.3.2 Urban Sprawl	412
11.4	Water Resources	414
11.5	Snow and Glacier	416
	11.5.1 Snow Studies	416
	11.5.2 Glacial Investigations	419
11.6	Wetland Management	424
	11.6.1 Remote Sensing of Wetland Ecosystems	426
	11.6.2 Wetland Inventory of India	426
11.7	Coastal Zone Management	430
	11.7.1 Coastal Zone Ecosystem	430
	11.7.2 Coastal Regulation Zone	432
	11.7.3 Use of Satellite Data for Coastal Management	433
	11.7.4 Integrated Coastal Zone Management	437
11.8	Marine Fisheries	437
	11.8.1 Introduction	437
11.9	Desertification	441
	11.9.1 Desertification Status Mapping	443
	11.9.2 Monitoring Change in Desertification Over a Period of Time	445
	11.9.3 Susceptibility to Desertification	446
	11.9.4 Desertification Mitigation	447
11.10	Archaeology	447
	11.10.1 Archaeological Signatures	448
	11.10.2 Data Collection and Processing	449
	11.10.3 Examples of RS in Archaeology	451
11.11	Remote Sensing for Earth System Science Studies	453
12.	**Geographical Information System (GIS)**	**456**
12.1	Data Model	458
12.2	Data Entry	462
12.3	Data Analysis and Modelling	464
12.4	A Practical Example—Urban Land Use Suitability	466
12.5	GIS in the Internet Era	468
12.6	Spatial Data Infrastructure	469
Colour Plates		**471**
Appendix 1	*Influence of Atmosphere on Remote Sensing*	491
	A1.1 Optical Depth and Visual Range	495

	A1.2	The Radiance Received by the Sensor	496
	A1.3	Effect of Turbulence	500
	A1.4	Partial Cloud Cover	501
	A1.5	Atmospheric Correction	501
		A1.5.1 Atmospheric Correction Over the Ocean in the OIR Region	502
		A1.5.2 Atmospheric Correction for Extraction of Sea Surface Temperature	503
Appendix 2	*Atmospheric Sounding*		506
	A2.1	Principle of Atmospheric Sounding	507
	A2.2	Limb Sounding	510
	A2.3	Absorption Techniques for Sounding	512
		A2.3.1 Solar Backscattering Observation	512
		A2.3.2 Occultation Methods	513
	A2.4	Active Sounding of Atmosphere	514
		A2.4.1 Backscatter LIDAR	514
		A2.4.2 Differential Absorption LIDAR (DIAL)	514
		A2.4.3 Raman Backscatter LIDAR	515
	A2.5	Sensors for Atmospheric Sounding	516
		A2.5.1 Spectral Selection Techniques	517
Appendix 3	*Decibels*		519
Appendix 4	*Map Projection*		521
	A4.1	Projection Geometries	523
Appendix 5	*Visual Interpretation*		529
Appendix 6	*Hyperspectral Image Analysis*		533
Appendix 7	*GNSS Remote Sensing*		544
	A7.1	GNSS Meteorology	545
		A7.1.1 GNSS Radio Occultation (GNSS RO)	545
		A7.1.2 GNSS Meteorology—Ground Based	549
	A7.2	GNSS Reflectommetrry (GNSS-R)	549
Appendix 8	*Acronyms*		552
References			559
Index			600

1 Introduction

Remote sensing is a recently coined term, for an activity each one of us has been carrying out since birth. Reading this book and hearing the sounds around you involve remote sensing. However, the associated energy in the two processes is different; in the case of seeing it is light energy while for hearing it is sound energy, the sensors being the eyes and ears respectively. These sensors are not in contact with the object that is being sensed. On the other hand, if we have to measure the body temperature using a clinical thermometer, the thermometer comes in contact with the body whose temperature is to be measured. We may call it *in situ* measurement. For remote sensing we may give the following generalised definition.

Remote sensing is the science of making inferences about objects from measurements, made at a distance, without coming into physical contact with the objects under study. That is, remote sensing refers to any method, which can be used to gather information about an object without actually coming in contact with it. In this context, any force field—acoustic, gravitational, magnetic, electromagnetic, and so on, could be used for remote sensing, covering various disciplines, extending from laboratory testing to astronomy. However, currently the term remote sensing is used commonly to denote identification of the features of the earth by detecting the characteristic electromagnetic radiation that is reflected/emitted by the earth system.

With extensive application of remote sensing for resource management, the definition used by the United Nations, (as part of the general assembly resolutions A/RES/41/65, 95th Plenary meeting, 3 December, 1986), seems to be more appropriate.

Remote sensing means sensing of the earth's surface from space by making use of the properties of electromagnetic waves emitted, reflected or diffracted by the sensed objects, for the purpose of improving natural resource management, land use and the protection of the environment.

Before we get to appreciate the profoundness of the scope of coverage of the subject, let us consider some daily experiences to understand the basic principle behind remote sensing. As mentioned earlier, visual perception of objects is the best example of remote sensing. We see an object by the light reflected by it. Here, the eye is the 'sensor', the head is the 'platform' on which the sensor is placed and the nervous system carries the information to the brain, which acts as an 'interpreter' for the identification of the object. In doing so, the brain recalls past experiences and completes the cycle of viewing and understanding. Let us consider a common experience. We all know that a papaya is ripe when it turns yellow. The following process takes place in leading us to this conclusion.

(i) Ripe papaya has a characteristic colour due to certain processes in the fruit.

(ii) We have been told by knowledgeable persons with previous experience that when papaya turns yellow, it is ripe.

(iii) This information is stored in our brain and comes in handy when we come across a similar situation.

(iv) When we see the characteristic colour of the skin of the fruit, this 'data' is compared with the information stored in our brain and if it matches we conclude that the fruit is ripe. (We cannot say whether it is sweet; that requires *in situ* sensing!)

Modern remote sensing is an extension of this natural phenomenon. However, apart from visible light, electromagnetic radiation extending from the ultraviolet to the far infrared and the microwave regions is also used for remote sensing of the earth resources. If the observation is made based on the electromagnetic radiation from the sun or self-emitted radiance, it is called *passive remote sensing*. It is also possible to produce electromagnetic radiation of a specific wavelength or band of wavelengths to illuminate the object or terrain. The interaction of this radiation can then be studied by sensing the scattered radiance from the target. This is called *active remote sensing*.

The basic process involved in remote sensing is the interaction (or emission) of the electromagnetic radiation with (from) matter. Electromagnetic radiation is made up of electric and magnetic fields and spans a large spectrum of wavelengths—from very short wavelength gamma rays (10^{-10} m) to long radio waves (10^6 m). The entire range of the electromagnetic radiation is called electromagnetic spectrum. Visible light occupies only a small portion of the electromagnetic spectrum extending from about 0.4 to 0.7 μm wavelength. While remote sensing may avail of a much broader part of the spectrum in comparison to what is useful for human eyes, the whole of the electromagnetic spectrum is not available for remote sensing for reasons that we may dwell upon at a later stage.

1.1 SUN AND ATMOSPHERE

The sun is the most important source of electromagnetic radiation used in passive optical remote sensing. The sun may be assumed to be a blackbody with surface temperature around 6000 K. The sun's radiation covers ultraviolet, visible, infrared and radio frequency regions. Maximum radiation occurs around 0.55 μm which is in the visible region. However, solar radiation reaching the surface of earth is modified by the atmospheric effects. All bodies at temperatures above absolute zero emit electromagnetic radiation at different wavelengths as per Planck's Law (Section 2.7). Hence, if the earth can be treated as a blackbody at 300 K, it emits electromagnetic radiation with a peak at around 9.5 μm. Thus during the day, if we observe the earth, we have solar radiation reflected by the earth's surface and the emission from the surface. Further, beyond about 5 μm, the radiation from the earth is mainly due to the emission process.

Solar radiation has to pass through the atmosphere before it interacts with the earth's surface. In passing through the atmosphere, the radiation is scattered and absorbed by gases and particulates. The strongest absorption occurs at wavelengths shorter than 0.3 μm primarily due to ozone. However, certain spectral regions of the electromagnetic radiation pass through the atmosphere without much attenuation. These are called *atmospheric windows*. Remote sensing of the earth's surface is generally confined to these wavelength regions: 0.4–1.3, 1.5–1.8, 2.2–2.6, 3.0–3.6, 4.2–5.0, 7.0–15.0 μm and 1 cm to 30 cm.

Even in the regions of atmospheric windows, the scattering by the atmospheric molecules and aerosols produces spatial redistribution of energy. The scattered/diffused radiance entering the field of view of a remote sensor, other than that from the target of interest, is called *path radiance*. The path radiance reduces the contrast of the image generated by the sensor, and thereby the visual 'sharpness' of the image is reduced. In addition, it corrupts the actual radiance leaving the target, that is characteristic to it. That is, the apparent radiance of the ground targets, as measured by the remote sensor, differs from the intrinsic surface radiance because of the intervening atmosphere, thus producing radiometric error. Since the aerosol concentration in the atmosphere varies with position and time, the amount of correction to be applied in order to remove the radiometric error, also varies. In principle, the additional radiance rendered by path radiance could be removed if the concentration and optical properties of the aerosol are known throughout the field of observation. A number of methodologies have been developed to provide at least approximate corrections.

The atmosphere including haze and clouds, is much more transparent to microwave than to optical and infrared regions. Hence, microwave remote sensing using active sensors such as Side Looking Airborne Radar (SLAR), Synthetic Aperture Radar (SAR), and so on, have an all-weather capability. However, emission from the atmosphere can affect the brightness temperatures of the target under observation even in the microwave regions, thus producing a certain amount of radiometric error. But the advantage of this is that the atmospheric absorption/emission can be used to derive information on atmospheric constituents and the vertical temperature profile.

1.2   CONCEPT OF SIGNATURES

Electromagnetic radiation when incident on a surface gets reflected, absorbed, re-radiated or transmitted through the material depending upon the nature of the object and the wavelength of the incident radiation.

Since the nature of interaction of the electromagnetic radiation with an object depends on its cumulative properties, the study of these interactions can lead to an understanding of the objects under observation. In remote sensing, the basic property which allows identification of an object is called the *signature*. In the example of the papaya cited above, the yellow colour is the signature showing that the fruit is ripe. In general parlance, the concept of signature in remote sensing is similar to how you are identified at the bank with your signature (or fingerprint) in your transactions. The basic assumption is that each individual has an unique signature or fingerprint, with which he can be identified. In general, we can say that any set of observable characteristics, which directly or indirectly leads to the identification of an object and/or its condition is termed as its signature. Spectral, spatial, temporal and polarisation variations are four major characteristics of the targets which facilitate discrimination.

Spectral variations are the changes in the reflectance or emittance of objects as a function of wavelength. The colour of objects is a manifestation of spectral variation in reflectance in the visible region. Spatial arrangements of terrain features providing attributes such as shape, size and texture of objects which lead to their identification are termed as *spatial variations*.

Temporal variations are the changes in the reflectivity or emissivity with time. They can be diurnal and/or seasonal. The variation in reflectivity during the growing cycle of a crop helps to distinguish crops which may have similar spectral reflectances, but whose growing cycles may not be the same. A plot of spectral reflectance vs growth stages of a crop provides a phenologic pattern, which is characteristic of a crop, even at the species level. Therefore, remote sensing data acquired over the same area at different times can make use of the temporal characteristics to discriminate between crops in a better way.

Polarisation variations relate to the changes in the polarisation of the radiation reflected or emitted by an object. The degree of polarisation is a characteristic of the object and hence can help in distinguishing the object. Such observations have been particularly useful in the microwave region.

Signatures are not however, completely deterministic. They are statistical in nature with a certain mean value and some dispersion around it.

1.2.1 MULTI-SPECTRAL CONCEPT

Spectral variation is the most often used signature, especially in the optical-IR region. Figure 1.1 gives the spectral variation of some of the natural objects in the 0.4 to 2.4 μm range. However, it is not easy (though not impossible) to generate continuous spectra for identifying objects. Therefore a practical solution is to make observations in a number of discrete spectral regions, usually referred to as spectral bands.

To understand the advantage of taking measurements in a multiple wavelength region to separate different classes of objects, let us consider some actual data from the Indian Remote Sensing Satellite (IRS) camera LISS-III (Chapter 6). We have chosen three classes—crop, water (turbid) and barren soil. The radiance values of these are extracted from the image for two spectral bands—red (band 3) and near IR (band 4). (These are pure classes based on ground identification.) The radiance values in the image are at times referred to as DN (digital numbers), since they are transmitted as digital values or grey level values. Figure 1.2(b) gives the number of times

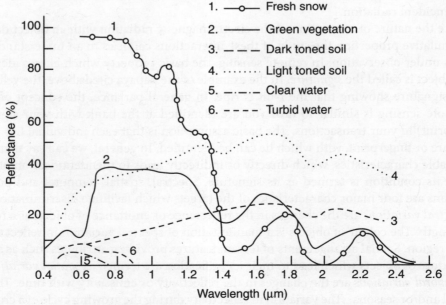

Fig. 1.1 Typical reflectance spectra of some land cover.

each DN value has occurred in band 3 for the whole data consisting of the three classes. Such a plot is called a *histogram*. To separate each class from the observation of band 3 alone, the histogram should have shown the distinct distribution for the three classes. Figure 1.2(b) shows that barren is distinct from the rest, while water and crop classes are mixed. Figure 1.2(a) gives a similar plot for band 4 data. Here crop and barren are mixed. This simple example shows that information from only a single band cannot distinguish all the classes. In Fig. 1.2(c), we combine the information from both bands. Here for each picture element (pixel), the band 3 values are plotted on the *x*-axis and the corresponding band 4 values are plotted on the *y*-axis. Such a plot is called a *scatter plot*, since it represents how the DN values are 'scattered' in two dimensional space. (This is also referred to as *feature space*.) With *n* number of bands, we can have an *n*-dimensional feature space.

Figure 1.2(c) shows how the three classes are distinctly separated, which was not possible by using either band 3 or band 4 alone. Here, we have chosen three classes to explain the concept. In practice, in a scene, the number of classes are not limited to three. As the number of classes increases, the possibility of overlap between the classes increases [Fig. 1.2(d)] which will require additional bands for separating the classes. However, it does not mean that separability (or more rigorously referred to as classification accuracy) increases linearly with an increasing number of bands. After 3–4 bands, for most features, the classification accuracy increases only marginally, while the computer time requirement increases faster. In fact, more than the number of bands, the specific choice of band locations is crucial in feature separation for specific themes.

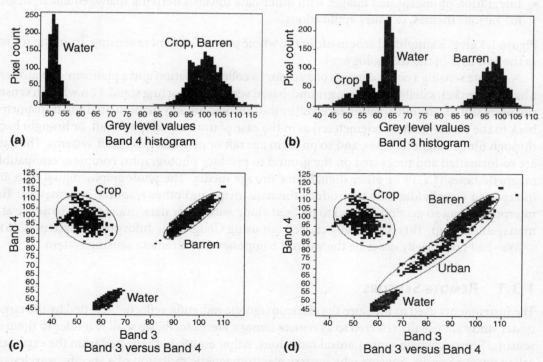

Fig. 1.2 Schematics showing the advantage of multi-spectral imaging for class separation.

Multi-spectral classification is only one of the 'multi' approaches in remote sensing. Other 'multi approaches' include multi-temporal (imaging the same area at different times/seasons), multi-directional, multi-polarisation, and so on.

1.3   REMOTE SENSING SYSTEM

With the general background treatise on remote sensing we have made so far, it would now be easier to make an analysis of the different stages in remote sensing. They are

- Origin of electromagnetic energy (sun, transmitter carried by the sensor).
- Transmission of energy from the source to the surface of the earth and its interaction with the intervening atmosphere.
- Interaction of energy with the earth's surface (reflection/absorption/transmission) or self-emission.
- Transmission of the reflected/emitted energy to the remote sensor placed on a suitable platform, through the intervening atmosphere.
- Detection of the energy by the sensor, converting it into a photographic image or electrical output.
- Transmission/recording of the sensor output.
- Pre-processing of the data and generation of the data products.
- Collection of ground truth and other collateral information.
- Data analysis and interpretation.
- Integration of interpreted images with other data towards deriving management strategies for various themes, or other applications.

Figure 1.3 gives a simplified schematic of the whole process of remote sensing, from the source to the end user of the technology.

A remote sensing system consists of a sensor to collect radiation and a platform – an aircraft, a balloon, rocket, satellite or even a ground-based sensor-supporting stand – on which a sensor can be mounted. The information received by the sensor is suitably manipulated and transported back to the earth—may be telemetered as in the case of unmanned spacecraft, or brought back through films, magnetic tapes, and so on, as in aircraft or manned spacecraft systems. The data are re-formatted and processed on the ground to produce photographs, computer compatible magnetic tapes (CCT) or other digital data storage media. The photographs/digital data are interpreted visually/digitally to produce thematic maps and other resource information. The interpreted data so generated need to be used along with other data/information to arrive at a management plan. This is generally carried out using Geographic Information System (GIS).

We shall now briefly describe the various components of a remote sensing system.

1.3.1   REMOTE SENSORS

The instruments used to measure the electromagnetic radiation reflected/emitted by the target under study are usually referred to as *remote sensors*. Henceforth, we shall just refer to them as sensors. Sensors, which sense natural radiations, either emitted or reflected from the earth, are called *passive sensors*. Sensors which carry electromagnetic radiation of a specific wavelength or band of wavelengths to illuminate the earth's surface are called *active sensors*.

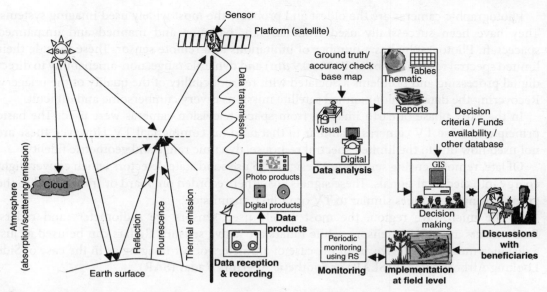

Fig. 1.3 Schematics showing remote sensing system for resource management from source to end use.

The major parameters of a sensing system which can be considered as indicators of the quality of data and which have bearing on optimum utilisation for specific end use include:

- Spatial resolution—the capability of the sensor to discriminate the smallest object on the ground of different sizes; usually specified in terms of linear dimension. As a general rule, higher the resolution, smaller the object that can be identified (Plate 1.1).
- Spectral resolution—the spectral bandwidth with which the data is collected.
- Radiometric resolution—the capability of the sensor to discriminate two targets based on its reflectance/emittance difference; it is measured in terms of the smallest reflectance/emittance that can be detected. Higher the radiometric resolution, smaller the radiance differences that can be detected between two targets.
- Temporal resolution—the capability to view the same target, under similar conditions, at regular intervals.

These four resolutions are the most basic requirements of any sensor system. There are no unique acceptable values for them. It depends on specific applications. For example, to study the motion of clouds (cloud motion vector), spatial resolution of about a km is acceptable, while the frequency of observation (temporal resolution), should be 30 min. or better. This is because cloud formation characteristics are spatially large, but they are subject to dynamic mobility. On the other hand, for agricultural studies, a few tens of metres of spatial resolution is desirable with a few days temporal resolution. This is because, the land use changes in small spatial units, while change due to growth occurs gradually over a few days. There are other aspects like dynamic range (the minimum to maximum radiance that can be faithfully measured), radiometric accuracy, geometric fidelity, and so on which should be borne in mind, while designing, realising and utilising a sensor.

Photographic cameras are the oldest and probably the most widely used imaging systems. They have been successfully used from aircraft, balloons and manned and unmanned spacecraft. Photography has a number of limitations as a remote sensor. These include their limited spectral response (about 0.45 to 0.9 μm) and dynamic range, non-amenability to direct digital processing and problems associated with reproducibility of the quality of the imagery. Recovering the data from unmanned satellite missions is very cumbersome and difficult.

In the early phase of earth imaging from space, television cameras were used. The basic principle of these TV cameras is similar to that used for commercial TV. However, these are not used now due to the limited spectral response, dynamic range and geometric fidelity.

Of late, remote sensing sensors are designed to use solid state detectors which convert light energy into electrical signals. These signals are either recorded on board or transmitted to the ground using techniques similar to TV or radio transmission.

In the microwave region, the most widely used sensors are radiometers and radars. Radiometers are passive sensors, while radars are active sensors. Radars can be used as just a distance measuring device, as in the case of altimeters or for imaging as in the case of Side Looking Airborne Radar (SLAR) or Synthetic Aperture Radar (SAR).

1.3.2 Platforms

Sensor systems need to be placed on suitable observation platforms and lifted to a pre-defined altitude. Platforms can be stationary (like a tripod for field observation) or mobile (aircraft, spacecraft) depending upon the needs of the observation mission and the constraints. For an imaging system, in general, spatial resolution becomes poorer as the platform height increases, but the area coverage increases (Fig. 1.4). Thus a trade-off has to be carried out between resolution and synoptic view in choosing the platform altitude. Further, the platform's ability to support the sensor system, in terms of weight, volume, power, and so on, and the platform stability have to be considered. Though aircraft, balloons, rockets and satellites have been used as platforms, the most extensively used ones are aircraft and satellites and hence our discussion will be restricted to them.

Aircraft are mainly useful for surveys of local or limited regional interest. One of the major advantages is their ability to be available at a particular location at short notice. Aerial remote sensing can be done from low altitudes (~1 km) to few tens of kilometers depending on the aircraft. Currently there are aircraft fitted with multiple sensors, capable of observations covering the whole range of the electromagnetic spectrum. The major limitation is the high cost for global coverage and for regional coverage on a repetitive basis.

Earth observation from a satellite platform provides a synoptic view of a large area. Further, it can be made under near constant solar zenith angles providing similar illumination conditions. Another major advantage of the satellite is its ability to provide repetitive observations of the same area with intervals of a few minutes to a few weeks depending on the sensor and the orbit. This capability is very useful to monitor dynamic phenomena such as cloud evolution, vegetation cover, snow cover and forest fires.

As the distance of a satellite from the earth increases, the period of revolution also increases. At about 36000 km, the period of the satellite is exactly equal to that of the earth's revolution and a satellite kept at the equatorial plane at that height (called *geostationary orbit*), it appears

Data products are generated after correcting these errors so that the interpretability of the original information of the scene (in terms of geometry, radiometry and information content) is retained. The data product is generally standardized for transmission or in photographic or digital form to allow further analysis.

A photographic product for a computer display is generated, from each spectral band gives different shades of grey. To which we may say that we can produce black and white pictures (from each band). A digital data of up to three bands can be combined to give a colour imagery. Images are taken one colour band and red, blue, the data combined to give natural colour, in the case of false colour, the reflectance normally take place in the near-IR. To take advantages of the remote sensate satellites combines green and IR bands, —control blue, green, and red—are transformed image to colour IR, results in what is commonly referred to as false colour IR product. Since the colour represented is not the natural colour, the IR colour is state, false colour, as seen on IR, as in false colour IR appears red.

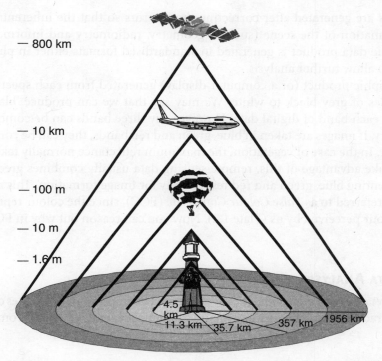

Fig. 1.4 Schematics showing the increase in viewing area with height.

stationary with respect to earth. Thus the satellite can have a constant view of a particular part of the earth.

Observation from the geostationary orbit is generally used to derive information on meteorological parameters.

The frequently used near-earth orbit height varies from a few hundred kilometers to a few thousand kilometers. The most useful orbit in this category for remote sensing is the circular, near polar, sun-synchronous orbit. In a sun-synchronous orbit, all points at a given latitude (say on a descending pass) will have the same local mean solar time. Further, the ground trace of the sun-synchronous satellite can be made to recur over a scene exactly at intervals of a fixed number of days by maintaining the height and inclination of the orbit to a close tolerance, thus ensuring repetitive observations of a scene at the same local time. Since fixed local time provides near identical solar illumination, it provides definitive advantages for interpretation of satellite data, while monitoring dynamic changes that occur on earth.

1.3.3 DATA PRODUCTS GENERATION

Acquired data has number of errors due to

- imaging characteristics of the sensor,
- stability and orbit characteristics of the platform,
- scene/surface characteristics,
- motion of the earth, and
- atmospheric effects.

Data products are generated after correcting these errors so that the inherent quality of the original information of the scene (such as geometry, radiometry and information content) is retained. The data product is generated in standardised formats either in photographic or digital form to allow further analysis.

A photographic product (or a computer display) generated from each spectral band gives different shades of grey-black to white. We may say that we can produce 'black and white' pictures from each band of digital data. However any three bands can be combined to give a colour imagery. If images are taken in blue, green and red bands, they can be combined to give natural colour. In the case of vegetation, the maximum reflectance normally takes place in the near-IR. To take advantage of this, remote sensing data usually combines green, red and IR bands, representing blue, green and red respectively for image formation. This results in what is commonly referred to as *False Colour Composite* (FCC), since the colour represented is not the actual colour perceived by us (Plate 1.2). Now you can reason out why in FCC, vegetation appears red.

1.3.4 Data Analysis

Visual interpretation and digital image processing are two important techniques of data analysis needed to extract resource-related information either independently or in combination with other data.

Visual Interpretation

Visual interpretation has been the traditional method for extracting information from a photograph based on the characteristics such as tone, texture, shadow, shape, size, association, and so on. Though this approach is simple and straightforward, it has some shortcomings. The range of gray values produced on a film or print is limited in comparison to what can be recorded in digital form. Though the number of colour tones recognised by the human brain is quite large, it is still limited. Hence full advantage of radiometric resolution of the instrument cannot be made use of while visually interpreting the data. In addition, the interpreter is likely to be subjective in discerning subtle differences in tones and hence visual interpretation tends to be qualitative rather than quantitative. In addition, when photographic products are generated from digital data, the contrast is further degraded. Visual interpretation poses serious limitations when we want to combine data from various sources. Above all, when a large volume of data has to be analysed, it cannot meet the throughput requirements.

Digital Techniques

Digital techniques facilitate quantitative analysis, make use of full spectral information and avoid individual bias. Simultaneous analysis of multi-temporal and multi-sensor data is greatly facilitated in digital methods.

In digital classification, the computer analyses the spectral signature, in order to associate each pixel with a particular feature of imagery. The reflectance value measured by a sensor for the same feature will not be identical for all pixels. For example, in a wheat field, all the pixels will not have identical reflectance values. That is, response variation within a class is to be expected for any earth surface cover due to various reasons. Therefore the radiance value for a class will have a mean and a variance, as seen in Fig. 1.2. We have seen in the feature space [Fig. 1.2(c)] a natural clustering of classes in three groups indicating the signature differences of the three classes. When the clusters corresponding to different ground covers are distinct, it is possible to associate localised regions of the feature space with specific ground covers. Such distinct clusters do not happen in real life situations. The digital classification technique essentially partitions this feature space in some fashion so that each pixel in the feature space can be uniquely associated with one of the classes (when we have n bands, we can have an n-dimensional feature space). The partitioning is achieved by suitable statistical methods and a number of such algorithms are established and available.

1.3.5 END UTILISATION

The information generated from remote sensing can be represented in many ways. It could be generated as tabular data, say, the area under different crops in each district, or as maps. Maps illustrate geographic relationships which are not readily apparent when viewing tabular data. To make a decision on the strategy of resource management and various possible options, one requires information from multiple sources and just one thematic map may not be adequate. For example, we would like to reclaim wasteland and put it to productive use. Remote sensing can generate images of wasteland from which thematic experts may produce wasteland maps. For what purpose the wasteland can be used, will require other information such as soil type, groundwater potential, road network, and so on. Each of this can be represented as thematic maps from the remote sensing data. Apart from these, we would like to know the socio-economic status of the people in that village/district or the funds available for development. To have an optimal solution, we need to take into consideration all of these factors. The importance and priority one attaches to each of these inputs could be different. Traditionally the analyst has been doing this manually by overlaying different maps and integrating all the data. This has been found to be time-consuming and manual methods have very limited capabilities to generate various development scenarios. Currently this task is carried out by the Geographic Information System (GIS). GIS is essentially a computer-based system designed for capturing and storing both spatial and tabular (attribute) data and combining them, to which one can apply spatial analysis tools as per the analyst's requirements/models. Because GIS-based analysis can be performed quickly, multiple scenarios can be evaluated efficiently and effectively. Although these development plans for resources can be generated in the confines of the office rooms, it would be prudent to involve the end user and stake holders such as farmers and fishermen for the efficient and useful implementation of such plans.

1.4 WHY OBSERVE EARTH FROM SPACE?

You may be wondering why we need to observe the earth and that too from space involving all these technical intricacies of science. It has been often said that the earth is a self-contained spaceship. The only external supply is solar energy; the rest of the resources are with us and cannot be replenished. However, the increase in population and increasing consumerism place a heavy burden on the limited natural resources, due to the increasing demand for food, fodder, fuel and minerals. Recurring natural disasters such as floods, droughts, landslides,

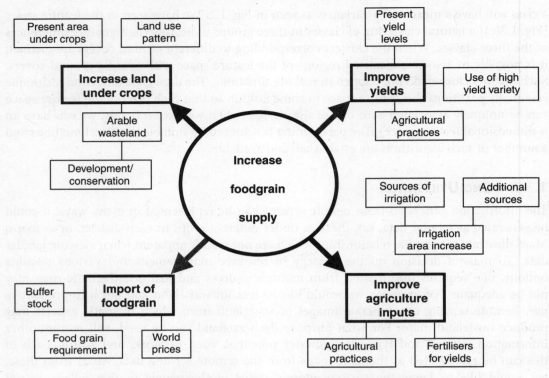

Fig.1.5 Information requirement scenario for increasing food grain supply.

earthquakes and forest fires further erode the natural resource base. The industrial era along with the comforts it promised to humankind also brought about environmental pollution and degradation, thus affecting our fragile ecosystems. Therefore, the highly competing and conflicting demands on our natural resources from the increasing population and the aspiration for improving the quality of life, need management strategies to use our resources optimally, to meet the present day need while not endangering our earth so that the needs of the future generation can be met—this is referred to as *sustainable development*. Even localised over-exploitation of certain resources, such as uncontrolled depletion of forests, has measurable global impact. Remote sensing, by providing timely and repetitive information on the phenomena occurring on earth and its environment can help in achieving worldwide economic and social development, by managing natural resources while minimising adverse impact on the earth's resources, environment and climate.

To realise any objective, one has a number of possible options, and a manager chooses the route that optimally uses the available resources without degrading the ecosystem. To arrive at such a decision, the manager requires reliable information about various aspects related to the problem he is contemplating to solve.

Let us consider the issue of meeting the increased demand for food. Figure 1.5 gives some of the possible options. One temporary possibility is to import foodgrains (if you have the money!) but it is not a long-term solution. Other possible alternatives are shown in Fig. 1.5.

Let us consider the option of increasing the land under cultivation which in our view is a possible path to sustainable development. To pursue this path, we require information on aspects such as, the present area under cultivation, land use pattern, arable wasteland, and so on which can be obtained through remote sensing at the local and global scale. Accurate and reliable information on these parameters is a prerequisite to take decisions on how to go about increasing the land under cultivation. Therefore, reliable and cost effective technologies to generate such an information system all over the world becomes apparent. We could extend this analogy to other areas of resource management as well. To sum up, relevant information is a vital element for resource management. The quality of decision-making would depend upon accuracy, timeliness, repetitive and updated information. Improper decisions could be not only more expensive, but may also affect the environment by further degradation of ecological quality. The ability of the remote sensing technique to provide repetitive coverage from the regional to the global scale enables planning the utilisation of our resources on a scientific basis rather than by intuition or habit.

But why do we have to go far way from earth to understand the earth? As we observe from greater heights, we get a larger coverage of the earth and observe a larger region (Fig. 1.4) but the details we can discern will be less. If you just look outside the window you see the road ahead and probably a few buildings nearby. If you go to the roof top of a building, you see nearby road network and where it leads to, different types of buildings, and so on. Thus, from the rooftop one gets a better understanding of the surroundings. If you fly in an aircraft, you see fields, habitation, water bodies and its interlinkages. It is these interlinkages that enable you to better understand the earth. To study the earth as a system you will have to understand all the features and their interdependence. This is only possible if we are able to see all the features together to the extent possible. In other words we require a *synoptic view*. Apart from this there are certain features, such as lineaments and paleo channels which may be difficult to identify by standing on the earth, but possess immense importance in the understanding of the earth.

Apart from the synoptic view, imaging from satellites has other advantages. Since the satellite orbit is fixed in space, as the earth rotates, one sees newer areas during each revolution of the satellite. Thus you can cover the whole globe within a certain period. If we choose special orbits (sun-synchronous), one can get near identical solar illumination and also enable the revisiting of a point on earth periodically and at the same local time. This is important to study changing phenomena such as vegetative growth, snow melt run-off and others.

Till now, we have been considering the use of earth observation for monitoring and management of earth's resources such as forests, agricultural crops, water resources, minerals and marine resources, and in monitoring/assessing/warning impacts due to calamities such as land degradation, earthquakes, droughts, landslides and urbanisation. Another area in which remote sensing finds tremendous application is the scientific understanding of the entire earth system on a global scale by studying how its component parts and their interactions are evolved, how they function and how they may be expected to evolve in the future.

1.5 REMOTE SENSING—A HISTORIC PERSPECTIVE

The ability to have a permanent record of what we observe was first possible due to photography which dates back to 1826. Thus photography may be considered as the first step towards modern remote sensing. The initial photographs of earth were captured while still being on earth. We have always tried to reach greater heights – treetops, mountains, platforms and so on – to observe phenomena of interest, to decide habitable places, farming and such other day-to-day activities. This inquisitiveness to get a bird's eye view prompted us to take photographs of earth from elevated platforms. Balloons were the first elevated platforms used for photography in 1858 by the Frenchman Gaspard Felix Tournachon (known as Nadar) to photograph the village of Petil Becetre near Paris. Modern imaging concepts from up above mainly started as a military reconnaissance tool. During the American Civil War, balloons were used to photograph enemy positions. From the Civil War until the First World War, people experimented with other platforms such as kites and pigeons. The invention of the aeroplane in 1903, was a great step forward to having a stable platform for photography. The first aerial photography from a plane was made by Wilbur Wright in Italy in 1909. With the advent of the Second World War, capabilities of remote sensing were pushed beyond visible spectrum photography into infrared and radar systems.

The beginning of space-based remote sensing can be dated back to 1891, when Germans were developing rocket propelled camera systems and by 1907 gyro-stabilisation had been added to improve picture quality. In less than two years after the first man-made satellite (Sputnik 1, 4 October, 1957) was launched, United States' Explorer 6, in August 1959, transmitted the first picture of earth, to be ever taken from a satellite. However, systematic earth observation from space started with the launch of Television Infrared Observation Satellite (TIROS-1) on 1 April 1960, designed primarily for meteorological observations. Considering the reconnaissance potential of space imagery, the US initiated the highly secret mission CORONA in the 1960s for collecting intelligence photography. Space photography was also carried out by Gemini and Apollo missions. Many scientists realised the immense potential of these photographs for civilian applications. Sensor technology had advanced to take images from space beyond the limits of photography.

The term remote sensing was used by Evelyn L Pruitt, a geographer formerly with the office of Naval Research, to replace the more limiting term 'aerial' and 'photograph' (*http://www.geog.nau.edu/RemoteSensing*). In 1962, the Institute of Science and Technology at the University of Michigan organised the first symposium on remote sensing of the environment. From that day, civilian remote sensing as a discipline began to come of age (Stephen H S, 1992). The first multi-spectral photography from space was from the Apollo 9 mission in 1968 using four Hasselbled cameras with different film filter combinations and bore-sighted to see the same area.

A new era in remote sensing began on 23 July 1972, when the United States launched the first earth observation satellite dedicated primarily for land observation, called Earth Resources Technology Satellite (ERTS-1). This was the first satellite available for systematic and repetitive observation of the earth surface. With the launch of the second satellite in January 1975, the name of the series was changed to LANDSAT.

LANDSAT 1 and 2 carried a four-band Multi-spectral Scanner (MSS) and a three-band RBV camera. In LANDSAT 3, a fifth band in thermal IR was added to MSS. A large amount of data pouring from MSS revolutionised the application of space images for various themes. An advanced scanner called thematic mapper (TM) with better spatial and spectral resolution and additional bands in middle IR was included in LANDSAT 4 and 5. LANDSAT 7 launched in 1999 had an Enhanced TM (ETM) with an additional 15 m resolution panchromatic band.

The four-channel microwave radiometer carried by COSMOS-243 launched by USSR, was the beginning of spaceborne microwave remote sensing. The NIMBUS series launched by the

The Story of ERTS-1 and MSS

The first symposium on remote sensing of the environment, held at the University of Michigan, convinced many scientists of the exciting possibilities of various applications if a dedicated civilian remote sensing satellite was launched. William Fisher, a photo-geologist who attended the symposium convinced William T Pecore, of the Department of Interior that the time might be right for a civilian remote sensing satellite. NASA's participation was crucial to build a satellite, but NASA administrators were not interested in a civilian satellite programme, and the most generous interpretation for their reluctance is that it would have distracted time and resources from their mandate to put a man on the moon. According to LANDSAT historian, Pamela E Mach 'The military and the National Security Council did not like the idea of the civilian community looking at the earth at all. That was their prerogative'. Responding to continued pressure from the Interior Department, NASA began planning for a small unmanned satellite in early 1967. By 1968, the Interior Department had formally requested congressional money for its Earth Resources Observation Satellite programme, and NASA planned to adapt one of the NIMBUS weather satellite bus for the job. The key mapping instrument aboard the satellite would be three RCA television type cameras known as Return Beam Vidicon (RBV). The choice might have been because of the expectation that it would be a straightforward adaption of existing technology for remote sensing. *In April 1968, NASA received an unsolicited bid from a group of scientists at Hughes Aircraft company at California, headed by Virginia T Norwood, suggesting a different type of sensor called Scanner*, which they had been developing for the Advanced Technology Satellite (ATS) weather satellites.

Thus when LANDSAT was being conceived, the argument was, whether one should use RBV or the untested scanner on the satellite. As David Landgrebe of Purdue University put it, 'the whole community felt much stronger about a framing type instrument than a line-by-line instrument, because their background was in aerial photography'. The demonstration of the new sensor by the Hughes made NASA put both the sensors – RBV and the scanner – for the first mission.

Norwood's group knew how to build a scanner, but they did not know what spectral bands would convey the best information about the earth. By experimentation and consultation, the Hughes group first suggested a six-band scanner. Then NASA, short of space on satellites that were designed only to house TV cameras, sent Norwood back to the drawing board. In 1971, the Hughes team came back with the more modest four-band multi-spectral scanner. That is how the MSS got into the ERTS-1.

The post-launch performance of MSS, vindicated the decision to use a novel design which was not flight proven. If MSS had not found a place in ERTS-1, the operationalisation of remote sensing would probably not have come of age this fast!!

(The details given above are from the USGS website – *http://edcwww.cr.usgs.gov/ earthshots/slow/HelpGardenCity/groundtruthtext* – which is based on the book—Mapping the next millennium: The Discovery of New Geographies, New York, Random House, 1992, p. 52–70, Stephen S Hall.)

USA had a variety of microwave sensors designed primarily for meteorological applications. However, the first imaging active microwave sensor specifically designed for ocean application was the L band SAR carried onboard SEASAT in 1978. This had a capability to produce images with a 25 m resolution. This was followed by Shuttle imaging radar (SIR – A and B) in 1982 and 1984 with capabilities similar to SEASAT. The European Radar Satellite (ERS-1), launched in 1991 opened the avenue for systematic global observation in the microwave region using its C band SAR. RADARSAT of Canada launched in 1995, had improved modes of operation for its C band SAR.

Today, many countries, apart from the USA operate Remote Sensing satellites – France (SPOT), Japan (ADEOS), India (IRS), China (Yogan), Korea (Kompsat), Thailand (Theos), Russia (Resurs) – the list is not exhaustive. USA, France and India have planned a series of satellites, with continuity of mission and improved capability, so that the users are assured of uninterrupted supply of earth observation data.

A quantum jump in the capability of imaging from space was enabled with the launch of IKONOS on 24 September 1999, which has 1 m resolution in panchromatic and 4 m resolution in multi-spectral; IKONOS was also the first commercial venture by a private company. Since then a number of commercial earth observation satellites have been launched with improved resolution. The WV-3 owned by DigitalGlobe provides 31 cm resolution for panchromatic channel and 1.24 m resolution for the multispectral bands. Thus civilian satellites have imaging capabilities approaching those of military spy satellites.

1.6 INDIAN REMOTE SENSING PROGRAMME

The Indian space programme had its modest beginnings in 1962 with the establishment of a rocket launching station at a place in the southern part of India through which the geomagnetic equator passes. Subsequently, the Department of Space (DOS) was established by the Government of India, in 1972, to promote development and application of space science and technology for identified national socio-economic objectives. The Space Commission, which is the apex body of decision-making on national space programmes and policies, lays down the framework of important space activities and advises the Government on major policies and programmes of space activities. DOS functions directly under the Prime Minister of India. The space technology and applications activities are carried out through the constituent centres/units of Indian Space Research Organisation (ISRO) and the autonomous institutions established for specific programmes.

As a developing country with a large population, space systems can address many developmental needs of the country. Thus, the Indian Space programme was initiated with a vision to use space technology for national development in the thrust areas of communication, navigation, resource survey/management and meteorological applications. Towards meeting these objectives, two major operational systems have been established—the Indian National Satellite (INSAT) for telecommunication, television broadcasting and meteorological services, and the Indian Remote Sensing Satellite (IRS) for monitoring and management of natural resources and disaster management support. India has also established a constellation of Indian regional navigation satellite system (IRNSS) to provide accurate position information service. These systems have taken the benefits of space technology to the society at the grassroots level. In addition to the application driven programs, front ranking scientific investigations are being carried out in the fields of astronomy, atmospheric sciences and planetary exploration. Over the years, the space programme has become largely selfreliant with the capability to design and build satellites for providing space services and to launch them using indigenously designed and developed launch vehicles.

Some of the major goals of India's EO programme include:

- conduct national natural resources census,
- realise large scale cartographic maps for the nation,
- establish Ocean State Forecasting system and an operational Ocean Information Service,
- facilitate improved weather forecasting,
- support information needs for a disaster management system,
- position a viable spatial information business in the country.

We shall now describe the evolution and future plans of the Indian Earth Observation (EO) programme. It all started with aerial photography, first used in India in 1920 in a survey experiment (Bhavsar, 1980). The first use of aerial photography in an application other than land survey was made in 1926 for flood assessment of the river Indus at Dera Ismail Khan, then part of undivided India. Since then, black and white aerial photography has been widely used for preparation of maps on a scale up to 1 : 15,000. The aerial photographs, mainly in black and white, were also used on a limited scale for geological survey and to study river basins. However, remote sensing, as practiced presently using multi-spectral information, was first introduced in India by Professor Pisharoty and his colleagues in 1970 with the conduct of an experiment aimed at early detection of coconut plantation disease – coconut wilt – using false colour infrared photographs taken from an airborne platform (Dakshinamurti et al., 1970). This was followed by a number of experiments using aerial flights and Landsat imagery for various themes across the country, in association with departments whose mandate was to monitor natural resources. Thus ISRO not only developed the technology of applying remote sensing input for natural resource survey and management but also created awareness across the end users by a joint demonstration of the potential of remote sensing in resource monitoring and management.

Another major step forward was the realisation of the need to establish a self-reliant operational remote sensing system. Towards this, DOS initiated various activities such as development of sensors, hardware/software for data products generation, visual/computer aided interpretation methodologies, development of interpretation equipment, application methodologies and so on. In addition, to take care of the operational needs of remote sensing in the country, the National Remote Sensing Agency (NRSA) was established in 1975 at Hyderabad, with the responsibility of establishing and operating earth stations for receiving remotely sensed satellite data and dissemination of data to various users, as well as application of remote sensing data for various national developmental needs. The NRSA ground station at Shadnagar about 50 km south of Hyderabad, is the remote sensing data reception and processing hub in the country. Apart from acquiring the data from all the Indian

Remote Sensing satellites, NRSA also acquires data from many other foreign satellites. As part of the 2001 Remote Sensing Data Policy (RSDP), NRSA has been identified as the national acquisition/distribution agency for all satellite data within India and has been allowed to enter into agreements for any foreign satellite data distribution in India. Even as NRSA undertook these data reception activities, it also initiated large scale projects in the use of satellite images for making inventory and maps of various natural resources – forests, water bodies, land use/ land cover, urban areas, soils – and slowly germinated the concept of natural resources thematic mapping for large areas, covering the whole nation. In 2008, NRSA was converted into a full-fledged government organisation and re-named as National Remote Sensing Centre (NRSC).

With the intention to gain experience and acquire expertise in satellite remote sensing, ISRO initially developed various remote sensors and associated data products for aircraft platforms (Bhavsar et al, 1981). These included multi-spectral scanners, radiometers, and so on (Joseph and Kamat, 1978). In the meantime, the development of the first satellite Aryabhatta, was a leap forward for satellite technology in India and also helped in setting up essential infrastructure and the capability to initiate a space-based remote sensing programme. Since the Indian space programme is directed towards the practical use of outer space for national development, it was decided that the second satellite should be an experimental Earth Observation Satellite. Thus, immediately following the Aryabhata, two Earth Observation Satellite missions (Bhaskara 1 and 2) were conceived, whose spacecraft designs were modifications of the Aryabhata satellite bus, but which incorporated remote sensing payloads relevant for practical applications. The payloads comprised a television camera system – which can picture a 341 km × 341 km of area on ground in a single frame with about 1 km spatial resolution – and a microwave radiometer system to study ocean wind and moisture contents in the atmosphere. The two Bhaskara satellites were launched with Soviet collaboration and provided an excellent training ground for conceiving future operational missions in remote sensing. Several experiments with practical applications involving users were undertaken to evaluate the efficacy of the data generated from a space platform.

Following the successful implementation of the experimental missions of the Bhaskara satellites, ISRO took a bold decision to have a dedicated remote sensing satellite series with capabilities comparable to the contemporary earth observation satellites, which could provide uninterrupted and assured operational services. This led to the conceptualisation of the Indian Remote Sensing Satellite programme and the first satellite IRS-1A, was launched in 1988. When compared to Bhaskara, considerable improvements were made in the satellite mission—orbit and attitude control, spatial and spectral resolutions of payloads as well as reliability aspects needed for an operational mission. Subsequent to IRS-1A, more satellites, namely IRS-1B, IRS-P2, IRS-1C, IRS-P3, IRS-1D, IRS-P4 (Oceansat), Resourcesat-1, Oceansat-2, Resourcesat-2 and Resourcesat 2A were launched in 1991, 1994, 1995, 1996, 1997, 1999, 2003, 2009, 2011 and 2016 respectively—this list is not exhaustive. Sub-metre imaging started with Technology Evaluation Satellite (TES) launched in 2001 which also tested a number of state-of-the-art technologies including a high resolution (1 m) imaging system. Cartosat-1 launched in 2005 was the first of a series giving stereo imaging capability. Figure 1.6 shows the imagery taken by the panchromatic camera from the Carto2 satellite. The launch of ISRO's first space borne Synthetic Aperture Radar (SAR) – Radar Imaging Satellite – RISAT-1 on 26 April

Fig. 1.6 Imagery taken over an airport by Cartosat-2 Panchromatic camera having spatial resolution of 0.65 m, from a 500 km height. The area covered is about $1.65 \times 1.65 \ km^2$.

2012, puts ISRO along with a select group of space agencies operating space borne C band SAR. The realisation of space borne state-of-the-art SAR is a milestone in the development of microwave remote sensors in the country.

Though IRS was started to meet the domestic remote sensing data needs, over the years it has become a global mission. The IRS programme has earned the credibility of being a continuous and dependable source for remote sensing data; thanks to the long-term planning of ISRO. Due to the robust IRS programme of ISRO, currently IRS data is marketed to a number of countries across the globe through a network of receiving stations and re-sellers spread across all continents thereby establishing a worldwide leadership by virtue of operating a constellation of state-of-the-art remote sensing satellites serving the global community. A major dimension in the Indian remote sensing programme is the operational capability of the launch vehicle, PSLV, to launch India's own earth observation satellites—the IRS satellites. In addition to the LEO missions, India has also developed earth observation capability from the Geostationary Orbit (GEO). Currently these data are used primarily for meteorological applications. In future ISRO will have a high resolution imaging system from GEO which has the potential for earth resource monitoring and management. The planned geostationary imaging system – GISAT – covers a broad spectral region extending from visible to thermal IR with different spectral and spatial resolution and is capable of imaging the full disk or any user specified region.

India has also established a strong applications programme which has successfully taken the technology of remote sensing to the grassroots level in support of locale specific development. Since the first coconut wilt disease experiment using a photographic camera, remote sensing applications have come a long way towards providing sustainable development solutions/ alternatives for land and water resources management. A number of joint experiment projects in remote sensing applications were carried out by the Department of Space along with different user departments/agencies, to demonstrate the potential of remote sensing for resource monitoring and management in different fields. Closely following these experiments and realising the need for an institutional framework for remote sensing applications, a National Natural Resources Management System (NNRMS), with the Department of Space as its nodal agency, was set up to coordinate remote sensing applications in the country.

Over the years, NNRMS has institutionalised a strong application foundation in support of national natural resources management. Today, remote sensing has been operationalised to cover diverse themes/areas such as forestry, agricultural crop acreage and yield estimation, drought monitoring and mitigation, flood monitoring and damage assessment, land cover/ land use studies, wasteland identification and reclamation, water resources development and management, groundwater targeting, marine resources survey, urban planning, mineral prospecting, environmental impact assessment and so on, thus encompassing almost every facet of sustainable resource development and management. Through NNRMS, the EO programme has reinforced the importance of remote sensing for the good of the public by enabling a systematic inventory of natural resources of the nation, providing operational meteorological services and establishing a National Spatial Data Infrastructure (NSDI).

As part of NNRMS, it was realised that for a wider outreach, the remote sensing applications programme needs to be backed up by appropriate infrastructure, in terms of trained manpower, technology base and so on. Thus, a programme for infrastructure development has been drawn up for setting up of facilities and training. Human resource development has been identified as a crucial element and thus both academic and professional training programmes have been identified. Yet another step taken was to involve private industry in a technology transfer mode, which can lead to commercial production and marketing of equipment and application services.

The availability of adequate services and facilities for interpreting and analysing satellite data is an important element for the extensive utilisation of remote sensing data. Keeping this in mind, five Regional Remote Sensing Service Centres (RRSSCs) were set up. The regional centre concept enables the users to use advanced technology without having to establish and maintain such facilities on their own. The RRSSCs are supposed to provide services to the users located around them to carry out remote sensing data analysis. These five centres have been geographically distributed and are located at Nagpur (Central region), Kharagpur (East), Jodhpur (West), Bangalore (South) and Dehradun (North). In addition, 23 states have set up State Remote Sensing Application Centres. As a result, the state centres are able to conduct application projects of relevance to their states and also participate in various national projects.

Starting with a modest experiment in the early seventies, the Indian Remote Sensing Programme has come a long way, all along maintaining emphasis on indigenous capacity-building and pursuing applications relevant to society. This focus for practical applications in the context of national needs combined with political support has ensured the sustainability of the programme. With data from improved sensors and the use of Geographic Information System, the use of remote sensing has emerged as an integral component of the decision-making process at various levels in the country. The application of satellite remote sensing in India is an example for many developing countries to demonstrate how relevant advanced technology can be used for the development of a country.

1.7 THE EARTH OBSERVATION EVOLUTION— THE PARADIGM SHIFT

Though earth observation from space really started with the launch of TIROS in 1960 for meteorological applications, the launch of Landsat-1 in 1972 provided the impetus to the application of remote sensing data for a wide variety of themes. Since then, the earth observation strategy has seen a number of changes both in terms of technology and management. After the launch of Landsat-1 in 1972, the United States was the only player in space-based remote sensing till the launch of SPOT-1 in 1986. Though there are now a number of nations that have Earth Observation Systems, it is the US programme of Earth Observation that dominates the scene of remote sensing. We shall briefly discuss the evolution of various remote sensing approaches.

The initial earth observation strategy was to use the space system to monitor land, ocean and atmosphere separately, using missions such as Landsat, Seasat, Upper Atmosphere Research Satellite (UARS), and so on. Since the land, ocean and atmosphere are coupled, it was found necessary to have simultaneous observation covering various disciplines to study global scale processes that shape and influence the earth system. Thus, the earth observation approach was in favour of making simultaneous observations to get information for different disciplines. The multi-disciplinary study requires a variety of sensors operating on various regions of the electromagnetic spectrum, in different modes. Thus NASA's Earth Observation System (EOS) was evolved to have a series of multi-instrument orbital platforms. This makes satellites very heavy and obviously expensive. In addition, the response or the gestation period to realise a mission is too long. For example, TERRA (formerly known as EOS AM-1) supports five instruments to study various aspects of land, ocean and atmosphere, covering a broad spectrum of the electromagnetic radiation. The satellite weighs about 4600 kg and produces 3 kW. This was in the planning stage for more than a decade, and was finally launched in December, 1999. The ENVISAT of the European Space Agency (ESA) has a similar story. It carries sensors covering visible–IR–NIR–TIR–microwave regions. The combination of sensors is chosen to make measurements of various processes of atmosphere, land and ocean. ENVISAT weighs 8200 kg and generates 6.6 kW. It took more than ten years to launch this satellite also.

If we plan for smaller satellites which will have a faster response to mission needs and are cheaper, the mission has to limit the number of sensors on board any one satellite, thus limiting the ability for multi-disciplinary observation, and hence going back to theme-specific missions. The Total Ozone Mapping Mission (TOMS), Tropical Rainfall Mapping Mission (TRMM), SeaWiFS (for ocean colour) are examples of this trend. But they do not have the capability of concurrent observation of a phenomenon/region in different spectral regions or using different observation strategies. The solution to this impasse is to have a number of small satellites carrying different observation capabilities to 'fly in formation'. The formation-flying of satellites is a relatively a new paradigm for space-based surveillance and remote sensing. In satellite formation flying, multiple satellites work together in a group to accomplish the objective of one larger satellite. A practical example of such a system is NASA's mission, called the Afternoon Constellation, or the A-Train. Here 'trailing formations' are created by five satellites orbiting on the same path. Each one follows the previous one separated by a specific time interval to either view a target at different times, or obtain varied viewing angles of the target. The satellites are in a polar orbit, crossing the equator north bound at about 1:30 pm local time, within seconds to minutes of each other. This allows near-simultaneous observations of a wide variety of parameters thereby achieving a multidisciplinary observation capability as in a big satellite. Each satellite is smaller, lighter and simpler to manufacture and hence the combined cost for all the satellites could be less expensive than having a big satellite accommodating all the payloads. Such an approach also reduces the risk of losing total observational capability due to malfunctioning of some subsystems or launch failure, apart from relatively higher reliability due to less complex systems. Another concept is cluster formations. A satellite cluster is a group of satellites that fly within very close range of each other (250 m–5 km). These satellites coordinate their activities, so that each satellite carrying antenna/telescopes by use of synthetic aperture techniques can simulate a single, very large satellite. The cluster operates as a 'virtual' satellite with a very large effective aperture, without the need for the heavy infrastructure that would be required for a monolithic satellite with the equivalent aperture. Another application of satellite clusters is interferometry. However, management of formation flying will require precise orbit and attitude control and increased automation for planning and scheduling, both in pre-flight mission planning and during operations.

Another shift in the earth observation scenario is the role of commercial operators in the space segment. The remote sensing satellite activity over the world was started as a national space agencies' funded programme. In the USA, concern regarding the Government's role in an operational system led the Congress to pass the Land Remote Sensing commercialisation act (LANDSAT Act) in 1984. According to this act, the National Oceanic and Atmospheric Administration (NOAA), who was operating the Landsat since 1979, was to delegate the management of Landsat 4/5 and their data distribution to the private sector. In addition, NOAA was to pursue procurement of future Landsat services from the private sector. The private company EOSAT won the competitive bidding and took over the operation of Landsat systems in 1985. However, the US effort to have the Landsat 4/5 programme as a commercial venture failed. In 1992, US Congress repealed the 1984 act and enacted the Land Remote Sensing Policy act and returned the responsibility of Landsat to the Government and also identified Landsat continuity as the fundamental goal of the Landsat programme. Thus Landsat-7 is managed by NOAA, with the United States Geological Survey/EROS Data Centre (USGS/EDC) having the responsibility of product generation, distribution and archiving. Thus Landsat is back as a national venture. However, in all the policy guidelines, the US government wants to promote and not preclude private sector commercial opportunities in Landsat-type remote sensing.

The US government (USG), as part of its commercialisation effort, licensed private agencies to develop a satellite system and sell satellite imagery with (initially) a 1 m resolution, though with certain restrictions referred to as 'shutter control'. (Under the shutter control, the USG reserves the right to interrupt or limit commercial operations should extraordinary circumstances warrant it.) The first such system is IKONOS launched in 1999. Following this, several private sector ventures emerged with goals to design and develop and operate high resolution Earth Observing Satellites having sub-metre spatial resolution in the panchromatic spectral band.

Thus high resolution images from space will be available from multiple sources; all operated fully by private entrepreneurs, without government support. The commercial viability of these high resolution systems is due to the large market for large scale mapping including urban facility mapping and also due to the military requirements for reconnaissance.

Thus the high resolution images which were accessible to only a few defence and intelligence agencies are now in the public domain. This could pose a major political and security problem. We shall address some of these issues later. However, it should be borne in mind that these high resolution systems will not have global coverage as Landsat/IRS/SPOT, because of their limited swath and hence poor temporal resolution; but they are very useful to study specific areas at a large scale. Thus these are special classes of satellites meeting the needs of only a certain class of remote sensing data users. The medium resolution data which can provide global coverage and which caters to scientific studies (as in global change) and natural resources management applications (as in land use, crop production estimation, watershed management and so on) is still government funded. The question also being debated is whether Landsat, SPOT or IRS class of satellites which are the work horses for natural resource management, can be commercially viable?

The earth observation technology has come a long way from its early beginnings in the 1960s. It is no more an issue of 'what the use of the images are' but is more an issue of 'meeting market demand, making commercial viability and maintaining security'. The technology and systems of earth observation are fast-changing—detailed, rapid and large volumes of data collection are being distributed efficiently across the globe and enabling a large suite of market economics and driven by government–private sector partnerships. With a large technological capability in earth observation (resolutions, bands, coverage, sophistication of measurements), the concept of the user segment has also seen a dramatic change. Today, a user of an earth observation satellite is no more the scientist/analyst in a lab but is the large-community of professionals in government, private sector, academia and even citizens, who seek a final solution to their problems. Thus, today an end user is interested in getting a solution for his problem and this may require analysis, fusion and integration of various images, maps, location data, social media data, complex tables, in an 'analysis model' that be customised as per user needs. Such a change in perspective and demand has brought about yet another trend in the form of large value addition and customisation market with earth observation images forming one big data element and the making of tailored solutions. Thus, a large market exists where users are ready to pay a cost for obtaining their solution needs, rather than just obtaining images and data.

1.8   LEGAL AND ETHICAL ASPECTS

The launch of the first artificial earth satellite Sputnik-1 on 4 October 1957, opened up new vistas of opportunities for mankind. This new capability also posed a number of legal issues, which were not thought of earlier. Every country has sovereignty over their airspace. What about outer space? Initially there was not much agreement about how high the airspace sovereignty extended. After extensive international consultation, the United Nations formulated the 'Treaty on principles governing the activities of states in the exploration and use of outer space including the moon and other celestial bodies'. The treaty highlights that the exploration of outer space shall be carried out for the benefit and interest of all countries. No nation can have sovereignty over space or any celestial bodies. All activities shall be carried out in the interest of maintaining international peace and security and promoting international cooperation and understanding. These are some of the highlights of the treaty. The treaty entered into force in October 1967. The outer space treaty can be considered as the basic framework on international space law. Both the USA and USSR realised the great potential of satellites to surreptitiously watch other's country. Thus a new chapter in spying started using satellite-borne imaging cameras. While this information is available only to a select few in the government, with the launch of Landsat-1, images from space, though with coarse resolution, are available in the public domain world-over. Soon nations realised the potential of such data for economic and military espionage. Many countries expressed concern of a country being watched without its knowledge. The outer space treaty covers only general issues relating to use of outer space, not specifically remote sensing. Based on extensive consultations and negotiations, the United Nations Committee on the Peaceful Uses of Outer Space (COPOUS), brought out a set of principles relating to remote sensing of earth from space, which was adopted by the UN General Assembly in 1986. The set of fifteen principles brought out by COPOUS include amongst others, 'the remote sensing activities shall be carried out for the benefit and in the interest of all countries and taking into particular consideration, the needs of the developing countries. The activities shall not be conducted in a manner detrimental to the legitimate rights and interests of the sensed state'. Principle XII states that 'as soon as the primary data and the processed data concerning the territory under its jurisdiction are produced, the sensed state have access to them on a non-discriminatory basis and on reasonable cost terms. The sensed state shall also have access to the available analysed information concerning the territory under its jurisdiction in the possession of any state participating in remote sensing activities on the same basis and terms, particular regard being given to the needs and interests of the developing countries'. The interpretation of these principles and its implementation in letter and spirit is not an easy task. These principles were enunciated, when only medium resolution data (10 m and above) were in the public domain. The situation has drastically changed since then. Now sub-metre resolution imagery of any part of the earth is available commercially. Thus, we are getting to a situation where imagery of any part of the world is available for a price to anyone, at resolution almost close to that which the best spy satellite gives (which is about 10 cm). How would you like someone peeping into your courtyard without your knowledge?! Are we reaching a situation where not only the national security is at risk but even personal privacy is encroached upon!! However, there is

---

Spy in the Sky

Imaging from space started for reconnaissance. Both USA and USSR realised the potential of the space platform to look into the other's territory without being interrupted as in the case of aerial reconnaissance missions. Corona was the first operational imaging satellite reconnaissance system of the USA. 18 August 1960 marked the first successful mission that returned film from space. [The US intelligence community used two sets of terminology to refer to the reconnaissance satellite activities, one that was a designator for the specific programme and second that was for the individual camera system. The programme managers referred to the satellite by their programme names—Corona, Argon, and so on. The users of the imagery referred to reconnaissance satellite and their imagery by the KEYHOLE (KH) designators that were assigned to the camera system (McDonald, 1997). The first Corona camera is KH-1.] Early missions had photographic cameras. The film after exposure was jettisoned to earth and recovered in mid-air. The quality of imagery improved over years from about 13 m for the first KH-1 camera to about 2 m towards the end of the Corona programme. KH-4 had dual cameras to get stereoscopic imagery. The Soviets also had successful photoreconnaissance satellites (Zenit) soon after the first US Corona. These photographic systems are broadly similar to the KH cameras.

Because of the high secrecy, all the technical details and capabilities of these satellites are not known to the public. The latest of the reconnaissance system KH-12 (improved crystal) operates in the visible, NIR and TIR regions. These sensors probably have low-light-level CCD-image intensifiers, which can provide night time images. The resolution achievable is said to be 10 cm (5 cm is the limit due to atmospheric effect, Appendix 1). A periscope-like rotating mirror reflects the image onto the primary mirror enabling the KH-12 to take imagery at very high angles of obliquity—hundreds of kilometers away from its flight path. The images acquired by KH-12 are transmitted in real time via Milstar relay satellites to appropriate ground stations. The imaging telescope is a folded Cassegrain with a 4 m diameter primary (IRS CARTO-2 primary diameter 0.7 m) and weighs 18 tons (IRS CARTO-2 weight ~ 1.5 ton). These do not have the capability to penetrate clouds. All weather capability is achieved by a SAR imaging system called LACROSSE, with a resolution capability of 1 m. The Defense Advanced Research Project Agency (DARPA) is working on a lightweight SAR system. The objective is to have a constellation of 24 satellites carrying SAR, which would allow for a rapid revisit rate (~ 15 m) to most areas of earth.

(Sources: Federation of American Scientist—FAS websites, Jane's Space Directory Website)

also a section who believe that the availability of such data will increase transparency, which will enhance stability by deterring aggression, providing assurance of benign intentions and also correcting unacceptable behaviour. On the negative side, the images may reveal military vulnerabilities that invite attack by regional adversaries (Mullen, 1999). There is no doubt that unrestricted availability of remote sensing data has done more good than harm.

Data is always neutral. It is how we use them that makes our living better on this planet. Probably the most basic principle to follow, individually and nationally is to *'treat others as you want them to treat you'*.

FOR FURTHER READING

1. Lillesand T M and Kiefer R W, *Remote Sensing and Image Interpretation*, John Wiley & Sons, Chapter 1.
2. *http://www.ldeo.columbia.edu/res/fac/rsvlab/fundamentals_e.pdf*
3. *http://geoinfo.amu.edu.pl/wpk/rst/rst/Front/tofc.html*
4. *http://www.itc.nl/library/papers_2009/general/PrinciplesRemoteSensing.pdf*
5. Mohammed J L, Automated Mission Planning for the TechSat 21 Formation Flying Cluster Experiment, *http://www.aaai.org/Papers/FLAIRS/2002/FLAIRS02-005.pdf*

2 | Electromagnetic Radiation

Since electromagnetic energy forms the basic source for remote sensing observations, it is useful to have an understanding of the basic properties of electromagnetic (EM) radiation. The intention here is not to provide a detailed account of electromagnetic theory, but to present the fundamentals and the basis for the reader to understand and appreciate its function in remote sensing. Electromagnetic waves are produced basically due to the motion of electric charge. Changing electric fields are set up by oscillation of charged particles and these changing electric fields induce changing magnetic fields in the surrounding medium. Changing magnetic fields set up more changing electric fields and so on. Thus, since a time varying electric field produces a time varying magnetic field and vice versa, once generated, the electromagnetic wave is self-propagating. The net result is that the wave energy travels across space. Thus, these waves consist of magnetic and electric fields. When propagating in homogeneous, isotropic media, the direction of the two fields are at right angles to each other and both the fields are at right angles to the direction of propagation (Fig. 2.1). The EM waves can be characterised by frequency, wavelength, intensity, direction of travel and plane of polarisation. Wavelength is the distance between two successive crests or troughs (Fig. 2.2). It is generally represented by λ and measured in metres or a fraction of it, nanometre (10^{-9} m), micrometre (10^{-6} m), and so on.

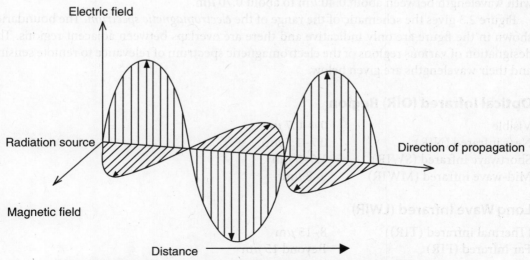

Fig. 2.1 Schematics showing the relation between electric and magnetic field and the direction of propagation.

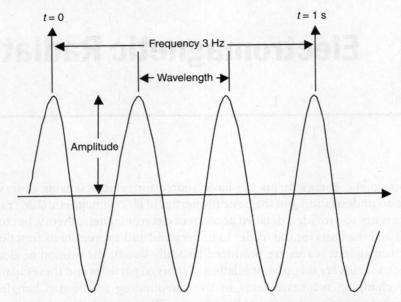

Fig. 2.2   Frequency, wavelength and amplitude of a wave. The x-axis is time for frequency measurement and distance for wavelength measurement, see also Fig. 2.5.

The frequency is the number of wave crests passing a fixed point in one second, measured in Hertz (Hz) or a multiple of it such as kiloHertz (10^3 Hertz), megaHertz (10^6 Hertz), and so on. Amplitude is the height of its crest from the midpoint. The square of the amplitude is proportional to the energy transported by the wave. Electromagnetic radiation covers a wide range of frequency (wavelength), extending from gamma rays (wavelength $<10^{-10}$ m) to radio waves (wavelength >1 m), called the electromagnetic spectrum. The visible spectrum, which we normally call light waves, occupies only a small portion of the electromagnetic spectrum with wavelength between about 0.40 μm to about 0.70 μm.

Figure 2.3 gives the schematic of the range of the *electromagnetic spectrum*. The boundaries shown in the figure are only indicative and there are overlaps between adjacent regions. The designation of various regions of the electromagnetic spectrum of relevance to remote sensing and their wavelengths are given below.

Optical Infrared (OIR) Region

Visible	0.4–0.7 μm
Near infrared (NIR)	0.7–1.5 μm
Shortwave infrared (SWIR)	1.5–3 μm
Mid-wave infrared (MWIR)	3–8 μm

Long Wave Infrared (LWIR)

(Thermal infrared (TIR))	8–15 μm
Far infrared (FIR)	Beyond 15 μm

(There is no universally accepted designation for the IR region beyond the visible region. In literature, there are also marginal differences in the range of wavelength shown.)

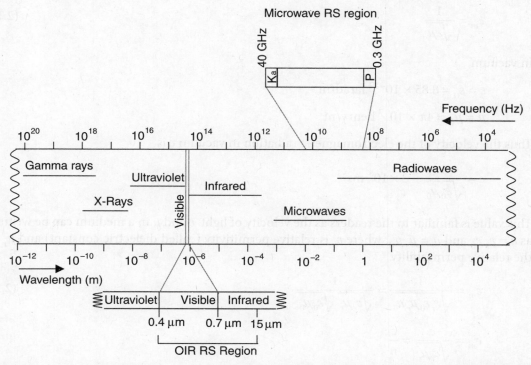

Fig. 2.3 The electromagnetic spectrum. Boundaries of various regions shown are not well-defined, different values are found in literature. However, all regions blend together into a continuous spectrum.

Microwaves

Band	Frequency (wavelength)
P band	0.3–1 GHz (30–100 cm)
L band	1–2 GHz (15–30 cm)
S band	2–4 GHz (7.5–15 cm)
C band	4–8 GHz (3.8–7.5 cm)
X band	8–12.5 GHz (2.4–3.8 cm)
Ku band	12.5–18 GHz (1.7–2.4 cm)
K band	18–26.5 GHz (1.1–1.7 cm)
Ka band	26.5–40 GHz (0.75–1.1 cm)

(Note: 1 GHz = 10^9 Hz)

2.1   VELOCITY OF EM RADIATION

Various properties of electromagnetic radiation can be deduced mathematically using four differential equations, generally referred to as Maxwell's equations. Readers interested in the mathematical formulation of electromagnetic theory may refer to Born and Wolf (1964).

Using Maxwell's equation it is possible to arrive at a relation between the velocity of the EM wave and the properties of the medium. The velocity c_m in a medium with the electric permittivity ε and the magnetic permeability μ is given by

$$c_m = \frac{1}{\sqrt{\varepsilon\mu}} \tag{2.1}$$

In vacuum,

$$\varepsilon = \varepsilon_0 \simeq 8.85 \times 10^{-12} \text{ farad/m}$$

$$\mu = \mu_0 \simeq 4\pi \times 10^{-7} \text{ henry/m}$$

Thus the velocity of the electromagnetic radiation in vacuum c is

$$c = \frac{1}{\sqrt{\varepsilon_0\mu_0}} \sim 3 \times 10^8 \text{ ms}^{-1}$$

This value is familiar to the readers as the velocity of light. ε and μ in a medium can be written as $\varepsilon = \varepsilon_r\,\varepsilon_0$ and $\mu = \mu_r\mu_0$, where ε_r is relative permitivity (called dielectric constant) and μ_r is the relative permeability.

$$c_m = \frac{1}{\sqrt{\varepsilon_r\varepsilon_0\mu_r\mu_0}} = \frac{1}{\sqrt{\varepsilon_r\mu_r}\ \sqrt{\varepsilon_0\mu_0}} \tag{2.2}$$

$$c_m = \frac{c}{\sqrt{\varepsilon_r\mu_r}} = \frac{c}{n}$$

That is, the velocity in a dielectric medium is reduced by a factor $1/\sqrt{\varepsilon_r\ \mu_r}$ compared to that in vacuum (frequency remains constant, and the wavelength is reduced). n is referred to as refractive index (RI). The media we consider are normally non-magnetic and hence $\mu_r = 1$. Therefore n $= \sqrt{\varepsilon_r}$. In general, ε_r can be complex (and hence n), in which case the medium is lossy, that is, the wave is absorbed. The imaginary part is responsible for the absorption of the wave; hence when ε_r is a real positive number, the medium does not absorb EM waves. (For subsequent discussions the subscript r is omitted for convenience, and the relative permitivity and relative permeability are simply expressed as ε and μ respectively.)

The wavelength λ, frequency v and the speed of the EM wave are related such that

$$c = v\lambda \tag{2.3}$$

Other quantities generally associated with wave motion are the period $T(l/v)$, wave number k $(2\pi/\lambda)$, and angular frequency $\omega(2\pi v)$.

2.2   POLARISATION

Polarisation of the EM radiation is an important parameter in remote sensing especially in the microwave region. As discussed earlier, the EM wave is made up of electric and magnetic fields, which are mutually orthogonal and transverse to the direction of propagation; hence the direction of one of the force fields can define the other. It is customary to consider the electric vector for the study of polarisation. If the EM wave is moving in the z direction, the electric vector will be in the xy plane, but can take any orientation. Polarisation defines

Permittivity is the property of a medium, which influences the force between electrical charges. The permittivity of a medium (material) is usually referred with respect to permittivity of free space and is called relative permittivity, also referred to as dielectric constant. Relative permittivity is the ratio of the permittivity of the substance to that of vacuum. Dielectric constant is a pure number and has no dimensions. Dielectric constant of pure water is 80. It means that the force between charges situated in water is eighty times less than if they were situated at the same distance apart in a vacuum. The higher the dielectric constant of a material, the poorer a conductor of electricity (or a more insulating material) it is.

Permeability is associated with the magnetic property of the medium (material). Permeability is a measure of 'conducting' the magnetic line of force into the material (when an iron is kept in a magnetic field the line of force 'crowds' into the iron as if they find it easier to go through the iron than through the air). Permeability is a measure of the extent to which magnetic lines of force (magnetic flux density) can penetrate a medium when a magnetising field is applied. Permeability is expressed as the ratio of the magnetic flux density (B) established within a material to the field strength (H) of the magnetising field ($\mu = B/H$). Usually the relative permeability, that is, the ratio of permeability of the material to that of vacuum is used. Relative permeability is a dimensionless number. Materials may be classified magnetically on the basis of their permeabilities. The force between the magnetic poles is inversely proportional to the permeability of the medium.

the orientation of the fields. For most sources of electromagnetic radiation, the radiation is composed of many waves with their electric vector randomly oriented with respect to each other. In such cases, the radiation is unpolarised or randomly polarised. This happens since each charge independently radiates a wave train in a short time ($\sim 10^{-8}$ s), which does not have any specific phase relationship with another wave train. When the electric field oscillates with the direction of the electric vector in a constant direction, we have a linearly polarised wave. This is also referred to as a *plane polarised wave*. If the electric vector is in the plane of incidence it is called *vertical polarisation* and if it is at right angles to the plane of incidence it is called *horizontal polarisation* (plane of incidence, is the plane containing the incident ray and normal to the reflecting surface at the point of incidence) (Fig. 2.4). When the end point of the electric vector sweeps a circle it is called *circularly polarised* and when the rotation is in the clockwise (looking towards the source) the wave is called *right circularly polarised*. If the rotation is anti-clockwise, we get *left circularly polarised* light. If the tip of the electric vector moves in an ellipse, it is called *elliptically polarised*. Light sources are in general partially polarised, that is, a mixture of unpolarised and polarised light.

2.3 COHERENT RADIATION

Two waves are said to be *coherent* with each other if there is a systematic relationship between their phases, which is referred as having a constant 'phase' relationship both in time and space. A description of the phase of a wave is required, to understand coherence. *Phase* of a wave is expressed as a fraction of a period with respect to a reference. It is usually specified by angular

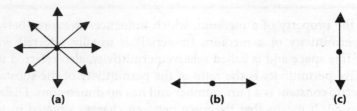

Fig. 2.4 Representation of polarisation. Viewed in the direction of motion (Head on). The arrows represent electric vector (a) unpolarised (b) horizontal polarisation (c) vertical polarisation. The plane of incidence is aligned with the arrow of (c).

measure, with one period being 360° (2π radians). The reference is taken from the previous passage through zero from the negative to the positive direction. In Fig. 2.5, the phase angle of the crest A is 90° (π/2) while the subsequent zero crossing B is 180° (π). The trough C has a phase angle of 270°. Points A and C are said to be 180° out of phase. Please note that the wave could be represented as variation with position at one time [Fig. 2.5(a)] or variation with time at one place [Fig. 2.5(b)]. For waves from a point source in an isotropic medium (that is, one in which speed is same along any direction), the phase is constant over a spherical surface drawn about the point source as a centre. The surface defined by the locus of points that have the same phase is called a *wave front*. The wave front will be perpendicular to the wave direction. The waves are named according to the shape of the wave front. For example, a wave whose surface of constant phase are parallel planes is called a *plane wave*. The absolute phase of a point on a wave is generally of no interest. What is of importance is the relative phase difference between the waves. Figure 2.6 shows two waves. At A, the waves 1 and 2 have a phase difference of π/2, which continues at all points. Two EM waves are coherent when the phase difference between them is constant in time and space. A perfectly coherent radiation is possible only when the beam contains a single frequency (single wavelength), that is, the radiation is monochromatic and the direction of motion of the waves are parallel, that is perfectly collimated. The types of coherence possible are (i) temporal coherence (ii) spatial coherence. A complete temporal coherence implies that the phase difference is maintained even after the waves have advanced through a distance. This is possible only if the waves are monochromatic. A spatial coherence means that the phase difference between two points in space is constant with time. Perfect spatial coherence is possible only for a pure plane wave (parallel beam). Superposition of the coherent waves produces interference. When the phase difference is 0 (or integral multiples of 2π), the amplitudes add up leading to *constructive interference*. When the phase difference is π (or odd multiples of π), the amplitude of waves cancel out giving *destructive interference*.

In practice there is no such thing as a perfectly coherent radiation. A perfect monochromatic radiation is only a mathematical proposition. In any practical situation there are a number of frequencies around a central frequency or wavelength. Thus a practical electromagnetic radiation we encounter will have a bandwidth Δv (or $\Delta\lambda$) around a central frequency v (or λ). If we consider a radiation with a bandwidth Δv, one can define a coherence length (Rees, 1990), that is, length over which there is a strong correlation between the amplitudes such that

$$l_{coh} = \frac{c}{\Delta v} = \frac{\lambda^2}{\Delta\lambda} \qquad (2.4)$$

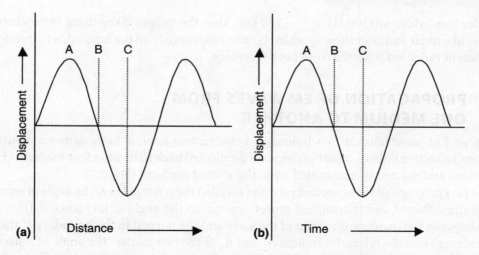

Fig. 2.5   (a) Wave showing amplitude variation with position at one time (b) Amplitude variation with time at one place.

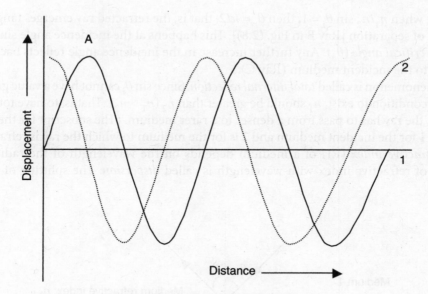

Fig. 2.6   Ilustration of phase difference.

The coherence time Δt_{coh} can be defined such that $\Delta t_{coh} = 1/\Delta \nu$. The significance of coherence length is that when the difference of the optical path is of the order of or much greater than the coherence length, interference effects are negligible or do not take place. Since the coherence length is inversely proportional to bandwidth, radiation with narrow bandwidths like laser and radar sources have long coherent lengths. For C band SAR, like one used in ERS-1, with a

Doppler bandwidth of 1300 Hz, $l_{coh} \simeq 230$ km. Thus the images taken using monochromatic sources like radar and laser show speckled (grainy) appearance on the image due to interference of coherent radiation reflected from nearby regions.

2.4   PROPAGATION OF EM WAVES FROM ONE MEDIUM TO ANOTHER

When an EM wave falls on to a boundary between two lossless homogeneous media with different refractive indices, a part of the wave is reflected back to the incident medium (Fresnel reflection) and the rest is transmitted on to the second medium (Fig. 2.7).

The rays propagated to the second medium is called the *refracted ray*. The angle of *refraction*, θ_r and the reflected and transmitted power depend on the angle of incidence θ_i (that is, the angle between the incident direction of the wave and the normal to the boundary at the point of incidence) and the refractive indices n_1 and n_2 of the two media. The angle of reflection is equal to the angle of incidence and the angle of refraction θ_r is given by the *Snell's Law*,

$$n_1 \sin \theta_i = n_2 \sin \theta_r$$

$$\sin \theta_r = \frac{n_1}{n_2} \sin \theta_i \tag{2.5}$$

In Eq. 2.5, when $n_1/n_2 \sin \theta_i = 1$, then $\theta_r = \pi/2$, that is, the refracted ray emerges tangent to the boundary of separation [Ray B in Fig. (2.8)]. This happens at the incidence angle $\sin^{-1}(n_2/n_1)$, called the *critical angle* (θ_c). Any further increase in the incidence angle reflects back the total radiation to the incident medium (Ray C).

This phenomenon is called *total internal reflection*. Since $\sin \theta_i$ cannot have a value greater than 1, for this condition to exist, n_1 should be greater than n_2 ($n_1 > n_2$). That is, to have total internal reflection, the ray has to pass from a denser to a rarer medium. (The subscript for the refractive index n is 1 for the incident medium and 2 is for the medium to which the ray is refracted.)

The *refractive index* (RI) of a medium depends on the wavelength of the radiation. The variation of refractive index with wavelength is called *dispersion*. The splitting of colours of

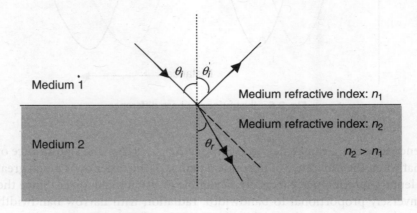

Fig. 2.7   Reflection and refraction of electromagnetic radiation.

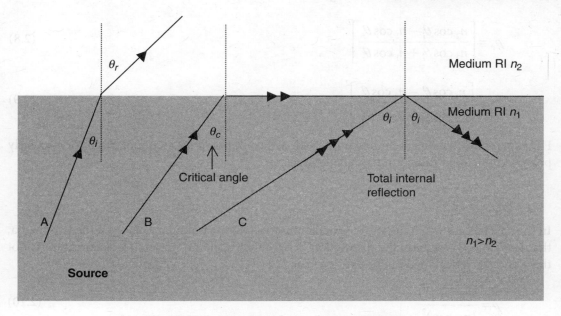

Fig. 2.8 Schematics showing total internal reflection.

white light, when it passes through a prism is due to this phenomenon. Since the refractive index of the colours are different (the RI of the prism material for red light is less than that for violet and for yellow light lies in between), they bend through different angles, while it enters and leaves the prism, thereby spreading the colour as white light leaves the prism, with the red rays least deviated and the violet rays most deviated.

2.4.1 FRESNEL RELATION FOR REFLECTION AND TRANSMISSION

We shall now consider the reflection and transmission when an EM wave is incident at an interface between two lossless dielectric media. The reflectance ρ and transmittance (t) depend on the wavelength, angular distribution and the polarisation of the incident wave. Without elaborating the derivation, we shall provide the final results for the reflectance for a specific wavelength (Born and Wolf, 1964).

$$\rho_v = \frac{\tan^2(\theta_i - \theta_r)}{\tan^2(\theta_i + \theta_r)} \tag{2.6}$$

$$\rho_h = \frac{\sin^2(\theta_i - \theta_r)}{\sin^2(\theta_i + \theta_r)} \tag{2.7}$$

v and h refer to vertical and horizontal polarisation and θ_i and θ_r refer to angles of incidence and refraction.

Through Snell's Law and several trigonometric transformations, the above can be written in terms of refractive index as

$$\rho_v = \left[\frac{n_2 \cos\theta_i - n_1 \cos\theta_r}{n_2 \cos\theta_i + n_1 \cos\theta_r} \right]^2 \tag{2.8}$$

$$\rho_h = \left[\frac{n_1 \cos\theta_i - n_2 \cos\theta_r}{n_1 \cos\theta_i + n_2 \cos\theta_r} \right]^2 \tag{2.9}$$

For a total reflected flux including both polarised component for an unpolarised (or circularly polarised) incident radiation the reflectivity is

$$\rho = \frac{\rho_v + \rho_h}{2}$$

In the special case when the wave is incident normal to the boundary between the two media, that is, θ_i and θ_r are zero, the distinction between vertical and horizontal polarisation is not there and the reflectance can be expressed as

$$\rho = \frac{(n_2 - n_1)^2}{(n_2 + n_1)^2} \tag{2.10}$$

For a normal incidence, the transmittance t is given by

$$t = \frac{4n_1^2}{(n_1 + n_2)^2}$$

We find from Eq. 2.6, when $\theta_i + \theta_r = \pi/2$

$$\rho_v = 0$$

That is, the reflected wave is completely polarised normal to the plane of incidence. This angle of incidence is called the *polarising angle* (or Brewster's angle).

We shall now calculate these values for water. In the optical region, the RI of water can be taken as 1.33. If the incident medium is air, we can take $n_1 = 1$. Equation 2.10 reduces to

$$\rho = \frac{(n_2 - 1)^2}{(n_2 + 1)^2} \tag{2.11}$$

The reflectance from water for vertical incidence works out to be ~2% and the Brewester's angle 53°. At microwave frequency, the RI of water is about 9, which gives reflectance for normal incidence at microwave region ~64% and Brewester's angle 84°. It is this higher reflectance in the microwave region that makes it possible to have radar altimetry at microwave frequencies for studies of ocean.

For normal incidence, Eq. 2.11 is modified for a complex refractive index $n' - in''$ (Section 2.5.1) as

$$\rho = \frac{(n' - 1)^2 + (n'')^2}{(n' + 1)^2 + (n'')^2}$$

Near the absorption band $n'' >> n'$ and then

$$\rho \cong 1$$

Thus if a band of electromagnetic radiation is incident on a polished surface, the reflected energy contains a relatively large portion of spectral energy around the absorption bands of the surface material. This is referred to as *restrahlen lines*.

2.4.2 SOME MORE WAVE PROPERTIES OF EM RADIATION

Diffraction

We generally think of light as travelling in a straight line. Therefore we expect a sharp geometric shadow when light encounters an obstacle in its path. However, waves have the characteristic of bending around the 'edges' it encounters. Since the EM radiation is a wave, it bends around an obstacle – an edge, slit, hole, and so on – producing some spreading of energy at the geometrical shadow. Thus the shadow produced by EM radiation is fuzzy and not sharp. The bending of waves around an obstacle is called *diffraction*. Diffraction is an important physical aspect inherent in all wave phenomena. Diffraction by an aperture depends on λ/d, where λ is the wavelength and d is the aperture width (diameter). The effect is prominent when λ/d is large. The diffraction pattern for a slit or hole consists of a bright central maximum flanked on either side by secondary maxima and minima, with the intensity of each succeeding secondary maximum decreasing as the distance from the center increases (see Section 5.3). Diffraction plays an important role in limiting the resolving power of imaging instruments. We shall deal with this aspect in a later chapter.

Doppler Effect

It is a common experience that the whistle of a train appears to increase in pitch as it approaches a stationary observer and the pitch becomes lower as the train moves away from the observer. This phenomenon of apparent change in frequency, with the relative motion of the source and the observer, is known as the *Doppler effect*. Thus an EM radiation received by an observer will have shorter wavelength if the source and the observer approach each other, and a longer wavelength if they recede from each other. The amount of change in wavelength is directly proportional to the net relative velocity along the line between the source and the observer (see Section 7.4.2).

The Doppler effect is used to find out the movement of stars from the observed shift of any characteristic wavelength. (The exact wavelength of the characteristic wavelength is known from laboratory measurement.) As the star moves away, the line is shifted to the longer wavelength, which is generally known as the *red shift*.

In remote sensing, this phenomenon is used in instruments like SAR (Chapter 7) and for atmospheric wind measurements by observing scattering of laser from tracers, such as aerosols.

2.5 ATTENUATION

When EMR passes through a medium, two phenomena take place (i) absorption and (ii) scattering.

2.5.1 ABSORPTION

In electromagnetics, materials can be broadly classified as conductors and dielectrics (insulators). There is no sharp line division between dielectrics and conductors. We may consider that when $\sigma/\omega\varepsilon > 1$, the material is a conductor, where σ is the conductivity. In good conductors, like metals, $\sigma/\omega\varepsilon$ is much larger than 1. Similarly for a good dielectric, $\sigma/\omega\varepsilon$ is much less than unity. Here our interest is to understand the effect of relevant parameters of the medium on the absorption of the EM radiation.

A lossy dielectric can be characterised by a complex dielectric constant consisting of a real and imaginary part such that

$$\varepsilon = \varepsilon' - i\varepsilon''$$

where $i = \sqrt{-1}$. Here the real part ε' corresponds to the lossless component and the imaginary part ε'' represents the lossy component. Since the refractive index $n = \sqrt{\varepsilon}$, the refractive index is also a complex number for a lossy dielectric such that $n = n' - in''$, where n' and n'' are the real and imaginary parts of the refractive index.

It can be shown that (Ulaby et. al., 1986)

$$\varepsilon' = (n')^2 - (n'')^2$$

$$\varepsilon'' = 2n'\,n''$$

In a lossy medium, as the wave propagates, the wave amplitude and hence the intensity gets progressively reduced. The power density (irradiance) (E_z) at a point z is given by

$$E_z = E_0 e^{-k_a z} \tag{2.12}$$

k_a is the power absorption coefficient and has the unit inverse of length. Another quantity of interest in remote sensing is *penetration depth (absorption length)* l_a.

$$l_a = \frac{1}{k_a}$$

The penetration depth may be defined as the depth at which the power is reduced by $1/e$.

When $\varepsilon'' << \varepsilon'$, the absorption length can be expressed as

$$l_a = \frac{\lambda_0 \sqrt{\varepsilon'}}{2\pi\varepsilon''} \tag{2.13}$$

Thus the penetration of the EM radiation depends on the free space wavelength λ_0 and the dielectric constant. From Eq. 2.13, it is seen that higher the wavelength, the longer distance it takes for the reduction to reduce to $1/e$ value. That is why L band SAR penetrates more than C band SAR.

2.5.2 SCATTERING

If the medium is not homogeneous (that is, it has dielectric discontinuities), the radiation in addition to being absorbed will also be scattered. By absorption we mean that the energy is transferred into other forms—say heat. However, both the phenomena reduce the intensity of the radiation from the incident direction. In case of scattering, the energy is not lost to the medium, but the radiation is scattered out to other directions, thereby reducing the amount of radiation in the original direction. As in the case of absorption, we have scattering coefficient k_s and *scattering length* l_s.

The combined effects of absorption and scattering in reducing the intensity from the incident radiation is called *attenuation* (sometimes referred to as *extinction*). In remote sensing we generally have inhomogeneous media (stalk of crops, trunk and crown of trees), we have both absorption and scattering. We can define the *attenuation length*, similar to absorption length, that is, the length over which the power falls by a factor of e due to the combined effect of absorption and scattering.

The attenuation (extinction) coefficient k_e is given by,

$$k_e = k_a + k_s$$

since k_a and k_s are wavelength dependent, the transport of radiation in the medium is also wavelength dependent.

The attenuation (extinction) length l_e

$$\frac{1}{l_e} = \frac{1}{l_a} + \frac{1}{l_s}$$

Another important parameter is single-scattering albedo (ω_0)

$$\omega_0 = \frac{k_s}{k_e}$$

ω_0 is essentially the probability that given an interaction between the photon and the particle, the photon will be scattered rather than absorbed. When the attenuation is primarily due to scattering, ω_0 is close to one, but when the attenuation is mainly due to absorption, ω_0 is near to zero.

When electromagnetic radiation propagates in the atmosphere, the attenuation is expressed in dB (decibels). The attenuation A in dB is given by (Rees, 1990).

$$A = 10 \log_{10} (I_1/I_2)$$

where I_1 is the incident intensity and I_2 is the attenuated intensity passing through the medium. In the OIR region, it is expressed as optical depth τ

$$\tau = \log_e (I_1/I_2)$$

2.6 QUANTUM NATURE OF EM RADIATION

The phenomenon of interference and polarisation require the EM radiation to behave like a wave, while for some interaction, like in the photoelectric effect, the radiation behaves like particles. Thus the EM radiation has a dual nature—wave and particle. The particulate nature of the EM radiation is explained in terms of the Quantum Theory. According to the Quantum Theory, the EM radiation moves in space as discrete packets or quanta of energy propagating with the same speed and direction defined by the Wave Theory. Each quantum of radiation – called *photon* – has an energy e_v related to the frequency such that

$$e_v = hv$$

where h is the Planck constant (6.63×10^{-34} Ws^2).

Since $c = v\lambda$, the energy of a photon e_λ in terms of wavelength is given by

$$e_\lambda = \frac{ch}{\lambda}$$

Let us calculate the energy of a single photon at 0.5 μm

$$e_{\cdot 0.5\mu} = \frac{6.63 \times 10^{-34} \times 3 \times 10^8}{0.5 \times 10^{-6}} = 40 \times 10^{-20} \text{ J}$$

In quantum physics, another unit of energy is electron volt (eV) defined as the energy gained by an electron, when it is accelerated through a potential difference of 1 volt. Though this is not generally used in remote sensing it is useful to be familiar with this terminology.

$$1\text{eV} = 16 \times 10^{-20} \text{ J}$$

What is the wavelength of photon, which gives 1 eV?

$$16 \times 10^{-20} = \frac{6.63 \times 10^{-34} \times 3 \times 10^8}{\lambda}$$

$$\lambda \cong 1.2 \ \mu m$$

In classical EM radiation, the radiant energy is dependent on the square of wave amplitude, whereas in quantum concept, the power depends on the number of photons N_p, which can be calculated from the spectral radiant energy Q_λ (See Chapter 3).

$$N_p = \int \frac{\lambda Q_\lambda}{hc} d\lambda$$

where the integral is over the whole wavelength contained in the beam. The photon flux ϕ_p is given by

$$\phi_p = \frac{dN_p}{dt}$$

For photon detectors, the current produced depends on the number of photons per second incident on the device.

2.7 THERMAL RADIATION

Any object above absolute zero emits electromagnetic radiation. Thus the objects we see around, including ourselves are thermal radiators! An ideal thermal radiator is called a black body, which emits radiation as per Planck's law given below.

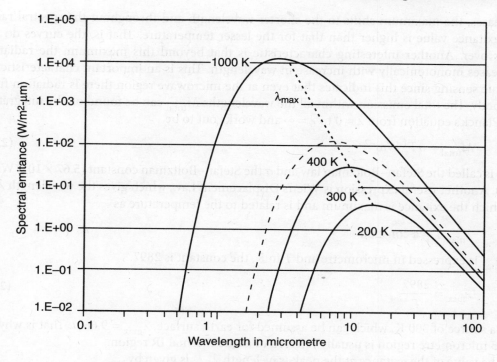

Fig. 2.9 Black body exitance at different temperature.

$$M_\lambda = \frac{2\pi hc^2}{\lambda^5[\exp(ch/\lambda kT) - 1]} \tag{2.14}$$

M_λ = spectral radiant exitance, h = Planck's constant: 6.6256×10^{-34} Ws^2,
c = velocity of light: 2.9979×10^8 ms^{-1}, k = Boltzmann's constant: 1.3805×10^{-23} WsK^{-1},
T = absolute temperature in K, λ = wavelength in m.

The value obtained after substituting for the parameters in Eq. 2.14, when divided by 10^6 gives M_λ in the conventional units of Wm^{-2} μm^{-1}.

A *black body* is an ideal surface such that

- it absorbs all incident radiation regardless of the wavelength or direction of the incident radiation,
- for a given temperature and wavelength, no body can emit more energy than a black body, and
- emission from a black body is independent of direction, that is, the black body is a diffuse emitter.

A practical black body assumes that the emission is from a cavity at a uniform fixed temperature (isothermal). It is a design challenge to minimise temperature gradients in a practical black body. Figure 2.9 shows the spectral exitance of a black body at various temperatures.

Studying the curves, a few observations can be made. The spectral exitance distribution curve is continuous and shows a single maximum for any temperature. As the temperature increases, the maximum shifts to the shorter wavelength and throughout the spectral range the exitance value is higher than that for the lesser temperature. That is, the curves do not cross over. Another interesting characteristic is that beyond this maximum, the radiation decreases monotonically with increase in wavelength. This is an important characteristic for remote sensing since this indicates that even at the microwave region there is radiation from the body. The total emission within all the wavelengths M_{total} can be found out by integrating the Planck's equation from $\lambda = 0$ to $\lambda = \infty$ and works out to be

$$M_{total} = \sigma T^4 \text{ Wm}^{-2} \tag{2.15}$$

This is called the Stefan–Boltzman law and σ the Stefan–Boltzman constant (5.67×10^{-8} Wm^{-2} K^{-4}). Another useful expression is Wien's Displacement Law, which gives the wavelength λ_{max} at which the exitance is maximum and is related to the temperature as

$$\lambda_{max} T = \text{a constant}$$

If λ_{max} is expressed in micrometre and T in K, the constant is 2897.

$$\lambda_{max} = \frac{2897}{T} \tag{2.16}$$

For a source of 300 K, which can be assumed for earth surface, $\lambda_{max} = 9.66 \, \mu$. That is why the 8–15 micrometre region is usually referred to as the thermal IR region.

The value of the exitance at the peak wavelength λ_{max} is given by

$$M_{\lambda_{max}} = b \, T^5$$

where $b = 1.286 \times 10^{-11}$ Wm^{-2} μm^{-1} K^{-5} $\qquad$ (2.17)

For 300 K, $M_{\lambda_{max}} = 31.2$ Wm^{-2} μm^{-1}

Equations 2.15 to 2.17 assume that the black body emits radiation into vacuum. On the other hand, if the back body is emitting radiation into a medium having a refractive index n, then in the Planck's equation, the wavelength and speed of light has to be modified by λ_m and c_m, where the subscript m refers to the respective values in the medium. Thus for example, Eq. 2.16 will be modified as $\lambda_{max} = 2897/nT$.

2.7.1   EMISSIVITY

We have been discussing the radiation emitted by an ideal black body, where the heat energy is converted to radiation at a maximum rate as per Planck's Law. However a real surface does not emit at this maximum rate. The emission from a real surface is characterised with respect to a black body. In order to do so, we introduce a term called *emissivity* which compares, the 'radiating capability' of a surface to that of a black body, which is an ideal radiator. Emissivity (e) is defined as the ratio of radiant exitance of the material of interest (M_m) to the radiant exitance of a black body (M_b) at the same temperature. That is

$$e = \frac{M_m}{M_b}$$

Emissivity is dimensionless, whose value lies between 1 and 0; zero for a non-radiating source and unity for a black body (see the box for more detailed definitions).

Based on the value of e, we can have three types of thermal radiators

(i)   Black body where $e = 1$, for all values of λ.
(ii) Grey body $e < 1$, but constant throughout the wavelength. That is, the emissivity is independent of the wavelength. For such bodies, the spectral exitance will be a fraction of that given by Planck's Law.
(iii) Selective radiator for which e varies with wavelength.

Spectral Directional Emissivity

The emissivity in general may depend on (i) the wavelength, (ii) direction (θ, ϕ) and (iii) temperature (T). Therefore, we may define a general term – *spectral directional emissivity* (e_λ, θ) – which is the ratio of the emitted spectral radiance of a body to that of the spectral radiance emitted by the black body under identical condition. That is

$$e_{\lambda,\theta}(\lambda,\theta,\phi,T) = \frac{L_{\lambda,m}(\lambda,\theta,\phi,T)}{L_{\lambda,b}(\lambda,T)}$$

where $L_{\lambda,m}$ is the spectral radiance from the material at wavelength λ, in the direction θ, at T K. (The parameters in the bracket show that $L_{\lambda,m}$ is a function of λ, θ, ϕ and T.) θ is measured with respect to the normal to the surface and the azimuth angle ϕ from any reference. However, it is reasonable to assume that, generally, $e_{\lambda,\theta}$ is independent of the azimuth angle ϕ.

$L_{\lambda,b}$ is the spectral radiance from the black body at wavelength l and temperature T K. Note that since the black body is a diffuse emitter, it does not have any angular dependence.

If directions are not specified, the emissivity referred to is, *spectral hemispherical emissivity e_λ* (λ, T), which represents an average over all directions

$$e_\lambda(\lambda,T) = \frac{M_{\lambda,m}(\lambda,T)}{M_{\lambda,b}(\lambda,T)}$$

That is, the ratio of radiant flux emitted by the material into the hemisphere between the wavelength λ and $\lambda + \Delta\lambda$ (that is, the spectral exitance) at a specified temperature T, to that emitted by a black body in the same spectral interval and temperature.

Another way of expressing emissivity is total *hemispherical emissivity e* (T), which represents an average over all directions and wavelengths.

$$e(T) = \frac{\int_0^\infty e_\lambda(\lambda,T)\,M_{\lambda,m}(\lambda,T)\,d\lambda}{\int_0^\infty M_{\lambda,b}(\lambda,T)\,d\lambda} = \frac{\int_0^\infty e_\lambda(\lambda,T)\,M_{\lambda,m}(\lambda,T)\,d\lambda}{\sigma T^4}$$

Unless specified, the emissivity given can be assumed as the average value, that is, e (T).

Table 2.1   Average emissivity of some objects at 10 μm

Objects	Emissivity
Grass	0.98–0.99
Leaves (dry)	0.96
Leaves (damp)	0.99
Wood	~0.9
Soil (dry sandy)	0.88–0.94
Soil (dry loamy)	0.92
Soil (moist)	0.94–0.95
Sand	0.95–0.96
Snow	0.97–1.00
Snow (compressed)	0.70–0.85
Glacier	0.85
Ice	0.98
Water	0.99
Asphalt paving	0.96
Concrete wall way	0.92
Brick	0.93

Source: Rees (1990)

The spectral emissivity is a function of the type of material and surface finish. It also changes considerably for the same material when the atomic/molecular arrangements change due to change of state (melting, vapourisation), oxidation, and so on. In general, metals have low emissivity compared to non-metals. For example, highly polished gold has an emissivity less than 0.02, while the emissivity of polished glass is around 0.9. Surface condition also alters emissivity. For example, polished brass may give an emissivity as low as 0.03 while a rough surface will give higher emissivity, and when the surface is oxidised, the emissivity could be as high as 0.6. However visual appearance can sometimes be deceptive. Human skin irrespective of colour are equally 'black' ($e \simeq 0.99$) beyond 2 micrometre. Probably a valid scientific reason to end racial discrimination! The average emissivity of some objects at 10 μm is given in Table 2.1.

In general, when energy is incident on a surface, three processes take place. A fraction of the energy is reflected (ρ), another fraction is absorbed (α) and the rest is transmitted (t), such that

$$\alpha + \rho + t = 1$$

The proportion of each will depend on the wavelength and the material property. For a black body since all the energy is absorbed there is no reflection ($\rho = 0$) and transmission ($t = 0$) and therefore $\alpha = 1$; that is, the emissivity is numerically equal to absorptance. Since an opaque material does not transmit, $t = 0$, $\alpha = 1 - \rho = e$. This is given by Kirchoff's Law, which states that 'under conditions of thermal equilibrium, the spectral emissivity of a material is equal to the spectral absorptance of that material'. This implies that *good absorbers are good emitters*.

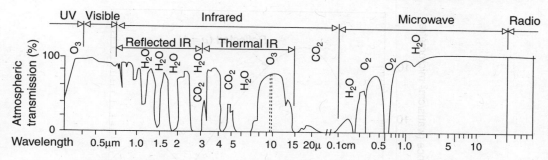

Fig. 2.10 Atmospheric windows. Gases responsible for absorption are indicated. (From: *Remote Sensing Principles and Interpretation,* Sabins F F © 1978, 1987, 1997, W H Freeman and Company/Floyd F Sabins, used with permission)

2.8 SOURCE OF EM RADIATION FOR REMOTE SENSING

The sun is the primary source of radiation in passive remote sensing in the optical and near IR wavelength region (about 0.4 to 2.5 μm). The sun may be assumed to be a blackbody with a surface temperature of around 6000 K. The sun's radiation covers ultraviolet, visible, IR and radio frequency regions and the maximum exitance occurs around 0.55 μm which is in the visible region. However, the solar radiation reaching the surface of the earth is modified by the intervening atmosphere.

In passing through the atmosphere, electromagnetic radiation is scattered and absorbed by gases and particulates. Besides the major atmospheric gaseous components of molecular nitrogen and oxygen, other constituents like methane, helium, water vapour, ozone, nitrogen compounds, and so on, play an important role in modifying the incident radiation energy spectrum. The strongest absorption occurs at wavelengths shorter than 0.3 μm primarily due to ozone. There are certain spectral regions where the electromagnetic radiation is passed through without much attenuation and these are called *atmospheric windows* (Fig. 2.10). Remote sensing of the earth's surface is generally confined to these wavelength regions. As mentioned in Chapter 1, atmospheric windows used for remote sensing are 0.4–1.3, 1.5–1.8, 2–2.26, 3.0–3.6, 4.2–5.0, 7.0–15.0 μm and 1 cm to 30 cm wavelength regions of the electromagnetic spectrum. Even in the atmospheric window regions, scattering by the atmospheric constituents produces spatial redistribution of energy.

When observing earth at wavelengths beyond a few micrometres, the emission of earth becomes the dominant source for passive remote sensing. That is, the observation is made essentially on the basis of change in temperature and/or emissivity. Figure 2.11 shows the solar reflected spectrum assuming sun is a black body at 6000 K. Also shown in the diagram is the emitted radiation of earth, assuming that the earth is at 300 K, which exceeds solar radiance beyond about 5 micrometres. This may look contrary to what we have seen in Section 2.7, where the emission at 300 K should have been less than the 6000 K curve at all wavelengths. This can be easily understood if we consider the fact that the sun is at an average distance of about 1.5×10^8 km (called 1 astronomical unit AU), and the angle subtended at the earth is only ~0.53°. Therefore the actual radiance of the sun at the earth's surface is only that fraction received through the solid angle of sun subtended at the earth.

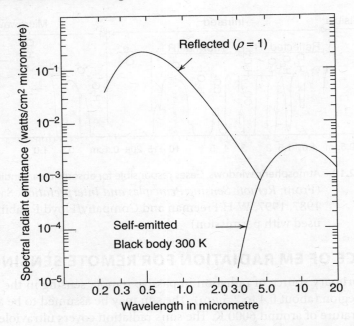

Fig. 2.11 Energy available for remote sensing. (Atmospheric absorption not considered and microwave regions not shown)

For active remote sensing, the sensors themselves carry the source of radiation. In the OIR region various types of lasers are used depending on the wavelength requirement. Currently active sensors in the OIR region are seldom used for earth resources survey. However they are very useful for studies of atmospheric constituents and winds. In the microwave region, active sensors like SLAR and SAR use pulsed EM radiation. These radiations are produced by suitable electronic circuits and the final power level is achieved by Travelling Wave Tube Amplifiers.

FOR FURTHER READING

1. *Remote Sensing: Optics and Optical Systems*, Slater P N, Addison–Wesley Publishing Company, Chapters 3 and 4.
2. www.electro-optical.com/bb_rad/bb_rad.htm
3. http://casswww.ucsd.edu/public/tutorial/Planck.html
4. http://astrowww.phys.univ.ca/~tatum/stellatm/atm2.pdf
5. http://light-measurement.com/reflection-absorption/
6. http://electron6.phys.utk.edu/optics421/modules/m5/Coherence.htm
7. http://www.physicsclassroom.com/class/light/Lesson-1/Polarization

3 Fundamentals of Radiometry

In remote sensing we are concerned with the quantitative measurement of the properties of electromagnetic radiation arising out of interaction with matter or emission of electromagnetic radiation from matter. We shall, in this chapter deal with some of the fundamental concepts and definitions necessary to describe measurement of electromagnetic radiation fields. We shall also discuss how this radiation is transferred from the source to the detector through a medium for quantitative evaluation, which can be broadly termed as *radiometry*. While radiometry deals with the total electromagnetic radiation, *photometry* is used to describe the light interaction detected by the human eye. However, in remote sensing since we deal with electromagnetic radiation outside the visible range as well, radiometry is relevant to the present discussion.

3.1 MEASUREMENT GEOMETRY—CONCEPT OF THE SOLID ANGLE

Central to the understanding of the measurement of radiometric quantities is the *solid angle*. In order to understand solid angle, let us start with *plane angle*, which is the angle contained within two straight lines intersecting at a point. If PR is rotated anti-clockwise around P to R′ and makes a straight line with PQ, the angle contained between PQ and PR′ is 180° (Fig. 3.1).

Another method of defining the plane angle is in terms of *radians*. If a circle is drawn with P as centre and r as radius, the arc length formed between the lines PQ and PR is s, the plane angle is expressed as

$$\theta = \frac{s}{r} \text{ radians (abbreviated as rad)}$$

How is a radian related to a degree? Since the arc length of a semi-circle is πr,

$$\text{Angle QPR}' = \frac{\pi r}{r} = \pi \text{ radians} = 180°$$

$$\text{That is: 1 radian} = \frac{180}{\pi} \cong 57.3°$$

We can extend the concept of radians in three dimensions to explain a solid angle. The cone subtended by an area on the surface of a sphere, at the centre of the sphere is called solid angle (Ω) and is equal to the ratio of the area (a) by the square of the radius (r) (Fig. 3.2). Thus the

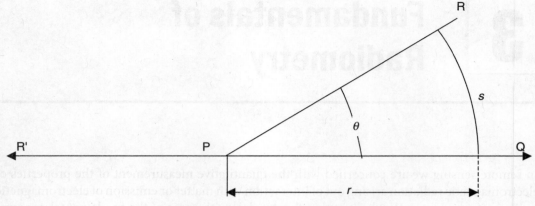

Fig. 3.1 Schematic showing plane angle.

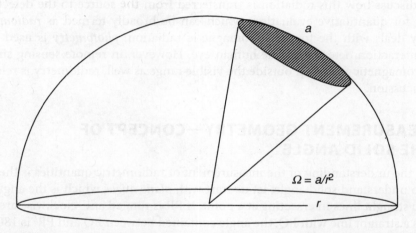

Fig. 3.2 Concept of a solid angle. The shaded portion represents an area a on the surface of the sphere.

solid angle is defined by a closed curve (area) and a point in space. The unit of solid angle is steradian (sr). In other words, a *steradian* is defined as the solid angle which has its vertex at the centre of the sphere, and cuts off a spherical surface area on the sphere equal to the square of the radius of the sphere. Since the area of a sphere is $4\pi r^2$, where r is the radius of the sphere, the solid angle subtended by the sphere is $4\pi r^2/r^2 = 4\pi$, that is, independent of the radius, the solid angle subtended by the sphere is 4π.

According to the above definition of solid angle, we consider the solid angle as subtended by a curved surface on to a point. But for many remote sensing measurements, we are more concerned with the solid angle subtended by a flat surface than a curved surface; for example the solid angle formed by a ground pixel at the lens. Flat area estimates can be used in place of spherical area, when the solid angle is less than 0.03 steradians, resulting in an error less than 1%.

If we have to calculate the solid angle at an angle θ to the normal of the surface, then the area to be considered is the projected area in the concerned direction (Fig. 3.3). The solid angle subtended by a at P is $-a\cos\theta/r^2$.

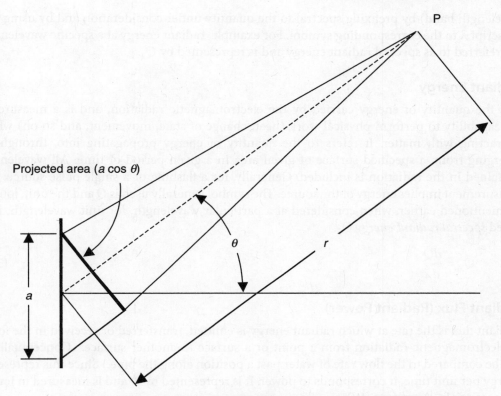

Projected area ($a \cos \theta$)

Fig. 3.3 Geometry for calculating solid angle in a direction θ normal to the surface.

Another terminology generally used is the prefix *element* or *elementary* to a term, such as an elementary beam, elementary area. It is an infinitesimally small quantity and is mainly a mathematical concept, not a measurable quantity. Each of such units can be treated independently and added up to get the total effect of a finite unit. The addition is mathematically carried out by integration. The elemental quantity is denoted by a preceding letter d as in the notation of calculus, that is, da, if a denotes area, da is an elemental area or if ω denotes solid angle, $d\omega$ represents an elemental solid angle.

3.2 RADIOMETRIC QUANTITIES

There are five quantities which are the basis of radiometry. These are:

(i) Radiant energy Q joule (J), (Ws)
(ii) Radiant flux (radiant power) Φ watts (W)
(iii) Irradiance E watts/metre^2 (Wm^{-2})
(iv) Radiant intensity I watts/steradian (Wsr^{-1})
(v) Radiance L watts/steradian/metre^2 (Wsr^{-1} m^{-2})

We shall now try to understand each of the above terms. Note that these quantities are wavelength dependent and could be expressed specific to a wavelength (in practice, to a narrow wavelength band) by prefixing spectral to the quantity under consideration and by using the subscript λ to the corresponding symbol. For example, radiant energy at a specific wavelength λ is referred to as spectral radiant energy and is represented by Q_λ.

Radiant Energy

It is the quantity of energy carried by the electromagnetic radiation, and is a measure of the capability to perform physical work (heat, change of state, movement, and so on) when interacting with matter. It refers to the quantity of energy propagating into, through or emerging from, a specified surface of given area in a given period of time. All wavelength contained in the radiation is included. Generally, for a flashing or a single pulse source, the measurement implies energy of the source. The symbol generally used is Q and the unit, joules. As mentioned earlier, when considered at a particular wavelength, for unit wavelength, it is called *spectral radiant energy* Q_λ.

$$Q_\lambda = \frac{dQ}{d\lambda}$$

(3.1)

Radiant Flux (Radiant Power)

Radiant flux is the rate at which radiant energy is emitted, transferred or received in the form of electromagnetic radiation from a point or a surface to another surface. (Conceptually it can be compared to the flow rate of water past a position along the pipe.) Since this represents energy per unit time, it corresponds to power. It is represented by Φ and is measured in joules per second (Js^{-1}) or watts (W)

$$\Phi = \frac{dQ}{dt}$$

(3.2)

The spectral radiant flux Φ_λ, is the radiant flux per unit wavelength interval at wavelength λ (watt per micron)

$$\Phi_\lambda = \frac{d\Phi}{d\lambda}$$

(3.3)

Irradiance

It is a measure of the radiant flux per unit area and is represented by the symbol E and the unit is watts per metre square (Wm^{-2}).

$$E = \frac{d\Phi}{da}$$

(3.4)

If the normal to the surface element da makes an angle θ to the direction of the radiation, then the projected area of the element in the direction of the radiation is to be taken and hence

$$E = \frac{d\Phi}{da.\cos\theta}$$

(3.5)

The flux density of radiant flux arriving at a surface is termed as irradiance (E), whereas the radiant flux emitted (leaving) from a surface is called exitance and is represented by M. The exitance from a point source follows the inverse square law, that is, the exitance is inversely proportional to the square of the distance from the source. It is easy to conceive this since the area of a sphere increases with R^2, the flux/unit area should fall off as $1/R^2$.

Radiant Intensity

It is the radiant flux leaving a source per unit solid angle in a given direction. It is represented by I and the unit is watts per steradian (Wsr^{-1}).

$$I = \frac{d\Phi}{d\omega} \tag{3.6}$$

If a point source radiates equally in all directions (isotropic) with a radiant flux Φ, the radiant intensity $I = \Phi/4\pi$. It is not possible to produce a true point source. In practice, a source can be approximated to a point source when its dimension is very much smaller compared to the observational distance from the source. A source dimension less than $1/10$ of the observational distance could be a good practical approximation to a point source.

Radiance

It is the radiant flux per unit solid angle leaving an extended source in a given direction per unit projected source area in that direction (Fig. 3.4). It is represented by L and the unit is watts per metre square per steradian ($Wm^{-2} sr^{-1}$).

In general, radiance is a function of position in a defined surface as well as the direction through the point to the observer (sensor). The radiance can be defined in general

$$L(x, y, \theta, \phi) = \frac{d^2\Phi(x, y, \theta, \phi)}{d\omega da \cos\theta} \tag{3.7}$$

Here (x, y) gives the coordinates of the position P, (θ, ϕ) gives the direction of the ray from P to the element da. The projection of da perpendicular to the ray direction is $da \cos\theta$. An important property of the radiance is that it is conserved in a lossless medium. *Thus the radiance in the object plane and image plane (lossless optics) is the same irrespective of optics diameter.*

Radiance describes the angular distribution of radiation, while irradiance is the addition of all these quantities within a solid angle (ω) giving an integrated value within the solid angle. Therefore, the relationship between radiance (L) and irradiance (E) is

$$E = \int_\omega dL(\theta, \phi) \tag{3.8}$$

The quantities, such as intensity, radiance and irradiance are defined for infinitesimal areas and solid angles. However, in practice, the measurements are carried out with detectors of finite area and optics with a finite field of view, and hence the measured quantities are average values.

For convenience, the radiometric quantities are summarised in Table 3.1.

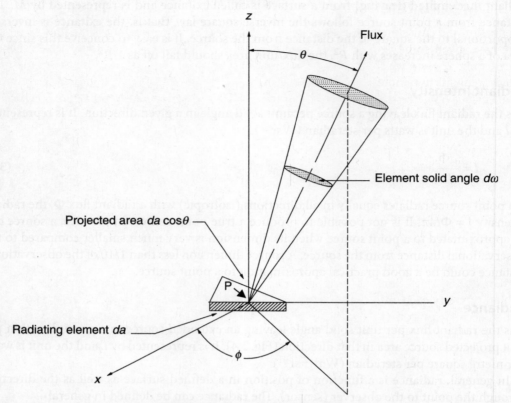

Fig. 3.4   Geometry for defining radiance.

Table 3.1   Radiometric quantities and units

S. No.	Quantity	Symbol	Unit	Definition
1.	Radiant energy	Q	joule	Quantity of energy carried. It is a measure of the radiation to do work.
2.	Radiant flux (radiant power)	Φ	watt	Radiant energy emitted or incident upon a surface per unit time. That is, rate of flow of energy.
3.	Irradiance	E	watt m^{-2}	Radiant flux falling per unit area of the surface.
	Exitance	M	watt m^{-2}	Symbol M is used for radiant flux emitted by unit area.
4.	Radiant intensity	I	watt sr^{-1}	Radiant flux leaving per unit solid angle, in a specified direction.
5.	Radiance	L	watt m^{-2}sr^{-1}	Radiant flux per unit projected area and per unit solid angle.

3.3 SURFACE CHARACTERISTICS FOR RADIOMETRIC MEASUREMENTS

Reflection and emission from targets are the two important phenomena used in remote sensing. We have given some general features of reflection of EMR and the emission characteristics in Chapter 2. Here we shall try to give some details specifically relevant for the radiometric measurements in remote sensing. A surface is said to be perfectly smooth if the reflection from that surface obeys Snell's law, that is, the angle of reflection is equal to the angle of incidence, and the incident ray, reflected ray and the normal to the plane of incidence are in the same plane. Hence when a parallel beam of light falls on a smooth surface, all the reflected rays (or refracted rays if the medium is transparent) are parallel. The reflectance from a surface which follows Snell's law is called *specular reflection*. Here, the direction of the outgoing ray is completely determined by the incoming direction. Reflection taking place from a mirror surface is a common example for specular reflection. Specular reflection, in general, does not mean that the amount of reflected flux is independent of the angle of incidence. Angular dependence is governed by Eqs 2.6 and 2.7. In general, as the angle of incidence increases, the reflected flux increases, but the sum of the reflected and refracted (medium lossless) flux will be equal to the incident value.

For diffuse reflection, even for a parallel incident beam, the rays have angles of reflection different from each other. This is because a diffuse surface has 'structures' of irregularly oriented micro-facets (Fig. 3.5), which in common parlance is referred to as roughness. Each point on the micro-facet appears smooth and hence specular reflection takes place, but the orientation varies over the surface area and hence the reflection over the area is distributed into a continuum of directions. Thus the aggregate behaviour from a rough surface results in light scattered in many directions. The angular distribution of the reflected ray varies with the surface property. If the emergent radiance is constant for all directions in a hemispherical solid angle then the surface is said to be a *Lambertian reflector* or emitter. Therefore, a sensor with a certain solid angle will give the same output when observing a Lambertian surface irrespective

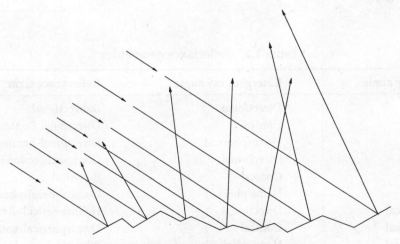

Fig. 3.5 Schematic showing diffuse scattering.

of the angle the sensor axis makes with the surface. The name 'Lambertian' has been given because the surface obeys *Lambert's cosine law*, which states

$$I(\theta) = I_o \cos\theta \tag{3.9}$$

where $I(\theta)$ = intensity as a function of angle from the perpendicular to the surface, I_0 = intensity at $\theta = 0$, θ = angle from the perpendicular.

The radiance is intensity per unit area. The projected area at an angle θ is proportional to $\cos\theta$ (Fig. 3.4) and therefore the radiance is independent of the viewing angle. For a Lambertian surface with exitance M, radiating into a hemisphere, the radiance is given by M/π. (Not $M/2\pi$ as intuitively assumed because the hemisphere has 2π radians. This is due to $\cos\theta$ dependence.)

We should not get confused between the 'isotropic' source and the 'Lambertian' source. Isotropic implies a spherical source that radiates the same in all directions (often called an 'isotropic point source'—a misnomer since a point source is not practicable). Here the intensity (W/sr) is the same in all directions. Lambertian refers to a flat radiating surface, whose intensity falls off as cosine of the observation angle with respect to the normal of the surface. Here the radiance (W/m^2/sr) is independent of direction.

The real surfaces we encounter are neither perfect specular reflectors nor perfect Lambertian surfaces. Whether the surface behaves as Lambertian or specular depends on the unevenness (that is height variation from a reference surface) of the surface relative to the wavelength of observation. Rayleigh's criteria for a rough surface is:

$$h > \lambda/(8 \cos\theta) \tag{3.10}$$

where h = rms height variation above a reference plane in units of λ, λ = wavelength, θ = angle of incidence.

Thus seashore sand which may appear as a diffuse reflector to the eye, will produce specular reflection in the microwave region. Before proceeding further let us clarify certain terminology used.

Table 3.2 Reflectance geometries

Incident ray angle	Emergent ray angle	Reflectance term
Directional	Directional	Bidirectional
Directional	Conical	Directional Conical
Directional	Hemispherical	Directional-hemispherical
Conical	Directional	Conical-directional
Conical	Conical	Biconical
Conical	Hemispherical	Conical-hemispherical
Hemispherical	Directional	Hemispherical-directional
Hemispherical	Conical	Hemispherical-conical
Hemispherical	Hemispherical	Bihemispherical

Reflectance (ρ) in general refers to the ratio of the reflected flux to incident flux and has a value between 0 and 1.

Reflectance factor (R) is the ratio of the radiant flux reflected within a solid angle in a direction to that reflected in the same direction by a Lambertian surface, of unit absolute reflectance, identically irradiated. If the surface has a large specular component in the direction considered, the reflectance factor could be larger than 1.

Albedo is another term generally used in planetary studies. It is the ratio of the total solar radiant energy returned by a body to the total solar radiant energy incident on the body. From the geometrical consideration it is a bihemispherical reflectance (See Table 3.2).

3.4 OBSERVATION GEOMETRY IN REMOTE SENSING

Let us first familiarise ourselves with the coordinate system used in radiometric measurement. How do we specify the geometry of the incident (source) radiation and the reflected radiation? One of the convenient coordinate systems used to specify the incident and reflected ray is an 'object-oriented' system defined with respect to a plane tangent to the surface at a point of interest (Woodham and Lee, 1985). The geometry is specified based on spherical coordinates (θ, ϕ) (Fig. 3.6). First consider a plane tangent to the surface at a point of interest. On the plane erect a Cartesian coordinate system (x, y, z), with the z axis aligned to the normal. However, the choice of x direction is arbitrary and can be aligned with any direction. The zenith angle (θ) is measured from the z axis and the azimuth angle, ϕ is measured counter-clockwise from the x-axis in the xy plane. Thus we have (θ_i, ϕ_i) referring to the incident ray and (θ_r, ϕ_r) referring to the reflected ray. Hence four angles are required to specify the incident and reflected rays, since the choice of the reference direction x is arbitrary. We will be using this coordinate system to define the reflectance properties in the subsequent sections.

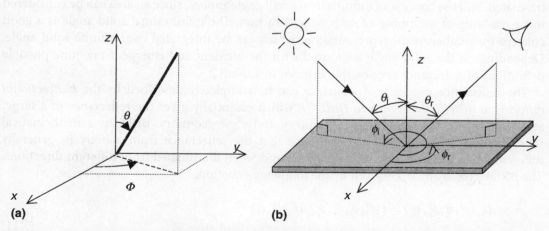

Fig. 3.6 (a) Representation of spherical coordinates θ and Φ. Zenith angle θ is measured from the z axis and azimuth angle Φ is measured counter-clockwise from the x axis in the xy plane. (b) The geometry for radiometric measurement. θ_i and Φ_i are solar zenith and azimuth angles. θ_r and Φ_r are the observational zenith and azimuth angles.

Infinitesimally
small solid angle

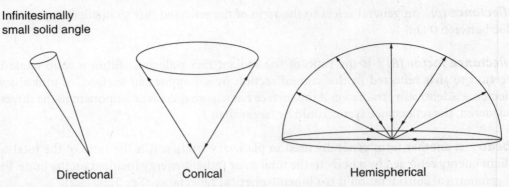

Directional   Conical   Hemispherical

Fig. 3.7 Geometry for directional, conical and hemispherical solid angles. (Reprinted with permission from *Introduction to Radiometry & Photometry*, WR McCluney, Artech House Inc., Norwood, MA, USA. www.artechhouse.com)

Other coordinate systems are (i) the 'viewer-centred' coordinate system, where the z axis is aligned to view direction; (ii) the 'earth-centred' coordinate system, where the x axis points towards the east, the y axis to the north and the z axis points vertically upward.

Any earth surface we study through remote sensing has directional dependence in response to the incident radiation. The incident radiation itself can have angular dependence. Therefore for the reflectance value to be meaningful, it is necessary to specify incidence and exitance angles. There are three kinds or sizes of solid angles that can be considered to define reflectance values (McCluney, 1994). The three solid angles are directional, hemispherical and conical (Fig. 3.7).

The term directional refers to an infinitesimally small solid angle in a specified direction (θ, ϕ) from the point P of interest. Hemispherical refers to a full 2π steradian of the hemisphere. Conical refers to an intermediate size of solid angle. In practice not a point but a surface is irradiated. Still the concept of infinitesimal small angle applies, since an area can be considered to be made up of a number of such pencils of rays. The infinitesimal solid angle is a good concept for mathematical representation, which can be integrated over a finite solid angle. Depending on the solid angle associated with the incident and emergent ray, nine possible definitions of reflectance are possible as given in Table 3.2.

The reflectance property of a surface can be completely described by the *bidirectional reflectance distribution function (BRDF)*, which essentially gives the reflectance of a target as a function of the illumination geometry and view geometry. BRDF is a mathematical representation of our practical experience that the reflectance from a body is, generally different when viewed from different angles and when illuminated from different directions. The BRDF $f(\theta_i, \phi_i, \theta_r, \phi_r)$ is given by the following equation,

$$dL_r(\theta_i, \phi_i, \theta_r, \phi_r) = f(\theta_i, \phi_i, \theta_r, \phi_r)\, dE_i(\theta_i, \phi_i)$$

$$\text{or, } f(\theta_i, \phi_i, \theta_r, \phi_r) = \frac{dL_r(\theta_i, \phi_i, \theta_r, \phi_r)}{dE_i(\theta_i, \phi_i)}$$

(3.11)

BRDF essentially transforms the incident irradiance into reflected radiance and has unit sr^{-1}. $dE_i(\theta_i, \phi_i)$ is the elemental incident irradiance from the direction (θ_i, ϕ_i), within an element of solid angle $d\omega_i$, $dL_r(\theta_i, \phi_i, \theta_r, \phi_r)$ is the reflected elemental radiance in the direction (θ_r, ϕ_r), into the solid angle $d\omega_i$ (Fig. 3.8). Since the reflection depends on wavelength, both dE_i and dL_i are spectral quantities though the subscript λ is omitted. Here the polar angles θ are measured from the surface normal and the azimuth angle measured from any arbitrary reference in the surface plane, most often the plane containing the incident beam.

By the definition, $dE_i = L_i \cos\theta_i \, d\omega_i$

Therefore, BRDF can also be represented by

$$f(\theta_i, \phi_i, \theta_r, \phi_r) = \frac{dL_r, (\theta_i, \phi_i, \theta_r, \phi_r)}{L_i \cos\theta_i \, d\omega_i} \tag{3.12}$$

For a Lambertian surface, the BRDF is $1/\pi$.

We should not confuse BRDF with reflectance (ρ) which is dimensionless. The nine reflectance categories given in Table 3.2 can be realised by integration of BRDF over the solid angles of incident and reflected radiation. Thus, the fundamental geometric descriptor of reflectance is the BRDF.

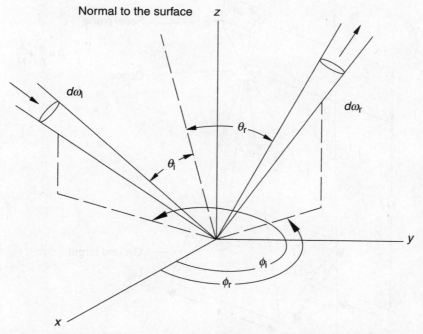

Fig. 3.8 Geometrical quantities referred to in the bidirectional reflectance distribution.

Since most earth surface objects are non-Lambertian reflectors, the same target viewed at different times of the day (or season) due to incidence angle variation and from different positions, due to view angle difference may appear to have different reflectance due to the bidirectional reflectance distribution. With a number of off-nadir viewing remote sensing satellites in the fray, when a target is viewed from different angles, unless the bidirectional characteristics of the target are taken into account, the intercomparison of reflectance values generated could lead to wrong conclusions.

3.5   RADIOMETRIC MEASUREMENT

To measure the radiance from a target, an optical system (in the visible and IR region) has to transfer the radiance of the target to the focal plane. This is carried out by a suitable optical system. Consider an optical system with a diameter D transferring the radiance from the target to the detector at the focal plane (Fig. 3.9). The radiant flux (power) delivered to the detector is given by

$$\Phi_d = \frac{\pi}{4} O_e \Delta\lambda L_\lambda \beta^2 D^2 \text{ watt} \tag{3.13}$$

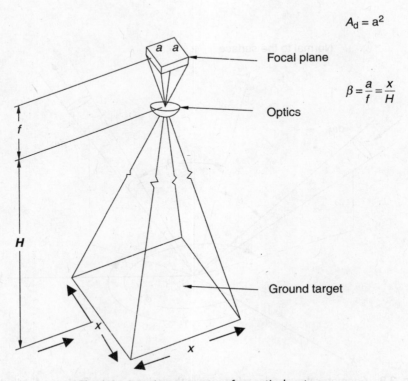

$$A_d = a^2$$

$$\beta = \frac{a}{f} = \frac{x}{H}$$

Fig. 3.9   Imaging geometry of an optical system.

where L_λ = the target radiance (watt m^{-2} sr$^{-1}\mu$m^{-1}), $\Delta\lambda$ = the spectral bandwidth of the radiation to be measured (μm), O_e = optical efficiency—transmittance of the optical system including atmosphere (<1), β = the system instantaneous field of view (IFOV) radians.

It may be noted that the radiant flux at the detector (that is, the detector output) is independent of the height H of the lens from the target. This is because, as the H increases, the area of the target covered increases for the same β (assuming the target size projected totally fills the detector) and hence compensates for the increased distance.

If A_d is the detector area, $\beta^2 = A_d/f^2$, where f is the focal length, the above equation can be rewritten as

$$\Phi_d = \frac{\pi}{4} O_e \Delta\lambda L_\lambda \frac{A_d}{f^2} D^2$$

$$= \frac{\pi}{4} \frac{O_e \Delta\lambda L_\lambda A_d}{(f/no)^2} \tag{3.14}$$

where f/no (pronounced f-number) is f/D. The irradiance at the detector E_d, Φ_d/A_d is given by

$$E_d = \frac{\pi}{4} \frac{O_e \Delta\lambda}{(f/no)^2} L_\lambda \text{ watt m}^{-2} \tag{3.15}$$

The above expression gives the on axis image irradiance. A more exact expression for the irradiance in the image plane is given by (McCluney, 1994)

$$E_d(\theta) = \pi O_e \Delta\lambda L_\lambda \left[\frac{1}{1 + (2f/no)^2}\right] \cos^4 \theta \tag{3.16}$$

where θ is the angle of the image location with respect to the optical axis. For the image along the optical axis $\theta = 0$.

For remote sensing since f/no is usually > 2, the equation can be approximated to

$$E_d(\theta) = \frac{\pi O_e \Delta\lambda L_\lambda}{4(f/no)^2} \cos^4 \theta \tag{3.17}$$

If we observe the target for a time τ seconds (usually called *integration time*), then the energy, per unit area at the detector is given by

$$Q_d(\theta) = \frac{\pi O_e \Delta\lambda L_\lambda}{4(f/no)^2} \tau \cos^4 \theta \text{ Jm}^{-2} \tag{3.18}$$

This expression is often convenient to evaluate the output of the detector, since the detector responsivity is usually given in V/(μJ/cm^2).

3.6 SCENE REFLECTANCE MEASUREMENT

To interpret the remote sensing data collected by sensors on board aircraft/spacecraft, requires an understanding of the reflectance characteristics of the scene under varying conditions such as crop phenology, soil characteristics, snow morphology, and so on. In certain applications such as computer classification using multi-spectral data of a scene, we use statistical differences among the pixel counts (DN value) to distinguish surface features. In such cases we require only the relative reflectance value. However, some other applications like establishing a relationship between vegetation index and yield, water leaving radiance and chlorophyll, multi-temporal classification, and so on, require the absolute reflectance value. In this section, we shall discuss issues concerning radiance measurement using field instruments.

Ground reflectance measurements are carried out by radiometers/spectroradiometers. The radiometer gives the radiance value corresponding to a number of broad spectral bands, usually matching the satellite sensor (like MSS, TM, IRS-LISS) characteristics. That is, the information is available in a number of discrete spectral bands. There are a number of such instruments commercially available. They have a field of view, varying from a few degrees to ~15°. A narrow field of view can define the direction of view in a more unique manner. However, the smaller area coverage is prone to give more scene variance, which is not a true representation of the integrated field reflectance value measured by a satellite sensor. Please note that our interest is not to measure the reflectance from a single leaf or other component of the vegetation. Therefore, a judicious choice of field of view and observation height is required to get a realistic representation of radiance from the field.

Before we proceed further let us understand the terminology used to describe radiation sensing instruments. *Radiometer* is a general term used to describe an instrument for quantitatively measuring the radiance of electromagnetic radiation in some wavelength band in any part of the electromagnetic spectrum. It is usually used with an adjective—thermal radiometer, microwave radiometer, and so on. *Multi-spectral radiometer* is an instrument, which measures the radiance, in a number of spectral bands simultaneously. *Imaging radiometer* includes some kind of scanning capability to the radiometer in order to provide two dimensional information. A *photometer* is a radiometer making measurements in the optical region. A *spectrometer* is designed to measure the wavelength distribution (content) of the electromagnetic radiation. A spectroradiometer is a radiometre that measures the radiance in narrow spectral bands (almost continuous) within the spectral range of the instruments.

The radiometer has to be initially calibrated in the laboratory, so that a relationship can be established between the radiometer output voltage and the radiance sensed, which can be traced to a primary standard. This sounds simple, but it is extremely difficult to have an accuracy better than a few per cent. If we have to measure only the reflectance, it is not necessary to have the absolute radiance value since reflectance is the ratio between the reflected and the incident radiation. A faithful measurement of incident radiation is also quite complex. This is because a target in the field is illuminated by a number of sources. Of course, direct solar radiation is the dominant source of illumination. Diffuse skylight illumination can be up to ~20% depending on the wavelength, shorter the wavelength higher the skylight contribution. Scattering from the surrounding objects contributing to target illumination also needs to be accounted for. This could be the structure that supports the radiometer or even from the observer himself! One experimenter has suggested that the staff involved in field measurement wear black clothes to reduce the contribution of scattering by the observer. The reflectance is evaluated by measuring the target radiance and from the measurement of the irradiance on the target by an upward-looking radiometer, using a cosine receptor (that is, a sensor which shows no dependence upon the zenith or azimuth angle of incident flux), in order to get the hemispherical irradiance value. The two radiometers have to be cross-calibrated as calibration error is a major source of error in reflectance evaluation. The upward-looking radiometer's ability to respond faithfully to radiation from all directions in the hemisphere also limits the accuracy of measurement.

Since, generally, we are interested in the relative change in reflectance, it is enough to measure the reflectance factor. As defined in Section 3.3, the reflectance factor is the ratio of the radiant flux reflected in a direction to that reflected by an ideal Lambertian reflectance panel, under identical illumination and view conditions. Care should be taken to make sure that the reference panel size is large enough to cover the total field of view of the radiometer. However, in practice there is no ideal true Lambertian panel. Laboratory studies have shown that panels coated with $BaSO_4$ and other so-called Lambertian panels are far from perfect Lambertian surfaces. Therefore, the reflectance panel characteristics have to be carefully measured and an appropriate correction factor applied. The measurements can be sequentially on the target and the reference panel, in which case the radiometer calibration accuracy is not important. Some investigators have pointed out that large errors can arise in the reflectance factor due to changes in irradiance between the measuring radiance reflected from the target and the reference panel due to atmospheric variability between the two observations (Duggin and Cunia, 1983). To overcome this, simultaneous measurement of target and reference panel has been carried out by some investigators. However, this requires the use of two radiometers, matched over a wide dynamic range, sensing identical wavelengths, with an identical field of view. Thus, the simultaneous method will have reduced errors due to short-term temporal changes in irradiation, gained at the cost of complexity in cross-calibration of the two radiometers.

Measurement is usually carried out with the optical axis parallel to the target normal (unless specifically planned to study the directional effect). If we neglect the irradiance due to sky and nearby objects, the reflectance factor is given by

$$R(\theta_i, \phi_i, \theta_r, \phi_r) = \frac{V_T}{V_R} R_R(\theta_i, \phi_i, \theta_r, \phi_r)$$

where θ_i is the solar zenith angle, V_T and V_R are the radiometer outputs (subtracted for dark current) for the target and reference panel respectively and R_R is the correction factor for the non-Lambertian characteristics of the reference panel (which is essentially the reflectance factor of the reference panel with respect to a Lambertian surface of unit reflectance). The reflectance factor so measured represents reasonably well (except for the path radiance), the geometry of the satellite observation from LANDSAT (MSS, TM), IRS (LISS-1,2,3) and so on. However, understanding of data from sensors with a wide swath like AVHRR, SPOT vegetation and the off-nadir viewing instruments like SPOT HRV, IRS PAN, IKNOS, and so on, will require the knowledge of the angular distribution of the reflected radiation. Natural objects are not Lambertian surfaces and hence the reflected intensity varies with the angle with which it leaves the surface. Sensors like POLDER onboard ADEOS specifically designed to study the surface angular distribution of the reflectance will provide valuable information on the bidirectional reflectance characteristics of the earth surface (Barnsky et. al., 1994).

In the field, the primary source of radiation is from the sun defined by the zenith angle θ_i (angle from the vertical) and the azimuth angle (the angle measured in the horizontal plane from a reference surface). To specify the reflectance property of the target completely, the reflectance must be measured at all possible source/sensor position, that is, the BRDF (Eq. 3.11). Unfortunately, the BRDF cannot be measured directly, because it is a ratio of the infinitesimal elements of the solid angle and wavelength and does not include measurable quantities of radiant flux. The radiometers used for measurement have a finite field of view. Therefore, we are actually measuring biconical reflectance value. Another problem of estimating BRDF in the field is the diffuse component of the illumination (since BRDF refers to a monodirectional illumination and all possible angles of collection). The diffuse component reaching the surface in the visible wavelength range varies from 3% of the total flux for an aerosol-free atmosphere to as much as 26% for a moderately aerosol-loaded (horizontal visual range $V_0 = 23$ km) atmosphere (Cierniewski, 1993). If the sensor field of view is sufficiently small (~2°) and field measurements are taken under clear sky conditions with predominantly direct radiation, the measured value can be considered to closely resemble BRDF.

Various types of radiometers suitable for field measurement are commercially available. With extensive applications of satellite remote sensing data, radiometers are available with bands tuned to LANDSAT (MSS, TM), SPOT HRV, IRS LISS, and so on. These are compact light-weight instruments (<1 kg) and can be operated either as hand-held or tripod-mounted. The BRDF measurement in the field is carried out by mounting the radiometers on suitable arms with capability for zenith and azimuth movement. One of the important requirements for BRDF measurement is to obtain multiple view angle measurements of ground surfaces in a short period of time to minimise the effects of changing sun position, sky conditions and the vegetation's dynamic biophysical conditions during the sampling period. There are currently a number of commercially available instruments with fast response. True BRDF estimation needs suitable correction for the atmospheric effect. The error contribution for not correcting atmospheric effect, increases with higher aerosol loading and lower wavelengths.

FOR FURTHER READING

1. *Introduction to Environmental Remote Sensing*, Barrett E C and Curtis L F, John Wiley & Sons Inc., Chapter 2.
2. *Physical Principles of Remote Sensing*, Rees W G, Cambridge University Press, Chapter 2.
3. *Theory and Applications of Optical Remote Sensing*, Asrar G, John Wiley & Sons, 1989, Chapter 2.
4. *Digital Photogrammetry*, Schenk T, Terra Sciences, 1999, Chapter 6.
5. *Remote Sensing: Optics and Optical Systems*, Slater P N, Addison–Wesley, 1980, Chapters 5, 6 and Appendix 3.

6. *http://www.cs.uscb.edu/~mturk/imaging/Misc/ILT-light-Measurement-Handbook.pdf*
7. *http://www.2.geog.ucl.ac.uk/~mdisney/teaching/PPRS/papers/schaepmanetal.pdf*
8. *http://www.photonics.com/EDU/Handbook.aspx?AID=25123*
9. *http://www.dii.unisi.it/~garzelli/documenti/03-SOME%20DEFINITIONS%20IN%20RADIOMETRY.pdf*
10. *http://photonics.intec.ugent.be/education/IVPV/res_handbook/v2ch24.pdf*
11. *https://www.umb.edu/spectralmass/terra_aqua_modis/modis*

Fundamentals of radiometry   65

6. http://www.es.ucr.edu/~chun/Imaging/HistoLight/Measurement-Handouts.pdf
7. http://www.z-gang.net/acton/multiwave/products/PBS/images/radiometry_primer.pdf

8. RADIOMETRIC DESIGN AND OPTIMIZATION 3.5.10

RADIOMETRY.pdf

10. http://photonics.intec.ugent.be/education/ivpv/res_handbook/v1ch04.pdf

Physical Basis of Signatures

In remote sensing we are interested in recognising an object or a feature from its surroundings. To do so, we should know what characteristic feature of the object distinguishes it from its surroundings. This characteristic feature which forms a 'key' to enable an object to be identified/recognised is called *signature*. If this is achieved through the difference in the reflectance/emittance characteristics with respect to wavelength (that is, the reflectance/emittance as a function of wavelength), then it is called *spectral signature*. There can be many other characteristics other than the difference in the spectral reflectance/emittance characteristics that are useful in target identification. For example, the differences in scattering cross-section with respect to polarisation especially in the microwave region provide characteristic signatures. In yet another case, if we measure the temperature using the thermal IR region, thermal inertia could provide signatures for distinguishing certain types of objects. Temporal variation such as the growth profile differences of plants can act as signatures for differentiation of crops in agricultural remote sensing. The parameters leading to a signature can be quantified, thus making it amenable for computer processing. However, signatures are not completely deterministic. They are statistical in nature with a certain mean value and some dispersion around it (Fig. 4.1). Understanding the physical basis of signatures is very important to define a sensor system, its time and frequency of observation as well as interpreting it. We shall now discuss these aspects on the basis of interaction of electromagnetic radiation on matter and some of the bio-geochemical process. In this chapter, we shall deal only with earth surface targets. Processes in the atmosphere shall be dealt with separately. The features on the earth's surface for this purpose may be broadly classified as

- vegetation,
- soil, rocks, minerals,
- water/ocean,
- snow, and
- man-made features.

Since the interaction mechanism in the various regions of the electromagnetic spectrum is different, it is convenient to deal with them in the three broad regions

  (i) reflective optical infrared region (ROIR, 0.4–3 μm),
 (ii) thermal infrared region (TIR, 8–14 μm), and
(iii) the microwave region (1–30 cm).

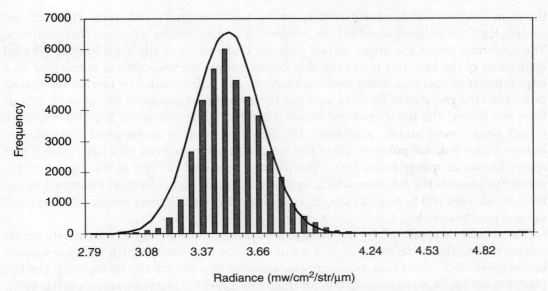

Fig. 4.1 Frequency distribution of wheat pixels. Each pixel is identified as pure wheat by supervised classification. The continuous curve is a Gaussian fit to data sets. (Data source IRS-1D/LISS-III)

4.1 SIGNATURE IN THE REFLECTIVE OIR REGION

As mentioned earlier, the source of energy in this region is the sun. Though there are a few studies using active sensors such as lasers for fluorescence studies, their practical applicability on an operational basis is limited and shall not be dealt with here. We shall now discuss the physical processes which give rise to signatures for various earth surface features.

4.1.1 VEGETATION

Vegetation either as agriculture or other forms of flora such as forest cover, bushes, shrubs, and so on, are vital for human existence. In addition, it plays an important role in regulating CO_2 through photosynthesis and in balancing radiation in the atmosphere which affects the weather and overall climate. Therefore, monitoring of vegetation is one of the most important applications of remote sensing technology.

Looking at vegetation from space, one sees the integrated effect of leaves, stems, branches, flowers and other appendages of the plants along with the background soil. The scattering and reflection by the vegetative cover alters the direction and spectral composition of the incident radiation in a complex manner. Since a major contribution to the reflected energy from a vegetation canopy comes from leaves, it is essential to understand why a leaf reflects more of certain wavelengths than of others. Hence, it is useful to first understand the structure of a leaf.

Structure of Leaves

Leaves show a wide range of variations in shape, size and surface as well as internal characteristics. These differences are responsible for the specific spectral characteristics of the plant canopies which are different in species, nutrition, stress, and so on. However, leaf morphology can be generalised for the purpose of understanding reflection characteristics. The epidermis covers the upper surface (adaxial epidermis) and the lower surface (abaxial epidermis) of the leaf (this is like the skin of our body). The epidermis is intercepted by a large number of openings called *stomata*. Each stomata is surrounded by two kidney-shaped cells called the *guard* cells. Stomata regulates the exchange of gases and loss of water vapour from the leaves. The tissue enclosed between the two epidermal layers is called *mesophyll* (Greek origin, *meso* middle, *phyll* leaf). The mesophyll consists of elongated cells arranged in rows called *palisade parenchyma* and/or irregularly arranged cells with large intercellular spaces known as *spongy parenchyma*. The palisade cells tend to form in the portion of the mesophyll towards the side from which light enters the leaf. Hence in most horizontal leaves, the palisade cells will be towards the upper surface. The parenchyma cells are filled with cell sap and protoplasm (Fig. 4.2).

The cellular structure of the leaf is large (~15 μm) compared to the wavelengths under consideration. The epidermal cells have a thin waxy cuticle overlay which is highly variable in thickness (3–5 μm). Chloroplasts are suspended within the cellular protoplasm. The leaf pigments are found in the chloroplasts. The pigments generally found are chlorophyll (~65%), carotenes (6%) and xanthophylls (28%), though the percentage distribution is highly variable (Gates et. al., 1965). There are two types of chlorophyll with a slight difference in the chemical structure namely chlorophyll-*a* ($C_{55}H_{72}MgN_4O_5$) and chlorophyll-*b* ($C_{55}H_{70}MgN_4O_6$). Chlorophyll-*a* is found in all photosynthetic plants and chlorophyll-*b* in most but not in all. Both *a* and *b* have absorption bands in the blue and red region. Other pigments have absorption bands around the blue region only.

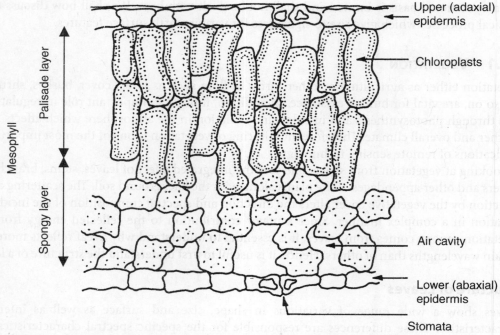

Fig. 4.2 The morphological structure of a normal green leaf. (Adapted from Fitzgerald, 1974)

Plants absorb very efficiently throughout the ultraviolet and the visible regions of the spectrum where energy is required for photosynthesis. In the near-IR region there is very little absorption, however, at wavelengths greater than about 2.5 μm, plants are good absorbers. At longer wavelengths, there is not much solar input. However plants get radiation from the surroundings. But as good absorbers they also act as good radiators and cool themselves by radiation thus controlling the temperature.

Interaction of Reflective OIR Radiation with Leaf

Now let us consider in a very general manner what happens when the sun's rays fall on a leaf. Obviously, the rays first encounter the leaf surface. About half of the total reflectance from a leaf in the visible spectrum is from the surface (cuticle) of the leaves and does not enter or interact with the leaf (Woolley, 1971). The amount and nature of the cuticular reflectance depends on the wax layer characteristics, which varies according to the species. Much of this reflectance is specular (mirror-like) and hence can be polarised.

The radiation that enters the leaf interacts with the internal leaf component and structure. The four leaf constituents which take part in the interaction are the cell wall, chloroplasts, cell sap and air. When a number of parallel rays are incident on a leaf, each ray will encounter different geometrical internal surfaces and consequently will be reflected and transmitted in different directions (Fig. 4.3). Reflection/refraction is caused due to the discontinuities in the indices of refraction of the interfaces such as cell wall–air, cell sap–cell wall, cell sap–chloroplasts, and so on. The reflection/refraction changes the direction of the incident ray. Some radiation gets reflected back and others pass through; a certain amount of scattering also takes place due to the constituents which are of dimensions comparable to the wavelength. Radiation also gets absorbed depending on the pigments and water.

A number of theoretical models have been developed to understand reflection from leaves. For this purpose, the leaf is specified by four optical parameters.

(i) The equivalent water thickness—a number that specifies the amount of water in a leaf.
(ii) The void area index (VAI)—a measure of the inter-cellular air space in a leaf.
(iii) The effective index of refraction.
(iv) The effective absorption coefficienct.

An excellent review of theoretical models is given in *Manual on Remote Sensing*, Vol. 1 (Chapter 3). A number of experimental works have also been carried out to find out the reflectance pattern of leaves/canopy under various conditions. The spectral reflectance mechanism of a typical leaf can be categorised as follows.

Visible spectral region (0.4–0.7 μm)   Absorption by leaf pigments dominates the reflectance characteristic in the 0.4–0.7 μm region. The incident radiation is absorbed in the blue (~0.45 μm) and red (0.67 μm) regions corresponding to the absorption bands of chlorophyll (Fig. 4.4). However, the absorption by the leaf is much broader than the sharp chlorophyll absorption band. This broadening is partly due to certain physical processes such as anomalous dispersion near an absorption band and also due to pigments other than chlorophyll. Thus in the reflectance spectra, a green leaf shows a characteristic peak at about 0.55 μm. However, leaves with low chlorophyll content or predominantly other pigments will have entirely

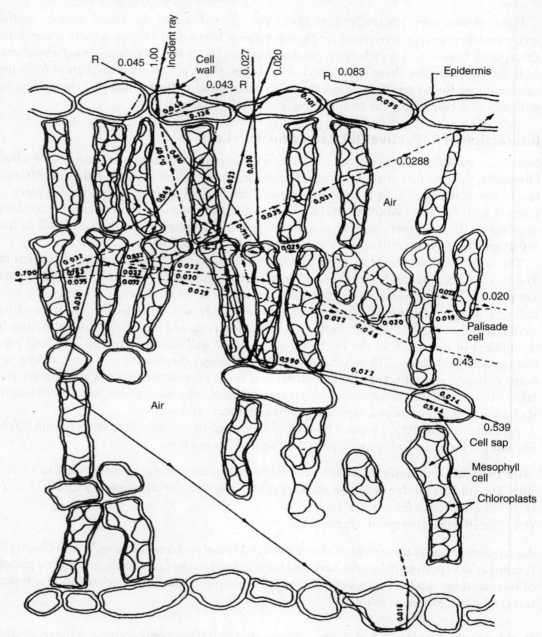

Fig. 4.3 Pathway of a light ray through a leaf cross-section. R denotes the reflected ray. Solid lines show the pathway of light considering the cell wall, chloroplasts, cell sap and air as the optical media. Dotted lines show the pathway of light considering only the cell wall and air as the optical media. The numbers along the rays denote their total intensity. The rays whose total intensity is less than 0.018 are not shown. (Adapted from Kumar and Silva, 1973)

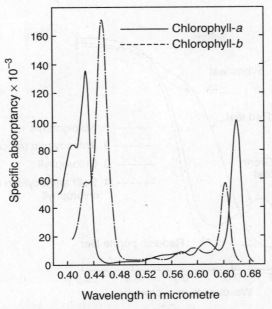

Fig. 4.4 Absorption spectra of chlorophylls *a* and *b*.

different reflectance characteristics. This is well-illustrated in Fig. 4.5, which shows the spectral response for four pigment conditions.

Near-infrared region (0.7–1.3 μm) The internal structure of the leaf primarily controls the reflectance in the near-IR region and the differences in the internal structure of various leaves essentially show up as the difference in reflectance in the 0.7 to 1.3 μm region. Leaves typically reflect 40%–50% and absorb less than 5% of the incident energy in this wavelength region. The process responsible for the reflection/transmission in this region is the multiple reflections in the internal mesophyll structure, caused by the differences in the refractive index of the cell walls and the inter-cellular air cavity. The mesophyll arrangements have the most influence on the reflectance/transmittance/absorptance in this wavelength region since the interaction of the radiation in this wavelength region is primarily a function of the cell shape, size and the intercellular space. Since the near-IR radiation passes through many more interfaces inside the leaf, than the visible light, the reflected rays in the 0.7–1.3 μm region is more diffuse than the visible portion. As the internal structure of leaves often varies considerably among species, differences in reflectance are generally greater in the near-IR region than in the visible region.

Short wave infrared region (1.3 to 2.7 μm) There are three strong water absorption bands in this region which occur at 1.4, 1.9 and 2.7 μm. In this region, the water content of the leaf greatly influences the reflection and transmission characteristics. Absorption depends on the equivalent water thickness which in turn, is a function of the moisture content of the leaf and its thickness. Two broad reflection peaks are observed between the three absorption bands. As the moisture content of the leaf decreases, the reflection in this region increases.

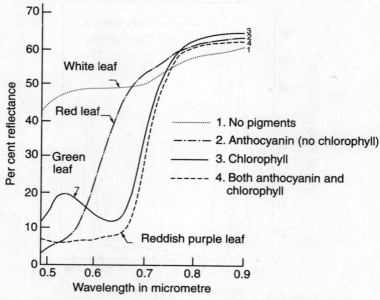

Fig. 4.5 Spectral response in the 0.5–0.9 μm region for four pigmentation conditions. (Adapted from Hoffer and Johannsen, 1969)

The reflectance characteristics of a leaf can be summarised in the reflective OIR region as follows

- visible (0.4–0.7 μm) region characterised by pigment absorption wherein most of the incident energy is absorbed with low reflectance (< 20%),
- the near-IR region (0.7–1.3 μm) having high (> 50%) reflectance is primarily controlled by the cell structure, and
- the shortwave IR (1.3–2.7 μm) region reflection is characterised by the water present in the leaf.

These regions are shown schematically in Fig. 4.6.

Reflectance from Vegetative Cover

While the phenomenon governing the reflectance characteristics of a leaf helps us to understand the reflectance from a plant canopy, the actual reflectance of a canopy as seen by a remote sensor is much more complex. This is because from space we observe the interaction of solar radiation with plants which contain multiple leaves and other parts (stem, flower, and so on), with the soil background and even shadows. In addition, the orientation of these with the incident radiation and the direction of observation also varies. The radiation measured by the sensor is an integrated effect of all these variables. This is usually referred to as *canopy reflectance*. For example, it is rather obvious that when viewing a vegetation canopy we see the effect due to multiple leaves. With stacks of leaves, the general shape of the reflectance pattern is the same as that of a single leaf but the relative values in various regions of the wavelength spectrum varies. Obviously, those regions where the energy transmitted by the leaf is very low,

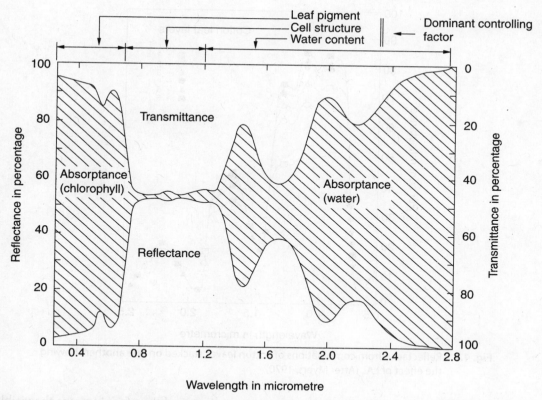

Fig. 4.6 Reflectance, absorptance and transmittance spectra of a typical green leaf. The hatched area shows absorptance. (Reprinted from *Remote Sensing of Environment*, Vol. I, Issue 1, Knipling, pp 156, 1970 with permission from Elsevier Science)

will not be affected much by multiple leaves, since the energy falling on the second leaf when further reflected and transmitted through the first leaf will be further attenuated. Therefore, the effect of multiple leaves is seen to be of maximum extent in the near-IR region, practically negligible in the visible region and very marginal in the shortwave IR region. This is well demonstrated in Fig. 4.7. As the number of leaves are increased from 2 to 4, about 10% increase in reflectance is seen in the near-IR region, whereas in shortwave IR it is 1%–2% and there is no change in the visible region. Increasing the number of leaves to more than four shows progressively lesser increase in reflectance in the near-IR region. The area of leaves within a canopy is usually quantified by *leaf area index* (LAI). The leaf area index is the one-sided leaf area per unit area of ground.

There are certain factors intrinsic to agronomy/physiology of the crop cover which gives different spectral reflectance values for different types of cover. This is the very basis of detection/identification using remote sensing. Since the leaf reflectance depends primarily on the pigments, internal cell structure and the equivalent water content, any change in these, either due to species difference or due to other factors like, stress, disease, cultural practices, or senescence, can give a different spectral reflectance. For example, the nitrogen nutrient in the plants markedly affect pigment concentration and subsequent leaf colour. A reduction in

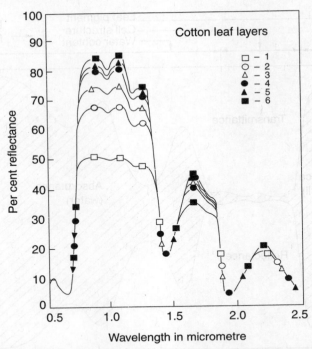

Fig. 4.7 Reflectance from combinations of cotton leaves stacked on one another showing the effect of LAI. (After Myers, 1970)

the nitrogen nutrient would reduce pigment concentrations and therefore increase the visible reflectivity because of decreased radiation absorptance (Thomas, 1970). Similarly, during plant senescence, because of chlorophyll degradation, there is high reflectance in the visible region (Knipling, 1970). Gausman et. al., (1971) have demonstrated the difference in reflectance spectra among 11 plant genera due to internal structure and water content. While we are looking for such differences in reflectance spectra to identify plant species/condition, there are extrinsic effects, which change the reflectance even when the plant physiology/agronomy remains the same. These are mainly background effects and illumination and view angle effects.

Background Effects on Vegetation Reflectance Spectra

The vegetative cover reflectance observed by a sensor is a mixture of reflectance from the vegetation, soil (litter) underneath and the shadow. At low values of vegetation cover, background reflectance could be quite important in affecting canopy reflectance. Discrimination of vegetation from these underlying background effects is an important aspect while applying remote sensing techniques to vegetation, especially in the case of agriculture. Many crops are planted in rows and for a considerable time during the early part of the growing season, the bare soil will be the dominant contributor of the reflected solar radiation. As the vegetation grows, it spreads out, covering the bare soil, after which, the major contribution comes from the vegetative cover. The relative contribution to the received radiation from plants, soil and the plant shadow in the background is dependent on the direction of the sun's rays and view direction. When plants are planted in rows and the sun's rays fall along the rows, the bare soil is fully illuminated, whereas when the sun's rays fall across the rows, the soil is mostly in the shadow of the standing vegetation. The relative contribution of the shadow will play a role in modifying the reflectance spectra.

To understand the effect of soil background, we shall compare the general reflectance characteristics of soil and vegetation. Figure 4.8 gives the typical spectral reflectance of dry soil, wet soil and vegetative cover. In the red region (~0.65 μm), the soil reflectance is higher than the vegetation. For a field with vegetation, one finds the reflectance in red decreases as the vegetation cover increases. In the case of NIR reflectance, the reverse happens (Colwell, 1974) (Fig. 4.9). Thus all other parameters remaining the same, in general, the reflectance in the visible band has a negative correlation with the per cent vegetative ground cover and the reflectance in NIR has a positive correlation. Obviously, the magnitude of variation will depend on the type of soil—dark, light coloured, moist, and so on. It is also worth noting that a partially covered canopy as in the case of some plantations/forests or grass, grown in between trees, can alter the spectral signature. A number of vegetation indices have been developed to separate the soil contribution.

View Angle Effects on Vegetation Reflectance Spectra

The reflectance characteristics of most vegetation canopies at the OIR region vary with both sensor view angle and solar zenith angle. This non-Lambertian behaviour is due to the geometrical characteristics of canopy such as leaf angle distribution, spatial distribution of plants, per cent canopy cover and optical properties of soil background. Understanding the dependence of reflection on the view angle is important to interpret off-nadir data. When using data from satellites with capabilities for off-nadir viewing (for example, SPOT, IRS-LISS4), the additional source of variation (which is not due to plant physiology) in the measured radiations due to view angle and solar zenith angle changes should be considered while interpreting the data.

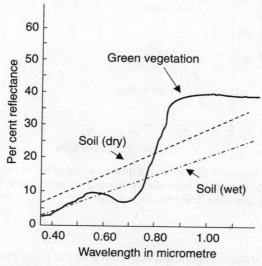

Fig. 4.8 Typical spectral reflectance of soil and green vegetation.

An incomplete canopy produces a greater effect on reflectance variation with sun and view angles than a completely covered canopy. In addition, as mentioned earlier, for plants in a row, the row direction with respect to illumination and view direction also matters. This can be intuitively expected, since with changing sun or view directions, the proportion of the four components of reflectance – sunlit vegetation, shadow vegetation, sunlit soil and shadow soil – viewed by the sensor, varies. For example, when the sensor looks straight down on a canopy with a well-defined row structure, the effect of sunlit and shadow soil on the scene reflectance is maximum. If the sensor views at right angles to the row, as the view zenith angle increases, proportionately more vegetation is viewed, since sensor FOV includes the sides of the plant rows. The effect is relatively less for a complete canopy cover compared to a partially covered canopy and the effect is more pronounced in the red (0.6–0.7 μm) than the NIR (0.8–1.1 μm) (Ranson et. al., 1985).

Thus the important parameters in determining the reflectance of a vegetation canopy include (Colwell, 1974)

- transmittance of leaves,
- amount and arrangement of leaves,
- characteristics of other components of the vegetation canopy (stalks, trunks, limbs),
- characteristics of the background (soil reflectance, amount of leaf litter),
- solar zenith angle,
- look angle, and
- azimuth angle.

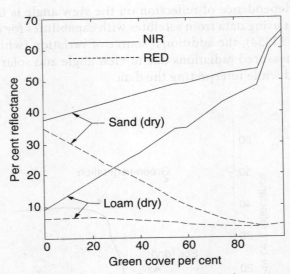

Fig. 4.9 Variation of reflectance with percentage of green canopy cover for red and NIR bands for two types of soil background. (Reprinted from *Remote Sensing of Environment*, Vol. 17, Issue 1, Heute et. al., pp. 41, 1985 with permission from Elsevier Science)

Vegetation Indices

The spectral reflectance data of vegetation are related to the plant parameters such as leaf area index and biomass, and plant status such as stress, disease and so on. However, utilisation of spectral data to derive such parameters have problems due to varying soil conditions, viewing and illumination geometry. It has been found that suitable combinations of data from different spectral bands can be used to reduce the effect due to some of these extrinsic variables and get a better correlation with the plant variable we are looking for. In some of the early experiments, the ratio of reflectance in IR to the reflectance in red (IR/RED) was used to relate crop parametres with reflectance data. Since then, a number of transforms have been used. One very extensively used transform is called *Normalised Difference Vegetation Index* (NDVI).

$$NDVI = \frac{IR - RED}{IR + RED} \qquad\qquad (4.1)$$

The NDVI can vary from −1 to +1 depending on the relative value of red and IR reflectance.

There are a few other transforms of the spectral bands such as, Perpendicular Vegetation Index, PVI (Richardson and Wiegand, 1977; Wiegand and Richardson, 1982), Soil Adjusted Vegetation Index, SAVI (Huete, 1988), Kauth–Thomas Tasseled Cap transformation (Kauth and Thomas, 1976), TM Tasseled Cap transformation (Crist and Cicone, 1984), and so on. However, these are not used for any operational applications and hence are not discussed here. The interested reader may look up the references cited.

Temporal Signatures of Vegetative Cover

All vegetation shows some seasonal changes in its characteristics. In the case of crops it is rather evident, since it goes through a process of germination, canopy growth, senescence and final harvest. In the case of deciduous forests, leaf shedding taking place in autumn gives a distinct reflectance. Therefore, imagery of the appropriate season (date) has to be chosen for optimal discrimination of the vegetation to be studied, from the background.

Let us consider the temporal effect for crops in a little more detail. When crops pass through different developmental stages, the vegetation index profile changes as follows.

(i) As the crop emerges after a period of sowing, the vegetation index profile rises above the threshold so that the crop becomes spectrally detectable. This time is the called *spectral emergence date.*

(ii) The vegetation index increases continuously as the crop cover increases over the soil background.

(iii) A maximum value (peak) is reached as the crop reaches the maximum green canopy development.

(iv) The vegetation index decreases as the crop begins to senesce.

(v) Finally the value falls below the threshold after harvest.

Although the exact values of the vegetation indices at different stages as well as the duration from one stage to other may vary from crop to crop, the general form of the growth curve remains similar. Figure 4.10 gives the growth profile of wheat, mustard and chickpea (Ajai et. al., 1984). It is clear that if a single observation is taken 100 days after sowing, the difference in the vegetation index for three crops are very little and can lead to misclassification. Thus, there are certain times during the year when it would be rather easy to identify a certain crop species and at other times, identification of the same species may be quite difficult. Hence,

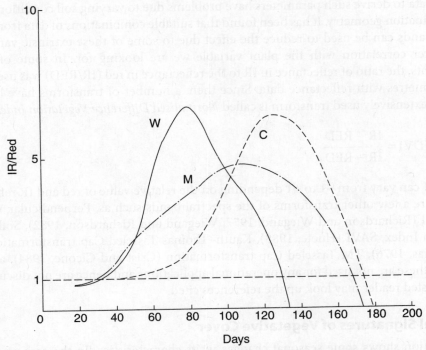

Fig. 4.10   Time profile of the ratio of IR reflectance to red reflectance after sowing for wheat (W), chickpea (C) and mustard (M). (Adapted from Ajai et. al., 1984)

information on the growth profile helps us to choose optimal dates for collecting the remote sensing data.

However, for operational application it is difficult to generate a growth profile from satellite data, since such frequent observation is not possible due to poor temporal resolution. Cloud cover also reduces the number of observations in a growth cycle for OIR sensors. Another approach is to fit an analytical model to the crop growth profile which can reduce the number of observations required. One growth profile developed by Badhwar (1984) based on greenness is as follows:

$$\rho(t) = \rho_o + (\rho_m - \rho_o) \, (2\beta \, e/\alpha)^{\alpha/2} \, (\, (t-t_o)^\alpha \exp[-\beta(t-t_o)^2] \tag{4.2}$$

where ρ_o is soil greenness, t_o is crop emergence date (day of year), ρ_m is the maximum value of greenness attained at time of peak $t_p (= \sqrt{\alpha/2\beta})$, and α and β are crop and condition related constants. [Greenness is a transformed parameter of the four bands of MSS developed by Kauth and Thomas (1976.) The general profile is also valid for other transforms like NDVI, in place of greenness.] Thus we have four crop related unknowns (α, β, ρ_o and t_o) which could be solved with at least four observations, preferably two on either side of the peak. The above equation has two inflection points t_1 and t_2 (Fig. 4.11), the difference essentially gives the width of the curve $\sigma^2 = (t_2 - t_1)^2$. The model, thus, permits the conversion of multi-temporal–multispectral data to three well identified features, ρ_m, t_p and σ, which have been shown to carry greater than 95% of the information contained in the raw spectral space. Figure 4.12 is a frequency histogram of t_p of corn and soybean. The soybean peak is about 2 weeks later than corn. Additional separability is possible with a classifier using ρ_m, σ and t_p. However this is seldom used in practice for crop classification.

Polarisation Signature from Vegetation

We have seen in Chapter 2 that electromagnetic radiation undergoing Fresnel reflection gets polarised. A good portion of the radiation from a plant canopy, especially in the visible wavelength is specularly (mirror-like) reflected. The diffuse radiation from a leaf is generated by the solar radiation entering inside the leaves and interacting with pigments, cell walls, and so on. On the other hand, the specular reflection is produced at the first surface the radiation strikes, that is, the cuticle having a wax layer. It is this layer of wax which provides most of the surface details of plant tissue on a microscopic and optical scale. The cuticle properties are related to species, developmental stage, and other physiological parameters of the plant and the environment. Therefore data on polarisation could give additional information on the vegetation which is not available or complementary to that got by measurement of diffused reflectance. However, polarisation measurements are currently carried out only as research investigations and there is no provision to make measurements on the polarisation of the radiation received in the current operational remote sensing satellites such as LANDSAT, SPOT, IRS and so on. A number of experimental studies have been carried out in the field and laboratories to understand the polarisation property of leaves and plant canopy. The polarisation from a plant canopy depends on

- the light polarising properties of each piece of foliage,
- the geometric arrangement of foliage in the canopy (leaf angle distribution and so on), and
- the direction of illumination and view.

The amount of polarised light from a wheat canopy decreases significantly with the advent of heading development stage (Ghosh et. al., 1993). This is due to the fact that heads, which are poor specular reflectors (and therefore poor polarisers), tower above the leaves and significantly reduce the amount of specularity in the reflected radiation. Similarly, the polarisation is decreased when the corn canopy is at the flowering stage (Rondeaux and Herman, 1991). Thus polarisation information can be a good supplementary/complimentary information to use with other remotely sensed data.

4.1.2 SOIL

For a common person the term soil usually means, the surface layer of the earth. However, soil scientists consider soil as a three-dimensional body formed due to the physical, chemical and biological weathering of rocks giving rise to spatial variation both in the horizontal and vertical direction.

A vertical section of the soil in the field shows more or less distinct horizontal layers. The vertical section (a plane at right angles to the surface), extending into the parent material is called 'profile' and the layers 'horizons' (Plate 4.1). Horizons have relatively uniform materials that extend laterally and run approximately parallel to the surface of the ground. Adjacent horizons have distinct properties which differ in many chemical, physical (colour, structure,

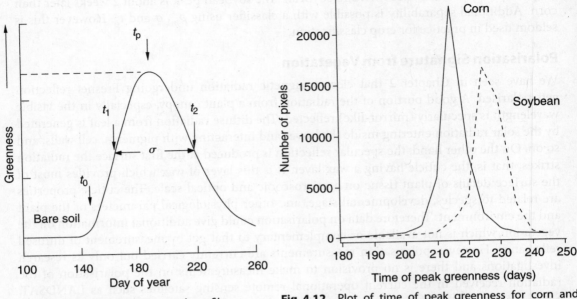

Fig. 4.11 Badhwar's growth profile.

Fig. 4.12 Plot of time of peak greenness for corn and soybean calculated from TM/TMS data. The soybean peak is about 2 weeks later than corn. (Reprinted from *Remote Sensing of Environment*, Vol. 16, Issue 2, Badhwar, pp. 178, 1982, with permission from Elsevier Science).

texture) and biological properties, characteristic of the soil forming process. The transitional layer between two adjoining horizons is called *boundary*. Boundaries vary in distinctness (thickness) and are uneven. For the purpose of soil survey a practical lower limit for study is bedrock (parent material) or 2 m, whichever is shallower (*Soil Survey Manual*, 1993). To have a better understanding of the reflectance characteristics of soil, it will be useful to have some understanding of the basic aspects of soil formation and physical and chemical characteristics of soils.

About 98% (by weight) of the earth's crust consists of elements such as oxygen (46.6%), silicon (27.7%), aluminium (8.1%), iron (5%), calcium (3.6%), sodium (2.8%), potassium (2.6%) and magnesium (2.1%). Various combinations of the earth's elements have produced a wide variety of minerals. The original minerals have been produced dominantly in primate rocks. Weathering, namely the disintegration (reduction in size) and decomposition (chemical alteration) of the exposed rocks over years lead to soil formation (Steila, 1976). All minerals do not decay at the same rate. Soluble materials like calcium, magnesium, and so on, are removed depending on the moisture condition. Thus, depending on the original rock type, climatic conditions and topography, the soil composition varies geographically.

Soil is composed of particles of varying size. They are grouped depending on the size—called soil separates. Depending on the particle size they can be broadly classified as clay, silt and sand. The classification of the soil particle according to size is given in Fig. 4.13. The major sand mineral is quartz (SiO_2). Secondary silicates dominate clay. The texture of a soil

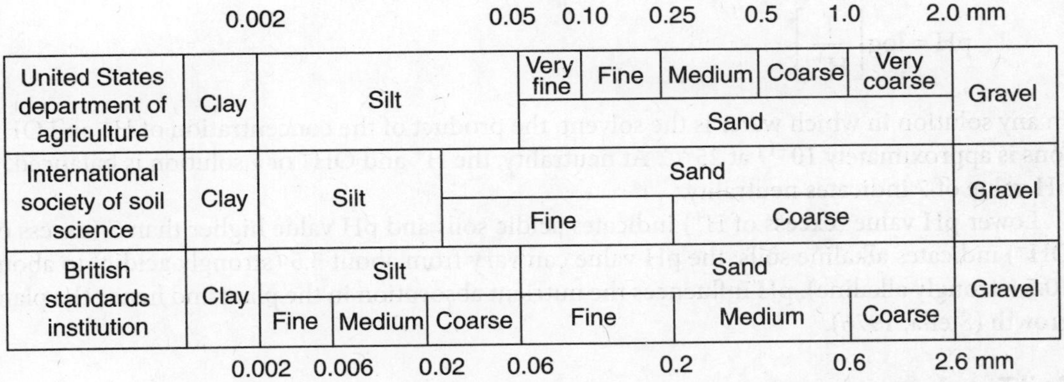

	0.002			0.05	0.10	0.25	0.5	1.0	2.0 mm	

United States department of agriculture	Clay	Silt		Very fine	Fine	Medium	Coarse	Very coarse	Gravel
				Sand					
International society of soil science	Clay	Silt		Sand					Gravel
				Fine			Coarse		
British standards institution	Clay	Silt			Sand				Gravel
		Fine	Medium	Coarse	Fine		Medium		Coarse

	0.002	0.006	0.02	0.06	0.2	0.6	2.6 mm

Fig. 4.13 Classification of soil particles according to size. (Adapted from Brady, 1974)

depends on the relative proportions of the soil separates. For example, loam is a soil texture class containing 7%–27% clay, 28%–50% silt and less than 52% sand (Brady, 1974).

Another important aspect is soil structure, that is, the physical arrangement and aggregations of soil particles into larger secondary units called *peds*. Four primary types of soil structure are recognised—plate-like, prism-like, block-like and spheroidal. The nature and origin of parent material, organic content, climate and so on, primarily influence the development of structure (Steila, 1976). Many soil properties such as soil water movement, porosity, aeration and bulk density, are dependent on the structure, texture and composition of the soil.

Soil organic matter is an important constituent influencing soil property for plant growth. Soil organic matter consists of decayed plant and animal residues and the micro-organisms that dwell in the soil, which decompose the plant/animal remnants. On the basis of organic content, two general groups of soils are commonly recognised—inorganic and organic. Inorganic soils vary in the amount of organic matter from trace to as high as 30%. Those with higher organic matter are called *organic soils*. The inorganic soils also called mineral soils cover a major portion (over 95%) of the world land surface (Steila, 1976).

The major components of soil are

- mineral material,
- organic matter,
- water (solution containing dissolved compounds), and
- air, all of which are intimately mixed.

For example, the volume composition of silt loam consists of 50% pore space (water and air) and 50% solid space, of which 45% is mineral and 5% organic matter. Compared to the top soil, the subsoil has a higher percentage of minerals and water and considerably lower content of organic matter and air (Brady, 1974).

Another aspect of soil which is of interest to soil scientists is the soluble salts in the soil. As the soil moisture content is reduced by evaporation, the concentration of soluble salts in the soil solution rises. Under excessive irrigation coupled with poor drainage and low rainfall, the salt concentration can increase to an alarming proportion interfering with plant growth. The acidity or alkalinity of a soil is usually expressed in terms of pH. The pH value of a solution is the reciprocal of the logarithm of the hydrogen ion concentration, that is

$$pH = \log\left[\frac{1}{H^+}\right]$$

In any solution in which water is the solvent, the product of the concentration of H^+ and OH^- ions is approximately 10^{-14} at 25°C. At neutrality, the H^+ and OH^- of a solution is balanced, a pH value of 7 indicates neutrality.

Lower pH value (excess of H^+) indicates acidic soils and pH value higher than 7 (excess of OH^-) indicates alkaline soils; the pH value can vary from about 3.5 (strongly acidic) to about 10.5 (strongly alkaline). pH influences the nutrient absorption in the plant and hence the plant growth (Steila, 1976).

Soil Taxonomy

According to the US Department of Agriculture's (USDA) classification system, soil can be classified under six categories: order (the broadest category), sub order, great group, sub group, family and series (the most specific category). There are 11 orders. The order category is based on soil forming processes, as indicated by the presence or absence of certain major features. The nomenclature of order category is always suffixed by 'sol' (derivative from latin *solum* = soil) and prefixed with a formative element such as, 'ert' or 'ent' in the case of vertisol and entisol respectively (Brady, 1974). The sub order has two syllables. The first denotes the diagnostic properties of the soil and the second is the formative element from the name of the order. For example in Usterts, ust (from latin *ustus,* burnt) meaning dry climates usually hot in summer followed by 'ert' the formative element of vertisol. There are 47 sub orders. Profiles

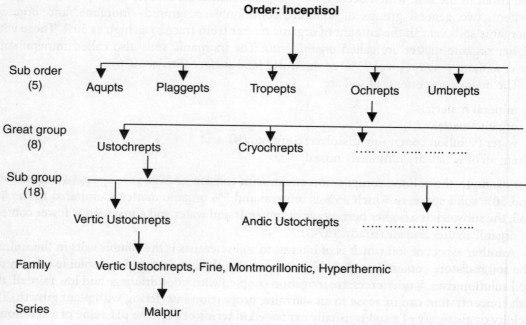

Fig. 4.14 Representation of soil classification for order Inceptisol.

having horizons similar in arrangement are called series. As an example the hierarchy of the Malpur series found in Dhar, Madhya Pradesh is shown in Fig. 4.14.

Spectral Reflectance of Soil

Soil reflectance in the visible and IR region has been extensively studied by various investigators both in the laboratory and field (Stoner and Baumgardner, 1981; Cipra, et. al., 1971; Condit, 1972; Bowers and Hanks, 1965; Coulson, 1966). The reflection properties of the soil in the visible region give a specific observable colour. Very little of the incident solar flux is transmitted and hence the reflectance of the soil mostly depends on the property of the top layer. Vegetation cover and changes in the bare soil surface condition (due to tillage or plant residue) render the study of soil using remote sensing techniques difficult. Although soils are composed of granular mineral materials which are generally mixed in their surface layers with organic matter, the reflectance property of the soil is less affected by the chemical composition than by moisture, texture and structural arrangement (Mulders 1987). In general, the spectral reflectance from any surface will be influenced by the absorption bands (due to electronic and vibrational transitions), which are shown as characteristic absorption features in the reflected spectra. The atomic constituents of soil minerals such as silicon, aluminium, magnesium, and so on, have neither electronic nor vibrational transition lines in the visible and near-IR region. The majority of the discernible features in the reflectance spectra occur as a result of water and hydroxyl ions. The absorption bands of the liquid water molecule which appear in the shortwave and near infrared are ~1.875 μm, ~1.454 μm, ~1.38 μm, ~1.135 μm and ~0.942 μm. However, in the spectra of minerals and rocks, whenever water is present, two bands appear prominently, one at 1.4 μm and the other at 1.9 μm. Hence the presence of the 1.4 μm and 1.9 μm features together is completely diagnostic of the presence of molecular water (Seigal, 1980). The hydroxyl ion, OH^- very frequently occurs in inorganic solids. The OH groups such as Al–OH and Mg–OH produce features near 2.2 μm and 2.3 μm respectively. The carbonate minerals display features around 1.9 μm, 2.0 μm, 2.16 μm, 2.35 μm and 2.55 μm (Seigal, 1980).

We shall now discuss how factors such as organic matter, moisture, particle size, surface conditions and minerals actually influence the reflection in the optical IR region.

Soil Moisture

Wet soil generally appears darker. This is because of the decreased reflectance in the visible region with increase in soil moisture. This has been explained on the basis of total internal reflection within the film of thin layer of water covering the soil surface. A characteristic feature seen is the decrease in the reflectance in the water absorption band (1.4, 1.9 and 2.7 μm). The laboratory measurements made by Bowers and Hanks (1965) on silt loam under varying moisture content is shown in Fig. 4.15.

As can be seen from the figure, increasing moisture content lowered the reflectance, but did not change the shape of the spectra. They have also shown that the percentage reflectance at 1.9 μm gives a good fit to soil moisture (Fig. 4.16). A linear relationship between albedo (0.3 to 2.5 μm) and moisture content of the surface layer of loam was also reported by Idso et. al., (1975). However, it should be borne in mind that this is a laboratory experiment and in field operations, other factors also affect the reflectance so that each soil will have a different moisture reflectance curve. Thus estimation of soil moisture through reflectance measurement

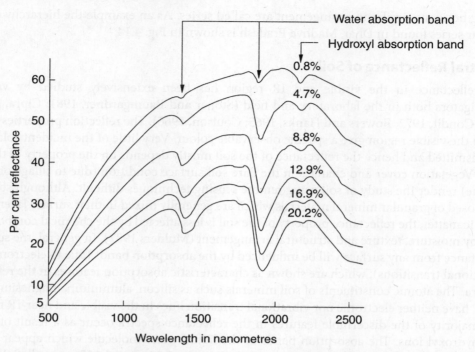

Fig. 4.15 Silt loam reflectance spectra for various moisture contents (moisture content indicated directly above each curve). (Adapted from Bowers and Hanks, 1965)

becomes practically difficult. For example, an increase in organic content can reduce reflectance even when the moisture content is not changed.

Particle Size, Soil Texture and Surface Condition

Other factors remaining same, the soil reflectance increases as particle size decreases (Fig. 4.17). Bowers and Hanks (1965) have shown that the most notable increase occurs at sizes less than 400 μm. For particle size higher than 400 μm, the effect of particle size on reflectance is marginal. The laboratory studies of Hunt et. al. (1971) for a number of mineral samples also show that with increase in particle diameter, the reflectance decreases. The conclusions arrived at in the laboratory may not always hold good in the field due to the interrelation between texture, moisture retention and structure. Reflectance of undisturbed soils measured in the field is generally the inverse of that measured in the laboratory. When measured with a spectrometer in the laboratory, sand generally has a lower reflectance than clay throughout the wavelength interval from 0.45 μm to 2.50 μm. However, reflectance from identical soils, measured in an undisturbed condition in the field shows that sand has the highest reflectance and fine textured soil, the lowest (Colwell, 1983). This is attributed to the fact that in the undisturbed case, fine textured soils generally have a structure which gives them the characteristic of aggregates coarser than sand (Myers and Allen, 1968).

The structure of the soil plays an important role in soil reflectance. It has been observed that the influence of structure is dominant over that of texture (Colwell, 1983). Surface roughness (soil aggregation) as governed by tillage treatments, has a substantial influence on the reflectance of soils which tend to aggregate. Rougher soil surface resulted in lower reflectance.

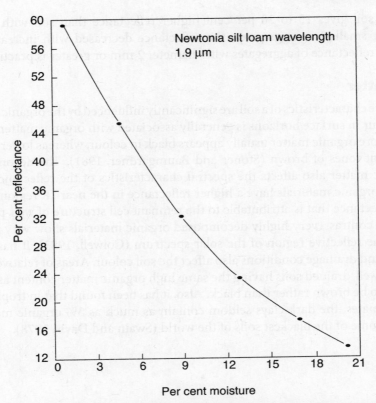

Fig. 4.16   Per cent reflectance vs surface moisture content for incident radiance energy of 1.9 μm. (Adapted from Bowers and Hanks, 1965)

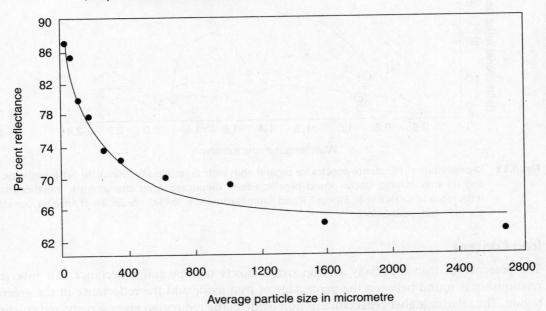

Fig. 4.17   Per cent reflectance vs particle size for incident radiation of 1.0 μm wavelength. (Adapted from Bowers and Hanks, 1965)

Structureless soil gives 15 to 20 per cent higher reflectance than soil with a well-defined structure. For small-sized aggregates, the reflectance decreased with increase in diameter. However, the reflectance of aggregates with diameter 2 mm or greater is practically constant.

Organic Matter

The reflectance characteristics of a soil are significantly influenced by the organic matter content. The dark colour in surface horizons is generally associated with organic matter content. A soil with 5% or more organic matter usually appears black in colour, whereas lower organic matter shows different tones of brown (Stoner and Baumgardner, 1981). The decomposition stage of the organic matter also affects the spectral characteristics of the reflectance spectra. Less decomposed organic materials have a higher reflectance in the near-IR region because of the enhanced reflectance that is attributable to the remnant cell structure of well-preserved fibres (Fig. 4.18). In contrast, very highly decomposed organic materials show very low reflectance throughout the reflective region of the solar spectrum (Colwell, 1983). It has been inferred that climatic and drainage conditions also affect the soil colour. Areas of relatively high annual temperature, well-drained soils having the same high organic matter content as soils in cooler regions tend to be brown rather than black. Also, it has been found that in tropical and warm-temperate climates, the dark clays seldom contain as much as 3% organic matter; yet these soils include some of the blackest soils of the world (Swain and Davis, 1978).

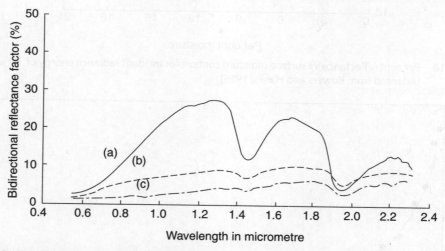

Fig. 4.18   Representative reflectance spectra for organic soils with: (a) minimally (fibric); (b) partially (hemic) and (c) fully (sapric) decomposed organic fibres. (Reprinted from characteristic variations in reflectance of surface soils, Stoner E R and Baumgardner M F, *Soil Science Society of America Journal*, 45, 1981 with permission)

Iron Content

The presence of iron especially as iron oxide affects the spectral reflectance. An inverse relationship is found between the percentage of iron oxide and the reflectance in the green region. The relative higher reflectance of iron oxide in the red region gives a 'rusty' red colour to the soil containing iron. Iron-dominated soils have strong absorption in the shortwave IR region (>1.3 μm) to the extent that the 1.4 and 1.9 μm water absorption feature is obliterated [Fig. 4.19, curve (e)], (Stoner and Baumgardner 1981).

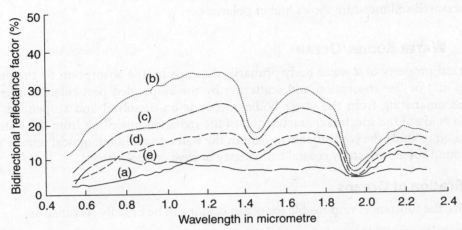

Fig. 4.19   Representative reflectance spectra of surface samples of 5 minerals soils; (a) High organic content, moderately fine texture; (b) Low organic, low iron content; (c) Low organic, medium iron content; (d) High organic content, moderately coarse texture and (e) High iron content, fine texture. (Reprinted from characteristic variations in reflectance of surface soils, Stoner E R and Baumgardner M F, *Soil Science Society of America Journal*, 45, 1981 with permission)

Generalisation of Soil Reflectance Characteristics

There have been a number of studies to classify the reflectance characteristic of soils in terms of some typical representative curves (Condit, 1970; Stoner and Baumgardner, 1981; Price, 1990). These studies have shown that soil reflectance curves can be reconstituted using a linear combination of a few 'basis' curves, that is, the *soil response* is the weighted sum of a few unique soil reflecting features. Huete and Escadafal (1991) have shown that all measured soil curves can be reconstituted from linear combinations of five unique 'basis' curves. Each basis curve is supposed to represent a unique soil spectral property and the amount needed of each curve to reconstitute a soil signature is a measure of the significance of that property in the soil sample. In addition, they have found that four or five 'key' bands are needed to completely characterise and reconstruct a soil spectrum. The 'key' bands in order of importance are 0.41, 0.90, 0.61, 0.54, 0.78, 0.48, 0.45 and 0.57 μm, which are similar to that proposed by Condit (1972).

These laboratory studies are very useful to understand the reflectance property of soils. However, they are not of much direct relevance in interpreting remote sensing data.

Polarisation Effect of Soil Reflectance

Polarisation studies on the soil have been carried out by a number of investigators—Coulson, et. al., 1965; Coulson, 1966; Genda and Okayama, 1978. Their major findings are

(i) Dark surface polarises reflected radiation more strongly, compared to a highly reflecting surface. Therefore, reflectance from desert sands are less polarised compared to the reflectance from darker soils.

(ii) The phase angle (that is, the angle between the illumination direction and the view direction) is the main geometric variable controlling the degree of polarisation.

(iii) Degree of polarisation decreases with increasing wavelength.

(iv) Increased soil moisture shows higher polarisation.

4.1.3 WATER BODIES/OCEAN

The optical property of a water body primarily depends on the absorption by the dissolved material and/or the absorption and scattering by the suspended particulate matter. Thus, radiation emanating from the water bodies depends on dissolved and suspended matter. Hence, a study of the spectral characteristics of the radiation upwelling from the water body can be used to study the constituents present in the water. In addition, optical remote sensing is also found suitable to study coastal bathymetry in clear coastal waters.

Classification of Oceans

In oceans, the substances responsible for ocean colour can be broadly classified as

- phytoplankton,
- non-chlorophyllous particles of biological or terrestrial origin, and
- dissolved organic matter, known as yellow substance.

Phytoplankton are microscopic plants, which occupy the first link in almost all aquatic and marine food chains. They are responsible for converting solar energy and dissolved carbon and nitrogen into organic biomass which is then available to higher trophic level organisms.

Phytoplankton contains the photosynthetically active pigment, chlorophyll-a (chl-a) which strongly absorbs near 0.443 μm (blue), while the chl-a absorption is much weaker in the green region (0.52 and 0.55 μm). Thus, as the phytoplankton content increases, the backscattering increases in the green region but the blue region is absorbed rapidly. Hence, water rich in phytoplankton (chlorophyll) appears green, while water that is poor in phytoplankton will appear deep blue in sunlight (Fig. 4.20). As the turbidity increases, the upward radiance peak shifts towards red and that is why one sees muddy water as brown. Morel and Precur (1977) has classified ocean water as Case 1 and Case 2 according to the relative importance of phytoplankton and their co-varying detrital products compared to various inorganic and organic sediments.

Case 1 water always contain the following

- Living algal cells—phytoplankton.
- Associated debris originating from grazing by zooplankton and natural decay.
- Dissolved organic matter liberated by algae and their debris (marine yellow substance).

Case 2 water may (or may not) contain the above component, but should contain at least one of the following components

- Suspended sediments from the bottom along the coast line and in shallow waters.
- Particles brought in by rivers and glacial run-off (yellow substance).
- Dissolved organic matter brought in by land drainage (yellow substance).
- Anthropogenic influx of particulate and dissolved matter.

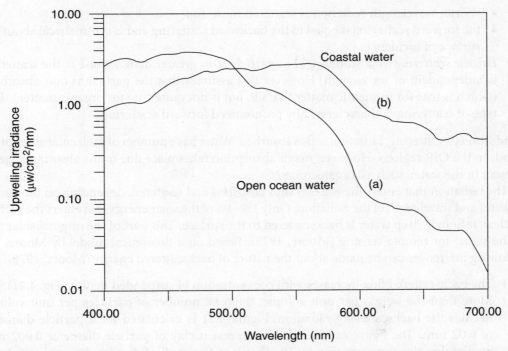

Fig. 4.20 Upwelling spectra for (a) Open ocean water (b) Coastal water. Data obtained during ship campaigns in the Arabian Sea during October, 1997. Since coastal water is rich in chlorophyll, the blue radiation is reduced due to absorption and there is enhanced radiation in green. Due to this coastal water appears green. (Chauhan, 2002)

In summary, Case 1 waters are those in which phytoplankton and their derivative products play a dominant role in determining the optical properties of the ocean, and Case 2 waters are those in which inorganic/organic sediments make the dominant contribution. Oceanic waters, as a rule, form Case 1 water. Case 2 water of diverse kinds are normally encountered in the coastal zone (estuaries, shelf areas, inlets) and possibly, in the case of extended shelves or shallow banks far from the coast (Gordon and Morel, 1983).

Upwelling Radiation from Water

We shall now discuss the interaction of the sun's radiation in the OIR region with water giving rise to the upwelling radiation which is sensed by remote sensors.

The sun's radiation reaching the water surface undergoes reflection and the remainder gets refracted and enters the water as per Snell's law (Chapter 2). The amount of radiance reflected depends on the angle of incidence. For up to about 45°, the reflectance is only about 2%. Thus 98% of the energy enters the water at angles of incidence less than 45° (for the present, we assume a 'calm' surface since reflection and refraction are functions of surface roughness). The light rays entering the water encounters two types of scattering.

(i) *Molecular scattering (Rayleigh scattering)* The scattering intensity in a direction θ is proportional to $(1 + \cos^2 \theta)/\lambda^4$. Therefore

- shorter wavelength radiation is scattered more and
- the forward scattering is equal to the backward scattering and is symmetrical about the surface of incidence.

(ii) *Particle scattering (Mie scattering)* For particle sizes greater than about 1 μ, the scattering is independent of wavelength. However this assumes that the particle is non-absorbant (which is true for inorganic matter like silt, but is not quite true for organic matter). This type of scattering is characterised by pronounced forward scattering.

In addition to scattering, radiation is also absorbed. Water has a number of molecular absorption bands in the OIR regions. However, major absorption takes place due to the absorbing agents present in the water, such as, organic matter.

The radiation that enters the water is thus absorbed and scattered, depending on the nature of water and wavelength of the radiation. Only 1%–3% of the solar energy that enters the surface of clear, infinitely deep water is backscattered to the surface. This part of the original solar flux is the signal for remote sensing (Moore, 1978). Based on a theoretical model by Moore, the following inferences can be made about the nature of backscattered energy (Moore, 1978).

(i) The backscattered flux increases with concentration of suspended matter (Fig. 4.21).
(ii) More than the weight per unit volume, the total number of particles per unit volume decides the backscattering radiation. Figure 4.21 is calculated for a particle diameter of 0.02 mm. The figure can be used to represent clay of particle diameter 0.002 mm by dividing the concentration by 10. That is, a few mg/l of dispersed fine clay provide the same signal as several thousand mg/l of suspended sand (diameter = 0.2 mm). This can be physically understood since more number of particles result in an increase in reflective area.
(iii) In a specific spectral band, the backscattered radiance increases and later levels off with increasing concentration of suspended particle (Fig. 4.22). Shorter wavelength bands produce higher backscatter.
(vi) Since the energy is attenuated (scattering + absorption) as it progresses down, most of the backscattered radiation comes from the top layers, the depth being dependent on the wavelength. In clear deep water, 50% of the signal for blue light (0.4–0.5 μm) could come from a depth up to about 15 m, whereas for red light (0.6–0.7 μm), most of the signal comes from a depth less than about 1.1 m (Fig. 4.23).

The properties which depend only upon the medium and are independent of the ambient light field within the medium are referred to as *inherent optical properties* (IOP). The IOP includes absorption, scattering and attenuation coefficients, single scattering albedo and volume scattering functions. These are associated with a wavelength-specific collimated beam of radiation propagating a volume of water. The *apparent optical property* (AOP) are those properties that depend both on the medium (IOP) and the directional structure of the ambient light field. An important AOP is the *diffuse attenuation coefficient* k_d. The *beam attenuation coefficient* k_e is defined in terms of radiant power lost from a single, narrow collimated beam. The *downwelling diffused attenuation coefficient* k_d is defined in terms of the decrease with depth of the ambient downwelling irradiance, which comprises photons heading in all directions (Mobley, 1994). Thus k_d also depends on the directional structure of ambient light apart from the inherent optical properties of the water body. In other words, k_d is a measure of

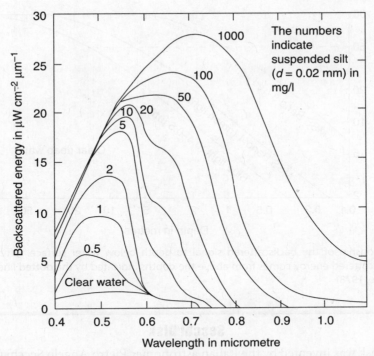

Fig. 4.21 Backscattered flux increases with concentrations of suspended silt (calculated for particle diameter of 0.02 millimetre.) The shape of all curves is similar for low to medium concentrations, because of the absorptance characteristics of water. At high concentrations, the curve shape is determined by the absorptance characteristics of particles. (Adapted from Moore, 1978)

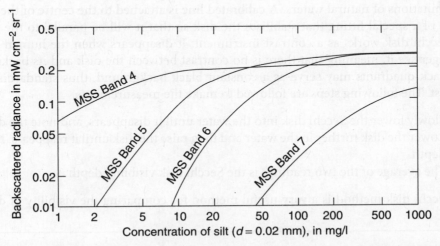

Fig. 4.22 The response of Landsat multi-spectral scanner to increasing concentrations of suspended silt. Note the exponential nature of the signal in all four bands. (Adapted from Moore, 1978)

water 'transparency'. Traditionally, a Secchi disk (a circular disc with white and black sectors) has been used in oceanography for the estimation of water transparency.

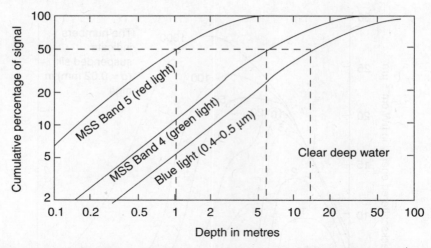

Fig. 4.23 Relationship of the backscattered signal to depth below water surface. Fifty per cent of the backscattered energy comes from above the depths indicated by the dotted lines. (Adapted from Moore, 1978)

Secchi Disk

The Secchi disk was invented by the Italian astronomer Pietro Angelo Secchi (1818–1878). The Secchi disk is one of the most inexpensive methods to measure the transparency of water for lake quality studies. The Secchi disk is a black and white circular plate, 20 cm in diameter that is used to determine the turbidity or degree of visibility in natural water supplies. The Secchi disk provides a very simple means of making transparency determinations of natural waters. A calibrated line is attached to the centre of the disk by means of a special fitting that stabilises the disk so that it will be parallel to the surface. The Secchi disk works as a contrast instrument. It disappears when the human eye can no longer see it, meaning that there is no contrast between the disk and its background. The black quadrants may serve as a constant black background, thus standardising the contrast. The following steps are followed to make the measurements.

(i) Slowly lower the Secchi disk into the water until it disappears, and note the depth.
(ii) Lower the disk further in the water and then raise the disk until it reappears. Note the depth.
(iii) The average of the two readings is the Secchi disk visibility depth.

The Secchi disk method is a very useful method for comparing the visibility of different waters.

Another associated terminology, which is of importance in ocean remote sensing is the penetration depth. The *penetration depth of light* (Z_{90}) in the sea has been defined for remote sensing purposes as the depth above which 90% of the back scattered radiation (excluding specular reflectance) originates. It is demonstrated that for a homogeneous ocean, this is the depth at which the downwelling irradiance falls to $1/e$ of its value at the surface $(1/k_d)$ (Gordon and McCluney, 1975). Their study shows that at around 475 nm, a maximum penetration depth of about 55 m can be expected in clear water. They have also shown that a mean penetration depth for broad band sensors as applied to the MSS, show that the maximum mean penetration depth expected for band 4 (0.5–0.6 μm) is somewhat less than 20 m, while for band 5 (0.6–0.7 μm), the result is about 2 m.

Ocean Colour

Light rays that fall on the ocean are refracted into the ocean depending on the angle of incidence and the refractive index (RI) of the ocean water (RI increases with salinity and decreases with temperature). The part of the sun's radiant energy (which includes direct sun radiation and the diffused sky radiation) which penetrates the ocean is partly absorbed and the rest is scattered, dependent on the nature and abundance of the particulates in the water. The scattered light is deflected to new directional paths, gets further absorbed/scattered while some are directed upwards and leave the water. It is this upward scattered light that determines the colour of the oceans as seen from above.

The spectral characteristics of the water-leaving radiance depends on the relative concentration of the optically active constituents of the ocean. In other words, changes in ocean colour are due to changes in the type and concentration of dissolved and suspended matter. In the visible region, for pure sea water, absorption by salt or other dissolved substances are negligible. However, the water molecules and salt ions produce Rayleigh scattering, by which the lower wavelengths are scattered more. The increase in the backscattering coefficient with shorter wavelength gives a deep blue colour for clear oceanic water.

The ocean colour variation with respect to turbidity and pigment content can be characterised in terms of the reflectance ratio $R(\lambda)$ for 'zero' depth. $R(\lambda)$ is the ratio of the upwelling irradiance just below the surface $[E_u(\lambda)]$ and downwelling irradiance just above the surface $[E_d(\lambda)]$.

$$R(\lambda) = \frac{E_u(\lambda)}{E_d(\lambda)} \qquad (4.3)$$

The reflectance ratio R is dependent on the inherent optical properties, namely the absorption coefficient and the backscattering coefficient. When the backscattering increases, R values increase more or less uniformly throughout the spectrum. Conversely, the rise in absorption diminishes R, especially in the spectral bands corresponding to the specific absorption of the various substances present, thus modifying the shape of the spectral reflectance curve.

In Case 1, the colour of the water is mainly decided by the phytoplankton. Their chlorophyll and related pigments have strong absorption in the blue and red region. When the concentration of the phytoplankton increases, a minimum appears progressively at 0.44 μm corresponding to the maximum of chlorophyll absorption (Fig. 4.24) . The peak in the red (0.685 μm) is due to the *in vivo* fluorescence of Chl-a. It should be realised that apart from the pigment concentration, the cell structure has an important influence on the absorption. Both pigment concentration and structure are variable, dependent on species composition, light

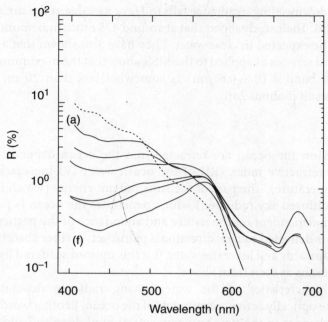

Fig. 4.24 Observed reflectance spectra for Case 1 water with different quantities of phytoplankton. The phytoplankton concentration increases from (a) to (f). The dotted line represents clear ocean water. (Adapted from Morel and Precur, 1977)

conditions and nutrient conditions which makes it impossible to have a standard absorption spectrum [and hence $R(\lambda)$] for all areas and seasons. Scattering by phytoplankton is in the domain of Mie scattering. The scattering is preferentially in the forward direction, with very small backscattering. In general, as the phytoplankton content increases, the backscattering increases in the green region, but the blue region is absorbed rapidly. Thus, water rich in phytoplankton appears green, while in Case 1, water that is poor in phytoplankton will appear deep blue in sunlight.

Radiance Received by Remote Sensors

A remote sensor in space, looking at the ocean will receive the following radiance.

(i) Radiance due to Fresnel reflection dependent on the angle of observation and solar zenith angle (sun glint).

(ii) Diffuse radiance produced by the scattering of the intervening atmosphere. The magnitude of the diffuse background depends on atmospheric visibility, that is, a clear atmosphere produces less diffuse radiation. The percentage of sky radiation to the global radiation (sun + sky) also depends on the wavelength and solar elevation.

(iii) Diffused radiation reflected from the water surface.

(iv) Radiation entering into the sensor field of view due to the reflection from an adjacent pixel and scattered by the atmosphere (adjacency effect).

(v) The sun and sky radiance refracted into the water are modified by the water and upwells to get out of the water body. This is the useful signal which contains the information characteristics of the water (this will also contain the radiation reflected from the bottom and attenuated and brought to the surface, when the depth of the water body is less than the penetration depth).

The contribution (ii), (iii) and (iv) are called *path radiance* and is the main component of the radiance reaching the sensor while observing water bodies; some authors do not consider (iii) as path radiance. Here we assume all radiation reaching the sensor other than the water-leaving radiation (v) as path radiance. The direction of view of the sensor determines not only the path length through the atmosphere, but also whether or not the specularly reflected sunlight is included within the field of view of the sensor. The sun glint can be avoided by suitably choosing the observation geometry. The radiance seen by the sensor L_t consists of

$$L_t(\lambda) = L_p(\lambda) + L_W(\lambda) \times T(\lambda)$$

where L_W is the water-leaving radiance, which is in our interest to measure, L_p is the path radiance, T is the diffuse atmospheric transmittance and λ in the bracket shows the spectral dependence of these terms.

L_W is a function of

- the radiance that entered the water surface,
- the absorption coefficient,
- the scattering function, and
- in shallow water, the bottom reflectance.

Thus, L_W gives the 'signature' of the water body. Figure 4.25 gives the computed values of L_t, L_W and L_p for two typical water bodies. We may notice that the shape of L_W is different, showing water-specific signature. Secondly, L_W is less than 10% of the total radiance L_t received by the sensor. These curves assume no reflection from the bottom. However, where a bottom reflected component is present, the L_W term may increase appreciably. The removal of path radiance is the major task to make useful inferences. The task is compounded since L_p varies with time and space. Some of the techniques used for atmosphere corrections can be found in Appendix 1.

Effect of Ocean Winds

Till now we have been assuming that the ocean surface is smooth. However, due to the action of wind, the surface of the sea is seldom smooth. The waves produced by the winds cause the effective reflectance of the surface to change significantly near the grazing incidence of the light entering the water from above. Similarly, when the surface is rough, the water-leaving radiance changes significantly for light emerging from below which are near the critical angle. This can be visualised since depending on the slope of the waves, the angle of incidence at the air/water interface will differ from a smooth sea surface, thus causing reflectance/transmittance changes. But for most wind speeds and viewing geometries of interest in remote sensing, the effect of wind on the magnitude of the time-averaged reflectance values is not major. However, the roughening of the surface does have a major effect in determining the portion of the sky that is reflected upward toward the sensor. Thus, for example, the angular size of the sun's glitter path will be determined by the windspeed. However, satellite sensors dedicated for ocean colour sensing have the capability to tilt the instrument, to avoid sun glint.

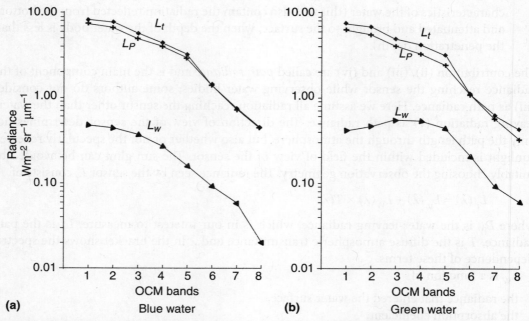

Fig. 4.25   IRS P4 OCM detected radiance of the ocean (Arabian sea). L_t is the total radiance detected at the top of the atmosphere, L_p is the computed path radiance, using data from NIR (0.768 nm and 0.867 nm), L_w is the water-leaving radiance. The horizontal axis indicates the eight discrete bands of OCM, namely 414(20), 442(20), 489(20), 512(20), 557(20), 670(20), 768 (40), 867(40) nanometres. The values in the bracket are bandwidth in nm. (Chauhan, 2002)

Chlorophyll Fluorescence

Till now we have considered the signature generated due to reflectance and penetration of sun's radiation at the air–water interface. A fraction of solar radiation absorbed by the phytoplankton is re-emitted in the red region. This phenomenon of re-emission of the absorbed radiation is called *fluorescence*. The chlorophyll fluorescence emission line shape can be approximated to a Gaussian distribution having a peak at 0.685 micrometre with a 25 nm width at half power (Gower and Borstad, 1990). This characteristic signal from the chlorophyll forms a specific signature and the height of the fluorescence line can be used to deduce the phytoplankton concentration. However, to get the line profile one has to use a spectrometer with a spectral resolution of about 2–3 nm. In addition it requires a 2000:1 signal to noise ratio to have a measurement accuracy of 0.1 mgm^{-3} chlorophyll concentration. One of the problems in data reduction (in addition to the atmospheric correction as in the reflectance measurement) is to establish a baseline over which the line height can be measured. Figure 4.26 gives the flourescence spectra measured using an imaging spectrometer with a spectral resolution of 2.5 nm, for two chlorophyll concentrations (Gower and Borstad, 1990).

4.1.4 SNOW

Snow cover gives the highest reflectance in the visible region compared to any other natural cover on earth. Snow also shows marked variations in its reflectance characteristics with time,

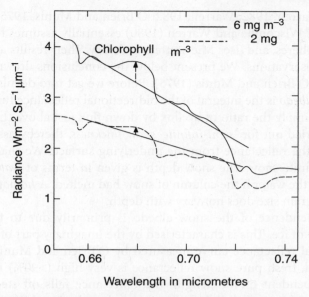

Fig. 4.26 Radiance spectra measured with an imaging spectrometer from an altitude of 152 m. (Adapted from Gower and Borstad, 1990)

due to metamorphism, melting, and so on. Snow cover also shows a wide variation in the grain size, density, and so on. Let us briefly review the formation of snow and its physical characteristics. Once the cloud temperature drops below freezing point, conditions are favourable for forming snow. Ice crystals (less than about 75 μm) formed through the process of ice nucleation is the initial stage in the growth of snow. When the ice crystal continues to grow, a snow crystal is formed. A snow flake is an aggregation of snow crystals. Snow flakes may consist of two to several hundred snow crystals joined together. In some cases, small (10–40 μm) cloud droplets freeze on contact with the snow crystal, forming 'rimed crystals' and in case of extreme riming, forming graupel particles (snow pellets). In general, snow may consist of snow crystals, rimed snow crystals and snow flakes as well as fragments of any of these. Thus, the ice particles formed in the atmosphere on their way to the ground undergo a number of transformations resulting from growth, disintegration and agglomeration. They can vary in density from 10 kg/m³ to 500 kg/m³ depending on the type of crystal, wind condition and other factors. After the snow is deposited, the particle shapes are modified by a process known as *metamorphism*. The grain size can vary from ~50 micrometre for fresh snow to ~5 mm with ageing. Snow cover also contains many impurities like ice nucleating particles, contaminants carried by falling snow and pollutants that enter the snow pack when it is on the ground. To summarise, snow is a collection of ice grains and air, containing soluble and particulate impurities and becomes liquid water at 0°C. The optical properties of snow depend on bulk optical properties and the geometry of ice grains, the liquid water present and the dissolved and suspended impurities.

Spectral Albedo from Snow

A number of theoretical and experimental studies have been carried out to characterise the snow albedo (Wiscombe and Warren, 1980; Warren and Wiscombe 1980; Dozier, et. al.,

1981; Dozier and Warren, 1982; Warren, 1982; O'Brien and Munis, 1975; Dozier, 1984). The theoretical model of Wiscombe and Warren (1980) essentially assumes that individual snow grains scatter like spheres, and uses Mie scattering theory. Their results agree fairly well with the experimental observations. We present below the conclusions drawn by Wiscombe and Warren (1980) and O'Brien and Munis (1975). Before we get into details, some of the terms need explanation. *Albedo* is the integral of the bidirectional reflectance function over the total reflection angle or simply the ratio of up flux by down flux just above the snow surface. The calculations are carried out for '*semi-infinite*' *snow thickness,* thereby assuming that there is no contribution to the reflectance from the underlying surface. We shall discuss later what constitutes semi-infinite snow. The snow depth is given in terms of *water equivalent height*. This is the height of the water if the column of snow had melted. A *homogeneous snow pack* is one whose average grain size does not vary with depth.

The spectral dependence of the snow albedo is primarily due to the variation in the absorption property of ice. This is characterised by the imaginary part of the refractive index (Fig. 4.27). A typical reflectance curve measured by O'Brien and Munis (1975) is given in Fig. 4.28. In general, fresh pure snow reflectance is very high (>90%) in the visible region and relatively independent of wavelength; the reflectance falls off steeply in the near-IR (0.8–1.5 μm) and remains generally low for longer wavelengths. Local maxima in the reflectance spectra are seen at around 1.1, 1.3, 1.8 and 2.2 μm corresponding to the local minima in the absorption coefficient. The snow albedo depends primarily on the following parameters: (a) wavelength; (b) grain size (hence age), (c) solar zenith angle, (d) liquid water content, (e) cloud cover (diffuse radiation), (f) snow pack thickness, and (g) contaminant present. We shall consider the effect of some of these parameters on snow reflection.

It is found that albedo falls at all wavelengths as the grain size increases (Fig. 4.29). This can be qualitatively understood since a photon has a chance to be scattered only when it crosses an air–ice interface and with increase in grain size, this probability decreases in volume, and hence the reflectance from snow containing larger grains decreases. The effect of grain size on reflection is maximum in the near-IR region, while in the visible region, the effect is relatively small.

The semi-infinite albedo is found proportional to the square root of grain radius in the 0.4 to 0.8 μm wavelength region (Fig. 4.30). The reflectance of snow decreases as it ages (Fig. 4.31). The decrease in albedo due to snow ageing can be mimicked by reasonable increase in grain size.

Since the refractive index of ice and liquid water is more or less the same, liquid water itself does not affect the snow reflectance. However, liquid water causes the snow to form grain clusters, which behave optically as a single large grain, causing decreased reflectance. O'Brien and Munis (1975) show that snow which is even slightly melting, when compared with nearly fresh snow, has a distinctly lower reflectance in the red region and is more pronounced in the near-IR region. Refreezing of snow, which has previously been exposed to melting temperatures, has relatively a minor effect, resulting in a reflectance curve generally resembling that of melting snow (Fig. 4.32).

The albedo for a thin snow pack is affected by the underlying surface. The depth necessary for the snow to be effectively 'semi-infinite' increases with grain size. For old melting snow, it could be around 20 cm liquid equivalent. Snow cover over the Arctic sea is often so thin that

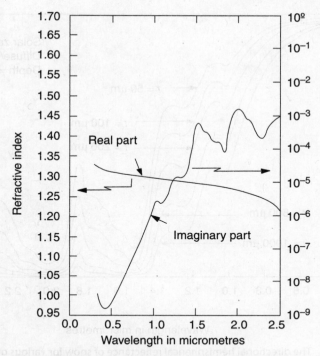

Fig. 4.27 Refractive index of ice. (Source—annonymous)

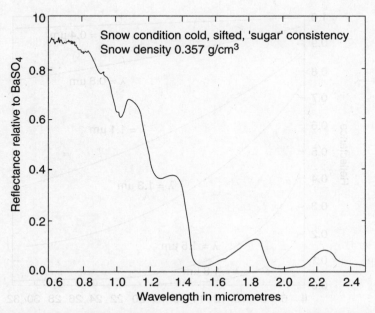

Fig. 4.28 Typical spectral reflectance curve of snow. (Adapted from O'Brien and Munis, 1975)

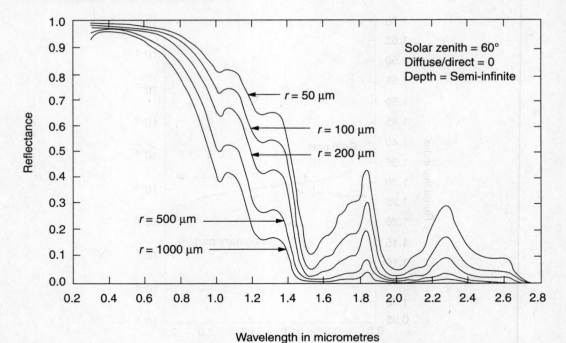

Fig. 4.29 The directional hemispherical reflectance of snow for various grain sizes.
(Adapted from Wiscombe and Warren, 1980)

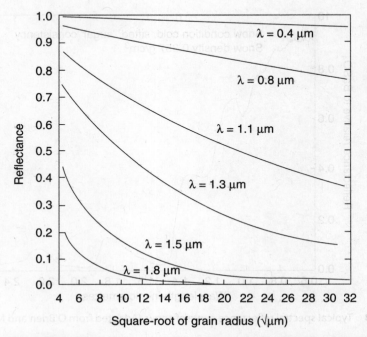

Fig. 4.30 Semi-infinite diffuse albedo versus square root of grain radius for seven discrete wavelengths.
(Adapted from Wiscombe and Warren, 1980)

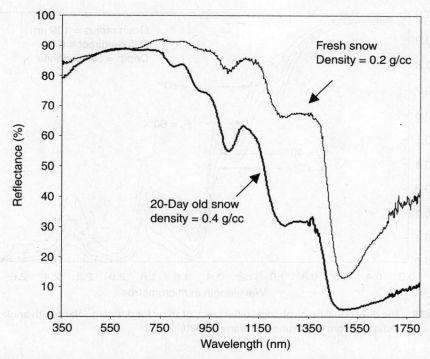

Fig. 4.31 Changes in snow reflectance with natural ageing. Measurements carried out at Manali. (Kulkarni, 2002)

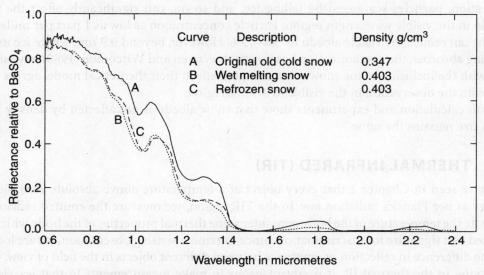

Curve	Description	Density g/cm³
A	Original old cold snow	0.347
B	Wet melting snow	0.403
C	Refrozen snow	0.403

Fig. 4.32 Effects of temperature on snow reflectance. (Adapted from O'Brien and Munis, 1975)

its albedo is reduced by the 'darker' underlying ice. Therefore, both grain size and snow depth should be known for understanding albedo of 'finite' snow packs.

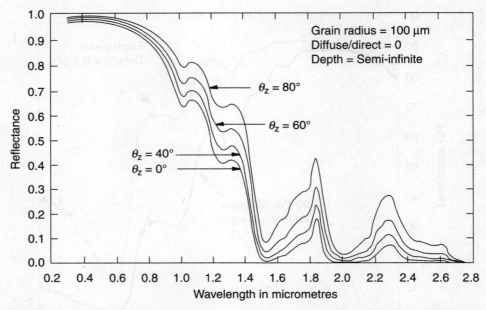

Fig. 4.33 The directional hemispherical reflectance of snow for different solar zenith angles (θ_Z). (Adapted from Wiscombe and Warren, 1980)

The albedo increases as the solar zenith angle is increased. The increase is only marginal in the visible region but substantial in the near-IR region (Fig. 4.33).

The contamination in the snow like soot, clay and mineral particles carried due to ice nucleation, particles scavenged by falling ice, and so on, can significantly affect the snow albedo in the visible wavelength region. Particle concentration as low as 1 part per million by weight can reduce the visible albedo by 5%–15%. However, beyond 0.9 μm, where ice itself is a strong absorber, the contamination has no effect. Warren and Wiscombe (1980) have shown that with the inclusion of the snow contamination effect, their theoretical model agrees fairly well with the observation in the visible to 2.5 μm region.

Both calculation and experiments show that snow albedo is not affected by density if the grain size remains the same.

4.2 THERMAL INFRARED (TIR)

We have seen in Chapter 2 that every object at a temperature above absolute zero radiates energy as per Planck's radiation law. In the TIR region, we measure the emitted radiance to estimate the temperature of the body or to infer some thermal properties of the body which can be used as a signature for discrimination. Since in remote sensing observation, we are looking for the difference in reflection or emittance between different objects in the field of view, while observing in the thermal IR, it is advantageous to make measurements in that wavelength region for which emittance is (M_λ) maximum for a change in temperature. In other words, we should observe at the wavelength for which ($\partial M_\lambda/\partial T$) is maximum. The wavelength (λ_e) for which the rate of change of spectral exitance is maximum for a given black body temperature T works out to be

$$\lambda_e = \frac{2411}{T} \qquad (4.4)$$

when wavelength is expressed in micron and temperature in K (Hudson, 1969). Wein's displacement law gives the wavelength λ_{max} at which the exitance of a black body is maximum as

$$\lambda_{max} T = 2897 \qquad (4.5)$$

Combining the above two equations we have,

$$\lambda_e = 0.832 \; \lambda_{max} \qquad (4.6)$$

Assuming earth as a black body of 300 K, λ_e works out to be about 8 μm while $\lambda_{max} = 9.66 \, \mu$m. Though 8 μm is in the atmospheric window, still the transmission is low. The peak wavelength 9.66 μm almost coincides with the ozone absorption band of 9.6 μm. To avoid this, the spectral region usually used for earth observation in the thermal IR is 10.5 to 12.5 μm.

Thus, if the emitted radiance in the 10.5–12.5 μm region is measured, in principle, the temperature can be calculated by inverting the Planck's law. However, we have seen that there are no ideal black bodies and at the best we have grey bodies. Therefore, the emittance from a grey body will be less than that from a black body, depending on the emissivity. Since the emissivity is always less than unity, the temperature estimated by measuring the emitted radiation (if emissivity is not considered) will always be less than the kinetic temperature (that is, the temperature measured by a thermometer).

Therefore, to estimate the kinetic temperature, the emissivity of the object should be known. How accurately should the emissivity be known in order to estimate the temperature within a certain accuracy? That is, everything else remaining same, we have to find out the change in temperature (ΔT) for a change in emissivity Δe. That is $\partial T/\partial e$, which can be evaluated from the Planck's equation for $M\lambda$. That is $\partial T/\partial e = \partial M_\lambda/\partial e / \partial M_\lambda/\partial T$. Figure 4.34 gives a plot of Δe verses ΔT for three values of T for $e = 0.95$. The graph can be used to find out the accuracy with which emissivity should be known so that the temperature estimated from the measured radiance is within the specified limit. For example, at $e = 0.95$ and at 300 K, for 1 K temperature accuracy 'e' should be known better than 0.013. Therefore, the accuracy with which we can measure the temperature using thermal radiometry (even without taking into account other errors like atmospheric absorption) is strongly dependent on the accuracy with which we know the emissivity of the target. This problem can be circumvented in theory (neglecting atmospheric effect), if we take measurements in two spectral bands, provided emissivity is the same for the two bands, which is a reasonable assumption if the two bands are not far apart or within any characteristic absorption band of the material. However, the atmospheric contribution makes the measurement of absolute temperature by remote sensing more complex.

The measured temperature itself is used directly for specific applications such as sea surface temperature for meteorological application. However, the primary objective of temperature measurement is to infer something about the nature of the composition and other physical properties of the earth's surface. The temperature difference of the earth's surface is caused by difference in thermal properties of the surface material. Three basic thermal properties decide how the surface is getting heated and its variation with time (diurnal variation) and depth. They are thermal conductivity, thermal capacity and density.

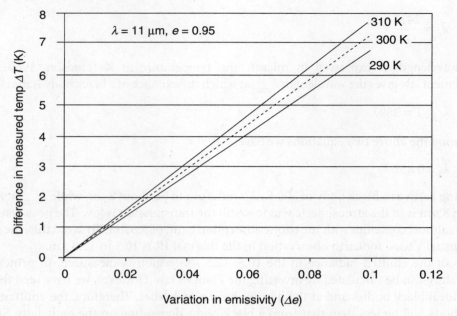

Fig. 4.34   Effect of emissivity on the temperature measurement.

Thermal conductivity (k) is the number of calories of heat that will pass through a one centimetre cube of material in 1 s when the opposite faces are maintained at a 1°C difference in temperature (cal cm^{-1} s^{-1} °C^{-1}). That is, thermal conductivity is a measure of the rate at which heat will pass through a material.

Thermal capacity is the ability of a material to store heat. It is generally expressed as specific heat (c) which is the ratio of the amount of heat energy in calories required to raise the temperature of 1 gram of substance by 1°C at 15°C to the heat supplied in raising the temperature of 1 gram of water by 1°C (cal g^{-1} K^{-1}), at the same temperature.

A derived product of k, c and density (d) which is of interest in thermal studies is the thermal inertia P, given by

$$P = (kdc)^{1/2} \text{ cal cm}^{-2}\text{sec}^{-1/2} \text{ K}^{-1} \tag{4.7}$$

Thermal inertia (TI) essentially gives a measure of the 'resistance' of the material to change in temperature. The variation in ground surface temperature depends on this property. Hence, thermal inertia determines the temperature difference in a diurnal cycle. Rocks and soils in general have low thermal inertia and show high temperature during the day and cools fast to low temperatures at night, while wet clay with a higher thermal inertia will have a smaller temperature difference between day and night. The temperature distribution in the soil as a function of depth and time depends on solar heating (which is the driving force) and the thermal properties of the material.

Figure 4.35 shows how the temperature varies over a day for materials of different thermal inertia. An interesting feature that can be seen is that just before sun set and about two hours after sun rise, irrespective of the thermal inertia, all objects have the same temperature.

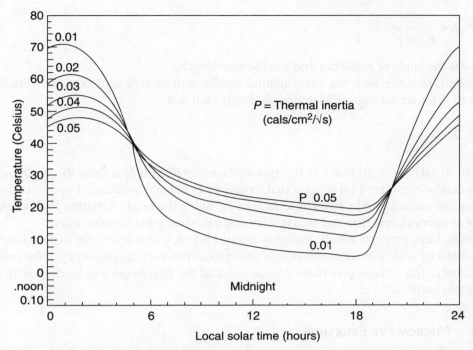

Fig. 4.35 Diurnal temperature variation for materials with different thermal inertia. (Reprinted from 'Geologic Applications of Thermal Infrared Images, Watson, *Proceedings of IEEE*, January 1975, with permission)

Therefore, these times are least suited for thermal imaging. The maximum temperature difference is seen between early morning and early afternoon.

It should be borne in mind that the day and night temperature difference ΔT can be influenced by factors, other than thermal inertia, such as topographic relief and meteorological conditions like the wind. TI could be misleading in agricultural areas because surface evaporation reduces the amplitude of the soil heat flux compared to amplitudes in dry areas and hence TI should not be used in regions having variability in surface moisture. Though a satellite Heat Capacity Mapping Mission (HCMM) was specifically launched for TI measurement, its utility turned out to be limited (Price, 1985).

4.3 MICROWAVE REGION

The two basic parameters on which the microwave emission and scattering depends on are surface roughness and dielectric constant. In Chapter 2, we have seen that the surface roughness is dependent on the wavelength. Thus, a surface irregularity of a few microns is an excellent smooth surface in the microwave region, but an extremely rough surface for application in the optical region. A *smooth surface* is generally meant to mean a specular surface that obeys Fresnel's reflection laws. The surface roughness is characterised by the standard deviation h of the surface height variation (rms height variation from any reference plane). As discussed in Section 3.3, the usually accepted criteria (Rayleigh criterion) for a surface to be smooth is

$$h < \frac{\lambda}{8 \cos \theta} \tag{4.8}$$

where θ is the angle of incidence and λ is the wavelength.

However, to agree with the experimental results, a more stringent criterion (Fraunhofer criterion) is found necessary (Ulaby, et. al., 1982) such that

$$h < \frac{\lambda}{32 \cos \theta} \tag{4.9}$$

Thus, at 30 GHz ($\lambda = 10$ mm), if the rms surface variation is less than about 300 μm, the surface can be considered smooth for that frequency at normal incidence. In practice for a one dimensional surface profile, h can be found out by taking the height variation from a reference surface at intervals less than or equal to $\lambda/10$ and calculating the rms deviation.

Another basic property affecting microwave interaction with matter is the dielectric constant of the material which in turn influences other properties such as emissivity, reflectivity and conductivity. The influence of these parameters and the roughness will be dealt with in the subsequent sections.

4.3.1   MICROWAVE EMISSION

The Planck's equation (Eq. 2.14) shows that the exitance from a body extends beyond infrared all through the electromagnetic spectrum. However, at the microwave region, the Planck's Law can be approximated to a simple relation. For example, let us consider 30 GHz, a normally used region for microwave radiometry. The corresponding wavelength is 1 cm. At this wavelength $ch/\lambda kT \approx 4.7 \times 10^{-3}$ and hence $[\exp(ch/\lambda kT)-1] \approx ch/\lambda kT$.

Therefore for a body at a temperature T, the spectral radiant exitance given by Planck's equation reduces to

$$M_\lambda = \frac{2\pi ck}{\lambda^4} Te(\theta, \phi) \tag{4.10}$$

where, $e(\theta,\phi)$ is the emissivity of the body at λ and T.

This is called Rayleigh–Jeans approximation, a special case of Planck's law. Thus at the microwave frequency, the emission is proportional to $Te(\theta,\phi)$. The product $Te(\theta,\phi)$ is called the brightness temperature T_B. Therefore, in passive microwave radiometry what we observe is the brightness temperature, which is the product of the physical (kinetic) temperature and the emissivity.

For terrestrial objects, the maximum temperature variation is at the most 60 K, which will produce only ~20% of variation with respect to an average temperature of the earth surface, say 300 K. But the emissivity variation is much more. At the lower end it could be close to zero for a good conducting surface and at the higher end it could be close to unity for a rough dry soil or very wet snow. Thus for the same physical temperature, the brightness temperature of terrestrial objects can vary over a wide range due to the variation of emissivity. Hence, to properly interpret the microwave emission signature, we should have a better understanding of the emissivity.

For an object in thermodynamic equilibrium, absorption (α) and emission (e) must be equal, that is, $\alpha = e$. Energy conservation requires that for an opaque body (no transmission) $\alpha = e = 1 - \rho$, where ρ is the reflectance. That is, if the reflectance is high, the emissivity is low. We have seen in Eqs 2.8 and 2.9 that reflectance depends on the refractive index. However, the refractive index $n = \sqrt{\varepsilon}$, where ε is the dielectric constant. Therefore, the brightness temperature is dependent on dielectric constant. Since an increase in dielectric constant increases the reflectivity, the emissivity decreases and consequently the brightness temperature is lower.

Increasing surface roughness increases the emissivity of both H and V polarised components. For a perfectly Lambertian surface, the emissivity is polarisation and angle independent (Ulaby et. al., 1981).

The emissivity of a material in general depends on the frequency (wavelength) of observation, polarisation, observation angle, surface roughness, chemical composition, dielectric constant and temperature. Based on a number of theoretical models and observations, Ulaby et. al., (1982) have shown (Fig. 4.36) the range of variation of the microwave nadir emissivity for some of the common targets covering the earth. The ranges of values given in the figure should be taken in a very general sense since it is based on a wide range of frequencies (1–100 GHz). This should be used only to get a general idea of the variability of emissivity.

Another factor to be noted in microwave radiometry is the depth to which we get the contribution to the observed brightness temperature. We have seen in Section 2.5, that the penetration depth depends on the wavelength and the dielectric constant. Given the reversibility of the EMR emission and absorption, the penetration depth is indicative of how deep the emitted radiation comes from. From Eq. 2.13, it is clear that lower the frequency

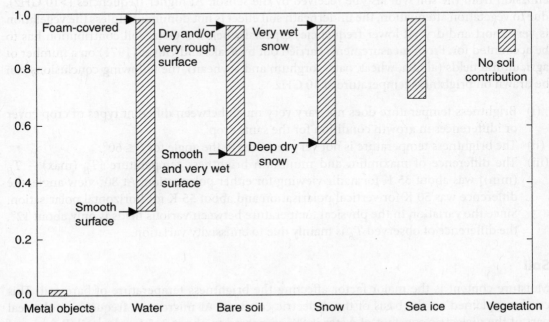

Fig. 4.36 Microwave nadir emissivity range for various classes of targets. (Reprinted with permission from *Microwave Remote Sensing—Active and Passive* by Ulaby, Moore and Fung, Artech House Inc., Norwood, MA, USA. *www.artechhouse.com*)

(higher λ), deeper is the emission, and higher the conductivity, lower is the penetration depth. In general, microwave emission depth is higher than that in the thermal region.

The microwave emission leaving the earth's surface and reaching a spaceborne sensor is influenced by the atmosphere in many ways. The effects caused by the influence of atmosphere, on the measured brightness temperature to be considered include:

(i)   Attenuation by absorption and scattering, which reduces the energy.
(ii) Emission from atmospheric constituents, which adds to the signal.
(iii) Extra-terrestrial radiation incident on the atmosphere, though the effect is not serious.

Even in a clear sky, oxygen and water vapour contribute to absorption. The major contribution to attenuation is liquid water or rain rate. Both attenuation and atmospheric radiation are frequency-dependent. At microwave frequencies below about 10 GHz, the atmospheric absorption and emission is small and can be neglected (see Section 7.2).

Vegetation

Both biomass and geometric structure of vegetation canopies influence microwave emission measured from above. Unlike the case of thermal emission, the microwave radiation emitted by the soil underneath a vegetative canopy is not totally absorbed, hence a portion is transmitted through the vegetation and adds to the emission from vegetation. Therefore, a radiometer viewing the vegetation receives radiations consisting of emission from the vegetation layer and emission from the soil underneath attenuated through the vegetation cover. In addition, in an agricultural field, in general, the vegetation canopy does not fully cover the soil and direct emission from the soil will also be received by the sensor. At higher frequencies (>10 GHz), due to vegetation attenuation, the underneath soil effect is not dominant, unless the vegetation is very short and dry. At lower frequencies especially below 5 GHz, soil contribution has to be accounted for. From measurements carried out by Peaks and Oliver (1971) on a number of agricultural fields (alfalfa, wheat, oats, sorghum and soybean), the following conclusions can be drawn on brightness temperature at 10 GHz.

(i)   Brightness temperature does not vary very much between different types of crop cover or idifferences in growth condition for the same crop.
(ii) The brightness temperature is not very sensitive to the angle for $\theta \leq 60°$.
(iii) The difference of maximum and minimum brightness temperature $[T_B$ (max) $- T_B$ (min)] was about 35 K for nadir viewing for either polarisation. At 80° view angle, the difference was 50 K for vertical polarisation and about 55 K for horizontal polarisation. Since the variation in the physical temperature between various fields is only about 12°, the difference of observed T_B is mainly due to emissivity variation.

Soil

Moisture content is the major factor affecting the brightness temperature of bare soil. This can be explained on the basis of the dielectric constant. At microwave frequencies, the real part of the dielectric constant of water is 80, compared to about 3–5 for dry soil. Because of this large difference, as the moisture content of soil increases, the dielectric constant increases and hence the emissivity decreases. The sensitivity of emissivity to soil moisture $S_s = (\partial e_s / \partial m_v)$

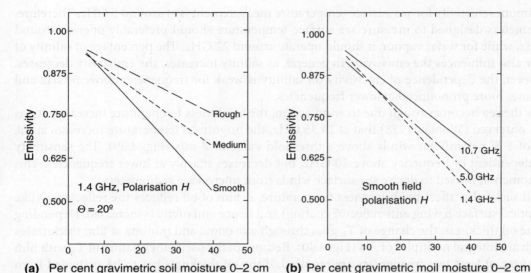

(a) Per cent gravimetric soil moisture 0–2 cm   **(b)** Per cent gravimetric moil moisture 0–2 cm

Fig. 4.37   Sensitivity of emissivity to soil moisture on surface condition (a) and frequency (b). (Reprinted from 'Soil Moisture Information and Thermal Microwave Emission', Newton, et. al., *IEEE Transactions on Geoscience & Remote Sensing*, Vol. GE-20, No. 3, July 1982, with permission)

increases as the surface becomes smoother and with decreasing frequency (Fig. 4.37). Based on various studies it is found that, for moisture estimation using passive radiometers, the optimum wavelength falls in the L band (20–30 cm), operating at near-nadir look angles and horizontal polarisation (Jackson and Schmugge, 1989). It has also been established that the emissivity is better correlated with volumetric soil moisture in the 0–5 cm surface layer. In a real life situation, the effect of vegetation cover has to be taken into account while deducing the soil moisture from the observed brightness temperature. A number of models have been developed to tackle this problem (Jackson et. al., 1982; Kirdiashev et. al., 1979; Wang, 1985). Processing of radiometer data for soil moisture also requires the knowledge of the surface temperature.

Surface roughness is another parameter, which affects the emissivity of soils. Surface roughness results in an increase in emissivity over that of an equivalent smooth surface. For a dry field, since the emissivity is already > 0.9, the effect of surface roughness on observed soil emissivity will be small, whereas for wet soil since emissivity is lower, the effect of surface roughness is more pronounced [Fig. 4.37(a)]. O'Neill and Jackson (1990) have shown that change in organic matter content of the soil at a given moisture level with similar texture and structure does not affect the emissivity. Schmugge (1980) has shown that S_s is higher for soils with low clay content compared to soils with high clay content.

Ocean

The emission from the surface of the sea is dependent on its salinity and temperature. In addition, the sea roughness and foam, produced by winds have pronounced effect on the emissivity. Sensitivity of brightness temperature to various geophysical parameters is dependent on frequency of the EM radiation being observed (Fig. 4.38). As seen from the graph, the maximum sensitivity for sea surface temperature measurement is at around 5 GHz. Therefore, radiometers designed to measure sea surface temperature should preferably operate around 5 GHz, while for water vapour, it should operate around 22 GHz. The percentage of salinity of water also influences the emissivity. In general, as salinity increases, the emissivity decreases. However, the dependence of emissivity on salinity is weak for frequencies above 5 GHz and becomes more pronounced at lower frequencies.

As the sea becomes rough due to wind action, the brightness temperature increases. It has been observed (Wilheit, 1978) that at 19.35 GHz, the brightness temperature increases at the rate of 1 K per m/s for winds above a threshold value of 7 m/s (Fig. 4.39). The sensitivity is independent of frequency above 10 GHz, but decreases sharply at lower frequencies. This phenomenon is used to derive sea surface winds from microwave radiometers.

Oil slicks also affect the brightness temperature. A film of oil reduces the reflectance (like an optical surface having anti-reflector coating) and hence emissivity is increased. Depending on the oil thickness, the change of T_B goes through a maxima and minima at film thicknesses which are integral multiples of $\lambda/4$ (Fig. 4.40). Because of the oscillatory nature of T_B with film thickness, at least two frequencies are required, if the oil thickness has to be evaluated from the brightness temperature.

Sea surface salinity (SSS) is a key parameter in determining ocean circulation and in climate modelling. The dielectric constant of sea water depends on both SSS and SST. So, in principle, it is possible to obtain SSS information from microwave radiometry if the other factors influencing T_B can be accounted for. T_B at the L band seems to be correlated with SSS. The European Space Agency (ESA) as part of the Living Planet programme is planning a

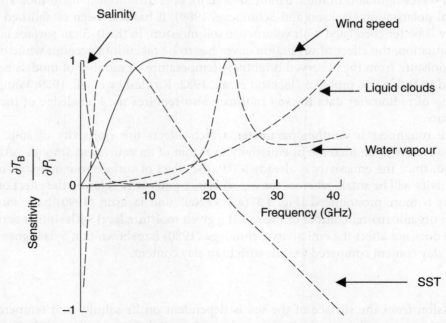

Fig. 4.38 Normalised sensitivity of brightness temperature (T_B) to various geophysical parameters (P_i), such as salinity, wind speed, and so on, as a function of frequency (schematic). (Adapted from Wilheit T, Chang A T C and Milman A S, 1980)

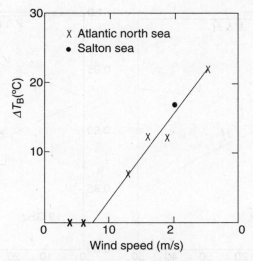

Fig. 4.39 Increase of T_B at 19.35 GHz caused by wind at the ocean surface.
(Adapted from Wilheit T T, Jr, 1978)

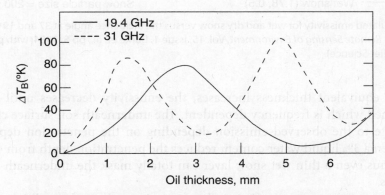

Fig. 4.40 Increase of T_B at 19 and 31 GHz as a function of oil slick thickness.
(Adapted from Hollinger and Mannella, 1973)

mission to find out the feasibility of using the L band brightness temperature to estimate SSS. The mission – SMOS – uses a multi-beam radiometer operating in the interferometric mode to estimate T_B at the L band (ESA web site).

Snow

Microwave emission from snow depends on parameters such as snow wetness, snow particle radius and snow depth. Emissivity is the lowest for dry snow and increases significantly for wet snow approaching unity. This is because of the drastic change in the complex dielectric constant of the wet snow due to the presence of water. In addition, the emissivity difference for V and H polarisation is negligible for wet snow conditions (Fig. 4.41).

As snow particle radius increases the emissivity decreases (Fig. 4.42).

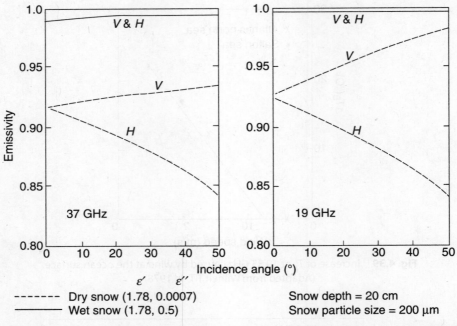

Fig. 4.41   Calculated emissivity for wet and dry snow versus the incidence angle at 37 and 19 GHz. (Reprinted from *Remote Sensing of Environment*, Vol. 15, Issue 1, Burke et. al., pp 5, 1984, with premission from Elsevier Science)

As the water equivalent thickness increases, the emissivity decreases until a 'saturation' depth is reached which is frequency dependent. The underneath soil surface characteristics also contribute to the observed emission depending on the penetration depth and snow thickness. Even a 3% liquid water content reduces the penetration depth from 4.8 m to 4 cm at 10 GHz. Thus even a thin wet snow layer can totally mask the underneath soil emission characteristics.

The response of microwave emission due to various physical conditions of snow are summarised in Table 4.1. (Burke et. al., 1984).

Table 4.1   Response of microwave emissions due to various physical conditions of snow

Physical condition	Microwave emission response
Physical temperature	Increases linearly as temperature increases
Snow particle radius	Decreases as radius increases
Snow depth	Decreases as depth increases until the saturation depth which is a function of wavelength
Snow wetness	Increases rapidly in the presence of free water until a certain degree of wetness is reached
Background surface	Affects the signature for thin and dry snow conditions

Source: Burke et. al., (1984)

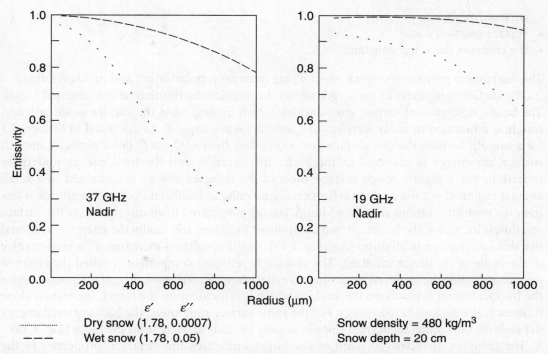

Fig. 4.42 Calculated emissivities versus snow particle radius for various types of snow at 37 and 19 GHz (Nadir). (Reprinted from *Remote Sensing of Environment*, Vol. 15, Issue 1, Burke et. al., pp 5, 1984, with premission from Elsevier Science)

4.3.2 MICROWAVE SCATTERING

The energy of a microwave pulse scattered from an object provides information on the characteristics of the target. Usually, an antenna pointing sideways from a moving platform transmits narrow pulses and the same antenna receives the energy scattered back from the targets. Such instruments are generally termed as *radar*. For such a system, the received power P_r is given by

$$P_r = \frac{P_t G^2 \lambda^2 dA}{(4\pi)^3 R^4} \sigma°$$ (4.11)

where, P_t = transmitted power, G = gain of the antenna, R = distance between target and sensor, λ = wavelength of radiation, dA = scattering element on the ground and $\sigma°$ = backscattering cofficient.

The *backscattering coefficient* $\sigma°$ is a measure of the strength of the radar signals reflected by a distributed scatterer (refer to Chapter 7). Because of a large dynamic range, $\sigma°$ is expressed in decibels (dB).

For a particular instrument, platform height and look angle, variation in the received power depends on the scattering coefficient $\sigma°$, which describes the nature of the ground target. The properties of the target which influence $\sigma°$ are

- surface roughness,
- surface geometry, and
- the complex dielectric constant.

The instrument parameters which affect $\sigma°$ are frequency, polarisation and incidence angle.

The surface roughness of the target affects the angular distribution of the returned signal. The height difference of surface irregularities, which distinguishes the surface as smooth and rough, is a function of radar wavelength λ and incidence angle θ. As discussed in Section 4.3 for a smooth surface, the rms surface deviation is less than $\lambda/32 \cos \theta$. For a perfectly smooth surface, no energy is scattered in the backward direction and the total energy undergoes reflection. For a slightly rough surface, most of the reflected energy is contained in a small angular region about the angle of reflection conforming to Snell's law, but its magnitude is less than the perfectly smooth case. In addition, energy is scattered in all directions. As the surface roughness increases, the backscattered component increases and finally the energy is scattered in a diffused manner in all directions (Fig. 4.43). As the roughness increases, $\sigma°$ is less sensitive to the angle of incidence variation. The specularly reflected component is called the *coherent component*, while the scattered component is called the *diffuse* or *non-coherent component*. Since the backscattering depends on the angle at which it is incident on the target, the terrain slope influences the backscattered energy. For the same surface roughness, the backscattered energy depends on how much the terrain slope is sloping towards or away from the radar (Fig. 4.44).

The complex dielectric constant of the target influences the electrical properties of the surface and hence influences the reflectivity of the radar pulse. An increase in the dielectric value increases the reflectivity and therefore the magnitude of the return signal. The dielectric constant of a natural material is considerably enhanced due to the change in the moisture content. This is because of the large difference in the dielectric constant of naturally occurring materials (3 to 8) compared to water (~ 80). Thus, wet soil gives a higher radar return compared to dry soil of similar roughness. Similarly, radar return from vegetation is stronger when there is more moisture.

What we have discussed is surface scattering, occuring at the dielectric discontinuity between the atmosphere and the ground (target). However, in certain cases, when the electromagnetic radiation penetrates the medium and encounters dielectric inhomogeneity, scattering takes place within the volume of the target. This is called *volume scattering*. In volume scattering, microwave energy penetrates in the inhomogeneous media and interacts with dielectric 'particles' within the media. In volume scattering $\sigma°$ is proportional to the dielectric discontinuities within the medium and the density of the inhomogeneity inside the medium (compared to surface scattering wherein the scattering strength depends on the complex dielectric constant of the surface). Since the spatial locations of discontinuities are random, the wave is scattered in all directions. Radar return from natural terrain in general, can contain both surface and volume scattering. For example, returns from vegetation contains scattering from the air-canopy top interface, air-soil interface (surface scattering) as well as scattering taking place within the ground and canopy at the various parts of the plant (Fig. 4.45).

The radar instrument parameters which influence $\sigma°$ are frequency, polarisation and look angle. The variation due to frequency is attributed to surface roughness and complex dielectric constant which are dependent on frequency. For the same surface, as frequency increases, it becomes more rough. Through dielectric constant, the penetration depth changes with wavelength, which in turn influences the relative contribution of the surface and volume scattering. In general, lower frequencies have higher penetration depth, thus contributing more to volumetric scattering.

The transmit and receive signal can be of the same polarisation or can be cross-polarised. Thus, there can be four combinations:

  (i) transmit horizontal polarised (H) and receive H (HH),
 (ii) transmit vertical polarised (V), and receive V (VV),
(iii) transmit H and receive V (HV), and
 (iv) transmit V and receive H (VH).

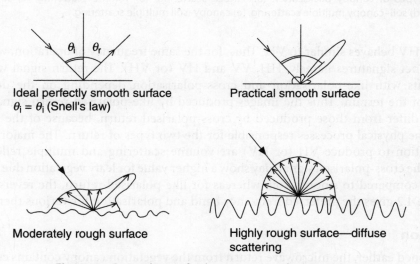

Fig. 4.43   Dependence of radar return on surface roughness.

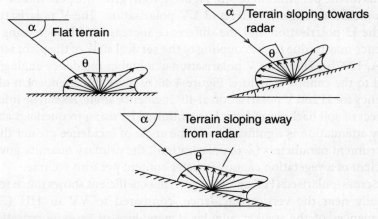

θ = Angle of incidence, α = Angle of depression

Fig. 4.44   Effect of local slope on radar return.

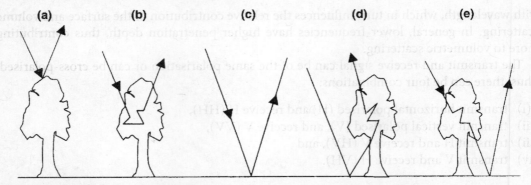

Fig. 4.45 Types of canopy backscatter: (a) surface scattering, (b) volume scattering, (c) soil scattering, (d) soil–canopy multiple scattering, (e) canopy–soil multiple scattering.

Generally HV behaves similar to VH. Thus, for the same frequency of operation, we can have three distinct signatures namely, HH, VV and HV (or VH). The return signal will contain components with like-polarisation and cross-polarisation depending on the depolarising property of the terrain. Thus the images produced by like-polarised return signals (HH or VV) may differ from those produced by cross-polarised return, because of the differences between the physical processes responsible for the two types of return. The major reason for depolarisation to produce VH (or HV) are volume scattering and multiple reflection. For example, the cross-polarised signal may show a higher value for leafy vegetation due to multiple scattering compared to smooth soil, whereas for like-polarised return, the reverse could be true. Table 4.2 gives the preferred frequency band and polarisation for various themes.

Vegetation

As mentioned earlier, the microwave return from the vegetation canopy contains components due to scattering from the canopy surface, volume scattering and backscattering from the underlying soil surface (Fig. 4.45). The relative contribution of vegetation and underlying soil depends on the penetration depth. Figure 4.46(a) gives the penetration depth of a corn canopy versus incidence angle for HH and VV polarisation. The V polarisation is attenuated more than the H polarisation and the difference increases with increasing incidence angle. This difference may be due to the coupling of the vertical stalk of the plant with vertical polarisation (NASA, 1987b). Therefore V polarisation at a higher incidence angle gives more information related to the canopy structure. Figure 4.46(b) gives the attenuation of a corn canopy versus frequency for H and V polarisation at 40° incidence angle. As can be inferred from Fig. 4.46(b), the effect of soil background can be minimised by using frequencies above 8 GHz (where the canopy attenuation is significant) and the angle of incidence greater than 40°. For a given set of instrument parameters (λ, θ, polarisation), the primary quantity governing the attenuation coefficient of a vegetation canopy is water content per unit volume.

The cross-polarised (HV or VH) scattering coefficient shows much less angular dependence especially near the vertical incidence, compared to VV or HH (Fig. 4.47). One of the consequences of the weaker angular dependence of cross-polarisation over like-polarised signal is that the cross-polarised SAR images will be less sensitive to slope variation. In addition, two crops with similar geometry may not be distinguishable in their like-polarisation

Table 4.2 Summary of frequency and polarisation requirements of SAR for various applications*

	L-band	C-band	X-band	HH	VV	HV
Glaciology						
Sea ice type discrimination	3	2	1	1	1	2
Sea ice dynamics	3	2	1	1	1	2
Lake and river ice observations	1	?	?	1	1	
Ice sheets and shelves	?	?	?	1	1	
Snow pack extent, condition	1	1	1		1	1
Hydrology						
Soil moisture	2	1		1	1	1
Surface roughness, erosion	1	1		1	1	1
Landform patterns	1	2	3	1	1	
Land–water boundaries	1	2	3	1	2	
Snow pack extent, condition	1	1	1		1	1
Vegetation						
Standing biomass	1	1	1	1	1	1
Canopy moisture	1	1	1	1	1	2
Surface boundary layer state	1	1		1		
Oceanography						
Currents, fronts and eddies	1	1		1	1	
Internal, surface waves	1	1		1	1	
Surface wind stress	1	2	1	1	1	
Bathymetric features	1	?	?	1	1	
Geology						
Crystal structure, tectonics	3	1	2	1	2	1
Arid land studies	1	2	3	1		2
Desertification	3	2	1		1	2

1 = Best; 2 = Next best; 3 = Third choice; ? = Unknown

Source: NASA, 1987b.

scattering behaviour alone, but could be separated when cross-polarised information is also used. Figure 4.48 gives a two dimensional feature space of σ^0 for HV and HH, showing discriminability between various crops. In summary, the σ^0 from vegetation depends on plant height, LAI, water content, plant row direction, growth stage and canopy structure, and the instrument parameters such as frequency, incidence angle and polarisaton.

We have seen in the section on the temporal signatures of vegetative cover that the NDVI for crops has a temporal profile. Similarly, back scattering coefficient of a crop also exhibits a temporal signature (Fig. 4.49). We shall explain this for paddy crop. During its early growth stage, fields are mostly flooded. As a consequence of this, radar backscatter is low since most of the radar waves are reflected specularly by the water surface. During the vegetative phase of crop growth, there is an increase in the number of tillers and development of leaves. Physically, this means that there is an increase in the vegetation volume due to the expansion in the vertical

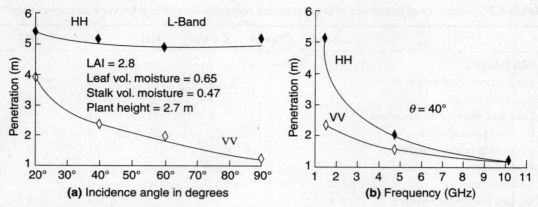

Fig. 4.46 (a) Penetration depth of a corn canopy versus incidence angle for HH and VV polarisation. Higher the penetration, lower the attenuation. (Adapted from NASA, 1987b) (b) Penetration depth of a corn canopy versus frequency at 40° incidence angle. (Adapted from NASA, 1987b)

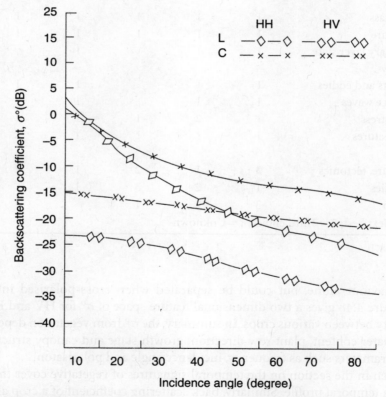

Fig. 4.47 Mean backscattering coefficient of vegetation canopies at L- and C- bands. (Adapted from NASA, 1987b)

and horizontal direction which covers the background flooded surfaces, and the volume scattering from plant canopy dominates over the background. As a result of this, backscattering

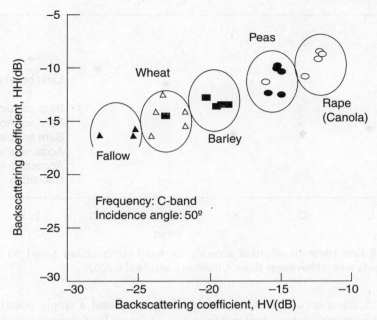

Fig. 4.48 Classification of five crop types using like and cross-polarised backscattering measurements made with a C-band scatterometer at 50°. (Adapted from NASA, 1987)

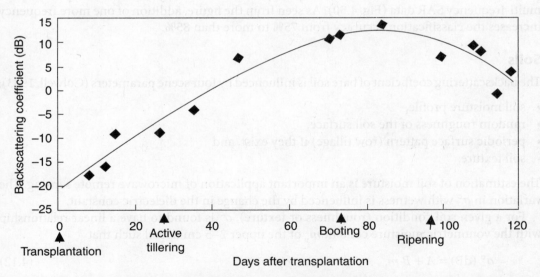

Fig. 4.49 Temporal profile of paddy crop in Ahmedabad district measured using ground based scatterometer at C-band and 40 degree incidence angle. Continuous line (–) shows the best fit. (Mohan et. al., 1992)

coefficients continue to increase. The plateau region approximately corresponds to constant biomass, moisture and height. During the ripening phase, the plant loses its moisture content which results in the decrease of dielectric constant causing a decrease in backscatter.

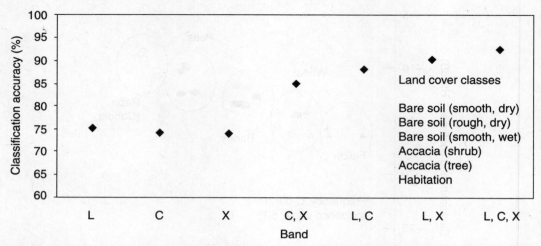

Fig. 4.50   Overall land cover classification accuracy for band combinations based on SIR-C SAR data. The study area is Bhavnagar, Gujarat. (Mohan S and Patel P, 2002)

The crop classification accuracy using a single frequency and a single polarisation is very poor (~80%). Accuracy can be improved by using additional information such as additional polarisation, multi-frequency and multi-temporal observations. Mohan and Patel (2002) have carried out land cover classification accuracy evaluation using SIR-C, multi-polarisation, multi-frequency SAR data (Fig. 4.50). As seen from the figure, addition of one more frequency increases the classification accuracy from 75% to more than 85%.

Soils

The backscattering coefficient of bare soil is influenced by four scene parameters (Colwell, 1983):

- soil moisture profile,
- random roughness of the soil surface,
- periodic surface pattern (row tillage) if they exist, and
- soil texture.

The estimation of soil moisture is an important application of microwave remote sensing. The variation in $\sigma°$ with wetness is influenced by the change in the dielectric constant.

For a given soil condition (roughness or texture), $\sigma°$ is found to have a linear relationship with the volumetric moisture content m_v of the upper 2–5 cm of soil such that

$$\sigma° \ (dB) = A + B \ m_v \tag{4.12}$$

For a given instrument parameter (frequency, polarisation, look angle), the empirically derived constants A and B are found to be dependent on soil surface roughness and soil texture. The term A depends on surface roughness and polarisation. The HH and VV polarisation yielded equivalent A, while cross-polarisation produced substantially lower value of A. The term B depends on soil texture, frequency and incidence angle. The value of B gently decreases with either increasing frequency or angle of incidence. However, polarisation does not seem to affect B. The linear relationship does not hold good near saturation, and $\sigma°$ levels off without being sensitive to added increments of water. Dobson and Ulaby (1985) further noticed that supersaturated and flooded soils behave more like a specular reflector, producing lower backscattering at nadir angles than non-saturated, but wet soils.

Ulaby et. al., (1978) have conducted an experiment using a truck mounted scatterometer for different frequencies (L, C and X bands), for varying surface roughness but with the same soil texture and approximately same moisture content. Figure 4.51 shows the results of their study for the L-band.

From their study, the following conclusions can be drawn.

- The variation in $\sigma°$ with respect to surface roughness is minimum around 7–10° incidence angle (where the curves intersect).
- The variation of $\sigma°$ with incidence angle is less for higher roughness.
- The dispersion of $\sigma°$ with roughness is less for higher frequency. Thus higher frequencies are preferred for reducing the variance in $\sigma°$ related to surface roughness; but attenuation and scattering by canopies also increases with increasing frequency.

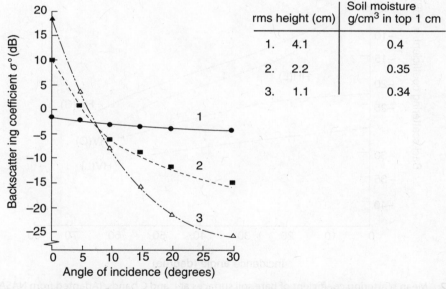

rms height (cm)	Soil moisture g/cm^3 in top 1 cm
1. 4.1	0.4
2. 2.2	0.35
3. 1.1	0.34

Fig. 4.51 Angular patterns of scattering coefficient at 1.1 GHz and HH polarisation for three bare soil fields with different surface roughness. (Ulaby et. al., 1978)

As in the case of vegetation, the cross-polarised backscattering coefficient is low and shows a much weaker angular dependence (particularly near the normal incidence angle) compared to the like-polarised scattering coefficient (Fig. 4.52).

An optimisation analysis by Ulaby et. al., (1978) has led to the conclusion that for a soil moisture study, the optimum frequency is from 4–5 GHz with an incidence angle range between 7–17° and HH polarisation. The ERS-1 SAR operates at 5.3 GHz and 23° look angle, which is very close to the recommended optimum configuration. However, even under this optimum condition, the roughness effects can be a significant source of error in soil moisture estimation. One way to improve accuracy is to concurrently extract the surface roughness using multi-frequency or cross-polarised returns and then model for the roughness effect correction. Alternately, instead of estimating absolute values, change in soil moisture can be evaluated with better accuracy since surface roughness varies slowly with time for agricultural fields in the absence of tillage operations. Another possible source of error is vegetation cover. The presence of a vegetation canopy over the soil surface affects the observed back scattered energy in two ways:

(i)   the vegetation attenuates the back scattering from the soil and
(ii) vegetative cover gives its own contribution to back scatter.

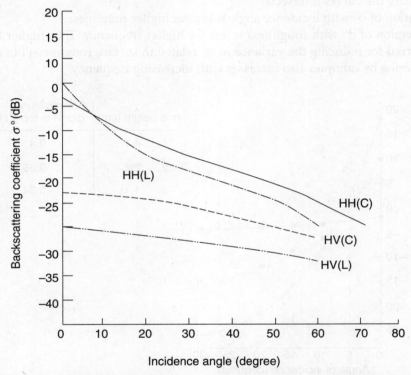

Fig. 4.52   Mean scattering coefficient of bare soil surfaces at L and C bands. (Adapted from NASA, 1987)

Thus A and B in Eq. 4.12 get modified as the vegetative cover increases. Results of an experimental observation using ERS-1 SAR for varying vegetative cover is given in Fig. 4.53. As expected, $\sigma°$ sensitivity to soil moisture decreases, as vegetative cover (NDVI) increases. To take care of vegetative cover, OIR data can be used to identify vegetative cover and suitable modelling has to be carried out to correct its effect.

It may be noted that remote sensing techniques provide estimates of soil moisture content of a surface layer of about 5 cm (Schmugge, 1983). However, soil moisture information is required for many applications down to the root-zone which is about 1–2 m deep for many crops. Statistical correlation techniques and theoretical modelling are used to estimate root-zone soil moisture from surface measurements (Blanchard et. al., 1981, Jackson, 1980).

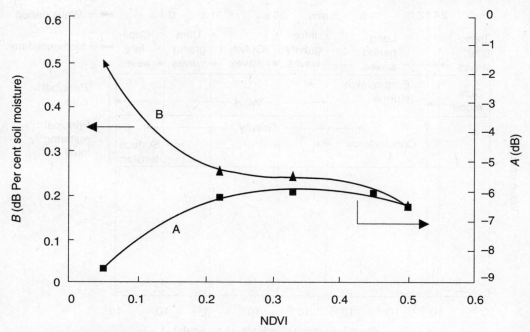

Fig. 4.53 Dependence of parameter A and B of (4.12) with NDVI. B represents change of so for a change of m_v. As NDVI increases, B decreases, showing less sensitivity of $\sigma°$ for the moisture content (m_v) change. (Adapted from Mohan, 1997)

Ocean

The backscattering in the microwave region from the ocean depends on the surface undulations generated due to various types of waves and currents. Waves of various wavelengths and heights are present in the ocean with the largest waves produced by tides at one end and ripples produced by light air at the shorter wavelength end, with varying amounts of energy (Fig. 4.54).

The cause of most ocean waves is the wind, which varies in speed from less than 1 m/s (light air) to hurricanes with speed in excess of 30 m/s which can produce very high waves and cover the sea with white foam. As the wind blows over the ocean surface, at first, small rounded waves with V-shaped troughs called *capillary waves* are generated whose wavelength is less than 1.74 cm. As more energy is transferred to the ocean, the capillary waves increase in height and length. The factors that affect the increasing energy in the wave are

- wind speed,
- the duration of the wind which blows in one direction, and
- the distance over which the wind blows in one direction referred to as fetch.

When the wavelength exceeds 1.74 cm, the wave takes on the shape of a sine wave and becomes the gravity wave. With increased energy, the steepness of the wave increases and when H/λ reaches 1/7, the wave becomes unstable and 'breaks', forming white caps (Thurman, 1975). As waves move out of the generating area or when the wind dies, the steepness of the waves decrease, they become long period waves called *swells*. Swells can travel thousands of kilometers

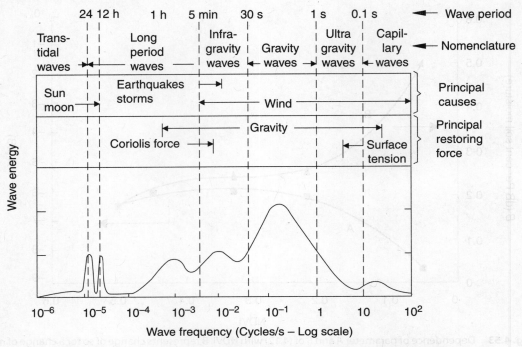

Fig. 4.54 Wave classification by wave period. (Adapted from Blair Kinsman, 1965)

without losing energy. They finally release their energy near the continent in the surf zone. Apart from the surface waves we discussed above, internal waves also produce surface features which affect the reflection of electromagnetic radiation. Surface waves occur at the interface between air and water, while internal waves are found at the interface between water layers of different densities. All these surface undulations affect the backscattering from the ocean.

Instruments used to study the interaction of microwaves on the ocean surface are altimeter, SAR and scatterometer, all of which function basically on the principle of radar and will be discussed in detail in Chapter 7. Scatterometers, which measure the back-scattered energy from the ocean surface provide information on ocean surface winds. The physical phenomenon that is relevant for sea surface wind measurement is the presence of gravity-capillary waves on the water surface. These waves with a wavelength of a few centimetres respond almost instantaneously to the strength of the local wind, that is, the amplitude increases with the wind speed. Hence, the strength of the radar backscatter, which is proportional to the amplitude of these waves (the surface roughness) is related to the wind speed near the surface. Thus the microwave return from the ocean can be related to wind velocity via suitable geophysical model functions/empirical models. The empirical models usually relate $\sigma°$ to the wind at a 10 m height above the ocean surface (the height 10 m is chosen simply because such measurements are widely available for validation).

The radar return from the ocean shows three distinct regions with respect to the incidence angle (Fig. 4.55). At near vertical incidence ($\theta < 20°$), the $\sigma°$ is high and is dominated by specular reflection from a 'facet' like surface oriented normal to the direction of the incident radiation. In the $\theta = 30-70°$ region, one finds only a slow variation of $\sigma°$ with the angle, like a diffuse reflection, and at the near grazing angles $\sigma°$ falls sharply. The $\sigma°$ at most angles of incidence is strongly related to the speed and direction of the wind. Various studies have shown that:

- $\sigma°$ in general increases with frequency,
- $\sigma°$ increases continuously with wind speed from a few m/s to 30 m/s (Fig. 4.56),
- the wind speed dependence is strongest for up wind observations, somewhat weaker for down wind and weakest for cross-wind observations,
- VV$\sigma°$ is always larger than HH$\sigma°$, and
- there is a well-defined periodicity with respect to the azimuth angle. This is shown in Fig. 4.57. Because of this, one measurement of $\sigma°$ cannot give a unique wind direction. The ambiguity can be reduced by making measurements with antennae at different angles. There are a number of algorithms to reduce the ambiguity using measurements of $\sigma°$ from different angles (Gohil and Pandey, 1985).

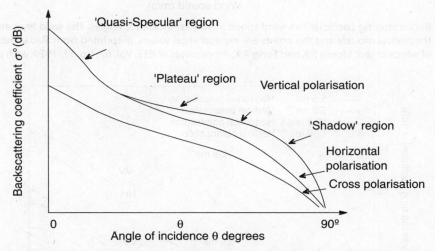

Fig. 4.55 General characteristics of radar return variation with incidence angle. (Reproduced with permission from *Microwave Remote Sensing—Active and Passive*, Ulaby, Moore and Fung, Artech House Inc., Norwood, MA, USA. *www.artechhouse.com*)

Another application of microwave scattering is to use it as distance measuring instrument—*radar altimeter*. The three geophysical parameters that is retrieved from a radar altimeter observing ocean are

(i) sea surface elevation,
(ii) significant wave height, and
(iii) wind speed.

Sea surface elevation The satellite altimeter essentially gives the height of the satellite above the closest point on the ocean at each radar pulse. The satellite height is measured with respect to a reference ellipsoid by tracking the satellite from a globally-distributed network of laser/Doppler stations. The trajectory and the height of the satellite are further refined by using orbit

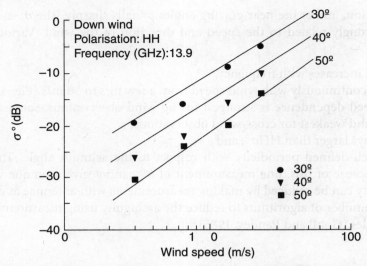

Fig. 4.56 Backscattering coefficient vs wind speed at various incidence angles. The solid lines are based on theoretical models and the points are experimental values. (Reprinted from 'Radar determination of winds at sea', Moore R K and Fung A K, *Proceedings of IEEE*, Vol. 67, No. 11, 1979, with permission)

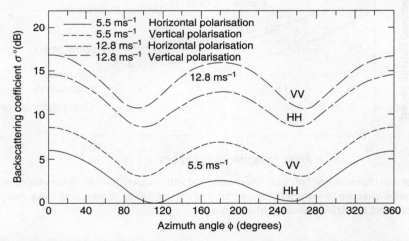

Fig. 4.57 Azimuthal variation of the backscattering coefficient of the ocean surface $\phi = 0$ corresponds to the upwind direction. (Reprinted with permission from *Microwave Remote sensing — Active and Passive*, Ulaby, Moore and Fung, Artech House Inc., Norwood, MA, USA. www.artechhouse.com)

modelling. The difference between the orbital height and the altimeter measured range gives the height of the sea surface above the reference ellipsoid (Fig. 4.58). However, the sea surface topography is measured with respect to the *geoid*, which is the equipotential surface of the earth's gravity field. (This coincides most closely with the undisturbed mean sea level extended continuously under the continents. Because of the irregular distribution of the earth's internal masses, the geoid is an irregular surface, which cannot be represented by a simple geometric figure. The direction of gravity is perpendicular to the geoid at every point.) To get the true

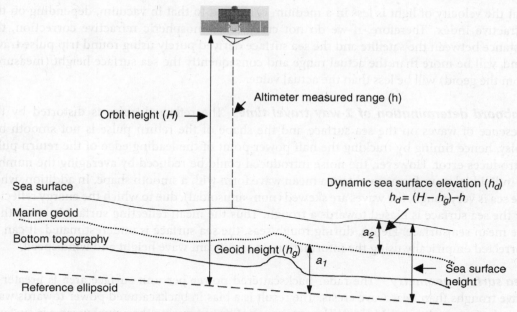

Fig. 4.58 Schematics showing the dynamic sea surface elevation (sea surface topography)
It is the displacement of sea surface from the geoid.

height from altimetry, the data has to be corrected to take into account the errors caused from a number of sources. These are briefly described here.

Atmospheric refraction The speed of light is constant (~3×10^8 m/s) only in perfect vacuum. Since the path between the satellite and sea-surface is not a perfect vacuum, the speed of light varies along the path. It will be dependent on the refractive index of the medium. The total refractive index can be decomposed into those caused by

- dry air,
- water vapour,
- liquid water, and
- free electrons in the ionosphere.

Since the atmospheric dry constituents are known fairly well, the correction due to dry air can be well-modelled. Generally, since the 'wet atmospheric' effect is the most varying, suitable multi-frequency microwave radiometers are co-located with the altimeter to view the same path. From the radiometer data, the actual integrated water vapour density can be evaluated, which can be used in the appropriate model to find out the required correction. Ionospheric range correction requires vertically integrated electron density values at each altimeter measurement location. This could be taken from global models. However, they are not very precisely known and could vary. Since the ionospheric range correction varies with frequency (proportional to square of frequency), altimeters operating in two frequencies can compute the ionospheric effect to give a more accurate correction. Topex altimeters uses two frequencies, namely, C-band (5.3 GHz) and Ku-band (13.6 GHz). We have seen in Chapter 2, that the velocity of light is less in a medium compared to that in vacuum, depending on the refractive index. Therefore, if we do not carry out atmospheric refractive correction, the distance between the satellite and the sea surface derived purely using round trip pulse travel time, will be more than the actual range and consequently the sea surface height (measured from the geoid) will be less than the actual value.

Onboard determination of 2-way travel time   The reflected pulse is distorted by the presence of waves on the sea surface and the shape of the return pulse is not smooth but noisy, hence timing by tracking the half power point of the leading edge of the return pulse introduces error. However, the noise introduced could be reduced by averaging the number of individual wave forms to obtain a mean wave form with a smooth shape. In addition, when the sea is very rough, the waves are skewed (non-sinusoidal), due to which the energy reflected by the sea surface is biased towards a trough. Thus the mean reflecting surface is lower than the mean sea surface. Hence, during rough seas, the sea surface is underestimated. It can be corrected empirically using the information on significant wave height and wind speed.

Sea surface geometry   The radar backscattered power per unit surface area is greater in wave troughs than near wave crests. The result is a bias in backscattered power towards wave troughs (referred to as EM bias). Thus we may not be measuring the actual mean sea surface.

Instruments   Clock instability, antenna mispointing, and so on, also add to possible error in height measurement. Current satellite radar altimeters can provide height accuracies of a few centimetres.

Significant wave height   In a pulse-limited operation of the altimeter, the return pulse energy increases linearly with time, followed by a near constant plateau (the plateau decays because of lower gain of antenna as the angle increases) (Chapter 7). If there are large waves present on the surface of the sea, there will be some radiation reflected from the top of the waves corresponding to a slightly smaller value of h and hence having a lower round trip time compared to the mean sea level; in the same way, there will be an extra delay experienced by the radiation reflected from the trough of the waves. Hence as the wave height increases, the leading edge of the return pulse shape becomes more and more stretched due to the spread of the returns from wave crests and wave troughs at the satellite nadir (Fig. 4.59). The significant wave height (SWH) at the satellite nadir is proportional to the rise time of the leading edge of the wave form. Thus the SWH can be estimated from the slope of the leading edge of the return pulse wave form. The actual SWH value is obtained through an empirical relationship. [The significant wave height (SWH) or sometimes represented as $H_{1/3}$ is defined as the average height of the highest 1/3 of all the waves (during a period) and is usually taken as four times the standard deviation of the sea surface elevation.]

Wind speed   A perfectly calm sea surface acts as a specular reflector, returning most of the energy to the transmitter. However, the wind over the sea surface increases its roughness, in a way proportional to the speed of the wind itself. As the sea surface roughness increases, the scattered energy gets distributed over a wider angle, thereby reducing the fraction reaching

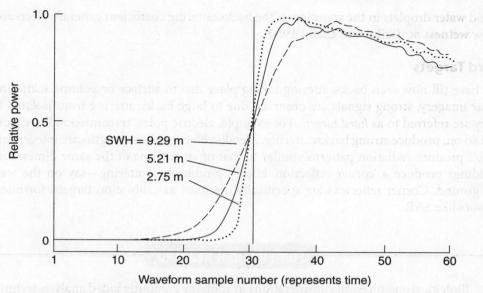

Fig. 4.59 Schematics showing the difference in the rise time of received power for different significant wave heights. (from SEASAT measurement) (Adapted from Chelton, 1988)

the satellite. Thus with increasing wind speed, the received backscattered power decreases. Therefore, the wind speed can be estimated using empirically related $\sigma°$ to the wind speed. At the Ku-band, the attenuation by water vapour and dry gases in the atmosphere is generally small. However, integrated liquid water (clouds) produce attenuation thereby reducing $\sigma°$. If not corrected, this reduction in $\sigma°$ would lead to overestimation of wind speed.

Snow/Ice

Dry snow can be considered as consisting of ice crystals embedded in an air background. For dry snow, the imaginary part of the dielectric constant (loss factor) is very low, of the order of 10^{-3} in the microwave region and therefore has higher penetration depth. The penetration depth also depends on snow density and ice particle radius. Depending on the snow thickness and frequency (that is, essentially based on the penetration depth), the scattering from snow consists of both surface scattering and volume scattering and from underneath soil surface. In general $\sigma°$ for snow increases with frequency.

In the case of sea ice, one has to take into account the entrapped brine and salt crystals. If the ice contains an appreciable amount of salt (first year ice), it is highly lossy and the penetration depth will be only a few millimeters and hence the radar return is controlled by the surface roughness. However, for multilayer sea ice, the upper portion has low salinity and hence low loss, thereby producing volume scattering within the ice.

As snow heats up during the day, the snow medium becomes a mixture of ice particles, water droplets and air. The amount of water droplets is a measure of 'snow wetness'. The snow wetness m_v is expressed as the volumetric fraction occupied by the water droplets. $\sigma°$ from wet snow is dependent on the surface roughness at the snow–air interface and on the amount of liquid water droplets in the snow layer. The backscattering coefficient generally decreases with snow wetness m_v (Stiles and Ulaby, 1980).

Hard Targets

We have till now seen backscattering taking place due to surface or volume scattering. In a radar imagery, strong signals are observed due to large backscattering from isolated targets. They are referred to as *hard targets*. For example, electric poles, transmission lines, buildings, and so on, produce strong backscattering. Metallic objects whose lengths are integer multiples of $\lambda/2$ produce radiation patterns similar to that of an antenna of the same dimensions. The buildings produce a 'corner reflection' effect by multiple scattering—say on the walls and the ground. Corner reflectors are specifically designed as calibration targets, for microwave sensors like SAR.

FOR FURTHER READING

1. Biological and physical considerations in applying computer aided analysis techniques to remote sensor data, Hoffer R M, *Remote Sensing: The Quantitative Approach*, Swain and Davis, Ed. 1978, McGraw-Hill Publishers.
2. *Manual of Remote Sensing,* Vol. 1, Colwell, Ed., ASPRS.
3. *http://www.dtic.mil/dtic/tr/fulltext/u2/a239496.pdf*
4. *http://www.ioccg.org/reports/report5.pdf*
5. *ftp://oceane.obs-vlfr.fr/pub/marcel/Book%20Chapters/Ruddick/Firs%20draft/ HABWATCH-RUDDICK.pdf*
6. *http://stars.library.ucf.edu/cgi/viewcontent.cgi?article=6339&context=etd*
7. *http://www.agrometeorologia.it/documenti/rivista9_1/Basso2004_1.pdf*
8. *https://www.hindawi.com/journals/js/2017/1353691/*
9. *http://repository.ias.ac.in/89353/1/31P.pdf*
10. *https://www.ncbi.nlm.nih.gov/pmc/articles/pmc3675549/*
11. *http://www.mdpi.com/1424-8220/15/2/3262/htm*

5 Remote Sensors—An Overview

Remote sensors are instruments that measure the properties of electromagnetic radiation leaving a surface/medium due to scattering or emission. Generally, radiance is the property measured and it is measured as a function of wavelength, but could include other parameters such as state of polarisation. This information could be collected over a spatial extent including the angular dependence of the observation and in certain cases (such as atmospheric sounding) as a function of distance along the line of sight of the instrument.

5.1 CLASSIFICATION OF REMOTE SENSORS

Remote sensors can be broadly classified as *passive sensors* and *active sensors*. Sensors which sense natural radiation, either emitted or reflected from the earth are called passive sensors. It is also possible to produce electromagnetic radiation of a specific wavelength or band of wavelengths as a part of the sensor system. The interaction of this radiation with the target could then be studied by sensing the scattered radiation from the targets. Such sensors, which produce their own electromagnetic radiation are called active sensors. The technology involved in developing sensors throughout the electromagnetic spectrum is not the same. Since the technology for developing microwave sensors is quite different from that of optical-infrared (OIR) sensors, from the standpoint of understanding the design and realisation of the sensors, it is convenient to classify the sensors (both passive and active) as those operating in the OIR region and those operating in the microwave region. The OIR and microwave sensors could be either imaging or non-imaging sensors. Imaging sensors give a two dimensional spatial distribution of the emitted or reflected intensity of the electromagnetic radiation (as in a photographic camera), while the non-imaging sensors measure the intensity of radiation, within the field of view, and in some cases as a function of distance along the line of sight of the instrument (for example, vertical temperature profiling radiometer—VTPR). Figure 5.1 gives a possible classification of remote sensors.

5.2 SELECTION OF SENSOR PARAMETERS

The information collected by the remote sensors is meant to identify and map various earth surface objects. Therefore, we may say that the performance of the sensor is evaluated based on its classification as well as its mapping accuracy requirements. It is reasonable to assume that this will depend on the instrument's ability to detect small differences in the emittance/reflectance of the earth's surface in a number of spectral bands for as small an object as

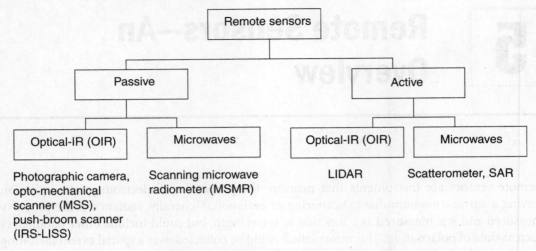

Fig. 5.1 Classification of remote sensors.

possible and as often as possible. Then the important question is 'what is the optimum set of specifications for a remote sensor?'. Unfortunately, there is no unique answer, since the choice of the optimum parameters depends on the theme under study. Even if we identify an ideal set of parameters, the realisation of a combination of these parametric values (that is, spatial resolution, number of spectral bands, spectral bandwidth, signal-to-noise ratio, and so on) in a sensor system is a complex problem due to the strong interrelationship these parameters have with one another and the engineering requirements of the sensor. We may consider the sensor parameters under four domains—(i) spatial (ii) spectral (iii) radiometric and (iv) temporal.

5.3 SPATIAL RESOLUTION

In a very general sense, the spatial resolution is a measure of the sensor's ability to image (record) closely spaced objects so that they are distinguishable as separate objects. Thus, a sensor with a 1 m spatial resolution can reproduce 'finer details' of the scene image compared to a sensor with a 10 m resolution. There are a number of sensor design parameters, which influence the resolution. We shall deal with them, when discussing the sensor design and realisation.

The theoretical limit of resolving two objects by an imaging system, say lens, is due to diffraction, [the phenomenon of electromagnetic radiation (EMR) 'bending' at the edge of an object on its path] of the EMR around its aperture. To understand this phenomenon, let us consider a perfect lens without any aberrations (which is not possible in practice). In the absence of any aberration, one expects the lens to image a point object as a point in the image plane. However, this does not happen due to diffraction. Thus, the image of a point object at infinity produced by an aberration-free imaging system will consist of a bright disc surrounded by concentric bright and dark rings called an *Airy pattern*. The central disc is called an *Airy disc*. The distribution of energy in the Airy pattern due to a circular aperture is as shown in Fig. 5.2. It has a main peak followed by a number of minima and maxima. The energy contained between the first minima is 84% of the total energy. The diameter of the first minima is 2.44 (λ/D) f, where D is the aperture of the lens, f the focal length and λ the wave-length of observation.

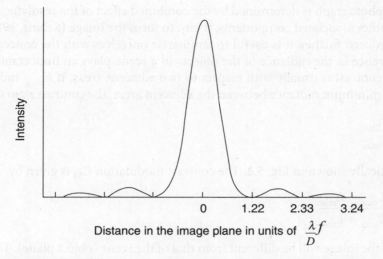

Fig. 5.2 Airy pattern of a circular aperture. 0 corresponds to the location of the optical axis in the image plane.

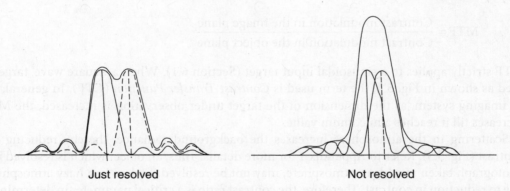

Just resolved   Not resolved

Fig. 5.3 Resolution limit. Two points are said to be just resolved when the principal maxima of the Airy pattern of one point falls at the first minima of the other point.

Two objects can be just resolved if the peak of the Airy pattern of one object falls on the first minima of the other (Fig. 5.3). That is, two objects separated by 1.22 $(\lambda/D) f$ can be just, resolved. This is the theoretical resolving limit of two objects. It is convenient to specify that in terms of angular resolution, this is 1.22 λ/D radians. Let us consider an IRS PAN camera, with an entrance aperture of ~22 cm, the limit of resolution at 0.5 μm wavelength is 2.7×10^{-6} $(1.22 \times 0.5 \times 10^{-4}/22)$ radians. From an altitude of 810 km, the spatial resolution limit is 2 m $(810 \times 10^3 \times 2.7 \times 10^{-6})$, while the instrument resolution is 5.6 m. However, if we were to use the same optics for imaging at shortwave IR (SWIR) at 2 μm, the diffraction by optics itself limits the resolution to 8 m.

It is necessary to understand the subtle difference between resolving power and resolution. The term 'resolving power' applies to the components of the imaging system such as lens, film and so on, while 'resolution' applies to the image produced by the system. That is, the resolution of a photograph is determined by the combined effect of the resolving power of the lens, film and other associated components, if any, to form the image (Sabins, 1986).

Before we proceed further, it is useful to familiarise ourselves with the concept of *contrast ratio*. The difference in the radiance of the objects in a scene plays an important role in their detection. The contrast is usually with respect to two adjacent areas. If L_{max} and L_{min} are the maximum and minimum radiance between the adjacent areas, the contrast ratio C_R is given by

$$C_R = \frac{L_{max}}{L_{min}}$$

This is schematically shown in Fig. 5.4. The contrast modulation C_M is given by

$$C_M = \frac{L_{max} - L_{min}}{L_{max} + L_{min}}$$

The contrast in the image will be different from that of the scene (object plane). This is because the imaging system reduces the contrast. The degradation of the contrast by the imaging system is represented by the *Modulation Transfer Function (MTF)*. Theoretically, MTF can vary from 0 to 1.

$$MTF = \frac{\text{Contrast modulation in the image plane}}{\text{Contrast modulation in the object plane}}$$

MTF strictly applies to a sinusoidal input target (Section 6.1). When a 'square wave' target is used as shown in Fig. 5.4, the term used is *Contrast Transfer Function* (CTF). In general, for an imaging system, as the dimension of the target under observation is increased, the MTF increases till it reaches a maximum value.

Scattering in the atmosphere increases the background radiance, thereby reducing the contrast (Fig. 5.5). Refer to Appendix 1 for more details. Thus, an object which is resolved in a photograph taken in a 'clear' atmosphere, may not be resolved if taken in a hazy atmosphere, due to reduction in contrast. Therefore, the contrast ratio is a critical parameter in determining the ability to resolve and detect objects. Other parameters remaining the same, an object with a higher contrast ratio can be more easily identified than a low contrast object.

The resolution of a photographic product is usually specified as line pairs per mm (one line pair is one 'dark' and one 'white' line adjacent to each other) [Fig. 5.6(a)]. This is evaluated by observing, on the photo product, a 'resolution target', which has alternate black and white bars of equal width.

A standard resolution chart has a number of such bars with different widths, thereby having different pairs of black and white lines of unit length [Fig. 5.6(b)]. The photograph is examined under magnification and the observer finds out the most closely spaced set of line pairs for which the bars and space are discernible. The spatial resolution of the photographic system is given as the number of line pairs per millimetre (lpm) on the photograph of the resolved target. Note that line pair means a pair of black and white bars [Fig. 5.6(a)]. Thus 5 line pairs per millimetre means each black is 0.1 mm thick, separated by a white bar of equal thickness. That is, a black and white bar together gives 0.2 mm and hence the line pair is 5 per millimetre (1/0.2). Therefore, if 5 lpm is resolved, it means you can resolve 0.1 mm in the photograph. What it means on the ground is that, it is dependent on the focal length of the lens and the

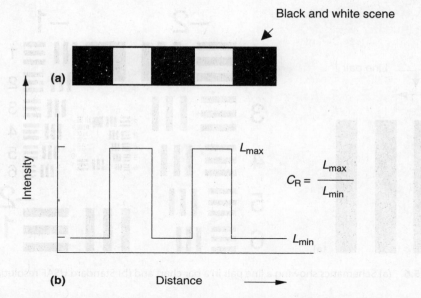

Fig. 5.4 Concept of contrast ratio; (a) a scene with black and white bars; (b) their intensity distribution.

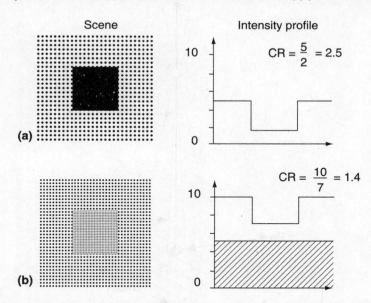

Fig. 5.5 Effect of scattered light on the contrast ratio of an image; (a) without scattering; (b) with five brightness unit added by scattered image. (Adapted from Sabins, 1986)

height from which the photograph is taken, which can be easily computed using elementary trigonometry.

$$\text{Ground resolution} = \frac{1}{2}(1/Rs)\frac{H}{f}$$

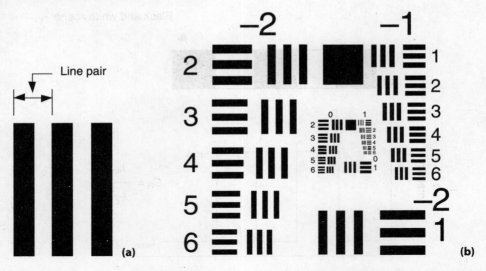

Fig. 5.6 (a) Schematics showing a line pair in a bar chart and (b) Standard USAF resolution chart.

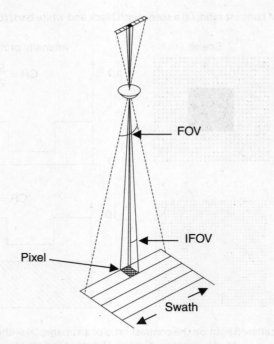

Fig. 5.7 Concept of IFOV and FOV.

where Rs is the resolution of the system in line pairs/unit length, f the focal length of the lens and H the observation height. The term ½ appears, to specify the dimension of the 'bar' on the ground (against pair). This method of evaluation of resolution is subjective, since it involves human judgment and depends on the target contrast. The instrument designer will prefer to evaluate the camera for an 'infinite contrast' target so that the system appears to have the best resolution. However, such targets do not often occur naturally on the earth and hence are not meaningful to the user. There is no universally accepted contrast which should be used for evaluation of the camera.

Another term associated with photographic products is 'scale'. Map scale is defined by the US Geological Survey (USGS) as follows: 'To be most useful, a map must show locations and distances accurately on a sheet of paper of convenient size. This means that all things included in the map – ground area, rivers, lakes, roads, distances between features, and so on – must be shown proportionately smaller than they really are. The proportion chosen for a particular map is its scale.' Thus, map scale is the ratio of the distance measured on a map to that measured on the ground between the same two points. It is expressed as, say for example, 1:100,000, which means, 1 cm on the photograph measures 100,000 cm on ground. One source of confusion to beginners are the terms *large scale* and *small scale*. For example, a map (photograph) of 1:5,000 is said to be large scale compared to a 1:50,000 map—that is, larger the ratio, smaller is the map scale. One way to remember (and appreciate) the terminology is that an object will appear larger in a large scale image compared to a small scale image.

When electronic sensors using discrete detectors are used for generating imagery (like LANDSAT, MSS, IRS LISS, and so on), spatial resolution is used to denote the projection of the detector element on to the ground through optics (Fig. 5.7). Thus when one speaks of the 5.8 m resolution of an IRS 1C/1D PAN camera, it only means that the projection of one CCD element on the ground through the imaging optics from the satellite orbit is 5.8 metres, that is, the *'footprint'* of the detector element on the ground—the *Instantaneous Geometric Field of View* (IGFOV). What the detector measures is the integrated radiance from the IGFOV reaching the focal plane. IGFOV is also referred in the literature as *'resolution element'/pixel*. [Readers may note that there is a subtle difference between the term *picture element* known as pixel and IGFOV though they are used without distinction. 'Pixel or picture element is the data sample in the output product to which a radiance value is assigned' (UN A/AC 105/260). That is, it is the smallest unit of a digital image that can be assigned colour and intensity. It has dimensions which are not necessarily related to the sensor system parameters since the data can be sampled at different spacing compared to the detector footprint.] In terms of angular measurement, it is referred to as the 'Instantaneous Field of View' (IFOV). If d is the dimension of the detector element and f the focal length of the imaging system, d/f gives IFOV in radians. The advantage of using IFOV, is that it characterises the sensor, irrespective of the altitude from which the image is taken. The *field of view* (FOV), is the total view angle of the camera, which defines the swath.

Unfortunately, spatial resolution as defined above alone is not a measure of the smallest object that can be detected. It depends on other parameters like modulation transfer function (MTF), signal-to-noise ratio (SNR) and object contrast. It may be possible to detect in an image, an object smaller than the resolution element. A common example of detection below the specified resolution is roads (at times even railway lines) in IRS LISS-1/LANDSAT MSS imagery which has a spatial resolution of about 74/80 metres. This is possible because of the large contrast between the objects and their surroundings; that is, even though the road in the image plane of the MSS is only a fraction of the resolution element, the radiance from the road is high enough to generate a higher signal in comparison with the surroundings. This radiance difference along with the linear nature of the target makes the detection possible.

Let us now try to understand the effect of MTF and signal to noise ratio (SNR) in discriminating objects in imagery. Even if there is adequate contrast difference in the scene (object space) the sensor noise should be lower than the signal generated by the radiance difference between the targets to be distinguished. Therefore, only those targets can be distinguished whose radiance difference can be measured, which depends on the radiometric resolution of the system-NEΔL (Section 5.5). The differential radiance at the image space depends on the contrast in the object space and the MTF of the total system. Therefore the ability to distinguish two targets depends on the object contrast, MTF, and the noise equivalent radiance. Thus a camera with low MTF but high SNR may perform better than one with a higher MTF but lower SNR. Joseph (2015), suggested a figure of merit (FM) of a camera for spatial resolution as the ratio of MTF to Noise Equivalent Radiance at IGFOV, that is $\left[\frac{MTF}{NE\Delta L}\right]_{IGFOV}$. The higher the FM value, the better the discriminability between the targets having the same contrast difference.

Since IFOV alone cannot give an idea of the detection capability of a sensor, a criterion called *Effective Instantaneous Field of View* (EIFOV) has been introduced (NASA, 1973) to compare the performance of the sensors. EIFOV is the resolution (for a sinusoidal target) for which the MTF of the system is 50%. However, this definition does not have much rationale.

Generally, MTF is considered as an indicator of how sharp the edges are after contrast reduction during imaging. However, MTF is also a measure of how accurately the actual radiance from a pixel is measured, since a lower MTF indicates contribution from other pixels to the pixel under observation and vice versa (Fig. 5.11). Therefore, the question is 'what is the radiometrically accurate IFOV?'. Joseph (2000) has introduced radiometrically accurate IFOV (RAIFOV) as the resolution for which the MTF is higher than 0.95. Since this does not give a specific value for RAIFOV it is redefined as the resolution at which th MTF of the system is 0.95.

To add to the confusion, sensor designers have added a new term, *Ground Sample Distance* (GSD). This means that the data can be generated by sampling at certain specified ground distances, which are smaller than the IGFOV. I would like to caution that GSD should not be confused with IGFOV. Consider the pushbroom sensors, which are currently used in many (especially high resolution) earth observation systems. In the 'along track' direction, if radiometric and electronic performance allow, the GSD can be made smaller than the IGFOV, to achieve better image quality because of reduction of smear. Does across-track performance improve if the data is sampled at smaller intervals compared to IGFOV? Can a 5 m IGFOV sensor at 1 m GSD have the same performance as a 1 m IGFOV sensor? What is the maximum allowable ratio of IGFOV over GSD? These are issues not well addressed either by sensor designers or users.

Thus, the term spatial *resolution*, though used frequently, is in reality difficult to define uniquely. Subconsciously, we think that a camera with a better spatial resolution will provide better image quality. This is generally true for cameras with similar MTF and S/N characteristics. Despite all the above discussions to define spatial resolution, it still might be hard to understand precisely what spatial resolution is. Irrespective of the shortcomings, we shall hereafter refer to spatial resolution as the projection of the detector element on to the ground through the optical system collecting the radiation; that is essentially IGFOV. Based on this definition, the spatial resolution of LANDSAT MSS is 79 m, SPOT (multi-spectral channel) 20 m and IRS LISS-II 36 m.

What is the optimum spatial resolution? There is no unique answer. It depends on the feature you want to study. If the feature varies slowly in space, as in the case of sea surface temperature, then one can use a coarser resolution compared to the resolution required to study the vegetation dynamics on land (this is why spatial resolution of ocean observation systems for temperature, chlorophyll, and so on, is only a few hundred metres). In the same manner, the resolution required to study vegetation dynamics could have a poorer resolution compared to that required for town planning.

The spatial resolution at which data are acquired has two effects—the ability to identify various features and the ability to quantify their extent. The former relates to the classification accuracy and the latter to the ability to accurately take measurements. One important aspect for classification accuracy is the contribution of boundary pixels. Boundary pixels are those which cover the boundary of two features, thus the radiance measured here is the combined effect of the two features (Fig. 5.8). Since the boundary pixels do not conform to the radiance value of either of the features, they are sources of error in classification.

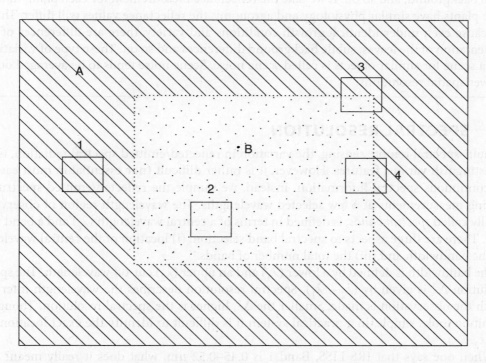

Fig. 5.8 Concept of pure pixels and boundary pixels. Feature A surrounds feature B. Four pixel footprints are shown. 1 is a pure pixel of A and 2 a pure pixel of feature B. 3 and 4 are boundary pixels. 3 covers more area of A, while 4 covers more of B.

The boundary pixel error is reduced with improved resolution. However, the classification accuracy cannot be improved by reducing the pixel size indefinitely, since the scene noise starts affecting the accuracy of classification as the pixel size is reduced below a certain level. The *scene noise*, in the present context, refers to the variability within a given land cover category. In any given scene, the change in classification accuracy with spatial resolution will be a function of the relative importance of scene noise and boundary pixels. The study carried out by Markham and Townshend (1981) shows that land cover classification accuracy degrades or remains constant as the pixel size is decreased below a certain value. This threshold value is dependent on the type of land cover.

It is obvious that the accuracy of measurement of an area will depend upon the accuracy of locating the boundary. Since it is not possible to locate with an accuracy better than a fraction of a pixel, the larger the pixel size, the more will be the error in the area estimation. The percentage error will obviously be higher for features having smaller area.

Scene Noise

The term *scene noise* refers to the variability in reflectance in a scene, even if it contains similar objects. For example, let us consider a scene having a wheat crop of the same variety, soil background, and so on. If we take the reflectance measurement for each plant, though the plants have similar physiology and agronomy, the reflectance values will differ. This is because even under identical growth conditions and variety, there are differences of the orientation of the leaves, subtle background differences and so on. These type of variations in a scene for similar objects is called scene noise. Scene noise tends to be averaged out at lower spatial resolutions.

5.4   SPECTRAL RESOLUTION

In multi-spectral remote sensing, the variation in reflected/emitted spectral radiation, is used to distinguish various features. However, it is rather difficult (nor essential in most cases) to get continuous spectral information. Instead, we sample the reflected/emitted spectrum by making measurements at a few selected wavelengths. The wavelength region of observation, usually called *spectral bands*, is defined in terms of a central wavelength (λ_c) and a band width ($\Delta\lambda$). There are three aspects to spectral band selection: (i) location of the central wavelength, (ii) the bandwidth and (iii) the total number of bands.

The bandwidth is defined by a lower (λ_1) and an upper (λ_2) cut-off wavelength. The spectral resolution $\Delta\lambda$ is given by ($\lambda_2 - \lambda_1$). Spectral resolution describes the wavelength interval in which the observation is made. Smaller the $\Delta\lambda$, higher is the spectral resolution. Though the definition looks simple, in a practical system it is difficult to identify the exact location of λ_1 and λ_2.

When one says that IRS LISS, Band 1 is 0.45–0.52 μm, what does it really mean? In an ideal system, the response should be 1 between the wavelengths 0.45 and 0.52 μm, and 0 for wavelengths outside this range [Fig. 5.9(a)]. Of course, this is not practical. Usually the bandwidth is defined in terms of 50% of the peak value on either side [Fig. 5.9(b)]. This definition holds best if the spectral response of the system is Gaussian or close to Gaussian. However, in a practical filter, the pass band response has a number of 'ringings' (Fig. 5.10) and assigning the peak value is not a straightforward process.

Palmer (1984) suggested a technique called the 'moments' method to compute λ_c and $\Delta\lambda$, which avoids the above problem of identifying the peak value. The analysis is based on determining the first and second moments of the spectral response curve R(λ) (Palmer, 1980). Following Palmer (1984), the central wavelength λ_c and $\Delta\lambda$ are given as

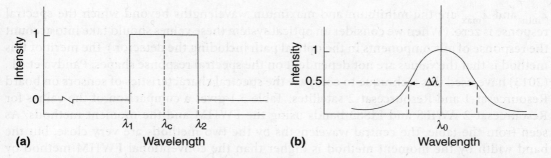

Fig. 5.9 Spectral bandwidth definition. (a) An ideal response, wherein response is zero below λ_1 and above λ_2. (b) A practical filter; the bandwidth $\Delta\lambda$ is the full width at half maxima (FWHM).

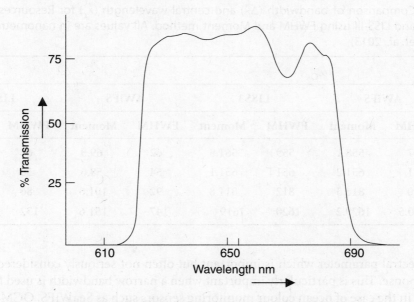

Fig. 5.10 Spectral response of a practical filter (LISS-B3).

$$\lambda_c = \frac{\int_{\lambda_{min}}^{\lambda_{max}} \lambda R(\lambda)\, d\lambda}{\int_{\lambda_{min}}^{\lambda_{max}} R(\lambda)\, d\lambda} \tag{5.1}$$

$$\lambda_1 = \lambda_c - \sqrt{3}\sigma \text{ and } \lambda_2 = \lambda_c + \sqrt{3}\sigma \tag{5.2}$$

$$\Delta\lambda = 2\sqrt{3}\sigma \tag{5.3}$$

where σ is given by $\sigma^2 = \dfrac{\int_{\lambda_{min}}^{\lambda_{max}} \lambda^2 R(\lambda)\, d\lambda}{\int_{\lambda_{min}}^{\lambda_{max}} R(\lambda)\, d\lambda} - \lambda_c^2$

λ_{min} and λ_{max} are the minimum and maximum wavelengths beyond which the spectral response is zero. (When we consider an optical system these values should take into account the response of all components in the optical path including the detector.) The merit of this method is that the values are not dependent on the spectral response shapes. Pandya et. al., (2013) have used this technique to compare the spectral characteristics of sensors on board Resourcesat-1 and Resourcesat-2 satellites. Table 5.1 gives a comparison of the values for Resourcesat-2 AWiFS and LISS3 bands using the FWHM and the moment methods. As seen from the table, the central wavelengths by the two methods are very close, but the band width by the moment method is higher than the conventional FWHM method by about 5% to 13%.

Table 5.1 Comparison of bandwidth ($\Delta\lambda$) and central wavelength (λ_c) for Resourcesat-2 AWiFS and LISS-III using FWHM and Moment method. All values are in nanometres. (Pandya et. al., 2013)

| | λ_c | | | | $\Delta\lambda$ | | | |
| | AWiFS | | LISS3 | | AWiFS | | LISS3 | |
	FWHM	Moment	FWHM	Moment	FWHM	Moment	FWHM	Moment
B2	557	558.1	559	561.5	62	69.5	66	69
B3	651	651.2	651	651.1	54	58.6	56	58
B4	820	816.5	812	811.8	92	101.6	86	95.1
B5	1630.5	1629.2	1620	1619	147	151.6	132	149.3

Another spectral parameter which is important but often not seriously considered is the out of band response. This is particularly important when a narrow bandwidth is used for spectral selection as in the case of ocean colour monitoring sensors such as SeaWiFS, OCM and so on. In the case of SeaWiFS, at the data product level the specification is less than 5% of the 'within the band' value. Within the band in this case is defined as the wavelength interval between the lower and upper 1 per cent response (Barnes et. al., 1999).

At the instrument level, the overall spectral response depends on the optics response, filter response and the detector response. At the data product level, the spectral content also depends on the input source spectral response shape which is difficult to assess in remote sensing since it depends on the target characteristics. The band shape of the interference filter chosen and its out of band rejection property should be consistent with the overall camera performance requirements.

The selection of bandwidth is a trade-off between the energy to be collected and spectral shape of the feature to be observed. If one is interested in observing some characteristic emissions lines, then obviously the bandwidth should be much smaller than the line width in order to sample a few points in the line spectra. For land observation in VNIR, a few 10s of nanometres is usually used, while for ocean observation 10–20 nanometres is used.

5.4.1 LOCATION OF SPECTRAL BANDS

The most important criterion for the location of spectral bands is that they should be in the atmospheric window and away from the absorption bands of atmospheric constituents. The LANDSAT MSS bands were chosen rather arbitrarily. However, field studies have shown that certain spectral bands are best suited for specific themes. The thematic mapper bands are selected based on such investigations. In Table 4.3, we have seen the preferred microwave bands for different applications. Table 5.2 gives the TM spectral bands in the OIR region, and their principal applications. The list is not exhaustive but indicative of the potential of various spectral regions.

Table 5.2 Applications of spectral bands (from An Introduction to Geographical Information System, Heywood, Cornelius & Carver, reprinted by permission of Pearson Educational Ltd., UK)

Spectral range (micrometres)	Principal applications
0.45 to 0.52	Sensitivity to chlorophyll; coastal water mapping, soil/vegetation discrimination, forest type mapping
0.52 to 0.60	Green reflectance for vegetation discrimination and vigour assessment
0.63 to 0.69	Sensitivity to chlorophyll; plant species identification; water type discrimination
0.76 to 0.90	Vegetation type, vigour, biomass determination; water body delineation, soil boundary and geological boundary mapping
1.55 to 1.75	Sensitivity to amount of water in plants; useful in drought studies and plant vigour studies, snow/cloud differentiation
2.08 to 2.35	Sensitivity to hydroxyl ions in minerals; useful in discrimination of mineral and rock types. Effective in identifying zones of hydrothermal alteration in rocks
10.4 to 12.5	Surface temperature mapping

The bands selected should be un-correlated to the extent possible, since correlated bands give redundant information, which does not help in improving the discriminability. There are a number of statistical methods to evaluate the correlation between the bands (Kondratyev and Pokrovsky, 1979). Unfortunately the outcome of such studies is scene-dependent and hence a certain amount of generalisation is required when one designs a camera for global coverage. Since the data rate increases directly with the number of bands, selection of an optimum number of bands is essential. It is important to have a minimum set of optimal bands. A study made by Sharma et. al. (1995), shows that addition of the middle IR band with any other band combination gives improved separability in agricultural classification (refer Chapter 10).

5.5 RADIOMETRIC RESOLUTION

The sensors respond only to those radiance values lying between the lower and upper radiance settings. The lower level is usually set close to zero radiance. The upper level is usually referred to as *saturation radiance* (SR) since for any radiance input beyond SR, the output of the sensor remains constant. Thus, the maximum radiance we can measure is SR. The SR setting depends on the mission objective. For example, for cloud/snow radiance measurement, the value is kept well above 100% reflectance, while for ocean colour measurement, 5%–10% reflectance may be adequate, since ocean leaving radiance itself is only a few per cent of solar irradiance (in practice, path radiance needs to be considered). In electro-optical sensors (Chapter 6), the output is usually digitised, to produce discreet levels. The digitisation is referred to as quantisation and is expressed as n binary bits. Thus, 7-bit digitisation implies 2^7 or 128 discreet levels (0–127).

Radiometric resolution is a measure of the capability of the sensor to differentiate the smallest change in the spectral reflectance/emittance between various targets. This is represented as the noise equivalent reflectance (or temperature) change—$NE\Delta\rho$ (or $NE\Delta T$). This is defined as the change in reflectance (temperature) which gives a signal output of the sensor equal to the noise at that signal level. Instead of $NE\Delta\rho$, it is more appropriate to use noise equivalent differential radiance ($NE\Delta L$), which is the only significant measure at instrument level. This can be defined as the radiance change at the input of the sensor, which produces an output signal change equivalent to the noise at that signal level. It depends on a number of parameters such as, the signal-to-noise ratio (S/N), the saturation radiance setting and the number of quantisation bits (Joseph, 2015). SPOT has 8-bit quantisation, while the IRS LISS cameras have 7-bit quantisation. In principle, both can have the same $NE\Delta L$ for a specific radiance, if S/N and saturation setting can be properly chosen. Current systems are being designed with 11 or more bit digitisation. Such systems, unless they have a corresponding S/N, do not imply a better radiometric resolution. Nevertheless, more number of bits increases the dynamic range so that measurement of objects with radiance varying from ocean to snow can be performed without any gain change.

5.5.1 RADIOMETRIC QUALITY

Radiometric quality of the image depends primarily on radiometric resolution, calibration accuracy and the modulation transfer function. Resolution in general is the minimum difference between two discrete values that can be distinguished by a measuring device. However, high resolution does not necessarily imply high accuracy. Accuracy is a measure of how close the measurement is to the true value.

Radiometric accuracy could be of two kinds.

(i) *Absolute accuracy* Using suitable calibration an electro-optical sensor output can be represented as, say, $mw/cm^2/sr/\mu m$. How close the sensor measured data is to a primary standard of radiance is the measure of absolute accuracy.

(ii) *Relative accuracy* This refers to the relative accuracy among bands with respect to a primary standard. For example, for a four band multi-spectral camera, though each band does not represent the radiance value accurately, if their ratio with reference to one band is the same as the true value ratio, then there is no relative error.

In computer classification of the features from a remotely sensed data, normally one looks at the statistical difference in the reflected value measured by the instruments. In this context, the absolute value of the reflectance (or radiance) is not important since one compares the relative reflectance value between pixels. However, when one is interested in using two date data for classification or combining information from two different sensors to find out how the reflectance has changed with time, it is necessary to have the absolute radiance value.

Radiometric errors are also introduced due to the Modulation Transfer Function (MTF) of the camera system. As mentioned earlier, the MTF essentially shows the contrast reduction from object space to the image plane. Because of this, the radiance measured by the instrument does not represent the actual reflectance of the pixel since the signals from the adjacent pixels spill over. Thus, the same object with different surroundings will have different signatures. This could lead to problems in multi-spectral classification, since the measured radiance of a pixel is dependent on the nature of the adjacent pixel. To summarise, the measured reflectance/emittance value is dependent on the surrounding pixels and the MTF of the instrument. An account of the effect of MTF on the radiance accuracy is given by Norwood (1974) (Fig. 5.11).

Another contribution to the radiometric error is due to atmosphere, since the atmosphere corrupts the actual reflectance reaching the sensor. The atmospheric effect is given in Appendix 1, where we have shown that the path radiance reduces the contrast and also adds to the actual

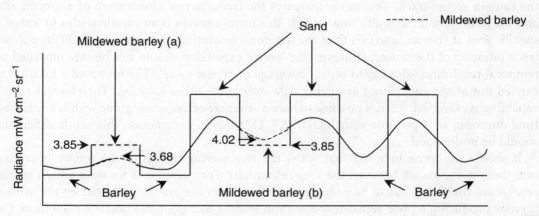

Fig. 5.11 Example showing the MTF effect on radiometric accuracy. The 'square wave' pattern gives the actual radiance from three targets—barley, mildewed barley (MB) and sand. There are two fields of mildewed barley—one amongst barley (a) and the other amongst sand (b). The 'sine curve' gives the radiance when the scene radiation is measured through a radiometer. The MTF of the radiometer modifies the radiance value. Mildewed barley both (a) and (b) have the same radiance (3.85). But due to the radiometer MTF, the MB at (a) shows a lower value (3.6), while MB at (b) shows a higher value (4.02). In the case of (b), the higher radiance from the sand spills over to MB, while the reverse happens in the case of (a). Thus the redistribution of the radiance due to MTF can give erroneous radiance value compared to actual field value. (Adapted from Norwood 1974)

reflectance value. The atmospheric effect of nearby pixels on the radiance of a given pixel (*adjacency effect*) makes the atmospheric contribution evaluation more complex (Kaufman and Fraser, 1984).

Radiometric errors generally lead to poor classification accuracy.

5.6 TEMPORAL RESOLUTION

One of the main advantages of satellite remote sensing is its ability to repeatedly observe a scene at regular intervals. Temporal resolution refers to the temporal frequency with which a given scene can be imaged, usually expressed in days. IRS-1C LISS-III camera has a temporal resolution of 24 days. This is also called *repetivity*. Repetivity depends on orbit characteristics and swath. In general, the larger the swath, the higher the temporal resolution. Thus SeaWiFS with a swath of about 3000 km has a temporal resolution of one day. Of course, highest temporal resolution is possible by geosynchronous observation systems like METEOSAT, INSAT VHRR, and others, with a temporal resolution ranging from a few minutes to 30 minutes, depending on the mode of operation. Higher temporal resolution enables monitoring occurrence of rapid changes, such as forest fires, floods, and so on, and also improves the probability of obtaining cloud-free imagery over areas that experience frequent cloud cover.

Here, the repetivity of 24 days of IRS-1C means that the sub-satellite track repeats (except for slight orbit perturbations) every 24 days. Hence any part of the globe (except around the pole) could be imaged every 24 days. In addition every image taken after 24 days has the same instrument view angle for any location, which is important so that Bidirectional Reflectance Distribution Function (BRDF) differences do not influence the data. With the launch of SPOT, we have, for the first time, the capability of imaging an area by tilting the view direction of the camera across-track. This mode increases the frequency of observation of a specific site and the term 'revisit capability' was added. This novel concept is an excellent idea to image a specific area at shorter intervals than the temporal resolution of 26 days of SPOT by across-track pointing of the sensor. However, the 'revisit capability' should not be misconstrued as temporal resolution (also called repeat coverage or repeat cycle). The revisit of a location is carried out at the cost of not acquiring data over some other location. Therefore, if revisit capability is exercised, it is not possible to have a coverage of the whole globe within a specified time duration, as is possible with LANDSAT TM/ IRS LISS cameras. This subtle difference should be understood.

It should be borne in mind that when the engineering design of the sensor is carried out, there is a trade-off between the four resolutions. For example, if we want a high spatial resolution, the IFOV has to be reduced, which reduces the energy collected by the sensor, thereby producing a poor signal-to-noise ratio leading to a poor radiometric resolution. On the other hand, keeping the spatial resolution the same, you can improve the radiometric resolution by increasing the spectral bandwidth (thereby collecting more energy), however, giving poor spectral resolution. Again, higher spatial resolution and increased swath results in increased data rate. Thus, in order to have an optimal sensor realisation for meeting the observation goals, a judicial choice of sensor parameters is necessary.

In general, the concept of resolutions mentioned in this chapter applies to OIR and microwave sensors, although explained only for OIR systems. Some aspects specific to microwave sensors will be further discussed in Chapter 7.

5.7 PERFORMANCE SPECIFICATION

The best use of any instrument depends on how well the user understands the performance characteristics of the instrument. Many of the earth observation camera parameters are not unambiguously defined and much worse, they are interpreted in many ways. There is a need to specify the optimal parameters of a camera to understand its potential and for inter-comparison with other sensors. For the benefit of all stakeholders, the earth observation camera manufacturers should present data about their sensors in a way that would help inter-comparison between sensors and products. The author – George Joseph (GJ) – has been championing the need to have a set of parameters to be specified for all electro-optical earth observation cameras (Joseph, 2000; Morain and Budge, 2004). GJ's specification matrix is given below (Joseph, 2015).

A. Spatial domain
   1. IFOV/IGFOV
   2. EIFOV
   3. RAIFOV
   4. FOV/Swath
   5. MTF at IFOV
   6. MTF at twice IFOV
B. Spectral domain
   1. Central wavelength
   2. Bandwidth (use moment method)
   3. Out of band contribution
C. Radiance domain
   1. Saturation radiance (SR)
   2. S/N at (a) at 90%SR (b) at 10%SR
   3. Number of digitisation bits

Though NEΔE can be derived from S/N, it is better if it can be explicitly expressed. These measurements are generally carried out in a laboratory. It is also necessary to have a broad agreement among the manufacturers and agencies who own the system regarding the procedures to be adopted to measure each of the above parameters. This will make the comparison between various sensors more meaningful. Some of the above parameters are carried out after launch also as part of the on-board characterisation of the camera (Joseph, 2015).

FOR FURTHER READING

1. *Remote Sensing: Optics and Optical systems,* Slater P N, Addison-Wesley Publishing Company, Chapter 2.
2. *Remote Sensing: Principles and Interpretation,* Sabins F F, 2nd Edition, Freeman and Company, Chapter 1.
3. *http://www.nrcan.gc.Ca/node/9379*
4. *http://www.montana.edu/jshaw/documents/18%20EELE582_S15_OTFMTF.pdf*
5. *https://www.edmundoptics.com/resources/application-notes*

6 Optical–Infrared Sensors

A sensor whose response covers a wavelength region extending from about 0.4 μm to 20 μm is considered an optical–IR (OIR) sensor. Here the radiation reception and analysis are carried out by instruments which are built on optical technology—lenses, mirrors, prisms, gratings. The OIR sensors can be further classified into two main categories—photographic and electro-optical. In the photographic system, the images are formed directly on to a film. In electro-optical sensors, the optical image is first converted into an electrical signal (video data) and further processed to record or transmit the data. The video data can be digitised and used for computer processing or can be converted back to an optical signal to produce an image on a photographic medium such as film or paper. The basic elements of an imaging system in the OIR region can be broadly classified as:

- collecting optic/imaging system,
- colour separation system,
- detectors,
- inflight calibration system, and
- associated electronics.

In addition, when mechanical scanning is involved as in the case of LANDSAT-MSS, the scanning mechanism also has to be considered. Details of some of these subsystems will be discussed in this chapter, as we deal with various sensors.

6.1 QUALITY OF IMAGE IN OPTICAL SYSTEMS

First let us understand the principles and limitations of an imaging system. An ideal imaging system should map every point in the object space to a defined point in the image plane, keeping the relative distances between the points in the image plane same as those in the object space. That is, geometrically, the image is an exact replica of the object except for the reduction in size. In addition, the image should faithfully reproduce the relative intensity distribution in the object space. However, such an ideal system is never realised due to various aberrations of the optical elements forming an imaging system. The basic concepts can be explained with reference to a simple lens.

A simple lens is formed by two curved surfaces. Let us familiarise ourselves with the terminology used in optics. *Optical axis* of a refractive or reflective optical element is an imaginary straight line that is coincident with the axis of symmetry of the surface (this is not true for an off-axis system). In a lens element, the optical axis is the straight line which passes through the centres of curvature of the lens surfaces—also referred to as the *principal axis*. An imaging lens usually has a number of simple lenses. In such cases, the optical axis is the line formed by the coinciding principal axes of the series of optical elements. The rays close and parallel to the optical axis (paraxial rays) converge at a point on the optical axis, called the *focal point* [Fig. 6.1(a)]. A plane at right angles to the optical axis passing through the focal point is called a *focal plane*.

Focal length is the fundamental parameter of an imaging system, which defines the scale of the image, that is, the size of an object in the image plane with respect to the object size (of course, it also depends on the distance between the object and the imaging system). For a thin lens, the focal length is the distance between the centre of the lens and the focal point on the optical axis. However, a practical lens consists of a number of individual lens elements. Then, how do we define the focal length? For a multi-element lens, two hypothetical planes (*principal planes*) can be considered at which all refraction can be considered to occur [Fig. 6.1(b)]. The separations between the planes are fixed for a given lens system. The point of intersection of the principal plane with the optical axis is called the *principal point*. Now the focal length of the system is the distance between the principal point and the focal point. However, locating the principal plane accurately in a multi-element lens system is not easy. The focal length can be measured accurately from the displacement of the image in the focal plane, when a paraxial ray is tilted by a small angle. If x is the shift in the image point in the focal plane for a tilt in the ray incident on to the lens through an angle θ degree, the focal length f is given by

$$f = \frac{x}{\tan \theta}$$

All optical systems have an *aperture stop*, somewhere in the system, which limits the amount of light reaching the imaging area. Thus the aperture stop controls how much light from the object reaches the film or the detector. In a multi-element lens it is usually between some of the lens elements [Fig. 6.2(a)].

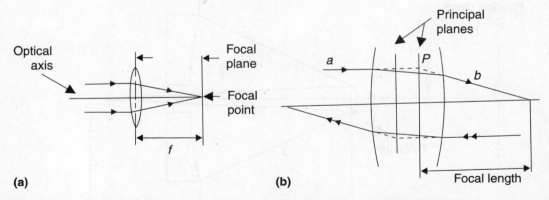

(a) **(b)**

Fig. 6.1 Concept of focal length f. (a) For a thin lens, the rays parallel and close to the optical axis converge to a point on the optical axis called the focal point. The distance between the centre of the thin lens and the focal point is the focal length. (b) For a multi-element lens if we trace the refracted ray b backward, it meets the projected incident ray at P. A plane can be constructed through P at which refraction of all the rays appear to take place. This is called the principal plane. The distance between the principal plane and the focal plane is the focal length.

The image of the aperture stop as seen from a point on the optical axis from the object space is called the *entrance pupil*. Similarly the image of the aperture stop as seen from the image plane is called the *exit pupil*. In a simple lens, or a simple telescope, like the Newtonian, the clear entrance aperture which allows the light rays itself forms the entrance pupil [Fig. 6.2(b)].

Another important parameter for an imaging system is the *f-number*. The *f*-number (*f*/no) is the ratio of the effective focal length to the entrance pupil diameter. It is usually written as *f*/5, which means that the entrance pupil diameter is 1/5ᵗʰ of the focal length. The irradiance at the image plane is inversely proportional to the square of the *f*/no. The systems, which have large *f*/no, are called *slow systems* (since the light gathering capability is low) and one with a smaller *f*/no is called a *faster system*.

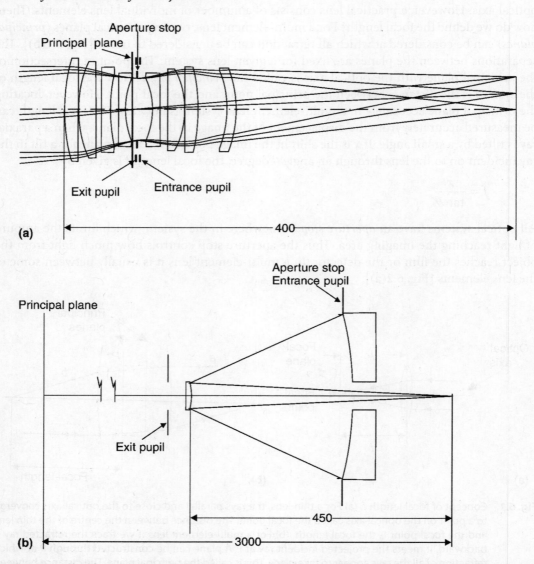

Fig. 6.2 Location of aperture stop in a practical optical system. (a) Double Gauss derivative (typical IRS LISS lens). (b) Cassegrain telescope (Typical VHRR telescope). Dimensions shown in mm.

What is of concern to sensor designers are the aberrations produced by the imaging system which affect the quality of the image. We have seen in Chapter 5, even for an ideal optical system, a point is never imaged as a point due to diffraction effect. Apart from this, a practical optical system has other aberrations. This can be broadly classified into two categories.

(i) Those that are wavelength dependent (chromatic aberrations).
(ii) Those that are wavelength independent (monochromatic aberrations).

Chromatic aberrations We have seen in Chapter 2 that, the angle through which a light ray bends when it passes from one medium to another depends on the refractive index. Refractive index of glass varies with wavelength. Therefore, every property of a lens that depends on refractive index also varies with wavelength, that is, focal length and hence image distance and magnification. When white light falls on a lens, the blue light is focussed close to the lens and the red light farthest away [Fig. 6.3(a)]. This change in the focus with wavelength is called *chromatic aberration*. Thus at the focal plane where the film or detector is kept, a sharp focus is possible only for one colour (wavelength); for other wavelengths it will be out of focus. However, there can be one plane, where the image size for a white light is minimum. Combining two or more lens elements having different refractive indices, one can eliminate chromatic aberration for a specific wavelength region. A lens corrected for chromatic aberration in all three primary colours (blue, green, red) is called *apochromat*. However, when a wide range of wavelength is to be covered, it is not possible to correct for the total wavelength region.

The reflection from a mirror surface is the same for all wavelengths and hence reflective optics do not suffer from chromatic aberrations. Therefore sensors, which cover wide wavelength regions, say, extending from visible to thermal IR, have to use reflective optics for imaging.

Even if we are imaging with a single wavelength, the image is not distortion free. Aberration occurs for both refractive (lens) and reflective (mirrors) systems. These aberrations are called *monochromatic aberrations*.

These aberrations also produce an extended image for a point object. Thus a beam of rays parallel to the optical axis does not focus to a single point and there is a spread in the energy. Generally it is possible to find a point on the optical axis where the image size is minimum. This is called the *circle of least confusion*.

Spherical aberration A spherical lens or mirror does not bring all the rays parallel to the optical axis at a single point. The rays, which are farther away from the optical axis, are brought closer to the lens than those close to the optical axis. This makes a point object appear as a blurred circle [Fig. 6.3(b)].

Astigmatism The rays from a point object lying in different planes form line images at different planes and at different distances. A point appears as an ellipse. The distance between the line image (and hence the circle of least confusion) is proportional to the square of the off-axis angle. In other words, the rays from two orthogonal planes have different foci and forms line images, which are orthogonal [Fig. 6.3(c)]. The plane containing the optical axis and object point is generally referred to as the *tangent plane* and the plane perpendicular to the tangent plane containing the principal ray is called the *sagital plane*.

Coma   This is an off-axis aberration which is only applicable to rays that are at an angle to the optical axis. Here each zone of the lens (or mirror) forms a circular image, where the size decreases with the size of the zone. That is, the ray of the outer zone produces the smallest spot. The overlapping image from all zones produces a comatic shape [Fig. 6.3(d)].

Distortion   The focal length of the lens for various points on the image plane (and hence the magnification) varies. Because of this, the image of a square object has sides that curve in (pin cushion) or curve out (barrel). Here every point may be in focus, but points on the image will not be in the proper places [Fig. 6.3(e)].

Curvature of the field   A planar object is imaged on a curved surface. That is, if the detector is a plane, as in the case of a film, a plane object cannot be in perfect focus at the centre and edge simultaneously. The optical system design aims at minimising various aberrations. This

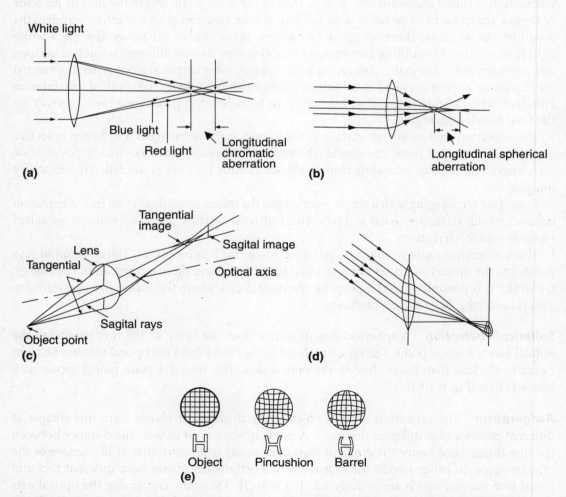

Fig. 6.3   Schematics showing aberrations in a lens. (a) Chromatic (b) Spherical (c) Astigmatism (d) Coma (e) Distortion.

is accomplished by using different lens materials, curvature or even using different surface shapes (aspherics). This is a major challenge for an optical designer. With modern computer aided optical design tools, it is possible to achieve a design such that most of the errors are eliminated and the performance is close to the theoretical limit due to diffraction, that is, diffraction limited design.

Ultimately what is of concern to the sensor designer is the 'quality' of the image. There are a number of parameters to evaluate the quality of image produced by the imaging sensor. The parameter widely used is the Modulation Transfer Function (MTF), which we discussed in Chapter 5. Another important parameter, which decides the usability of the data from electro-optical sensors is the signal-to-noise ratio (S/N). We shall deal with this in more detail later.

Let us first try to understand MTF in a little more detail. As explained in Chapter 5, MTF is a measure of the capability of the imaging system to preserve the contrast of the object after being imaged. We shall briefly describe the mathematical concept of MTF. A scene can be considered to have been formed by a combination of point sources. Even for an aberration-free lens, a point is imaged with finite size, which we referred to as airy disc. Aberrations, which we explained earlier, increase the spot size of the imaged point. The intensity distribution of the image of a point source is called *Point Spread Function* (PSF). The fourier transform of the PSF is known as the *Optical Transfer Function* (OTF). The amplitude of the OTF is MTF, which gives a measure of the decrease in the contrast modulation due to the imaging system as a function of spatial frequency.

What is the concept of spatial frequency in an image? When the reflectance value varies smoothly over a distance (length), the image has a low frequency content whereas when one experiences sudden change(s) in the reflectance value, the feature can be considered as having a high frequency component. Large monocropped areas, such as a wheat field in Haryana/Punjab, is an example of low spatial frequency. Many natural and man-made features in imagery such as geological faults, land–water boundary, roads and urban areas have high frequency components.

How do we quantify spatial frequency in an image? Let us consider the IRS LISS-III camera. The IGFOV on the ground is about 23 m. Since we talk about a line pair (one black plus one white), on the ground, the dimension of a line pair is 46 m. We can say that the LISS-III has a maximum spatial frequency of 22 line pair/km (1000/46). In the image plane, the pixel size is 10 μm with a pitch of 10 μm or we have for the IGFOV 50 line pairs per millimeter, at the image plane.

To measure MTF in the laboratory, a '*sine*' *target* – a dark and bright target whose intensity distribution varies in a sinusoidal manner – is projected at the input of the imaging system (through suitable collimators) and the contrast of the output of the imaging system is measured. Knowing the contrast modulation of input and the measured output contrast, we can calculate MTF. This can be repeated for targets with different spatial frequencies to generate the MTF curve. MTF = 1 indicates that the contrast of a sine wave frequency is perfectly retained in the image, while MTF = 0, that is, total contrast loss, indicates that the target is 'lost' in the imaging process, since our eyes require a minimum contrast (which is dependent on illumination), to distinguish between adjacent objects. In general as spatial frequency increases, the MTF decreases (Fig. 6.4). In the case of an imaging system using discrete detector arrays, such as CCD, the target should be aligned such that the bright bar falls specifically on a pixel and the dark bar falls on the adjacent pixel when the MTF at the IGFOV frequency is measured. If this precaution is not taken, the measured MTF will be lower than the true value.

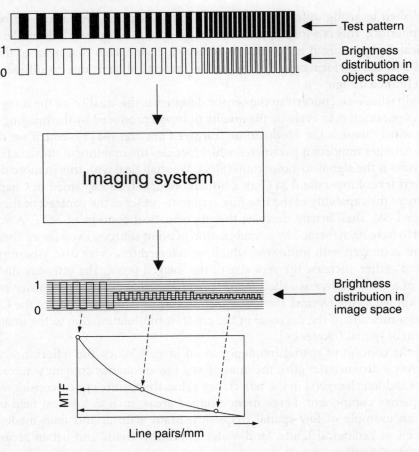

Fig. 6.4 Schematics showing how the MTF varies with spatial frequency. (Modified from http://www. schneideroptics.com/pressreleases/kino.htm)

Mathematically, MTF is applied to a sinusoidal input target. The system MTF is then the product of the MTF of the individual components like optics, detectors, image motion and even the atmosphere.

Thus the overall MTF of an imaging system is given by

$$\text{MTF}_{\text{system}} = \text{MTF}_{\text{optic}} \times \text{MTF}_{\text{detector}} \times \text{MTF}_{\text{image motion}} \times \text{MTF}_{\text{atmosphere}} \times \text{------}$$

For a perfect optics, the frequency at which MTF = 0, called *cut-off frequency* (n_c) is given by

$$v_c = \frac{1}{\lambda(f/\text{no})}$$

So, as (f/no) decreases the cut-off frequency increases. Therefore, theoretically, a faster system (low f/no) gives a better MTF compared to a slower system. However in practice, since the fabrication complexity and aberrations are relatively less for a slower system, the realisable MTF of a system will not strictly follow the f/no advantage as stated above.

One generally uses the square wave target for MTF measurement in the laboratory, since it is relatively easy to make, compared to a sine wave target. When a square wave target is used, it is generally referred to as the Contrast Transfer Function (CTF). The CTF is generally higher than the MTF, for the same spatial frequency (Fig. 6.5).

The square wave MTF, that is, CTF at a frequency v is related to the sine wave MTF as follows,

$$MTF(v) = \frac{\pi}{4}\left\{CTF(v) + \frac{CTF(3v)}{3} - \frac{CTF(5v)}{5} + \ldots\ldots\ldots\right\}$$ (6.1)

The second and higher term values are generally very low since the CTF falls as frequency is increased.

6.2   IMAGING MODE

In general, imaging can be carried out in three different ways.

(i) **Frame by frame**   Here a snapshot is taken at one instant covering a certain area on the surface depending on the sensor characteristics and platform height. A typical example is the conventional photographic camera. The imaging carried out by area array CCD or other types of area detectors also produce images in this mode of operation (at times it is referred to as *stairing mode*). Successive frames image a strip of terrain depending on the camera orientation. Generally, the successive frames are taken with a certain overlap [Fig. 6.6(a)].

(ii) **Pixel by pixel**   Here the sensor collects the radiation from one pixel at a time. Generally, a scan mirror directs the sensor to the next pixel in the cross-track direction and by the scan mirror motion, one cross-track line of width equal to one pixel is imaged. Successive scan

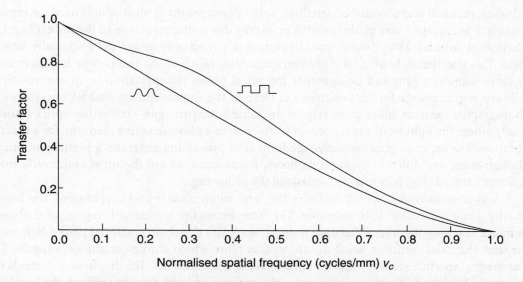

Fig. 6.5   MTF curves for an on-axis aberration-free lens for a sinusoidal and square wave input modulation. The abscissa is normalised frequency such that $v_c = 1/\lambda(f/no) = 1$.

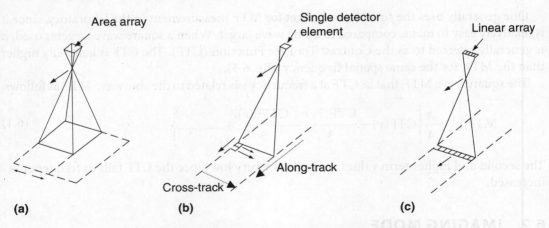

Fig. 6.6 Various modes in which an image can be generated.

lines are produced by the motion of the platform. This is the way opto-mechanical scanners image. This mode of imaging is sometimes referred to as *whiskbroom scanning* [Fig. 6.6(b)].

(iii) **Line by line** Here the sensor collects radiation from one 'line' in the cross-track direction at one instant. Successive lines are generated by the platform motion. Linear CCD/Photode arrays generate imaging using this mode. This is also called *pushbroom scanning* [Fig. 6.6(c)].

6.3 PHOTOGRAPHIC CAMERA

The term *photography* is derived from two Greek words *phos* (light) and *graphics* (writing). Photographic cameras are the oldest remote sensors, and are used even now in spite of various advancements in techniques of imaging. Though they have been used successfully from aircraft, balloons, manned and unmanned satellites, aerial photography is most widely used for remote sensing. Photography was made possible primarily due to the invention of the photochemical reaction at around 1840, which could produce a permanent image on a specially coated plate. This was the early form of a photographic film. Much of the technology improvements in aerial cameras, film and equipments for aerial photo interpretation is an outgrowth of military requirements for reconnaissance. Despite the improvements and advancements in photographic cameras, all of them rely on the same basic principle—collecting optics (mostly lens) gathers the light from the scene and focuses on to a photosensitive medium, for a specific duration. The exposed photosensitive medium after processing generates a permanent image. Though there are different types of cameras, frame cameras are the most commonly used. A frame camera (Fig. 6.7) mainly consists of the following.

A lens cone assembly, which includes the lens, filter, shutter and diaphragm. The lens is usually a multi-element lens assembly. The filter limits the wavelength region of the scene radiance reaching the film. Filters are transparent (glass or gelatin) material placed in front of the lens, the most common being the absorption films, which absorb certain wavelengths. The diaphragm (aperture stop) is located in between the lens elements. The diaphragm controls the aperture of the lens (*f*/no), which decides the amount of light passing through the lens. The diaphragm diameter can be adjusted to suit lighting conditions and film sensitivity. The shutter

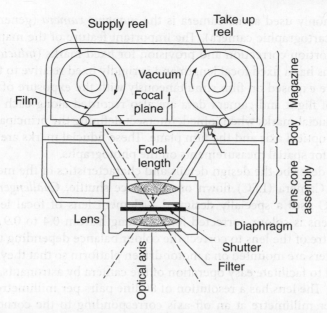

Fig. 6.7 Schematics showing a mapping camera. Reprinted from 'Remote Sensing and Image Interpretation', 1st Ed., by Lillesand and Kieffer, 1979, with the permission of John Wiley & Sons, Inc.

controls the duration of the exposure. The shutter is incorporated at the focal plane or within the lens assembly.

The camera magazine, which holds the film supply and take up reels, and can be invariably detached from the camera. During exposure, the film is held stationary and flat at the focal plane; for cameras designed for precision measurement, a vacuum system usually ensures this.

A camera body to which the lens cone and the film magazine are attached and also contains the film drive mechanism.

The important factors which determine the quality of the image are:

- lens resolution,
- film resolution,
- film flatness and its location in the focal plane, and
- accuracy of image motion compensation—a technique to reduce image degradation due to relative motion of the camera with respect to terrain during exposure.

With modern computer aided design and fabrication, the lens can approach diffraction-limited performance. Different methodologies of *image motion compensation* have also been developed to reduce the image blur due to motion of the camera during the exposure time. In the simplest form, this is achieved by moving the film in the opposite direction to the vehicle movement, to exactly compensate the forward motion of the vehicle, generally referred to as *Forward Motion Compensation* (FMC) *systems*. The FMC allows longer shutter speed and hence allows the use of slower films with higher resolution. However, in the case of aerial flights, the FMC does not correct for the angular motion in bad weather. To take care of this, an *Angular Motion Compensation* (AMC) device, which is essentially a gyro-stabilised platform for maintaining the camera orientation, is used along with FMC devices.

The most commonly used aerial camera is the *mapping camera* (generally referred to as metric camera or cartographic camera). The important feature of the mapping camera is its high degree of distortion correction and provision for fixed marks (*fiducials*) to be recorded on the film. The lens has a fixed focal length and is rigidly fixed relative to the film plane. The fiducial markers are exposed on film simultaneously with the exposure of the ground scene. Extensive details of flight and camera data are also recorded along each frame. Diagonally opposite pair of fiducial marks when joined, intersect defining the principal point, that is, the intersection of the optical axis and the film plane. These fiducial marks are used to define the frame of reference for spatial measurements on the photographs.

We shall briefly describe the design details and characteristics of the metric camera called the Large Format Camera (LFC) flown on the space shuttle, *Challenger* in October 1984 (Doyle, 1979). LFC uses a specially designed 8-element lens of focal length 305 mm and aperture $f/6$. The lens is colour-corrected for wavelength from 0.4 to 0.9 μm. Filters can be inserted in the centre of the lens to correct the colour balance depending upon the film used (Fig. 6.8). These filters are mounted on a motor driven platform so that they can be changed by external command to facilitate easy operation of the camera by astronauts. The image format is 230×460 mm^2. The lens has a resolution of 80 line pairs per millimetre with a minimum of 50 line pairs per millimetre at an off-axis corresponding to the corner of the film. The spatial resolution of the image depends on the flight altitude and the film used. The camera has a 'between lens' shutter, which can provide exposure time varying from 0.003 to 0.024 s by remote control. An image motion compensation system ensures that the relative motion between the film and the scene is compensated to provide high quality imagery. Along with the image, the film will contain fixed marks (which is transferred to the film through fiducial marks located on the plate at the focal plane) and other auxiliary information such as time of exposure, duration, flight number and so on. The camera magazine has a capacity for 1.2 km length of film sufficient for 2400 frames. The total camera weighs about 320 kg.

From a nominal altitude of 300 km, each picture frame covers 225×450 km^2 and provides a ground resolution of approximately 14 m when high resolution black and white film is used. The camera can be operated with varying overlaps to produce stereoscopic pairs to generate height information. The terrain height can be derived with accuracy better than 10 m.

While the metric camera is primarily used for cartographic mapping, multi-band camera plays the most important role for resources survey. Multi-band cameras enable simultaneous

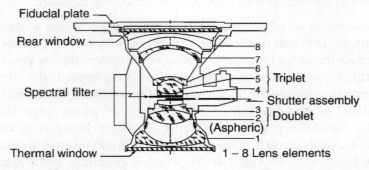

Fig. 6.8   Simplified schematic of LFC lens configuration. (Adapted from Mollberg, 1981)

photography of a ground scene in more than one spectral band. Multi-band cameras can be realised by using one of the following techniques:

- multi-camera installations,
- multi-lens cameras, and
- beam-splitter cameras.

In a multi-camera installation, three or more cameras with selected lenses are mounted on a single mounting frame. The cameras are bore-sighted to cover the same field of view. The shutters for all the cameras operate simultaneously. Appropriate filters are used for each lens and each camera magazine is loaded with the suitable film for that spectral band. Each camera's shutter speed and aperture stop can be set at the proper exposure for the film-filter combination. The first multi-band photograph of the earth from space in the NASA programme was taken by such a multi-camera system (S065) flown on Apollo 9 in March, 1969 (Slater, 1972). It consisted of four Hasselblad (brand name) cameras mounted on a suitable frame. The individual cameras were off-the-shelf items and were not specifically made to give matched multi-spectral data. Nevertheless, the imagery did show the utility of multi-spectral imaging from space.

The multi-lens camera consists of multiple lenses, with appropriate filters, mounted on a single camera frame. The lenses are carefully adjusted to have the same focal length, so that all the photographs of a multi-band set have the same scale. The lenses are bore-sighted to view the same area in all the bands. Initially, the design was such that the camera magazines could be loaded with only one type of film at a time; thus, images of all spectral bands were recorded on the same film. Though differences in the spectral sensitivity of the films are corrected by adjusting each lens aperture stop for the proper exposure, a single film cannot be optimal over a wide spectral region, and hence cameras cannot provide best performance in all bands. This was later overcome by accommodating individual magazines for each lens. The MKF-6M camera developed for USSR by Carl Zeiss Jena is a typical example of a six band multi-band camera.

One of the major problems in multi-band cameras is the registration between the images. Misregistration can be caused due to various factors such as focal length differences between the lenses, non-identical distortion among the lenses, bore-sighting errors (the optical axis of all lenses are not parallel), non-synchronisation of the mid-points of the shutter exposure, and so on. In the beam-splitter camera arrangement, a single lens is used for image formation. A beam-splitter assembly placed between the lens and the focal plane separates different colours. Separate film magazines are required and each spectral image is recorded on a separate emulsion. The emulsions can be selected for the spectral sensitivity for each colour band.

6.3.1 PHOTOGRAPHIC FILMS

Since photographic films (hereafter referred to as films) form one of the most crucial components in making photography practical, we shall give a broad outline of the basics of films and its characteristics. Films, in general, consist of a photosensitive photographic emulsion coated on to a base for support. The emulsion consists of silver halide crystals (generally referred to as grains), of different sizes, embedded in a gelatin matrix. When light falls on the emulsion, it undergoes a photochemical reaction forming a latent image. During the processing of the film, the chemicals used reduce the exposed silver salts to silver grains that appear black. The area on the film where light has not fallen, the silver halide is dissolved during the development process thus appearing transparent. Thus, we have a negative image—those areas not exposed to light (black in the object) appear bright. Positive images are produced on paper or on transparent positive (diapositive).

Photographic materials which are sensitive to a wide portion of the electromagnetic spectrum, ranging from 0.25 μm (ultraviolet) to 0.9 μm (infrared) are currently available. The films used for aerial/space photography can be broadly classified under three categories. They are:

- black and white,
- true colour, and
- colour IR.

Black and white (B&W) film sensitive to visible light is referred to as *panchromatic film*. Normally a minus-blue filter (which removes blue light) is used to eliminate the short wavelength blue light, which is responsible for haze. Another type of B&W film is, black and white infrared (B&W IR) film, which is sensitive to the spectral region covering both visible and near-IR region, usually covering from about 0.4 μm to about 0.9 μm. Here also a minus-blue filter is used to suppress blue light. Both these films record light intensity as shades of grey.

However, the brightness as seen on the photograph for the same objects differ in the B&W and B&W IR photographs, since the spectral region covered by the respective films is different. For example, since vegetation has a higher reflectance in the near-IR region, vegetation is shown in brighter tones in B&W IR photographs (prints) compared to B&W photographs. Similarly the boundary between water and land are much sharper in B&W IR photographs compared to conventional B&W photographs.

To understand the design of colour film, it is first essential to understand the psychophysical mechanism by which we perceive colour. We have three separate light receptors (sensors) in the retina, which respond to blue, green and red lights. The colour of an object we perceive depends on which combination of sensors are excited and the relative amount of excitement. Blue, green and red are termed *additive primaries*. Various combinations of the additive primaries can be used to produce other colours. However in order to mix colour by superposition of films, the three subtractive primary colours – yellow, cyan and magenta – are used. These are referred to as *subtractive primaries*, since each represents the remaining colour after one primary colour has been subtracted from white light. For example, when red is removed from white light, the colour cyan is produced (Plate 6.1). In the most basic form, a colour film (negative) consists of three layers of dye (Fig. 6.9). The top layer is sensitive to blue light, the second layer to green and the third to red.

Since the second and third layers are also sensitive to blue, a blue-absorbing filter is introduced between the first and second emulsion layer (the blue blocking filter is dissolved in the developing process). After developing the exposed film, the red sensitive bottom layer produces a complementary cyan image of the red portion of the scene. Blue and green sensitive layers produce magenta and yellow images respectively. White light falling on the film exposes all the three layers, thus transmitting no light, while a black object produces a transparent image, since none of the layers are exposed. After the exposed colour film has been developed we have the negative colour film. The negative can be projected on to special photographic paper, wherein the normal colour is reproduced, that is, the 'greens' on the ground appear as green in the photograph (print).

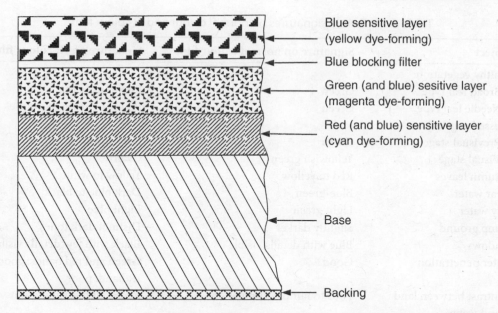

Blue sensitive layer
(yellow dye-forming)

Blue blocking filter

Green (and blue) sesitive layer
(magenta dye-forming)

Red (and blue) sensitive layer
(cyan dye-forming)

Base

Backing

Fig. 6.9   Generalised cross-section of a colour film. (Reprinted from 'Remote Sensing and Image Interpretation', 1st Ed., by Lilesand and Kieffer, 1979, with permission of John Wiley & Sons, Inc.)

In remote sensing, colour infrared (colour IR–CIR) film is more commonly used. In contrast to normal colour film, the colour IR film is designed to record green, red and near-IR portions of electromagnetic radiation. The emulsions are so sensitised that after developing, the colour IR print gives a blue image for an object which primarily reflects in the green wavelength, objects primarily reflecting in red will appear green, while a red image is produced by objects which reflect primarily in the near-IR region. With these films, a yellow filter is used over the lens, to cut off blue light, since all the three layers are sensitive to blue. Thus, the resultant image is not a true reproduction of colour as we see it and hence it is also known as a *false colour film*. Colour IR films were originally developed for military applications to detect, by aerial photography, the presence of objects painted with green paint which represented the colour of foliage. Since the IR reflectance characteristics of the paint is different from green vegetation, the CIR film can separate these. In remote sensing, CIR film is preferred over normal colour film. One of the most important uses of colour IR photography is in vegetation studies. This is because, since healthy green vegetation reflects maximum in the near-IR region, it appears bright red in CIR photography. Frequently, spectral differences between vegetative species or variations due to stress conditions are so small that they are difficult to see on regular colour film. However, spectral differences that may be very small in the visible wavelengths are often pronounced in the near-infrared wavelengths, and such differences will show clearly on colour infrared film; for example, soil moisture variations, in bare fields are often accentuated in CIR imagery. Table 6.1 gives the terrain signatures on normal colour and IR colour film.

What we have discussed till now was films, which produce a 'negative transparency' and which are used to generate the image on to a photographic paper. There are films, which can directly produce a positive image on the film itself. These are called positive transparencies

Table 6.1 Terrain signatures on normal colour and IR colour film

Subject	Signature on normal colour film	Signature on IR colour film
Healthy vegetation:		
Broad leaf type	Green	Red to magenta
Needle leaf type	Green	Reddish brown to purple
Stressed vegetation:		
Previsual stage	Green	Darker red
Visual stage	Yellowish green	Cyan
Autumn leaves	Red to yellow	Yellow to white
Clear water	Blue-green	Dark blue to black
Silty water	Light green	Light blue
Damp ground	Slightly darker	Distinct dark tones
Shadows	Blue with details visible	Black with few details visible
Water penetration	Good	Green and red bands: good
		IR band: poor
Contrast between land and water	Poor to fair discrimination	Excellent discrimination
Red bed outcrops	Red	Yellow

Source: Remote Sensing Principles and Interpretation by Floyd F Sabins © 1978, 1987, 1997 by Freeman W H and Company/Sabins F F. Used with permission

or diapositives. A diapositive can be used directly for interpretation on a light table, or after suitable projection.

6.3.2 CHARACTERISING FILM

We have seen how films are categorised based on their spectral sensitivity. We shall now discuss how the exposure is quantified. Exposure is the product of the intensity of light reaching the film (depends on *f*/no) and the length for which the light falls on the film (decided by the shutter speed). The amount of exposure is designated in terms of density. The density, *D*, is the logarithm of the opacity (*O*), where opacity is the reciprocal of transmittance (*T*).

$$D = \log_{10} O = -\log_{10} T$$

Thus in diapositives (transparency), overexposure results in lower density (more transparent) and underexposure causes more density. In negatives, the opposite is true. The *density curve* (also called *characteristic curve*) is graphic description of the optical density *D* of a developed photographic material as a function of exposure (Fig. 6.10).

At the beginning of the density curve (A), we have minimum density (D_{min}), where no image is produced. That is, the exposure is too low to produce a photochemical reaction. The region A to B is the threshold region where image generation starts. From A to B, the density increases, though slowly with exposure. This portion of the curve is called the *toe* (Lillfield and Kiefer, 1979). This is followed by a linear region (B to C). At the end of the straight line portion, the density is again non-linear on the characteristic curve (*shoulder*) and is followed by the

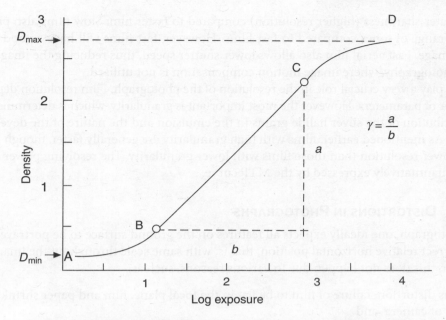

Fig. 6.10   Schematics of a typical characteristic curve of a photographic film.

overexposed region (D). The slope of the straight line portion of the characteristic curve is referred to as the *gamma* of the processed film. In general, the higher the gamma, the higher the contrast of a film. Gamma is a function of not only the emulsion type, but also the film development condition. Even in areas of no exposure, a minimum density D_{min} is seen due to some inherent density of the type of film used, D_{base}. Some density even develops when an unexposed emulsion is developed called *fog* (D_{fog})

$$D_{min} = D_{base} + D_{fog}$$

Features recorded at the extreme 'toe' and 'shoulder' will be underexposed or overexposed. Best results are obtained only when the scenes are recorded over the linear portion of the characteristic curve. However, each type of film has a characteristic exposure range referred to as the *latitude of exposure*, within which, if the film is exposed, it can reproduce the actual colour and tonal values of the scene photographed.

Another important parameter of the film is its speed. The film speed is defined as the emulsion's degree of sensitivity to light, and determines the amount of exposure required to photograph an object under a given lighting condition. Qualitatively, the speed is distinguished as 'fast' and 'slow'. Fast films are more sensitive to light compared to slow films. That is, fast film in general requires less change in exposure to produce a change in density at the 'linear' region of the characteristic curve. Quantitatively, they are designated by certain standards set by various organisations (ISO, DIN, and so on). The industry standard previously used in USA was ASA, such as ASA 100, ASA 200... The greater the ASA number, the faster is the speed. The film responsivity for panchromatic aerial films, by the American National Standard, is the Aerial Film Speed (AFS). Photographs taken with slower speed film appear less 'grainy' when enlarged. Because of the small size of the silver halide grains, slower films reproduce fine details with greater sharpness (higher resolution) compared to faster film. Slow films also produce a broader range of tones compared to fast films. However, fast films will have a good contrast on the image. Fast aerial film also allows lower shutter speed, thus reducing the image blur in aerial photography, where image motion compensation is not utilised.

Films play a very crucial role in the resolution of the photograph. Film resolution depends on a number of parameters. However the most important is granularity, which is determined by the size distribution of the silver halide grains in the emulsion and the nature of the development process. As mentioned earlier, films with high granularity are generally faster, though they will have a lower resolution than those films with lower granularity. The resolving power of a film can be quantitatively expressed by the MTF curve.

6.3.3 Distortions in Photographs

In a photograph, one ideally expects all features on the ground surface to be portrayed at their correct relative horizontal position, that is, with same scale throughout the image. However, this does not happen due to various reasons, such as:

(i) lens distortion, failure of film to be flat in the focal plane, film and paper shrinkage,

(ii) tilt of camera, and

(iii) the topography of the terrain.

Even if we consider an ideal (hypothetical) system, wherein (i) and (ii) of the above can be eliminated, the projection geometry of the photograph displaces any feature lying above or below the reference horizontal plane from its true planimetric position. Let us understand a little more about the projection geometry of a lens.

A photographic image is a 'central perspective'. This implies that all the light rays falling on the film passes through a single point called the *perspective centre* (the light rays actually pass through the lens, which is mathematically considered as a single point, that is, the perspective centre). Such a viewing geometry has two effects.

(i) Tall objects near the nadir can 'hide' objects away from the nadir and close to the tall objects. That is, tall objects block the view of the nearby objects away from the nadir.

(ii) It causes features lying above or below the horizontal datum to be displaced from their true planimetric positions.

This is called *relief displacement*. The relief displacement is outward for features whose elevations are above the datum and inward for points whose elevations are below the datum. This will give a different size, shape and location of the objects compared to a map, which is a vertical projection—top view (Fig. 6.11).

From simple geometrical consideration (Fig. 6.12), we can draw the following inference on relief displacement d

$$d \propto h$$

$$\propto r$$

$$\propto 1/H$$

Top view

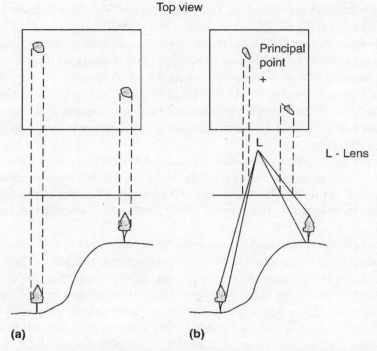

Fig. 6.11   The geometrical differences in a map. (a) orthographic projection and a vertical aerial photograph, (b) central projection. In the map (a), we have a top view of the object in its true relative horizontal position. (Reprinted from *Remote Sensing and Image Interpretation*, 1st Ed., Lillesand and Kieffer, 1979, with permission of John Wiley & Sons, Inc)

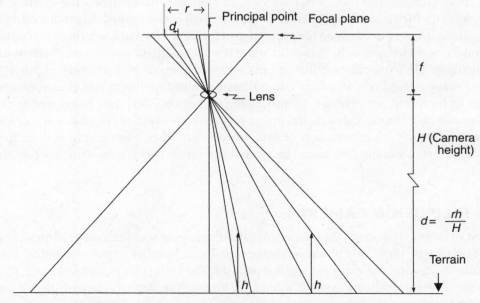

Fig. 6.12   Schematics showing relief displacement on a vertical photograph. For the same height *h*, the object closer to the optical axis has lesser relief displacement.

where, h is the elevation from the datum, r is the distance between the displaced image and the principal point, and H is the height of the camera above the datum.

Since the relief displacement (d) is inversely proportional to the height of the camera (H) for the same feature, a photograph taken from a satellite gives lesser relief displacement compared to an aerial photograph. The principal point (where the optical axis meets the film) has no relief displacement in a vertical photograph (a vertical photograph is one in which the optical axis is parallel to the local vertical). Though relief displacement is a nuisance in a map display, we can use this phenomenon to find out the height of objects, or difference in elevation between objects from a single photograph.

The scale of the aerial photograph also depends on the topography. Higher elevations are closer to the camera and hence show up on the image at a larger scale compared to areas of lower elevation that are farther from the lens. Air photo scale is thus a function of a number of factors such as focal length of the camera, flying height of the aircraft and ground elevation above sea level.

Aerial photographs cannot be used straight away for measurement of position or area due to the distortions produced due to topography, tilt, relief displacement, and so on. These distortions are corrected to produce an 'orthophoto' through a process called *orthorectification*. Orthorectification transforms the central projection of the photograph into an orthogonal view of the ground. Thus, an orthophotograph has the orthographic projection and the geometric properties of a map. There are a number of optical-mechanical instruments which can carry out this rectification. However, one can also digitise the photographs to generate 'digital imagery'. Digital techniques can then be used for orthorectification. Apart from accurate camera parameters, a digital elevation model is required to correct for relief displacement.

As a remote sensor, photographic cameras have a number of limitations. They have limited spectral response extending only up to about 0.9 μm. The shortwave IR and thermal IR regions which are of great interest cannot be covered with photographic cameras. The dynamic range of the camera, which essentially depends on the film used is also limited. Reproducibility of the quality of the imagery depends on the processing of the film, which unless stringently controlled, will produce degraded quality pictures and hence it will be difficult to compare different images quantitatively. Dimensional stability of photographic films is of particular importance in accurate mapping and reproduction. Dimensional stability applies to size changes caused by changes in humidity, temperature, by processing and ageing. The data being analog are not directly amenable to automated digital image processing—which is essential when one wants to process and analyse large amounts of data. In addition, when photography is done from an unmanned spacecraft, the film has to be ejected out for recovery, which further complicates the system.

6.4 TELEVISION CAMERAS

The first electronic system to take imagery of earth from space was a television camera. Starting from TIROS-1 in 1960, vidicon cameras were used in a number of meteorological satellites for routinely viewing the earth for weather studies. The early TIROS cameras used 12.7 mm (1/2 inch) slow scan vidicon, at 400 TV lines per frame. The improvement of the TV camera primarily depends on the improvement of the basic imaging tube. Typical imaging tubes used in spaceborne high resolution cameras include return beam vidicon, image dissector tube,

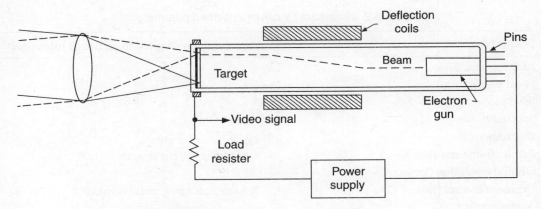

Fig. 6.13 Schematic diagram of a vidicon camera.

secondary electron conduction tube, and so on. Details of the operation of these tubes are well documented (NASA, 1973). As an illustration of how a TV camera operates, we shall describe the functioning of the basic vidicon tube.

In the vidicon camera, an optical system is made to focus the ground scene on to a photoconductive surface (Fig. 6.13). The incident photons vary the conductivity of the surface locally according to the intensity of the incident light. An electron beam is made to scan the photoconductive surface from the rear side. The resulting target current will be proportional to the conductivity of the photoconductive surface (and hence the intensity of light) and the signal is further amplified and recorded or transmitted. In the case of Return Beam Vidicon (RBV), the signal is derived from the depleted electron beam which is reflected from the photoconducting surface. This is further amplified by a multi-stage electron multiplier.

The best example of a high resolution TV camera operated in space, for resources survey, is the Return Beam Vidicon used in the LANDSAT series (Eastman, 1970). The LANDSAT television camera system consists of three RBV tubes with its associated lens filter assembly so that images can be taken in three spectral bands. The three RBV cameras are aligned in the spacecraft to view the same nominal 185 kilometres square ground scene. The cameras are exposed by operating mechanical shutters and the images are stored on the photosensitive surfaces of the camera tubes which are then scanned by electron beams to produce video signal outputs. Each camera is read out sequentially, requiring about 3.5 seconds for each of the three spectral images.

The Indian experimental remote sensing satellites, BHASKARA-I and II, carried a two-band television camera system (Joseph, 1982). Of the two bands, one operated in the 0.54–0.66 μm region and the other in the 0.75–0.85 μm wavelength region. Each picture frame covers about 400×400 km^2 with a spatial resolution of about 1 km. Table 6.2 gives the camera specifications.

The TV camera system, like the photographic camera, has a limited spectral response which depends on the material used for the photosensitive surface. Using a silicon diode array target, a response from about 0.4 μm to about 1 μm can be achieved. Though targets with pyro-electric materials have been developed to operate in the thermal IR band (8 to 14 μm) (Garn and Petito, 1977), they do not have the capability to produce high resolution imagery especially from spacecrafts. Other limitations of TV tubes include poor dynamic range and radiometric

Table 6.2   Bhaskara TV camera payload parameters

Sensor type	Slow scan vidicon coupled to an image intensifier
Imaging lens: f/no.	1.9
Focal length (mm)	18.46
Field of view (degree)	49.37
Spectral bands	0.54–0.66
(micrometres)	0.75–0.85
Picture frame size (km²)	341 × 341 for a 525 km altitude
Ground resolution (km)	~1
Exposure control (ms)	1, 1.5, 2 selectable by ground command
Average power (W)	22.5
Weight (kg)	44

accuracy and geometric distortions. Apart from all these, generating multi-spectral imagery is very cumbersome. In LANDSAT and BHASKARA, this is achieved by using separate camera tubes for each band and selecting the spectral band using appropriate filters. The principal disadvantage of such a system is the difficulty in registering all bands.

6.5   OPTO-MECHANICAL SCANNERS

Most of the limitations associated with photographic and TV imaging systems are overcome in opto-mechanical scanners. The principle of operation of an opto-mechanical scanner is shown schematically in Fig. 6.14. The radiation emitted or reflected from the scene is intercepted by a scan mirror, which diverts the radiation to a collecting telescope. In the normal case, the scan mirror is inclined at 45° to the optical axis of the telescope. The telescope focusses the radiation on to a detector. In this case, the detector receives radiation from an area on the ground which is determined by the detector size and focal length of the optics. This is called a *picture element* or a *pixel*. By rotating the scan mirror, the detector starts looking at adjacent picture elements on the ground. Thus, information is collected pixel by pixel by the detector.

Such an instrument when mounted on a moving platform, like an aircraft or spacecraft, with the optical axis aligned to the velocity vector of the platform, the rotation of the scan mirror collects radiation from a strip on the ground whose width equals a pixel and is at right angles to the nadir track. If the rate of rotation of the scan mirror is adjusted such that by the time the platform moves through one picture element, the scan mirror is set to the start of the next scan line, then successive and contiguous scan lines can be produced. Thus, in the cross-track direction, information is collected from each pixel (because of the scan mirror motion) to produce one line of image and in the along-track direction, successive lines of image in a contiguous fashion are produced by the platform motion. The scan frequency has to be correctly adjusted, depending on the velocity of platform and pixel dimension, to produce a contiguous image. To produce multi-spectral imagery, the energy collected by the telescope is channelled to a spectral dispersing system spectrometer. Such systems that can generate imagery simultaneously in more than one spectral band are called *Multi-spectral Scanners* (MSS). Figure 6.15 gives the functional block diagram of a multispectral scanner. Thus, the MSS has a scan mirror, collecting optics, dispersive system

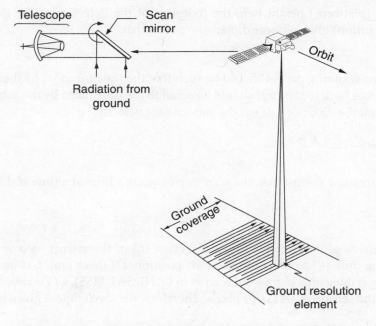

Fig. 6.14 Schematic of operation of an opto-mechanical scanner.

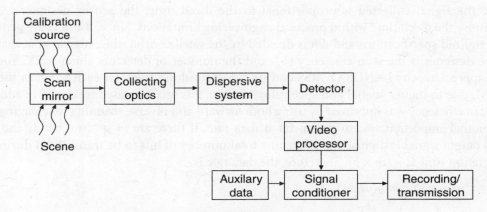

Fig. 6.15 Functional block of an MSS.

(which essentially spreads the incoming radiation into different spectral bands) and a set of detectors appropriate for the wavelength regions to be detected. The output of the detectors go through electronic processing circuits. The data from the scene along with other data such as attitude of the platform and temperatures of the various subsystems are formatted together and the combined information is either recorded on a suitable magnetic medium (as is usually the case with aircraft sensors) or transmitted through telemetry for spacecraft sensors.

We shall now work out the inter-relationship between various parameters of an opto-mechanical scanner. Let us assume a sensor with an IFOV of β radians and FOV of Ω radians.

If the satellite (platform) height is h, the footprint of the detector on the ground (that is, geometric resolution) gives a linear dimension r such that,

$$r = \beta h$$

The scan mirror scanning period should be such that the time taken (t) by the mirror to scan one line and come back to the start should be equal to the time taken by the sub-satellite point to move through the distance r. If v is the sub-satellite velocity,

$$t = \frac{r}{v} = \frac{\beta h}{v} = \frac{\beta}{(v/h)} \tag{6.2}$$

If n detectors are used along-track, the scan mirror scans n lines at a time and hence,

$$t = \frac{n\beta h}{v} \tag{6.3}$$

The time t consists of the time for forward motion (t_f) of the mirror to cover a swath of Ω radians and the time (t_r) to return to the start position. Of these only t_f is useful in imaging (when imaging is done only in forward scan as in LANDSAT MSS), t_f/t is called *scan efficiency* S_e. During t_f, the sensor views (Ω/β) pixels. Therefore, the *dwell time* is given by

$$\tau = \frac{tS_e}{\Omega/\beta} = \frac{n\beta^2 S_e}{(v/h)\Omega} \tag{6.4}$$

Since the signal collected is proportional to the dwell time, the sensor designer tries to maximise the dwell time within practical engineering limitations. Since, β and Ω are generally the required specifications and v/h is decided by the satellite orbit, the only variable available to the designer is the scan efficiency (S_e) and the number of detectors along-track. You will now appreciate why LANDSAT MSS had six detectors along-track for each band. In the case of TM, due to higher spatial and spectral resolution, this was increased to 16 and in addition, the scan efficiency was improved by using both forward and reverse scanning for imaging.

Another important system parameter is data rate. If there are m spectral bands and each band output signal is digitised to b bits, the total number of bits to be transmitted during the integration time is $n(m \times b)$. Therefore, the data rate is,

$$\frac{n(m \times b)}{\tau} = \frac{mb(v/h)\Omega}{\beta^2 S_e} \tag{6.5}$$

The above equation shows that the data rate is inversely proportional to the square of the IFOV. That is, when the resolution is doubled (IFOV halved), the data rate increases four times. Higher data rate is one of the major concerns for realising high resolution imaging systems.

The signal-to-noise ratio (S/N) is an important parameter, which decides the quality of the image. The S/N depends on the energy reaching the detector and the noise characteristics of the detector used (Joseph, 1996; NASA, 1973). We have seen in Chapter 3, the power received at the detector is (Eq. 3.13)

$$\phi = \frac{\pi}{4} O_e \Delta \lambda L_\lambda \beta^2 D^2 \text{ watts}$$

when the signal is integrated for τ s, the energy collected is

$$Q = \frac{\pi}{4} O_e \Delta\lambda L_\lambda \beta^2 D^2 \tau \text{ joules}$$

where, L_λ is the scene radiance, $\Delta\lambda$ is the spectral bandwidth, D is the diameter of the collecting optics and O_e is the optical efficiency.

Substituting for τ from Eq. 6.4,

$$Q = \frac{\pi}{4} L_\lambda O_e \Delta\lambda \beta^2 D^2 \cdot \frac{n\beta^2 S_e}{(v/h)\Omega}$$

$$Q = \left[\frac{\pi L_\lambda}{4(v/h)} \right] \frac{O_e S_e \Delta\lambda n \beta^4 D^2}{\Omega} \text{ joules} \tag{6.6}$$

If we have to improve the resolution by a factor of two (β halved), then $\Delta\lambda$ has to be increased by a factor of 16 (everything else remaining the same), to collect the same energy (poor spectral resolution) or double the optics diameter (increased weight and volume). Yet another possibility is increasing the number of detectors along-track by 16 times, that is, increased power and system complexity. This interplay between the various sensor parameters sets a limit on higher resolutions achievable from a sensor. A trade-off study between the resolution achievable in terms of engineering complexity – weight, volume and data rate – and cost is required to be carried out before a final choice is made.

The details of some of the major sub-systems to realise an opto-mechanical scanner are given below.

6.5.1 SCANNING SYSTEMS

In an opto-mechanical imager, the scanning can be carried out either in the object plane or in the image plane. In the image plane scanner, the scan mirror is kept after the collecting optics near the focal plane [Fig. 6.16(b)] and the mirror directs each point in the focal plane to the detector. Obviously, such a system requires the collecting optics corrected for the total field of view, which is quite difficult, especially if a reflective system has to be used. However, it requires a relatively smaller size scan mirror. Though image plane scanning has been used in some of the early opto-mechanical multi-spectral scanners (as in Skylab Multi-spectral Scanner, S-192, Abel and Reynolds, 1974), due to large field correction required for the total field of view, image plane scanning is not generally used. Moreover, due to availability of linear array CCDs, the scope of image plane scanning using mechanical systems is decreasing.

In object plane scanning, the rays from the scene fall on to the scan mirror, which reflects the radiation to the collecting telescope [Fig. 6.16(a)]. Here for the rays reaching the detector, the direction of rays at the collecting optics remains the same irrespective of the scan mirror position. Thus when object plane scanning is used, the collecting optics need to be corrected only for a small field around the optical axis. The extent of field correction depends on IFOV, and the distribution of detectors in the focal plane for reducing the scanning frequency or for additional spectral bands.

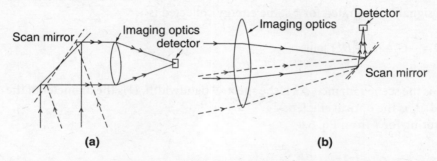

Fig. 6.16   Schematic of object plane and image plane scanning. (a) Object plane scanning. (b) Image plane scanning.

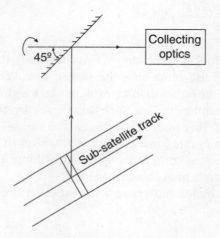

Fig. 6.17   Schematic of scan geometry.

Different techniques are used for realising an object plane scanning. In the simplest case, a plane mirror is kept at 45° to the optical axis and is rotated around the optical axis. In this configuration, all the radiation which is falling at 45° to the scan mirror normal and at right angles to the axis of rotation will be reflected along the rotational axis (Fig. 6.17).

This type of scanning has been extensively used in the meteorological payloads such as VHRR/AVHRR on NIMBUS, NOAA, and others. From a satellite altitude of 1000 km, even for a horizon-to-horizon scanning, the total angle to be covered is somewhat less than about 120°. Therefore, the time for which the scan mirror views the earth surface (scan efficiency) for such scanners is less than 30%. During the rest of the period, the scan mirror views either deep space or the instrument body. However, a part of the time when it views the instrument body, is used for calibration purpose. The scan efficiency can be increased by adding a second mirror so that while the first mirror sees upwards, the second mirror can scan the ground. Further improvement for scan efficiency can be achieved by a polygon of flat mirrors. In the case of high resolution imagers, to increase the scan efficiency (in order to have a higher dwell time), instead of rotating, the mirrors are oscillated to cover the required swath. The oscillation is carried out such that during the active period (when data is collected), the angular motion is a linear function of time and at the end of the scan it returns as quickly as possible. Such systems in practice can provide a scan efficiency of about 45% as in the case of LANDSAT MSS. Further improvement in scan efficiency can be achieved by using both forward and reverse motion, as used in LANDSAT, TM and can provide a scan efficiency better than 80%.

To reduce the weight and at the same time to keep high rigidity, scan mirrors are generally made of beryllium.

6.5.2 COLLECTING OPTICS

Collecting optics can be refractive, reflective or a combination of refractive and reflective elements called *catadioptic*. When the spectral bands of interest are spread over a broad wavelength region extending from visible to thermal IR, reflective optics is used to avoid dispersion. The three generally used basic reflective telescope systems are:

(i) *Newtonian*, which consists of a concave paraboloidal primary, with a flat mirror as secondary near the prime focus, so placed as to bring the focus to the side of the telescope [Fig. 6.18(a)].
(ii) *Gregorian* system, which is similar to the Cassegrain, except that the secondary is concave and kept outside the prime focus [Fig. 6.18(b)].
(iii) *Cassegrain* system, which has a concave primary and a convex secondary is placed inside the prime focus, so that it redirects the rays through a hole in the primary [Fig. 6.18(c)].

In the Cassegrain and Gregorian systems, the effective focal length is longer than that of the primary mirror. Of the three configurations, the Cassegrain system has the smallest tube length (distance between the primary and secondary) for the same effective focal length and primary mirror diameters. Since it is desirable to keep the tube length minimum, in order to reduce the weight and volume (which is one of the major considerations for spaceborne telescopes), the spaceborne opto-mechanical scanners generally use the Cassegrain configuration as the collecting telescope.

There are different ways of realising a Cassegrain type telescope system. In its classical form, the Cassegrain system consists of a concave paraboloidal primary and a convex hyperboloidal secondary mirror. In such a configuration, theoretically, on the axis there is no aberration. However, the off-axis image has comatic aberration. To improve the off-axis performance, an often used system is the Ritchey–Chretien system, wherein the primary and secondary are hyperboloidal mirrors. Since a convex hyperboloid is expensive to make, an inexpensive system at reduced performance is possible using a spherical secondary and aspheric (ellipsoidal) primary. Such a system is called a Dall–Kirkham system. Figure 6.19 gives a relative comparison of the aberration of the three systems, having the same primary and secondary *f*/no. and the same effective focal length.

The secondary mirror obscures a fraction of the area of the entrance aperture. Any central obscuration reduces the effective aperture thereby reducing the optical energy reaching the detector and more importantly lowering the MTF of the obscured system to a level lower than that of the unobscured system. Figure 6.20 gives the MTF comparison of an unobscured system with varying central obscuration. Because of the degradation of the MTF of a centrally obscured system, off-axis imaging systems are preferred to get the best MTF. However, off-axis systems are generally less compact compared to an equivalent diameter and focal length, centrally obscured telescope.

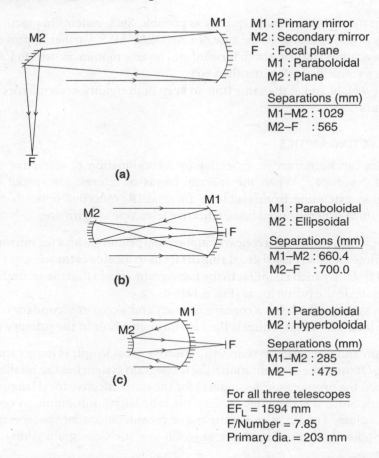

M1 : Primary mirror
M2 : Secondary mirror
F   : Focal plane
M1 : Paraboloidal
M2 : Plane

Separations (mm)
M1–M2 : 1029
M2–F   : 565

(a)

M1 : Paraboloidal
M2 : Ellipsoidal

Separations (mm)
M1–M2 : 660.4
M2–F   : 700.0

(b)

M1 : Paraboloidal
M2 : Hyperboloidal

Separations (mm)
M1–M2 : 285
M2–F   : 475

(c)

For all three telescopes
EF_L = 1594 mm
F/Number = 7.85
Primary dia. = 203 mm

Fig. 6.18 Comparison of the sizes of different telescopes. (a) Newtonian telescope (b) Gregorian telescope (c) Cassegrain telescope.

In an opto-mechanical scanner, unless one employs an image plane scanning, the rays are close to the axis, and hence large field correction is not necessary (except that required for accommodating focal plane detector arrays) and therefore usually an all-reflecting collecting optic is used. When it is necessary to achieve good image quality over a wide field of view, a catadioptic system which incorporates a corrective lens (such as a Schmidt corrector) is used. Another method to increase the field of view is to use a three mirror system. Such systems generally have an off-axis primary and hence do not have any obscuration for the incoming radiation, thereby also increasing the MTF. The third mirror gives additional flexibility for the optical designer to compensate for the off-axis aberration to get a wide field of view. IRS-1C/1D Pan uses such a three mirror optical system (see Section 6.7.2).

6.5.3 SPECTRAL DISPERSION SYSTEM

The collecting optics generally collects the reflected/emitted radiation in a broad spectral region. The spectral dispersion system selects the specific wavelength region for measurements by the detector. Historically, glass prisms were first used to break up light into its component colours.

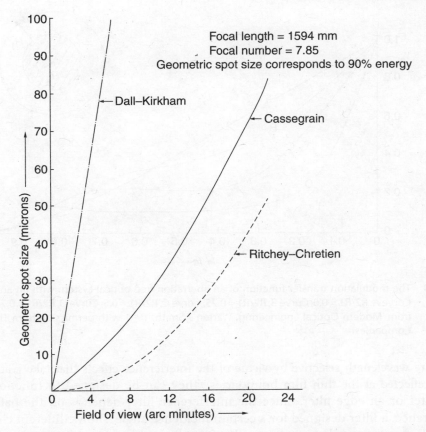

Focal length = 1594 mm
Focal number = 7.85
Geometric spot size corresponds to 90% energy

Dall–Kirkham

Cassegrain

Ritchey–Chretien

Fig. 6.19 Geometric spot size as a function of the field angle for the same focal length and f/no.

For a given prism material, the refractive index varies with the wavelength and hence the rays are bent (refracted) differently as they pass through the prism as per Snell's Law (see Chapter 2). The type of prism material used depends on its transmission characteristics and dispersion property. Since the index of refraction of optical glass varies by only a few per cent across the visible spectrum, different wavelengths are separated by small angles and hence can give only low spectral resolution.

A *grating* is another device used for spectral dispersion. A diffraction grating is a ruled mirror or transparent plate having many parallel grooves. Here, the light rays are diffracted at the groove and in a particular direction; only a specific wavelength will constructively interfere (reinforce), thereby spreading out the spectrum into different angles corresponding to the various wavelengths. Though prisms and gratings are the basic dispersing elements, additional imaging systems are required to form a sharp image at the detector.

Selection of a specific wavelength region can be achieved by using filters. The simplest is to use colour glasses. Here the spectral selection is by absorption. Colour glass filters are doped with material that selectively absorb light by wavelength. To pass a band of wavelengths (band pass filter), generally an *interference filter* is used. An interference filter consists of multiple thin layers of dielectric/metallic coatings having different refractive indices and thickness. The interference

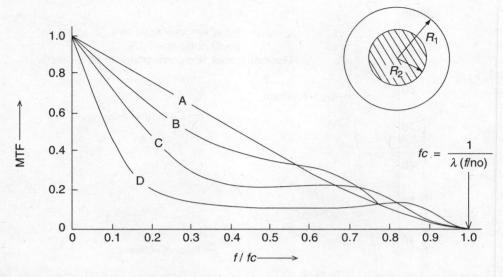

Fig. 6.20 The modulation transfer function of an aberration-free optical system with an annular aperture. Curve A, R2/R1 = 0.0; Curve B, R2/R1 = 0.25; Curve C, R2/R1 = 0.5; Curve D, R2/R1 = 0.75. (Reproduced from 'Modern Optical Engineering', Warren J Smith, 1991 with permission from The McGraw-Hill Companies)

filters are wavelength selective by virtue of the interference effects that take place among the waves reflected at the thin film boundaries. They can be designed to function as a band pass filter or an edge filter. Since the interference filter depends on the path length for interference, a filter designed for a certain incidence angle, shows different characteristics $(\lambda_c, \Delta\lambda)$ when operated at another angle of incidence. Therefore, the use of an interference filter to cover a large field of view poses problems. There are special beam splitters (dichroic beam splitters) based on the interference filter principle which selectively transmit/reflect a particular band of wavelength. The usage of such beam-splitters and appropriate band pass filters at the detector facilitates specific spectral band selection (Joseph and Kamat, 1978). In some of the other cases, discrete detectors are placed at the focal plane and each detector will have the band pass filter to choose the desired central wavelength and the bandwidth.

The next step is to measure the spectrally separated radiation using appropriate detectors.

6.5.4 DETECTORS

A *detector* is a device that produces an output signal, which depends on the amount of radiation falling on the 'active' area of the detector. The properties of O-IR radiation, which enables their detection, and typical detectors based on these properties, are schematically shown in Fig. 6.21. We have already discussed at length the principle of operation of various types of photographic films. The detectors based on the thermal and quantum effects, in general, convert optical energy into an electrical signal, which is then measured suitably. Therefore, these types of detectors can be broadly termed as *electro-optical detectors*. Opto-mechanical scanners use one or the other type of electro-optical detectors. We shall first familiarise ourselves with the performance

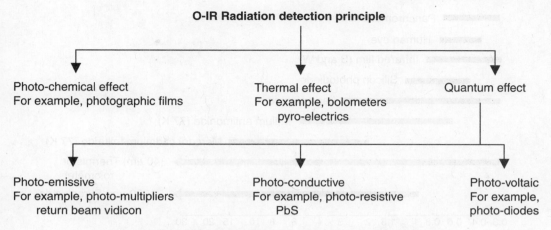

Fig. 6.21 Schematics showing basic classes of O-IR detectors.

characteristics terms commonly used to describe the detectors. To choose a detector for a specific application one would like to know its characteristics, such as, how sensitive the detector is to the radiant energy (responsivity), the spectral range over which the detector can be used, noise characteristics, response time, and so on. We shall now try to understand these terms.

Responsivity Responsivity (R) is essentially a measure of how effective (sensitive) the detector is to convert the radiant power to an electrical signal—current or voltage. For a detector that generates current output, the responsivity is the ratio of the root mean square (rms) signal current (in ampere) to the rms incident radiant power, that is, ampere/watts. For a detector that generates output voltage, it is given as volts/watts. Since, in general, the responsivity is not constant over the wavelength region, R is specified for a particular wavelength (R_λ). If I_s is the rms current generated for a spectral radiant rms power of Φ_λ, then

$$R_\lambda = \frac{I_s}{\Phi_\lambda \, d\lambda} \frac{I_s}{E_\lambda A_d d\lambda}$$

where E_λ is the spectral irradiance (w/cm^2/μm) and A_d is detector area in cm^2. It should be noted that the responsivity is dependent on the operating condition, such as detector bias (wherever it applies), temperature, chopping frequency, and so on.

The responsivity depends on the *Quantum Efficiency* (QE) of the detector, which is the ratio of the basic 'countable' events (such as photo-electrons or electron-hole pairs) produced by the incident photon to the number of photons incident. Thus, QE = 0.5 means that if 10 photons are incident, on an average, 5 photo-electrons (or electron-hole pairs) are generated. Thus QE is another way of expressing effectiveness of the basic radiant energy in producing an electrical signal in the detector.

Spectral response Each detector has a spectral region for which only it can be used. Figure 6.22(a) gives the useful spectral ranges for some typical detectors. Spectral response gives the variation of the responsivity with wavelength. It can be shown as a curve, with λ on the x-axis and $R(\lambda)$ on the y-axis, giving the absolute responsivity at each wavelength

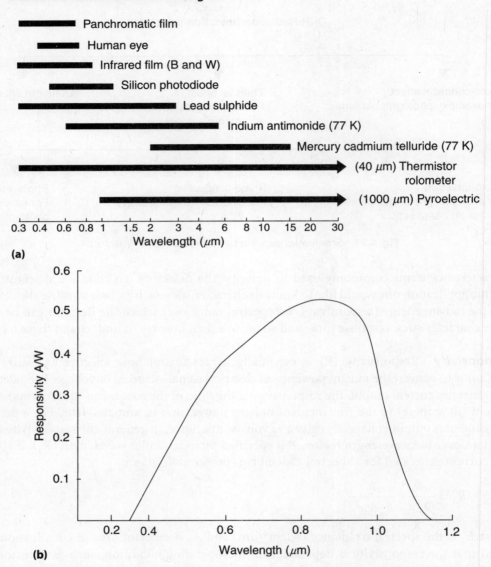

Fig. 6.22 (a) Useful spectral ranges for typical detectors (operating temperature of all detectors is 300 K unless otherwise noted) and (b) Representative spectral response for a silicon photodiode.

[Fig. 6.22(b)]. However, it is more commonly depicted as a relative spectral response curve, in which the peak of the response curve is set equal to 100%, and all other points are relative to this.

Noise equivalent power (NEP) A sensor designer is interested in knowing the minimum radiance that can be measured. This cannot be estimated from responsivity alone but requires a knowledge of the noise that the detector generates. In any detector, there are various sources of noise, which are generally random in nature, depending on the type of detector and its mode of operation. The NEP is defined as the rms input radiance at the detector which produces an output voltage equal to noise voltage, that is, a signal-to-noise ratio of unity. The NEP value should be stated at a specified wavelength, modulation frequency, detector area, temperature and electrical bandwidth used in the measurement. The electrical bandwidth is usually 1 Hz. The NEP increases as a square root of the measurement bandwidth and hence usually expressed as $W/Hz^{1/2}$. Please note that the detecting capability increases with decrease in NEP.

Note that even if we hypothetically assume that all the noise sources are eliminated, the ultimate limitation to detector performance is 'photon noise'. This is due to the random arrival of photons from the very source of radiant energy under measurement and background radiation, if any. The photon noise limited detector gives a signal-to-noise ratio proportional to $(QE \times N)^{1/2}$, where N is the number of photons arrived at the detector and QE the quantum efficiency.

Specific detectivity The NEP is dependent on the area of the detector. Therefore, it is difficult to compare the performance of two detectors without knowing its active area. An area independent figure of merit, the specific detectivity D^* (pronounced as D-star) is given by

$$D^* = \frac{\sqrt{A_d}}{NEP} \, cmHz^{1/2}w^{-1}$$

Time constant It is a measure of how fast the detector can respond to changes in the input radiation. If a detector is exposed to step input of radiation, then the time required for the output voltage (or current) to reach 0.63 of its asymptotic value is called time constant.

After having familiarised ourselves with the various terms which characterise the performance of an electro-optical detector, we shall now review some of the basic principles involved in realising the detectors.

Thermal Detector

Thermal detectors make use of the heating effect of the EM radiation. The consequent rise in temperature causes a change in some physical properties of the detector. The response of the thermal detector is only dependent upon the radiant power which they absorb and hence independent of wavelength (however, in practice, the absorption characteristic varies with wavelength, depending on the surface property of the detector). Some of the common thermal detectors include bolometers, thermocouples and pyroelectric detectors.

In *bolometers*, the change in temperature caused by the radiation changes the electrical resistance, which is suitably measured. In its earliest form, a thin blackened platinum strip was used. Advanced bolometers use semiconductors. Semiconductors exhibit a much more pronounced resistance variation with temperature change, compared to metals. The semiconductor bolometer material is called thermistor.

A *thermocouple* is formed by joining two dissimilar materials having different thermoelectric power. Two of the commonly used materials are bismuth and antimony. One of the junctions is blackened to absorb the radiation. The difference in temperature between the junctions produces a thermoelectric emf, which is a measure of the incident radiant power. In order to increase the sensitivity, a number of thermocouples are connected in series, called a *thermopile*.

When the temperature is below the curie temperature, certain ferroelectric crystals exhibit spontaneous polarisation with change in temperature. This is called the pyroelectric effect.

A *pyroelectric detector* is basically a ferroelectric capacitor that is thermally isolated and exposed to incident radiation. When the incident radiation changes the temperature of the detector element, it exhibits spontaneous polarisation, that is, opposite faces of the crystallographic orientation exhibit opposite electric charges in response to the temperature change. This can cause a displacement current to flow in an external circuit, which can be detected. Pyroelectric detectors respond only to changes in temperature. They have the maximum D^* and the fastest response time compared to other thermal detectors.

The time constant of thermal detectors is usually in milliseconds or more and hence they are not suitable for high resolution imaging.

Quantum Detectors

Quantum detectors, also referred to as photon detectors, respond to the rate at which the photon is absorbed. The spectral response of a quantum detector is shown in comparison to a thermal detector in Fig. 6.23. There is minimum frequency (maximum wavelength), when the responsivity starts. This corresponds to the minimum energy required to generate charge carriers in the detector.

As the wavelength is decreased, the photon energy increases, hence the number of photons per unit input power decreases. In a photon detector, since the response is dependant on the number of photons per second, the responsivity decreases as wavelength is decreased. On the other hand, since thermal detectors respond to the total energy absorbed, for a constant energy input, the response is independent of wavelength. There are three basic modes in which photon detectors perform—photoemissive, photoconductive and photovoltaic modes.

Photoemissive detectors If a photon of energy greater than a certain critical energy (that is, wavelength less than a critical value) is incident on certain materials, it can liberate an electron with sufficient energy to escape from the surface. This property is called the *photoelectric* or *photoemissive effect*. The energy required by the electron to escape from the surface of a material depends on the material property and is called *work function* (p). The kinetic energy (E) of the electron as it leaves the surface is

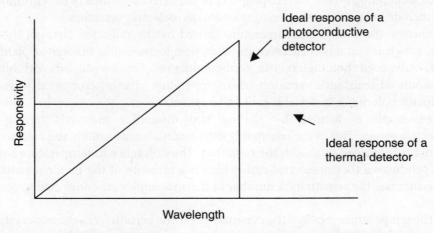

Fig. 6.23 Idealised spectral response curve of a thermal and quantum detector for a constant energy input.

$$E = h\nu - p$$

$$= \frac{hc}{\lambda} - p \tag{6.7}$$

where hc/λ is the energy of the photon. The minimum energy required by a photon to have the photo-electric effect is such that,

$$\frac{hc}{\lambda} - p = 0$$

that is, the electron just comes out with zero velocity. Thus we have a cut-off wavelength $\lambda_c = hc/p$. If p is expressed in electron volts and λ in micrometer then,

$$\lambda_c = \frac{1.24}{p} \tag{6.8}$$

Thus the lower the work function p, the longer is the cut-off wavelength.

Certain compound materials give a low work function compared to a single metal. The silver–oxygen–cesium surface gives a work function of 0.98 eV, giving a λ_c of 1.25 μm.

In the simplest form of a photoelectric detector, the photoemissive surface (photocathode) and a plate, are housed in an evacuated glass envelope. By applying a positive potential to the plate with respect to the photocathode, the photoelectrons generated are attracted to the plate and the resultant current can be measured by a suitable external circuit. The most widely used detector using the photoemissive effect is the photomultiplier tube (PMT). In a PMT, the photoelectron emitted from the photocathode falls on to successive *dynodes*; each dynode produces increasingly multiple photoelectrons, which are finally collected by the anode. Thus, PMT provides an internal gain, which enables very low light levels to be detected. Other detectors working on this principle are some of the television tubes.

Semiconductor detectors Before we proceed further, it is useful to understand some of the underlying principles, which make up a semiconductor, including the energy band theory. We know, as per Bohr's model, in an atom, electrons are confined to certain allowed orbits. That is, electrons in an atom can only have certain discrete energies. When atoms are brought together as in a solid, under the mutual influence of the nuclei, the allowable energy levels are broadened into energy bands. The lowest available energy is called the *valance band* and the electrons contained in this band are responsible for the chemical properties of the material. Here, the electrons are bound to specific lattice sites in the crystal. The next available energy is called the *conduction band*. The separation between the two bands (forbidden band) depends on whether it is a conductor, insulator or a semiconductor (Fig. 6.24).

In metals, the valance and conduction bands overlap and the thermally liberated electrons in the overlapping region can move freely in the conduction band and are thus amenable to producing electric current. In an insulator, the valance band is fully filled, and in order for an electron to conduct, it would have to jump to the conduction band crossing the band gap. If the band gap is larger than the energy that can be achieved by the temperature effect (KT), there will not be any conduction. In the case of a semiconductor, the forbidden band gap is between the conductor and the insulator. Thus, in semiconductors, the band gap is such that some

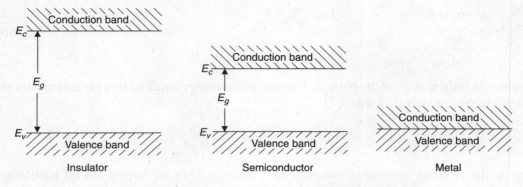

Fig. 6.24   Band structure in insulator, semiconductor and metal.

thermally excited electrons can cross the gap and conduct electricity at room temperature. For each electron pushed to the conduction band, an electron is missing from a normally occupied valance band. The electron vacancy is called a *hole*. If an electron moves from a nearby location to fill the vacancy, a new hole is created and thus can be thought of as a positive charge moving in the opposite direction to the electron.

Semiconductors typically fall into two categories—extrinsic and intrinsic. The intrinsic semiconductor is one made of single type atoms such as Si or Ge. It is possible to influence the properties of a semiconductor in a controllable manner by adding impurities (known as *doping*) and these semiconductors are called *extrinsic semiconductors*. Two types of extrinsic semiconductors can be created, depending on the parent material and the impurity doped. In the first type, the impurity is such that their valence electron is within the band gap, generally close to the conduction band of the parent semiconductor. These electrons are then more easily excited into the conduction band and constitute the *n*-type semiconductor. In the second case, the dopant is such that it accepts electrons from the valence band of the parent semiconductor, and thus creates holes. The resulting material is called a *p*-type semiconductor. Thus in an *n*-type semi-conductor, conduction is mainly due to the negative charge or electrons, with holes as minority carriers. In a *p*-type semiconductor, conduction is mainly due to positive charges or holes, with electrons as minority carriers.

Photoconductive detectors   We have seen earlier that a photon of sufficient energy can excite an electron from the valance band to the conduction band. If E_g is the band gap, the maximum wavelength for which this happens is given by

$$\lambda_c = \frac{1.24}{E_g}$$

where λ_c is in micrometre and E_g is in electron volt. The E_g for germanium is 0.66 eV, for silicon 1.12 eV and gallium arsenide 1.42 eV. When electrons are excited to the conduction band, the conductivity of the detector increases, and can be measured. Thus *photoconductive detectors* can be considered to be light sensitive variable resistors, whose conductivity varies with the number of photons absorbed. The band gaps and hence the cut-off wavelength can be altered by suitable doping. Some of the commonly used photoconductive detectors for remote sensing include indium antimonide, indium gallium arsenide, mercury cadmium tellunide (MCT). MCT is of particular interest, since by adjusting the relative concentration of CdTe and HgTe, it is possible to cover a wide range of wavelengths extending from near-infrared to thermal IR. The INSAT VHRR uses MCT for the detection of thermal (10.5–12.5 μm) and water vapour (5.7–7.1 μm) bands (Joseph et. al., 1994).

To realise a practical detection system, the detector is connected to a resistor and a supply voltage is applied. Depending on the variation of conductivity due to the incident radiation, the voltage across the detector (or resistor) varies and is measured by suitable amplifiers.

Photovoltaic detectors   When p and n extrinsic semiconductors are brought together, we have a p–n junction. There are various engineering processes by which this is achieved and we will not deal with them here. Instead, we shall try to understand the operation of a p–n junction. Initially both sides of the junction are electrically neutral. However, when the p and n sides are brought together, since the n-type region has excess electrons, the concentration gradient causes electrons to diffuse from the n-type region to the p-type region and holes from the p-type region to the n-type region. This diffusion generates a net positive charge at the vicinity of the junction on the n side and a negative potential on the p-side, thus creating an electric field. However, the electron–hole movement across the junction stops when the electric field generated is equal to the concentration gradient. The region over which the electric field extends is called the *depletion region*. (This could be given a physical explanation as follows: the region of n-type material in the immediate vicinity of the junction is depleted of electrons and a similar region in the p-type material is depleted of holes. The combined region from both sides could be thought of as the depletion region.) The potential difference created across the junction is called the *contact potential*. A device operating in this mode to detect radiation is called a *photodiode*.

When a photodiode is exposed to radiation with energy greater than E_g, additional charge carriers are generated. The additional charge generated increases the potential across the junction. The voltage generated across the junction (open circuit) increases logarithmically with the radiation intensity. However, if the photodiode is operated in the current mode, the current generated increases linearly (within limits) with intensity of radiation. This mode of operation in the zero bias mode is called the *photovoltaic mode*. Here, the photodiode is actually generating an electric potential.

Figure 6.25 gives the current versus voltage characteristics of a photodiode. If the diode is reverse biased (the n region is connected to the positive of the battery and p region to the negative), the reverse current is proportional to the intensity of radiation. This mode of operation is referred to as the *photoconductive mode* (unfortunately, this is wrong terminology and is widely used; we are still using a photodiode; only the operating region has shifted).

There are merits and demerits for both the operation modes. In the photovoltaic mode, in the absence of an applied bias, there is no dark current and hence the only source of noise is thermal noise. Hence very low light level intensities can be measured. When operated in the photoconductive mode, the reverse bias applied across the junction results in a wider depletion region and hence smaller capacitance and a shorter rise time. Hence, for applications involving faster response, the photoconductive mode of operation is preferred. This mode also provides a linear light response over a wide range of light intensities. However, with reverse bias, the dark current increases and hence the noise is larger.

Another form of a photodiode is a $p-i-n$ (p-intrinsic-n) diode, which has an intrinsic region between the p and n regions. A bias potential applied depletes the intrinsic region of the carriers, thus increasing the volume for light absorption and hence has a higher quantum efficiency. Also, because the p and n regions are farther apart than in the $p-n$ junction diodes, the $p-i-n$ diodes have less capacitance and hence show a faster response.

In all photon detectors, there is a current even in the absence of any light. This is called the *dark current* and is due to thermally excited electrons. Dark current is one of the noise sources, which limits the detection of low radiation levels. This is particularly true in the case of detectors tuned for IR detection because to have a higher cut-off wavelength, the band gap has to be small, and hence a substantial number of thermal electrons can contribute to the dark current. Higher the temperature, higher is the energy for the thermally excited electron. Therefore, to have reasonable performance, the IR detectors are cooled. In aircraft sensors, specially made dewars are used to carry liquid nitrogen (77 K), which through special arrangements cool the detector element. In satellite sensors, passive coolers which couple the detector element to space (which is at ~ 4 K) is generally used for cooling to ≃ 90–100 K. These radiation coolers require a very specialised surface property to enhance emittance and reduce absorptance. The location of these coolers on the spacecraft requires very careful planning to avoid any appendages of the spacecraft coming in the field of view of the cooler. Development of compact stirring cycle cooling systems is now becoming practical for space use.

We shall now describe some of the typical satellite-borne opto-mechanical scanners.

6.6   OPTO-MECHANICAL SCANNERS OPERATED FROM SATELLITES

6.6.1   LANDSAT MULTI-SPECTRAL SENSORS

The multi-spectral scanner system on board the NASA Earth Resources Technology Satellite LANDSAT-1, popularly known as MSS was the first operational satellite-borne opto-mechanical scanner for civilian applications. We shall briefly describe the MSS instrument and its operation. LANDSAT-1 and 2 MSS had four spectral bands in the 0.5–1.1 μm region. The subsequent LANDSAT MSSs had an additional band in the thermal IR region (Lansing and Cline, 1975). MSS onboard LANDSAT consists of a Ritchey–Chretien (RC) telescope with a 23 cm aperture. The RC design was selected for the telescope on the basis of its good off-axis performance, in order to cover the thermal IR band, which is separate from the first four bands in the focal plane. In addition, the RC design has reduced sensitivity to minor misalignments. The telescope has a focal length of 82.6 cm and an f/no. of 3.6. The mirrors are made of fused silica and coated with enhanced silver for high reflectance. The primary and secondary mirrors are coupled through an invar support structure. Near the focal plane, the energy passes through a rotating shutter, which includes calibration functions [Fig. 6.26(a)]. At the focal plane, 24 optical fibres are arranged in a 4 × 6 array, corresponding to the four spectral bands and the six detectors per band aligned in the along-track direction.

The square end of each single glass fibre forms a field stop of 86 micro-radians, subtending 79 m on the earth from the LANDSAT orbit. Light impinging on each glass fibre is conducted to an individual detector through an optical filter, specific to the spectral band concerned. The scanner covers 185 km wide swath (west-to-east) on the earth during the daylight, southbound

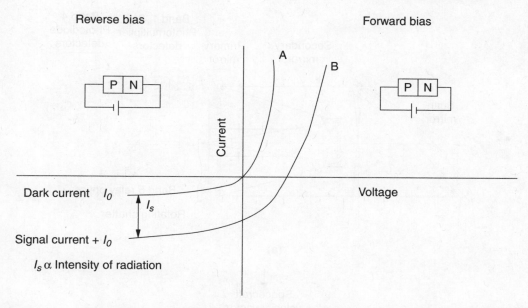

Fig. 6.25 I–V characteristics of a *p–n* diode. Curve A is in the dark. Curve B occurs when the diode is irradiated with light.

part of the orbit. The cross-track scan is achieved by motion of the object plane scan mirror, oscillating at a frequency of 13.62 Hz.

The along-track scan is produced by the orbital motion of the spacecraft. For the nominal orbit, along-track sub-satellite velocity is 6.47 km/s, neglecting spacecraft perturbation and earth rotation effects. By oscillating the scan mirror at a rate of 13.62 Hz, the sub-satellite point will move 474 m along-track during the 73.42 millisecond active scan and retrace cycle. The width of the along-track field of view of six detectors is also 474 m (6 × 79 m). Thus, the line scanned by the first detector in one cycle of the active mirror scan lies adjacent to the line scanned by the sixth detector of the previous mirror scan, producing contiguous images [Fig. 6.26(b)]. The use of 6 detectors per scan line reduces the scan rate, thereby increasing the dwell time.

The fifth band covering the thermal infrared region (10.4–12.6 μm) is relayed from the telescope focal plane and reimaged on to a mercury cadmium telluride detector, which is cooled to 100 K by a radiation cooler. The fifth band field stop, determined by detector dimensions, is 260 microradians, subtending 240 m on the ground. In this case, two detectors cover adjacent lines during the scan to sweep out the same area as the six lines of the other bands.

The video outputs from each detector in the scanner are sampled and commutated once in 9.95 microseconds and multiplexed into a pulse amplitude modulated (PAM) stream. The commutated samples of video are either fed directly to the analog-to-digital (A/D) converter for encoding or for bands 1, 2 and 3 are passed through a logarithmic signal compression amplifier and then to the encoder. This selection can be made by ground command. The data is encoded to 6 bits either in the linear or compressed mode (NASA, 1972).

A high gain mode is also selectable by ground command. In this mode, a gain of three is applied to the video signal, so that the full dynamic range of A/D converter is utilised for a

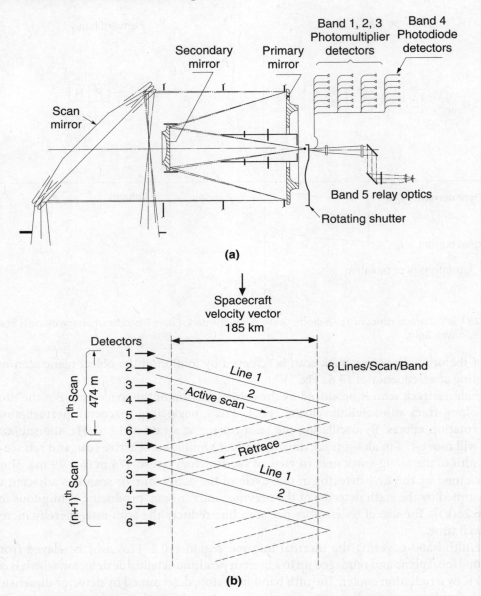

Fig. 6.26 LANDSAT MSS instrument and scan pattern. (a) Optical schematic of LANDSAT MSS, (b) Scan mirror sweep pattern in MSS. (Reprinted with permission from 'The Four and Five band Multi-spectral Scanners for LANDSAT' by Lansing & Cline, Optical Engineering, SPIE Vol. 14, No.4, 1975)

scene producing low irradiance into the sensor. Annotation on each image will indicate the setting of compression and gain. The important parameters of MSS are given in Table 6.3.

Thematic Mapper

The Thematic Mapper (TM) is an advanced second-generation opto-mechanical multi-spectral scanner first carried onboard LANDSAT-4. TM provides 7 narrow spectral bands

Table 6.3 LANDSAT MSS parameters

Optics	22.9 cm Ritchey–Chretien with 10.16 cm secondary $f/3.6$
Scan method	Oscillating mirror $\pm$ 2.9° at 13.6 Hz with 45% active scan
IFOV (in micro rad.)	86 (bands 1–4); 260 (band 5)
Swath (km)	185
No. of bands	5
No. of detectors	6 per band for bands 1 to 4 and 2 for band 5

Spectral bands and detectors	Band	Wavelength (micrometer)	Detector
	1	0.5–0.6	PM
	2	0.6–0.7	PM
	3	0.7–0.8	PM
	4	0.8–1.1	Si PD
	5	10.4–12.5	HgCd (Te)

Quantisation (bits)	6
Data rate	15 MBPS
Calibration	Halogen lamp, skylight
Power (W)	55
Weight (kg)	64

covering visible, near infrared, shortwave infrared and thermal infrared spectral regions with a 30 m resolution in the visible, near and shortwave infrared bands and 120 m resolution in the thermal infrared. Apart from the improved spatial and spectral resolution, TM provides a factor of two improvements over the MSS in radiometric sensitivity.

Considerable innovation in the electro-optical design was required to achieve such improvements (Blanchard and Weinstein, 1980). The thematic mapper uses an RC telescope with an aperture of 41 cm. The scanning is accomplished by a 41×53 cm^2 flat elliptical scan mirror mounted by flexural pivots on a fixed frame. Unlike the MSS, both forward and reverse scanning of the mirror are used for collecting data. This necessitated the inclusion of a scanline corrector preceding the detectors to compensate for the motion of the spacecraft so that the scanlines will be straight and aligned to the cross-track direction. The visible and near infrared bands use silicon photodiode arrays. Cooled indium antimonide (InSb) detectors are used for the middle infrared channels. The silicon photodiodes and InSb array have 16 detectors per band. The thermal band uses four cooled mercury cadmium telluride detectors. The total data rate with 8-bit digitisation is about 85 megabits per second. The weight and power consumption of a thematic mapper is about four times that of the MSS. The specifications of the thematic mapper are given in Table 6.4.

The descendant of LANDSAT-5, LANDSAT-7 has a thematic mapper called an Enhanced Thematic Mapper (ETM) with an additional band (panchromatic) providing 15 m resolution covering the spectral region from 0.5 to 0.9 μm. The improved resolution is achieved by locating 32-detectors/panchromatic band at the prime focal plane next to Band 1. The panchromatic band will generate data at the combined rate of bands 1–4. However, to limit the data rate for transmission, one of the following three modes can be used for transmission:

Table 6.4 LANDSAT thematic mapper parameters

Optics	40.6 cm Ritchey–Chretien $f/6$		
Scan method	Oscillating mirror 7Hz with 85% scan efficiency (bi-directional)		
IFOV (in micro rad.)	43.0 for 1–5, 7; 170.0 for 6		
Swath (km)	185		
No. of bands	7		
No. of detectors	16 for bands 1–5, 7; 4 for band 6		
Spectral bands and detectors	**Band**	**Wavelength (micrometre)**	**Detector**
	1	0.45–0.55	Si PD
	2	0.52–0.60	Si PD
	3	0.63–0.69	Si PD
	4	0.76–0.90	Si PD
	5	1.55–1.75	In Sb
	6	10.4–12.5	HgCd (Te)
	7	2.08–2.35	In Sb
Quantisation (bits)	8		
Data rate	85MBPS		
Calibration	Halogen lamp		
Power (W)	300		
Weight (kg)	243		

(i)   bands 1–7 like L4 and L5,

(ii) Pan plus B6, B4 and B5, and

(iii) Pan plus B6, B4 and B7.

The data that is not transmitted live at 85 Mbps can be recorded for a later transmission utilising the redundant multiplexer and the onboard tape recorder.

6.6.2 OPTO-MECHANICAL SCANNER FROM GEO-STATIONARY ORBIT

The sensors we have discussed so far are placed in low earth orbiting satellites, wherein along-track imaging is carried out due to satellite motion. If we have to image from a geostationary orbit, since the satellite is stationary with respect to earth, the instrument requires scanning in both axes. From the sensor point of view, the imaging system from a geosynchronous orbit can be broadly classified as cameras-on-board spinner and three-axis stabilised platforms. In the case of a spinner, the spin of the satellite produces a one scan line in the west–east direction. North–south scanning is carried out by stepping a scan mirror placed in front of the entrance aperture of the telescope. In the case of METEOSAT, which is a spinning satellite, the whole telescope is tilted at the end of each east–west scan to scan in the south–north direction. The METEOSAT is spun at about 100 rpm and can image the earth once every 30 minutes. Since the earth covers only about 17° from a geosynchronous orbit, the efficiency of scanning is very poor, because for the rest of the rotation period, the instrument sees deep space. Due to poor scan efficiency such instruments require larger collecting optics and higher data rate compared

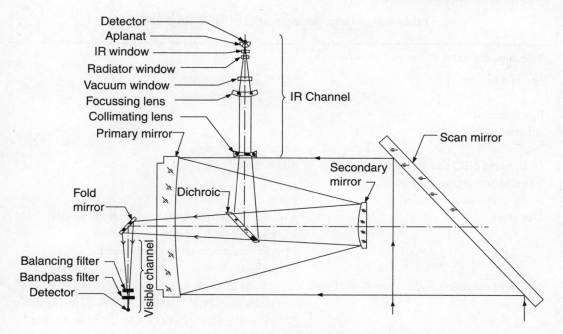

Fig. 6.27 Optical schematic of INSAT-2 VHRR.

to an instrument kept on a three-axis stabilised platform. However, it has the advantage of better spacecraft stability due to the rigidity of a spinning space platform.

The VHRR on board INSAT is a typical example of an opto-mechanical scanner from a three-axis stabilised geostationary orbit. Figure 6.27 gives the optical schematic of INSAT-2 VHRR (Joseph et. al., 1994). It essentially consists of a Ritchey–Chretien (RC) telescope with an effective focal length of 1594 mm.

Since the spacecraft is stationary with respect to the earth, a scan mirror with the ability to scan in two orthogonal axes is used to scan in the east–west and north–south direction. The east–west scan is accomplished in 1.2 s after which the mirror is stepped equivalent to 8 km, field of view. Four detectors are used in the visible and one detector in the IR region to cover 8 km in the N–S direction. The visible and IR radiation are separated by a special dichroic mirror. The reflected IR goes through a relay optics and falls on to the mercury cadmium telluride detector cooled to 105 K using a radiation cooler. The visible channel is detected by an array of 4 silicon photodiodes. The satellite operates in three modes:

(i) the full disk coverage (which covers $21.4° \times 20°$ field of view) in about 33 minutes,
(ii) normal mode of scanning which covers $21.4° \times 14°$ (N-S) in 23 minutes, and
(iii) a sector scan in which $4.5°$ in the north–south direction can be covered anywhere in the earth disc in 7.5 minutes.

Some of the salient features of the INSAT-2 VHRR are given in Table 6.5.

There are a number of other remote sensors, using the opto-mechanical scanner principle, which have been flown in spacecraft and aircraft. The instruments described above give a fairly good representation of the characteristics of the opto-mechanical scanners in general.

Table 6.5   Salient characteristics of INSAT-2A/B VHRR

Telescope diameter 203 mm		
Spectral bands:	VIS	0.55–0.75 micrometre
	IR	10.5–12.5 micrometre
Resolution at subsatellite point:	VIS	2 km
	IR	8 km
IR Channel NEDT at 300 K		0.25 K max
VIS Channel signal-to-noise ratio at 2.5% Albedo		6 min.
Detectors:	VIS	4 (main) + 4 (redundant) silicon photo-diodes
	IR	1 (main) + 1 (redundant) Mercury cadmium telluride operated normally at 105 K
Modes of operation Full frame: 21.4° (E–W) × 20° (N–S) in 33 min.		
		Normal frame: 21.4° (E–W) × 14° (N–S) in 23 min.
		Sector mode: 21.4° (E–W) × 4.5° (N–S) in 7.5 min. with 0.5° sector positioning capability
Quantisation levels 10 bit for VIS and IR		
Data rate		526.5 kbps
IR Calibration		Black body view and deep space

The major limitation of the opto-mechanical scanners is the limited dwell time as it scans pixel by pixel. This limitation is partly overcome by increasing the number of pixels along-track. Thus, as we have seen earlier, the LANDSAT TM, has to use 16 detectors along-track compared to 6 for LANDSAT MSS. This is in addition to using both forward and backward scanning for data acquisition and increased aperture for optics. The LANDSAT-TM design probably gives a practical (or engineering) limit to the spatial resolution from space platforms using opto-mechanical techniques. Joseph, 1996, has shown that if we were to realise a 10 m resolution similar to SPOT (Section 6.7.1), using an opto-mechanical scanner, to have the same S/N as in TM, the diameter of the collecting optics needs to be 69 cm compared to the actual SPOT optics diameter of 31 cm. Alternatively, if the optics entrance aperture is kept constant (as in TM), to achieve the same S/N, the increase in the number of detectors in the along-track direction will be 128 detectors per band (against 16 used by TM). This shows the complexity of achieving spatial resolution better than TM using opto-mechanical scanners. Therefore, for higher spatial/spectral resolution, we have to resort to other imaging technologies.

6.7   PUSHBROOM CAMERAS

In the previous section, we have seen the complexity of realising a high spatial resolution imaging system from a space platform using opto-mechanical scanners. The limitation primarily arises from the mode of imaging on an instantaneous geometric field of view (IGFOV) by IGFOV basis, thereby limiting the time to collect the radiation. The situation can be substantially improved if data are collected for an entire across track strip by imaging the complete swath at a time, since all the pixels of the strip get the integration time corresponding to the time taken by the satellite to move through one IGFOV. This mode of operation is made possible due to the development of a linear detector array consisting of a number of optically independent detector elements arranged along a line which is used as the detection system in the focal plane. We shall discuss the operation of such detector systems in a later section. Imaging system operating in this mode are called pushbroom cameras.

6.7.1 PRINCIPLE OF OPERATION OF PUSHBROOM CAMERA

A strip of the terrain is focussed by an optical system, say a lens, on to a linear detector array such as a charge-coupled device, CCD (see Section 6.7.2). At any given instant of time, only those points on the ground that lie in the plane defined by the optical centre of the imaging system and the line containing the sensor array (the optical centre is the imaginary point at which all the rays intersect) are imaged. This plane may be referred to as the instantaneous view plane. The radiation from the strip on the ground is received simultaneously by every detector element of the sensor and each detector element produces electrons proportional to the radiant flux received by that detector element and the duration for which the detector is exposed, also referred to as the integration time. Depending on the number of elements in the detector, one line of information generates that many pixels. When such a system is mounted on a moving platform (usually such that the array length is at a right angle to the velocity vector of the platform), as the platform advances, the view plane sweeps out a strip of the terrain that is continuously projected onto the CCD array. Normally, the detector is exposed for a duration equal to the time taken by the sub-satellite point to move through one IGFOV, referred to as the dwell time. Thus, due to the platform motion, every successive exposure produces contiguous image strips. Hence, a two dimensional image is produced—the linear array detector producing one image line across track (XT) and successive image strips along track (AT) by the motion of the platform (Fig. 6.28). When compared to opto-mechanical scanning systems, the scan mirror is avoided and instead the detector array is used to produce one scan line of information. This mode of scanning is referred to as pushbroom scanning. In this case, the total time taken by the sub-satellite point to move through one ground resolution element is available for integration of the signal for all the pixels along the linear array, thereby increasing the integration time compared to an opto-mechanical scanner of the same IFOV.

Let us consider the dwell time for a pushbroom scanner. In this case, the total time taken by the sub-satellite point to move through a one ground resolution element is available for integrating the signal for all the pixels along the CCD. Using the notation used in Eqs 6.2–6.4, the dwell time for a pushbroom scanner τ_p is given by

$$\tau_p = \frac{\beta}{v/h} \tag{6.9}$$

Here, the scanning is done electronically, and the scan efficiency is 1. If τ_o is the dwell time for an opto-mechanical scanner for $n = 1$, using Eq. 6.4, we have

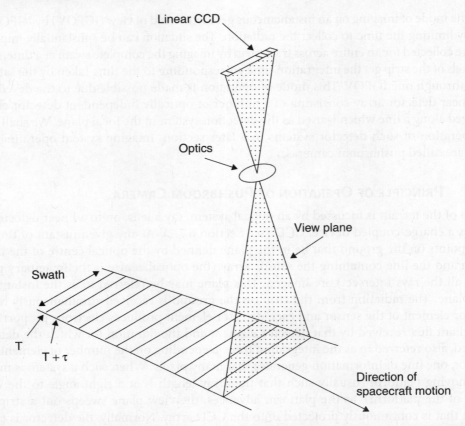

Fig. 6.28   Illustration of the pushbroom scan technique. τ is the integration time. (From Building Earth Observation Cameras by Joseph G, CRC press 2015, reproduced with permission via Copyright Clearance Centre)

$$\frac{\tau_p}{\tau_o} = \frac{\beta}{(v/h)} \frac{(v/h)\Omega}{\beta^2 S_e} = \frac{\Omega}{\beta S_e} \tag{6.10}$$

Ω/β is the number of elements on the CCD array (across-track pixels). Thus the dwell time is considerably longer in a pushbroom scanner compared to an opto-mechanical scanner thereby improving the signal-to-noise ratio. Hence, for the same aperture and S/N as that of an opto-mechanical scanner, a higher spatial/spectral resolution imagery can be produced with pushbroom scanning. The absence of mechanical motion increases the reliability and makes the system more compact. It is worthwhile to mention that all high resolution imaging systems are based on this principle. We shall now discuss some of the subsystems used in pushbroom cameras.

6.7.2   LINEAR ARRAY FOR PUSHBROOM SCANNING

Pushbroom scanning is made possible due to the development of solid state imaging detectors. The concept of solid state image sensors was experimented on from the early sixties (Weimer et. al., 1967). A practical imaging solid state camera with acceptable quality was possible only with the invention of the Charge Coupled Device (CCD) by Willard S Boyle and George E Smith in 1969, for which they were awarded Nobel Prize in 2009. Currently, solid state imaging focal plane arrays are used in various areas from industrial applications to scientific investigations. In this section we shall discuss some of the solid state imaging systems used in remote sensing with reference to pushbroom scanning.

6.7.2.1 Charge Coupled Device Linear Array

The detection of photons by a CCD is the same as that of a photodiode which is a light sensitive detector—it converts the light (incoming photons) into electrons which are stored as electrical charge in a capacitor formed by the depletion region. A number of such photo sensitive elements can be placed in close proximity and organised either as a two dimensional array (area array) or as a linear array. The photo sensitive elements are isolated as individual photon detectors by non-conducting channel stops and biased gate electrodes. When a scene is focussed on to such a device, each capacitor accumulates an electric charge proportional to the number of photons received at that location. The number of photons received depends on the irradiance at the focal plane and the exposure time. Thus, during the exposure period, the sensor accumulates a spatial charge distribution throughout the detector array that corresponds to the distribution of the number of incident photons. This is the first step in capturing the image.

Adjacent to the image sensing elements (photosites) is located a structure called *transfer gate* (Fig. 6.29). By applying suitable voltages to the transfer gate at the end of the integration period, the charge packets accumulated in the image sensing elements are transferred out in parallel to a shift register called the *transport shift register* or readout register (usually two, one each on either side of the array, connected to alternate pixels—odd and even pixels). The detector elements are then reset and ready to accumulate a new line of data. At the transport shift register, the charge corresponding to each pixel is stored in a separate capacitor. By manipulating various gate voltages, the charges in each of the capacitors is transferred to the adjacent capacitor sequentially and finally to the output amplifier. Thus, the charges from each

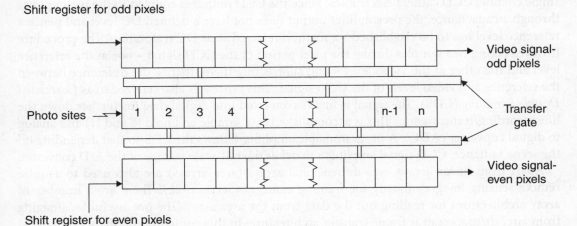

Fig. 6.29 Schematics showing the organisation of a linear CCD with two transport shift registers. (From Building Earth Observation Cameras by Joseph G, CRC press 2015, reproduced with permission via Copyright Clearance Centre)

Charge to Voltage Conversion in CCD

Figure 6.30(a) shows the conceptual schematics of the output stage of a CCD. The charge measurement is accomplished by dumping the charge from each pixel on to a 'sense capacitor' C_s located at the end of the transport shift register. The process begins by closing the FET switch 'S' with a reset clock (Φ_R) to pre-charge the sense capacitor C_s to the reference voltage V_r. Initially there is a 'reset feed through' due to the parasitic capacitive coupling of the switch to the output of the amplifier. This is followed by the reference level. Signal charge from the readout shift register is then transferred onto the node of C_s, whose potential changes linearly depending on the amount of the signal charge delivered. A voltage V is developed across the sense capacitor according to the relation $V = Q/C_s$. Since the electron charge is negative, the photon generated signal (here afterwards referred as video signal) goes negative from the reference level. The signal so generated is made available through a MOSFET source follower for off the chip processing. In summary, the output of the CCD is a sequence of stepped DC voltage for each pixel, consisting of reset feed through, reference level and pixel video level [Fig. 6.30(b)].

The difference between the reference level and the video level gives the actual signal produced due to the photons collected by the pixel, which is the information that we require.

When there are multiple readout shift registers in a CCD, they may be combined on the chip so that a single output is available, or each shift register may have its own output amplifiers producing multiple video outputs.

pixel, one at a time, reach the charge sensing output amplifier (sometimes referred to as the on-chip preamplifier) located at one end of the readout register where the electrons (which represent charge, Q) are converted to voltage. The output from the CCD is further processed usually by off the chip electronic circuits. Figure 6.31 gives a simplified block diagram of single channel CCD camera electronics. Since the CCD output is coupled to the preamplifier through a capacitance, the preamplifier output does not have a defined DC level and hence a reference level has to be established—a method referred to as DC restoration. The procedure involves taking two samples during the pixel period of the CCD signal – one at the reference level and the other at the video level – and subtracting them, that is, the difference between the reference and video levels of the CCD signal. This process is also referred to as *Correlated Double Sampling* (CDS). The signal is finally converted into digital data for further down the line recording/transmission. This is accomplished by a sample and hold (S and H) and analog to digital converter (ADC). A programmable amplifier follows the CDS so that depending on the scene radiance, CCD signal amplitude matches the full-scale voltage of the A/D converter.

Apart from linear arrays, two-dimensional arrays (area arrays) are also used to acquire remote sensing imagery mostly for framing cameras (Section 6.2). There are a number of array architectures for reading out the data from the area array. The one useful for imaging from aircraft/spacecraft is frame transfer architecture. In this configuration there is a parallel storage array that is *not* light sensitive. The captured scene from the photosensitive area is rapidly transferred to the storage array. Read-out from the storage array is then performed, while the photosensitive area records the image of the next frame.

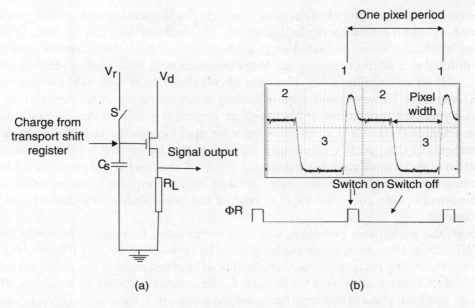

(a)   (b)

Fig. 6.30 (a) Schematics of CCD output charge detection amplifier. V_r — Reference voltage, V_d — drain voltage, C_s — sense capacitor, R_L — load resistor, S — switch. (b) CCD output voltage waveform. 1 — reset feedthrough, 2 — refrence level V_r, 3 — pixel voltage level. The difference between 2 and 3 gives the voltage due to the charge accumulated at the pixel photosensitive area. Width of 3 gives the video duration. (From Building Earth Observation Cameras by Joseph G, CRC press 2015, reproduced with permission via Copyright Clearance Centre)

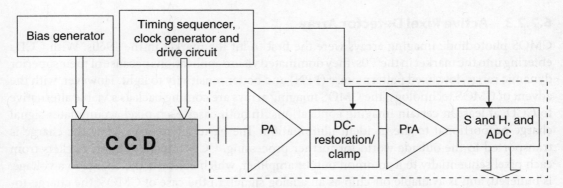

Fig. 6.31 Schematics showing the architecture of a single band CCD camera. The blocks in the dotted box perform off the chip signal processor functions. PA — preamplifier, PrA — programmable amplifier. (From Building Earth Observation Cameras by Joseph G, CRC press 2015, reproduced with permission via Copyright Clearance Centre)

6.7.2.2 Hybrid Arrays

Monolithic detector arrays (photon sensor and readout on same substrate) are generally silicon based. Silicon-based photosensitive devices do not respond to wavelengths beyond about 1 micron. Therefore, to have a detector array responding to wavelengths beyond 1 micron, one technique is to have the two functions – namely photon sensing and readout circuitry – separated—a hybrid detector array. In this scheme, the radiation detectors are made of suitable IR material and can be wire-bonded on to a silicon chip or the entire detector array can be bump-bonded to a silicon readout chip. Many detectors such as mercury cadmium telluride (MCT), indium antimonide (InSb), platinum silicide (PtSi), have been used for shortwave IR (SWIR) detection. However, they require cooling much below the room temperature, some even to cryogenic temperatures, so that the dark current is within acceptable limits. Indium gallium arsenide (InGaAs) is a possible choice for operating in the near-room temperature environment. $In_xGa_{1-x}As$ is a compound semiconductor. By varying x (that is, the relative proportion of indium and gallium), the optical, electrical and mechanical properties of InGaAs can be varied (Guntupalli and Allen, 2006). InGaAs having a response between 0.9 and 1.7 μm as photodetector with integrated CCD as readout has been used in IRS LISS-III and SPOT HRV cameras.

Though the pushbroom technique was used for imaging from space in visible, near IR and SWIR since 1986, imaging in the long wave IR region (10–14 μm) followed the opto-mechanical scanning route due to non-availability of long arrays. Mercury cadmium telluride (MCT) detectors have been used for decades for detecting long-wave IR radiation. Though moderate size focal plane arrays have been realised using MCT, there are technical difficulties in realising long arrays and yields are low. Quantum well infrared photodetectors (QWIPs) have emerged as an alternative for imaging in the thermal IR spectral region. Details on QWIPs can be found in the book by Henini and Razeghi (2002). There is rapid growth in developing high-performance QWIP, with both area and linear arrays. Landsat 8 launched in 2013 is the first space borne earth observation pushbroom imaging system operating in the thermal IR region using quantum well detector arrays.

6.7.2.3   Active Pixel Detector Array

CMOS photodiode imaging arrays were the first to hit the market in the 1960s. With CCDs entering into the market in the '70s, they dominated vision applications because of their superior dynamic range, low fixed pattern noise (FPN) and better sensitivity to light. However, with the advent of CMOS technology, the CMOS imaging arrays are coming back as a viable alternative to CCD, at least in certain imaging applications. In both cases each pixel accumulates signal charge proportional to the incident illumination. The basic difference is how the charge is transported to the outside world for further processing. CCD transfers charge packets from each pixel sequentially to a common output amplifier, which converts the charge to a voltage, is buffered, and is available off-chip as an analog signal. In the case of CMOS, the charge-to-voltage conversion takes place in each pixel which is multiplexed, and the output from each pixel is connected successively to a common output amplifier (Fig. 6.32). Since each pixel has an active circuit, this is also referred as *active pixel sensor* (APS). Using the CMOS process, it is possible to integrate many additional features on the chip along with photon detection. These include timing and control clock, bias generation, auto-exposure, automatic gain control, gamma correction, analog to digital conversion, and so on, thus providing a readout integrated circuit (ROIC) along with the photon detection function. Hence, we get a digitised output providing a robust, noise immune interface for further processing off the chip. Thus, it is a complete focal plane chip with only command signals and power as inputs to the chip.

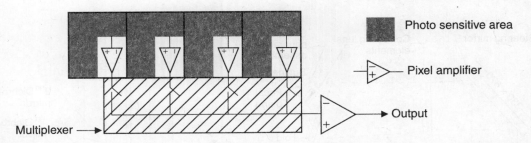

Fig. 6.32 Schematics showing the organisation of an active pixel linear array. Charge generation takes place at the photo sensitive area of photodiode. Charge-to-voltage conversion is carried out for each pixel by amplifiers. Multiplexer successively connects amplifiers to a common bus to transfer the data to outside for further processing. (From Building Earth Observation Cameras by Joseph G, CRC press 2015, reproduced with permission via Copyright Clearance Centre)

Digital image data is available as output. Because of combined functionality, miniaturisation and simplification of the sensor electronics, it is possible for CMOS APS to offer lower system power, increased functional flexibility and higher system reliability, all of which lead to reduced system assembly and test cost. The APS also has an advantage of reduced fabrication cost since the proven high yield CMOS fabrication technology can be adopted. Therefore, CMOS based detector arrays are extensively used in commercial applications.

6.7.3 COLLECTING OPTICS

In cameras employing object space scanning, the radiation from each IGFOV is collected close to the optical axis and hence the imaging optics need to be corrected only for a small field to cover the IFOV, or n times IFOV, if n detectors are used per spectral band in the along-track direction. The across-track field requirement depends on the arrangement of the detectors in the focal plane. In practice, the optics for opto-mechanical scanners needs to be corrected for less than 0.1°. However, in the case of pushbroom scanning, the optics has to cover the FOV in the cross track direction corresponding to the swath. For example the IRS LISS-I camera has a FOV of about 9.4° to cover a swath of 148 km. While it is possible to have refractive optics (using only lens elements) corrected for this FOV, when a reflective optics is used additional steps need to be incorporated to get the optics field corrected to accommodate wide FOV. There are two basic design concepts in realising a wider FOV telescope system as discussed in Section 6.5.2. In one configuration, the light collection is primarily by reflective optics and the correction to achieve a larger field/flat field is achieved by placing refractive elements in an appropriate location in the optical path. The refractive corrective system can be placed at the entrance to the collecting optics as in the case of the SPOT HRV camera (Fig. 6.33) or near the focalplane as in the IRS Carto series. As this scheme uses both reflective and refractive components, it is referred to as a catadioptric system. We have seen that two-mirror systems can provide a good image over a narrow field only (Fig. 6.19). One could add more reflective surfaces so that there are more parameters (such as surface profile and its location), which can be varied to compensate for aberrations over a wider FOV, thereby making an all reflective optical system. A three mirror system – three mirror anastigmatic (TMA) telescope – offers a diffraction-limited wide FOV with superior stray light baffling. This configuration is used

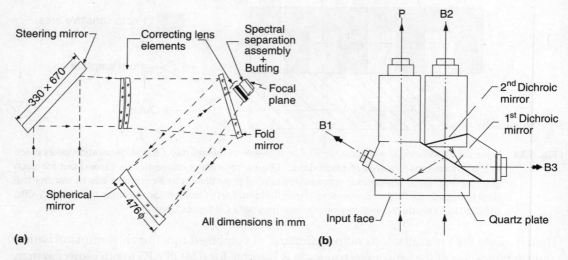

Fig. 6.33 SPOT HRV (a) Optical configuration used in SPOT (adapted from Chevrel et. al., 1981), (b) Optical schematic of a HRV beam-splitter. (Adapted from Jouan et. al., 1989)

in many space-borne earth observation cameras including IRS-PAN/LISS-IV cameras (Fig. 6.35a).

6.7.4 Pushbroom Cameras Operated from Satellite

The first space-borne pushbroom imager MSU-E (Multispectral Scanning Unit-Electronic) was built at the Russian Institute of Space Device Engineering (ISDE). The instrument had three parallel CCD arrays each of 1024 elements, thereby providing multispectral imagery in the visible–NIR spectral band with 28 m resolution and 28 km swath. The camera was first flown on board Meteor-Priroda-5 (Meteor I-30) on 18 June 1980 (Joseph, 2016). The SPOT-1 (Satellites Pour l'Observation de la Terre or Earth-observing Satellites) launched in 1986 is the first operational earth observation satellite based on the pushbroom imaging mode. This was followed by IRS-1A launched in 1988. We shall now discuss some of the technical details of a few space borne EO cameras operating in the pushbroom mode.

6.7.4.1 SPOT-HRV Camera

The first operational spaceborne remote sensing payload operating in the pushbroom mode was the HRV onboard the French earth observation satellite SPOT. It provides a three-band multi-spectral image (MX) with 20 m resolution and also has a panchromatic band (PAN) of 10 m resolution. There are two such cameras onboard, each providing a 60 km swath. One specific advantage of the SPOT system is that the view axis of the camera can be pointed in the cross-track direction within a range of ±27° from the nadir. We shall now discuss the important design details of the SPOT camera system.

The HRV optical system consists of a spherical mirror with lenses to correct for aberrations. The optical system has a focal length of 1082 mm with a $f/3.5$ aperture. The optical path is bent through 90° at the telescope entrance by a plane elliptical mirror (Midan, 1986). This mirror driven by a stepper motor allows off-nadir viewing. Off-nadir viewing enables the instrument to revisit a specific region within 5 days and produce stereo pairs from two different orbits, which can provide height information. A fold mirror is used to reduce telescope dimensions [Fig. 6.33(a)]. It is important to note that such a catadioptic design has the inherent limitation of not allowing a large field coverage. Therefore, two instruments are required to cover a reasonable swath of about 120 km.

The spectral separation and detection is carried out by a focal plane assembly, which consists of a beam-splitter assembly and an optical butting unit with associated CCDs. The optical schematic of a beam-splitter is shown in Fig. 6.33(b). The assembly essentially consists of a set of prisms with dichroic coatings at appropriate faces. The green band B1 is reflected by the dichroic mirror 1. The red (B2) and IR (B3) bands are separated by the dichroic mirror 2. The panchromatic band is directly transmitted through the prism. Spectral responses for each band are achieved by means of filters at the output ports. For each channel, the separator behaves as a plane parallel block of glass. To reduce the polarisation sensitivity arising out of dielectric mirrors a 'multi-wave' quartz plate is placed in front of the beam-splitters.

A CCD of 6000 detector elements is required to get a 10 m resolution and 60 km swath. This is achieved by optically butting four 1728 element CCDs.

In order to improve the radiometric accuracy of the instrument, and to correct for any changes that may occur during its lifetime in orbit (ageing of optical coatings, contamination of optical surfaces, degradation of CCD detectors), the HRV is equipped with a calibration system which can be operated by ground control. The signals generated by the CCDs are processed by two separate image processing electronics for the PAN and MX channels. The amplifier gain for each of the CCDs can be changed by command. The data are digitised to 8 bits. Due to higher resolution, the data rate of PAN is one-third more than the MX data rate. To overcome this, the PAN processing electronics includes a data compression function, which ensures that the PAN output bit rate is identical to the MX output. Each HRV delivers two 25 Mbps data streams corresponding to the PAN and MX modes. Major HRV parameters are given in Table 6.6.

Table 6.6 SPOT HRV characteristics

Optics	Catadioptic $f/3.5$; FL:108.2 cm
Detector	CCD
Spectral bands (micrometre)	0.50–0.59 ⎫
	0.61–0.68 ⎬ MX
	0.79–0.89 ⎭
	0.51–0.73 PAN
Ground resolution (m)	20 (MX)
(Nadir, 822 km)	10 (PAN)
Swath (km)	60
	117 (2 HRV Combined)
Off-nadir viewing (degree)	± 27
Quantisation (bits)	8 (MX)
	6 or 8 DPCM (PAN)
Data rate	85 MBPS

MX — Multi-spectral channel; PAN — Panchromatic channel

The second generation SPOT satellites, namely, SPOT 4/5 have an additional band in the Middle Infrared Region (MIR) for multi-spectral imaging (HRVIR) and also carry a new five bands imaging system called '*Vegetation instrument*' with a resolution of about 1 km (Arnaud, 1988). The addition of the middle IR band (1.58–1.75 μm), sensitive to vegetation water stress, is quite useful for various themes in agriculture as well as to inventorise various types of snow and for certain applications in geology.

The vegetation instrument is a separate and independent payload of the SPOT 4/5 satellites (Arnaud and Leroy, 1991). Unlike the HRV, for the vegetation instrument, each spectral band uses separate collecting optics. Of the five spectral channels, four are identical to HRVIR and the fifth band is 0.43–0.47 μm, useful for oceanic information. The vegetation instrument provides a spatial resolution of about 1 km and swath of about 2200 km with a 10-bit radiometric resolution.

6.7.4.2 IRS-LISS Camera

The first operational remote sensing satellite of India (IRS-1A) has two payloads employing linear imaging self-scanning (LISS) sensors.

(i) A camera operating in four bands (B1, B2, B3 and B4) in the 0.45–0.86 μm region with a geometric resolution of 72.5 m and a swath of 148.48 km. This camera is called LISS-I.

(ii) Two cameras (LISS-II) operating in four bands in the 0.45–0.86 μm band (similar to LISS-I) with a geometric resolution of 36.25 m, each with a swath of 74.24 km. The combined swath of the two LISS-II cameras, allowing for a 3 km overlap between them, is 145.48 km. The cameras operate in the pushbroom scanning mode using linear CCD arrays of 2048 elements.

We shall now briefly describe the design features of IRS-LISS cameras. The LISS cameras have a modular design. Each of the camera systems consists of four imaging lens assemblies (one for each band) followed by a linear CCD array (Fig. 6.34). This configuration has been chosen after detailed trade-off studies to choose between a single collecting optics (as in SPOT) and a multiple optical system. One of the many advantages of a system with a separate lens for each band is that it offers best MTF performance, as each lens needs only to be optimised for its own spectral band. Each imaging lens assembly consists of 8 elements (a double Gauss design). In addition to these elements, the first two elements are a neutral density filter and an interference filter. The imaging lens assemblies have focal lengths of 162.2 mm for LISS-I and 324.4 mm for LISS-II. Both cameras use a 13×13 μm^2 element size linear CCD having 2048 elements.

Considering various aspects such as diffraction limited performance, design/fabrication complexities, size, and so on, the camera system is designed to have an f/no. of 4.5 for both LISS-I and LISS-II. The spectral bands are selected keeping in mind the application needs as well as to minimise the effects of atmospheric absorptions. Moreover, band shapes have a steep rise and fall corresponding to a four-cavity interference filter.

The onboard calibration system uses LEDs. Two LEDs illuminate each CCD array from the two sides. The calibration system illuminates all the 2048 elements of the CCD. Using the ON-OFF combination of these LEDs, 12 non-zero intensity levels are generated covering the total dynamic range. The onboard calibration system enables the corrections required, if any, for the degradations that may occur in CCD detectors and associated video circuits.

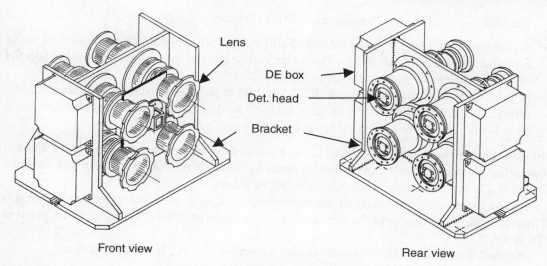

Lens

DE box

Det. head

Bracket

Front view

Rear view

Fig. 6.34 IRS-1A LISS-I camera mechanical configuration of the electro-optics (EO) module. Det. head — Detector head carrying CCD; DE box — Detector electronics box housing circuits to the drive CCD and pre-amplifier.

The signals generated by each CCD are processed and digitised to 7 bits using a separate chain for each band, thereby achieving modularity at the band level. Adequate redundancies are incorporated to ensure that a single point failure will not jeopardise the multi-spectral imaging capability. The radiance saturation value can be set to one of the four levels separately for each band. The LISS-I and LISS-II data are transmitted separately using S and X band transmitters respectively. Table 6.7 gives the IRS-1A/1B camera parameters.

Table 6.7 IRS-1A/1B camera parameters

	LISS-I	LISS-II
Optics	Multi-element lens	Multi-element lens
	f/4.5, FL = 162.2 m	f/4.5, FL = 324.4 mm
Ground resolution (m) (from 904 km height)	72.5	36.25
Swath (km)	148	74 (Two LISS-II combined 146.5)
Spectral bands (micrometre)	0.45–0.52	0.45–0.52
	0.52–0.59	0.52–0.59
	0.62–0.68	0.62–0.68
	0.77–0.86	0.77–0.86
Detector	2K CCD	2K CCD
Quantisation (bits)	7	7
Data rate (Mbps)	5.2	2×10.4
Power (W)	34	2×34
Weight (kg)	38.5	2×80.8

The follow-on to IRS-1A/1B satellites, IRS-IC/1D have

- A panchromatic camera in the 0.50–0.75 μm range with a geometric resolution of about 6 m and a swath of about 70 km. The swath can be steered in a range of ± 405 km (on the surface of the earth) with reference to the nadir.
- A four band multi-spectral camera (B2, B3 and B4 of IRS-1A/1B and an additional middle infrared band B5 in the spectral range of 1.55–1.7 μm) with a geometric resolution of about 23 m for B2, B3, B4 and about 70 m for B5, with a swath of 140 km.

In addition to these payloads, IRS-1C/1D also carry a wide field of view sensor (WiFS) operating in two spectral bands, B3 and B4 with a geometric resolution of about 188 m, and a swath of 770 km. This camera provides a revisit of 5 days.

All the three cameras operate in the pushbroom scanning mode using linear CCD arrays (Joseph et. al., 1995). Some of the important specifications of IRS-1C/1D cameras are given in Table 6.8.

We shall now discuss the important design aspects of IRS-1C/1D camera systems.

Panchromatic camera

A high resolution camera requires long focal length optics. However, the required angular resolution can be obtained by a number of possible combinations of detector size and optics focal length. The optics focal length can be decreased by decreasing the detector size. Though by decreasing the detector size, the size of optics can be reduced, it results in a penalty

Table 6.8 Specifications of IRS-1C/1D cameras

Parameters	Panchromatic	Multi-spectral	WiFS
Optics	All reflective off-axis telescope	Multi-element lens	Multi-element lens
Ground resolution (m) (from 812 km)	5.8	23.5, B2, B3, B4 70.5 MIR (B5)	188
Swath (km)	70	140	770
Swath steering Range (Deg.)	±26	Not applicable	Not applicable
Spectral band (micrometre)	0.5–0.75	B2 0.52–0.59 B3 0.62–0.68 B4 0.77–0.86 B5 1.55–1.70	B3 0.62–0.68 B4 0.77–0.86
Detector	3 × 4 k CCD	6 k CCD (B2-B4) 2 k CCD (B5)	2 k CCD
Quantisation (Bits)	6	7	7
Data rate (MBpS)	85	36 for B2, B3, B4 1.4 for B5	2
Power (Watts)	65	95	22
Weight of EO Module (kg)	120	85	20

of operating the system at a higher spatial frequency. For a $7 \times 7 \ \mu m^2$ CCD element size, the frequency of operation is ~ 70l line pair per mm. For such a high spatial frequency, obscured systems do not offer good MTF performance. Hence, PAN optics uses unobscured optical systems [Fig. 6.35(a)] consisting of three mirrors. A single CCD of 4 K pixels does not cater to the swath requirements, thereby necessitating the use of three CCDs to cover the required swath. A novel optical butting scheme is used wherein these three CCDs are cascaded to cover the required swath without incorporating any beam-splitter [Fig. 6.35(b)]. The mechanical configuration of the electro-optics module is shown in [Fig. 6.35(c)].

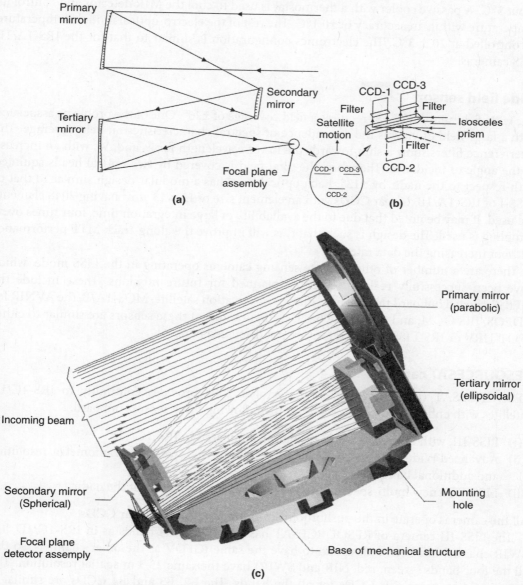

Fig. 6.35 IRS-1C pan optical configuration.(a) Schematics of collecting optics.(b) Focal plane optical butting scheme.(c) Mechanical layout of the EO module.

LISS-III camera

The LISS-III system design is similar to the LISS-I design. Band 1 is replaced by a middle infrared (MIR) band B5 (1.55–1.70 μm). In this band, InGaAs linear CCD array with a 26 μm pitch is used. The VNIR bands use a 6 K silicon linear CCD with a 10 μm pitch. The along-track MTF degrades due to the relative motion of the camera and scene during the integration time. To reduce this smear effect, the pixel size along-track is chosen to be 7 μm but data is sampled corresponding to a 10 μm interval. The geometric resolution of the MIR band is 3 times lower than that of VNIR bands. The MIR device is maintained at a temperature of about 5°C. A passive cooler with a thermostat is used to cool the MIR detector and control its temperature within an accuracy of ±0.1°C. The rest of the electro-optical module temperature is controlled at 20 ± 3°C. The electronics configuration is similar to that for the IRS-1A/1B LISS cameras.

Wide field sensor

The wide field sensor (WiFS) requires a field coverage of ±26°. One of the problems associated with a large field of view is the dependence of spectral characteristics on field coverage. The interference filters show a shift towards the lower wavelength for λ_c and $\Delta\lambda$, with an increase in the angle of incidence. Therefore, the total field is covered by two optical heads squinted with respect to the nadir by ±13°. Each optical head has a modular design similar to that of LISS-I of IRS-1A/1B. Linear CCDs with an element size of $13 \times 13 \ \mu\text{m}^2$ having 2048 elements are used. It may be noted that due to the availability of large integration time, four times over-sampling is used. The design is such that this will improve the along-track MTF performance without increasing the data rate.

There are a number of other remote sensing cameras operating in the LISS mode, which have been successfully realised, or being planned for future missions. These include the MESSR carried onboard the Japanese marine observation satellite, MOS-1A/B, the AVNIR for ADEOS, IRS OCM, and so on. The basic configurations of these sensors are similar to either SPOT-HRV or IRS-LISS and therefore are not discussed here.

RESOURCESAT camera

RESOURCESAT (IRS-P6) launched in October 2003 provides continuity to IRS-1C/1D satellites with enhanced capabilities. It has the following three sensors onboard.

(i) LISS-III, with improved SWIR resolution compared to IRS-1C/1D.
(ii) Advanced Wide Field Sensor (AWiFS), with improved spatial and radiometric resolution and additional bands.
(iii) LISS-IV, a new multi-spectral camera with a 5.8 m resolution at the nadir.

All the cameras operate in the pushbroom scanning mode using linear CCDs.

The LISS-III camera of RESOURCESAT has B2, B3 and B4 bands as in IRS-1C/1D. The SWIR channel has been redesigned to have the same IGFOV as the other channels, so that all the four bands (green, red, NIR and SWIR) have the same 23.5 m spatial resolution. This is achieved by using 6 K CCDs for all the bands. The B2, B3 and B4 CCDs are similar to those used in the IRS-1C/1D LISS-III. The SWIR CCD is a new device with a pixel size of

$13 \, \mu m \times 13 \, \mu m$ and the odd and even pixels displaced (centre to centre) by $26 \, \mu m$. The SWIR lens focal length is chosen so that the IGFOV matches the other bands.

The AWiFS is an improved version of the WiFS flown in IRS-1C/1D. The AWiFS has a spatial resolution of 56 m at the nadir and operates in four spectral bands as in LISS-III. It uses 6 K devices similar to those used in LISS-III. It has 10-bit digitisation and the dynamic range covers 100% reflection at all seasons. Thus snow/sand features will not be saturated and can provide new information. No other satellite sensor has this capability at this resolution. As in the case of IRS-1C/D WiFS, the total FOV is covered by two optical heads (squinted with respect to the nadir by ±12°) in order to provide a combined swath of 740 km.

The LISS-IV is a high resolution (5.8 m at the nadir) multi-spectral camera operating in B2, B3 and B4 bands. The basic optics is similar to that of PAN of IRS-1C/1D. However, the CCD is a 12 K (12,000 pixels) device, with a pixel size of $7 \, \mu m \times 7 \, \mu m$, with odd and even pixels staggered by $35 \, \mu m$ (5 pixels). To reduce the device read-out rate, each CCD has 8 output ports, so that each port gives the output from 1500 pixels. In order to accommodate three CCDs corresponding to three bands, an ingenious beam-splitter assembly is used. Reflective surfaces are used in the converging beam ahead of the focal plane (Fig. 6.36). B2 and B4 bands are separated by reflection while B3 passes through a slot at the centre. Each band output is digitised to 10 bits. However, due to transmission data rate constraints, only 7 bits are used for transmission. Any 7 consecutive bits from the 10-bit pixel data can be selected by ground command. Filters are placed in front of each detector for spectral selection. The swath covered is 70 km as in IRS-1C/1D PAN.

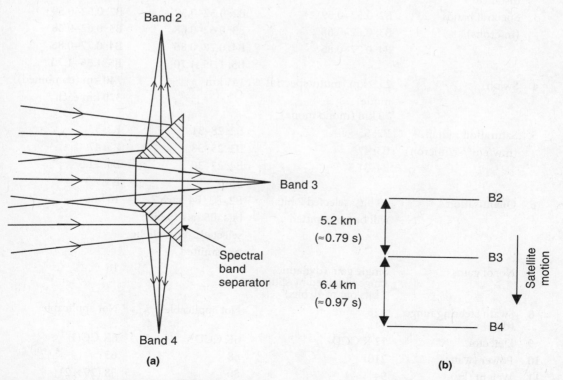

Fig. 6.36 Schematics showing (a) LISS-IV focal plane beam-splitter, (b) projection of detectors on the ground.

The LISS-IV camera can be operated in mono or multi-spectral mode. In the mono mode any single band (out of B2, B3, B4) can be transmitted at the full swath of 70 km. This is similar to PAN operation (except for spectral band details). Any band can be selected by ground command (nominal is B3 — red band). In order to keep the data transmission rate the same as that of IRS-1C/1D PAN only 1/3 of the swath is transmitted in the multi-spectral mode. The multi-spectral data can be selected using an electronic steering scheme for any 4 K contiguous pixels within the full swath of 12 K pixels by commanding the start pixel number. The three bands are displaced along track and this makes registration between the bands dependent on spacecraft dynamics. The LISS-IV camera has the additional feature of off-nadir viewing by tilting the camera by ±26°. This way, as in the case of IRS-1C/1D PAN, LISS-IV can provide a re-visit of 5 days for any given ground area and can also provide stereo pairs.

Since the bands are similar to that of LISS-III, it is much simpler and more representative to generate LISS-III + LISS-IV (mono) merged products.

The major specifications of IRS-P6 payloads are given in Table 6.9.

Table 6.9 Major specifications of RESOURCESAT-1 payloads

	Specification	LISS-IV	LISS-III	AWiFS
1	IGFOV (across track)	5.8 m	23.5 m	56 m (nadir) 70 m (at field edge)
2	Ground sampling distance	5.8 m	23.5 m	56 m
3	Spectral bands (microns)	B2: 0.52–0.59 B3: 0.62–0.68 B4: 0.77–0.86	B2: 0.52–0.59 B3: 0.62–0.68 B4: 0.77–0.86 B5: 1.55–1.70	B2: 0.52–0.59 B3: 0.62–0.68 B4: 0.77–0.86 B5: 1.55–1.70
4	Swath	23.9 km (multi-spectral mode) 70 km (mono mode)	141 km	740 km (combined) 370 km each
5	Saturation radiance (mw/cm^2/sr/micron)	B2: 55 B3: 47 B4: 31.5	B2: 28–31 B3: 25–38 B4: 27–30 B5: 7.5	B2: 53 B3: 47 B4: 31.5 B5: 7.5
6	Quantisation	10 bits; selected 7 bits will be transmitted	B2, B3, B4 have 7 bits. B5 has 10 bits; selected 7 bits will be transmitted	10 bits
7	No. of gains	Single gain (dynamic range obtained by sliding 7 bits out of 10 bits)	4	16
8	Swath steering range (deg.)	±26	Not applicable	Not applicable
9	Detector	12 K CCD	6K CCD	6K CCD
10	Power (watts)	210	68	65
11	Weight (kg) (EO module)	94	80	58 (29 × 2)

6.7.4.3 Landsat 8—Data Continuity Mission (LDCM)

Landsat satellites have been providing us with uninterrupted multispectral images of the earth since 1972. The workhorse in the Landsat series is the Multi Spectral Scanner (MSS) and its follow on Thematic Mapper (TM) and its variants (Section 6.6.1). These sensors are based on opto-mechanical scanning technology. In order to get a better performance the follow-on satellite in the Landsat series – Landsat 8 – is based on pushbroom technology. Landsat-8, previously known as the Landsat Data Continuity Mission (LDCM), was launched on 11 February 2013, with two independent instruments that are operated simultaneously— (i) the Operational Land Imager (OLI) with nine spectral bands in the visible (VIS), near infrared (NIR), and the shortwave infrared (SWIR) spectral regions; and (ii) the Thermal Infrared Sensor (TIRS) with two spectral bands in the thermal IR (TIR) region. In order to provide continuity of data to the Landsat data users, the Landsat-8 specifications such as ground resolution, swath, spectral location and so on, are compatible with the ETM+ specifications.

The OLI telescope is a four mirror off-axis anastigmatic design with an aperture of 13.5 cm, with an aperture stop in front and an effective focal length of 886 mm at the centre of the field of view (Fig. 6.37). The optics is positioned inside a lightweight, yet highly stable, carbon composite optical bench. The telescope provides a 15-degree field-of-view covering 185 km across-track ground swath from the nominal Landsat-8 altitude of 705 km. The OLI sensor collects image data in 8 multispectral bands extending from 0.435 to 2.294 micrometres with a spatial resolution of 30 m and a panchromatic band of 15 m resolution. The focal plane detector organisation is quite different compared to other similar pushbroom cameras. The visible–near IR (VNIR) and PAN bands use silicon photodiode (PIN) arrays and the shortwave–IR (SWIR) bands use mercury–cadmium–telluride (MCT) arrays for photon detection. Appropriately mounted interference filters provide the spectral selection. In order to take care of any failures there are redundant detectors—two for each silicon and three for each MCT detector. One of the two detectors can be selected for readout for the silicon bands, and one of the three detectors can be selected for the MCT bands. This arrangement introduces an offset that must be accounted for during data processing based on auxiliary data which identifies which detector elements are actively read out. The swath is covered by 14 staggered detector assemblies (sensor chip assembly, SCAs) each carrying 9 detector arrays (Fig. 6.38). The focal plane assembly (FPA) is passively cooled to keep the temperature of the detectors at less than 210 K. A focussing mechanism is incorporated in the FPA to adjust the focus by ground command. The OLI is digitised to 14 bits, but due to data rate transmission limitations, only 12 bits (the 12 highest bits or the 12 lowest bits) are sent to the ground.

Table 6.10 compares spectral details and the signal to noise ratio (SNR) for ETM+ and OLI. Both the cameras have the same spatial resolution and swath. However, OLI even with a better spectral resolution, provides a much higher SNR though the collecting optics aperture is only 13.5 cm compared to the ETM+ aperture of 40.6 cm. This is a good practical example demonstrating the advantage of a pushbroom camera over an opto-mechanical scanner as explained in Section 6.7.

The Thermal Infrared Sensor (TIRS) of Landsat-8 is the first instrument to image in the thermal IR in the pushbroom mode. The TIRS telescope is a temperature-stabilised four-

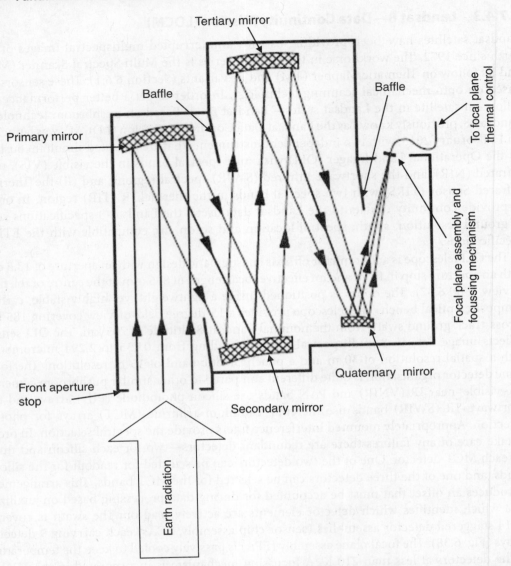

Fig. 6.37   Schematics showing OLI telescope layout and optical path. (Adapted from L8 EO portal https://directory.eoportal.org/web/eoportal/satellite-missions/l/landsat-8-ldcm#sensors)

element refractive lens assembly. It has three germanium (Ge) elements and one zinc selenide (ZnSe) element having a focal length of 178 mm and f number $f/1.64$, providing an FOV of 15° (Fig. 6.39). There is an ingenious non-mechanical way to adjust the focus, if the need arises, using the thermal dependence of the index of refraction of Ge. This property is used to adjust the focus by providing a provision to change the Ge lens temperature by ±5 K (Reuter 2009). The camera collects data in two spectral bands—10.6–11.19 μ and 11.5–12.51 μ. Two channels in the thermal region enable more accurate temperature extraction from the radiance data by correcting for atmospheric effect (refer Section A1.5.2). The instrument provides 100 m spatial resolution over a 185 km swath. The instrument uses GaAs Quantum Well Infrared

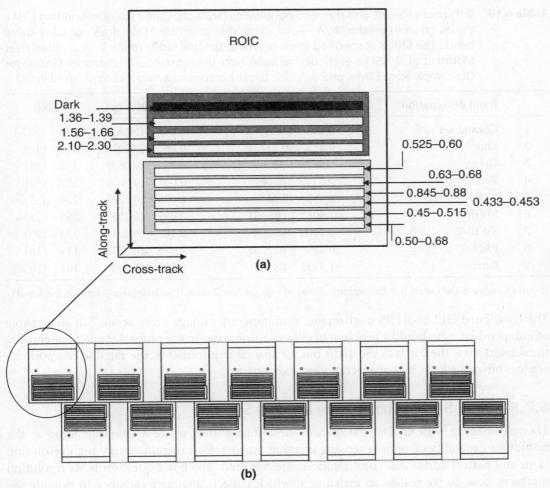

Fig. 6.38 (a) Detector layout in one Sensor Chip Assembly. Each SCA consists of rows of detectors, a read-out integrated circuit (ROIC), and a nine-band filter assembly mounted on a single plate. The numbers are the wavelength region in microns. (b) Focal plane layout of detectors in OLI. (Adapted from L8 EO portal https://directory.eoportal.org/web/eoportal/satellite-missions/l/landsat-8-ldcm#sensors)

Photo detectors (QWIPs) in the focal plane to measure the radiation—a technology flown for the first time on Landsat-8. The focal plane assembly consists of three identical Sensor Chip Assemblies (SCAs) staggered along-track with overlap so that the combined pixels cover the swath. The focal plane assembly is cooled to about 40 K by a two-stage mechanical cryocooler and is held stable to better than 0.05 K. To reduce the background thermal level, the focal plane enclosure is cooled to ~100 K. On-orbit radiometric calibration is carried out by looking at deep space and a black body source. For this purpose, at the entrance of the lens, a scene select mechanism is included which flips a flat mirror to change the look angle from the nadir (that is, earth view), either to the on-board blackbody calibrator or a deep space view. Data generated by TIRS are quantised to 12 bits. The noise equivalent differential temperature (NEΔT) of TIRS data is approximately 0.05 K at 300 K in both bands.

Table 6.10   OLI spectral bands and signal-to-noise ratios (SNR) compared to corresponding ETM+ values given in bracket. N/A — not applicable since the ETM+ does not carry these bands. The SNR is at specified levels of typical spectral radiance (for $L_{Typical}$ values refer Morfitt et. al., 2015) for each spectral band. Note the substantial improvement in SNR for OLI compared to ETM+, primarily due to pushbroom scanning technique used in OLI.

	Band designation	Central wavelength (μ)		Band width (μ)		SNR	
1	Coastal/aerosol	0.443	(N/A)	0.016	(N/A)	238	(N/A)
2	Blue	0.482	(0.4775)	0.06	(0.073)	364	(40)
3	Green	0.5615	(0.56)	0.057	(0.082)	302	(41)
4	Red	0.6545	(0.6615)	0.037	(0.061)	227	(90)
5	NIR	0.865	(0.835)	0.028	(0.126)	204	(35)
6	SWIR-1	1.6085	(1.648)	0.085	(0.202)	265	(36)
7	SWIR-2	2.2005	(2.2045)	0.187	(0,281)	334	(29)
8	PAN	0.5895	(0.7055)	0.173	(0.381)	149	(16)
9	Cirrus	1.3735	(N/A)	0.021	(N/A)	165	(N/A)

(Source Landsat 8 Data users handbook; https://landsat.usgs.gov/documents/Landsat8DataUsersHandbook.pdf)

The co-aligned OLI and TRS instruments simultaneously image every scene, but are capable of independent use, should a problem in either sensor arise. In the normal mode of operation, the sensors view the earth at the nadir but for special requirements, the satellite can point its sensors off-nadir ±15° by a spacecraft yaw manoeuvre.

6.7.5   High Spatial Resolution Imaging Systems

Though imaging with CCDs (the manner described above) made a quantum jump in the resolution capability of remote sensing imaging sensors, for imaging at very high resolution (1 m and better) additional considerations are required. The basic question is, as resolution increases how do we realise an instrument which collects adequate radiance to provide the desired signal to noise ratio? To have continuity we shall repeat what we discussed in Chapter 3, Section 3.5. The radiant flux delivered to the detector is given by

$$\Phi_d = \frac{\pi}{4} O_e \Delta\lambda L_\lambda \beta^2 D^2 \text{ watts}$$

If we observe a target for a time τ seconds (integration time/dwell time), then the on-axis energy received by the detector is given by

$$\Phi_d = \frac{\pi}{4} O_e \Delta\lambda L_\lambda \beta^2 D^2 \tau \text{ joules} \tag{6.11}$$

where L_λ is the target radiance (W m^{-2}sr$^{-1}\mu$m^{-1}), $\Delta\lambda$ the spectral bandwidth of the radiation to be measured (μm), O_e the optical efficiency transmittance of the optical system including atmosphere (<1), β the instantaneous field of view (IFOV) in steradian (β can be expressed as $\frac{A_d}{f^2}$ where A_d is the detector area and f is the effective focal length of the imaging optics and D is the effective aperture diameter of the collecting optics.

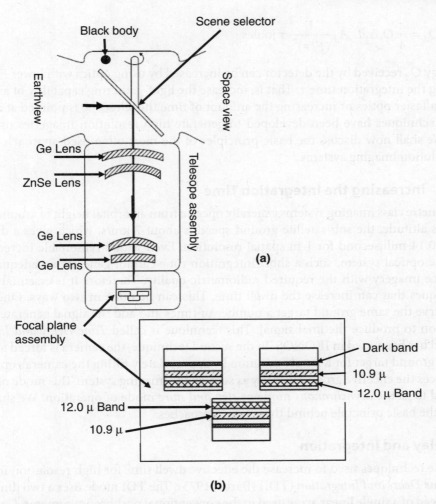

Fig. 6.39 (a) Schematics showing Landsat 8 TIRS electro-optical module. (b) Schematics showing the focal plane assembly. Each SCA contains a two dimensional detector array of which 32 rows are covered by the spectral filters that define the TIRS spectral bands. 32 active rows allow the correction of any pixel degradation by substituting from a row in which the corresponding pixel is functioning properly. 76 rows of pixels which are shielded from radiation (dark bands) are used for dark current estimation. (Adapted from L8 eo portal https://directory.eoportal.org/web/eoportal/satellite-missions/l/landsat-8-ldcm#sensors)

Substituting for β in terms of focal length, we can rewrite Eq. 6.11 as

$$Q_d = \frac{\pi}{4} O_e \Delta \lambda L_\lambda \frac{A_d}{f^2} D^2 \tau \text{ joules}$$

$$Q_d = \frac{\pi}{4} O_e \Delta \lambda L_\lambda A_d \frac{D^2}{f^2} \tau \text{ joules} \tag{6.12}$$

Replacing $\frac{f}{D}$ with the f number (F/#), Eq. 6.12 can be rewritten as

$$Q_d = \frac{\pi}{4} O_e \Delta \lambda L_\lambda A_d \frac{1}{(F/\#)^2} \tau \text{ joules} \qquad (6.13)$$

The energy Q_d received by the detector can be increased by using optics with lower $F/\#$ and/or increasing the integration time τ. That is, increase the light-gathering capability of a telescope by using a faster optics or increasing the amount of time the telescope is pointed at an object. Various techniques have been developed to generate high resolution imageries using CCD arrays. We shall now discuss the basic principles of the most often used approach to realise high resolution imaging systems.

6.7.5.1   Increasing the Integration Time

The sub-metre class imaging systems generally operate from an orbital height of around 650 km. From this altitude, the sub-satellite ground speed is about 7 km/s, which gives a dwell time of about 0.14 millisecond for 1 m spatial resolution. Even with a reasonable increase in the size of the optical system, such a short integration time cannot generate an adequate signal to produce imagery with the required radiometric quality. Therefore it is essential to resort to techniques that can increase the dwell time. This can be done in two ways. One method is to observe the same ground target a number of times and add the signal generated in each observation to produce the final signal. This technique is called *Time Delay and Integration* (TDI) and has been used in IKONOS. In the second technique, the camera is forced to 'stare' at the same ground target for a longer duration by appropriately tilting the camera's optical axis. This reduces the effective ground velocity as seen by the imaging system. This mode of imaging is referred to as the *asynchronous* mode or *step and stare* mode of operation. We shall briefly describe the basic principle behind these two approaches.

Time delay and integration

One of the techniques used to increase the effective dwell time for high resolution imaging is called *Time Delay and Integration* (TDI) (Barbe, 1975). The TDI mode uses a two dimensional array instead of a single linear array used in the conventional pushbroom cameras. Consider an array consisting of M pixels (across-track) and N rows (along-track). The charge accumulated in each row is transferred to the successive lines at a rate exactly compensating the image motion, thereby increasing the effective dwell time N times. The TDI techniques thus enable integration of charges for the same objects through multiple lines positioned along-track (Fig. 6.40). The signal increases linearly, while in general, the noise adds up incoherently, thereby producing an improvement of the S/N ratio by a factor of $(N)^{1/2}$. While TDI mode effectively increases the dwell time, full performance advantage can be achieved only if the charge transfer from each line to the next is in exact synchronisation with image motion. The spacecraft attitude stability, drift, and so on, should be controlled to meet this requirement.

The first civilian remote sensing satellite system to use TDI for generating high resolution (1 m GSD) is IKONOS. Apart from the panchromatic data at 1 m resolution, the system also takes 4-band multi-spectral (B, G, R, NIR) imagery with a 4 m spatial resolution. The instrument has a three-mirror telescope with a primary mirror of 0.7 m diameter and an overall telescope focal length of 10 m. Two flat mirrors are used to fold the optical beam in order to produce a compact instrument (Fig. 6.41). The detector for the PAN is a TDI CCD

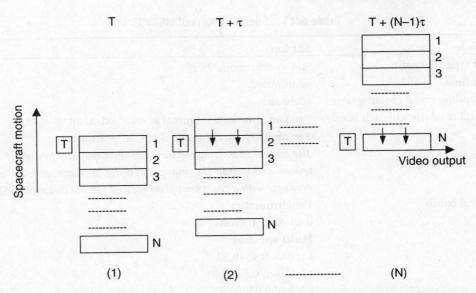

Fig. 6.40 Schematic showing concept of TDI. At (1) target 'T' is seen by the first array. When the sensor has moved through a distance corresponding to one integration time, at (2) the target is seen by the second array (2) and the information in array '1' is transferred to array '2'. This process continues till the last array N is reached after (N – 1) transfers and the data is read out serially from the Nth array.

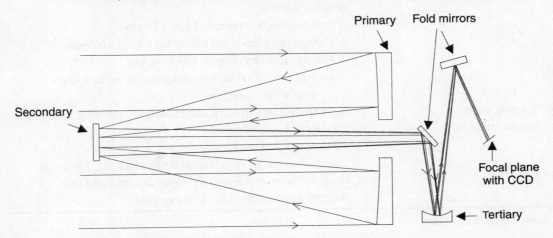

Fig. 6.41 Schematics of the optical layout of IKONOS telescope. The primary, secondary and tertiary are curved surfaces. The fold mirrors are used to reduce the size of telescope (not to scale). Based on a photograph at www.*birdseyeimages.com/cameraschema.html*

array with a 12 μm pixel size and 32 TDI stages having 13,500 pixels. The specifications of IKNOS imaging system/spacecraft are given in Table 6.11.

Effective ground track velocity reduction

In the conventional pushbroom technique, ideally, the optical axis is along the radius vector of the satellite orbit. The signal is usually integrated for a duration equal to the time taken by

Table 6.11   Specifications of IKONOS

Altitude	681 km
Orbit type/inclination	Sun-synchronous/98.1°
Orbit time	98 minutes
Descending nodal crossing time	10:30 am
Ground resolution of each band	1 m panchromatic (nominal at < 26° off-nadir)
	4 m multi-spectral (nominal at < 26° off-nadir)
	The ground processing software has the capability to rapidly process and mosaic the imagery in order to create seamless image products with a consistent pixel ground sample distance (GSD)
Spectral bands	**Panchromatic:**
	0.45–0.90 microns
	Multi-spectral:
	#1: Blue 0.45–0.52
	#2: Green 0.52–0.60
	#3: Red 0.63–0.69
	#4: Near IR 0.76–0.90
	(same as LANDSAT 4 and 5 TM bands #1–4)
Swath widths and scene sizes	Nominal swath width: 11 km at nadir
	Areas of interest:
	A nominal single image at 13 km × 13 km
	• strips of 11 km × 100 km up to11 km × 1000 km
	• image mosaics of up to 12000 sq. km
	• up to two 10000 sq. km contiguous areas in a single pass within a region
Viewing angle	Agile spacecraft—in track and cross-track pointing
Revisit frequency	2.9 days at 1 m resolution,
	1.5 days at 1.5 m resolution
	These values are for targets at 40 degrees latitude. The revisit times will be more frequent for higher latitudes and less frequent for latitudes closer to the equator

Source: spaceimaging.com

the sub-satellite point to move through one resolution element—dwell time. This mode of operation is called the 'synchronous' mode, since the data is collected synchronous with the satellite motion (or the optical axis moves synchronously with the sub-satellite). If we can reduce the relative velocity between the optical axis and the ground, we can increase the dwell time. In practice, this can be achieved by tilting the optical axis, so that its projection on the ground moves in the opposite direction with respect to the sub-satellite velocity vector, such that it 'stares' at the pixel for a longer time. This mode is asynchronous to the sub-satellite velocity and is referred to as the *asynchronous* mode or *step and stare* mode of operation. In Fig. 6.42, at $t = 0$, the sub-satellite point is at A. The optical axis is tilted such that its projection on the earth is at C. Now, as the satellite moves from A to B, the optical axis is continuously

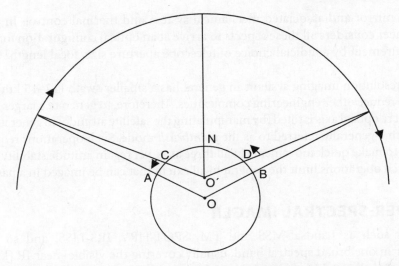

Fig. 6.42   Schematics showing asynchronous (step and stare) mode of data collection for a pushbroom sensor. In the synchronous operation, the optical axis continuously 'looks' at the centre of the earth. In the asynchronous mode, the optical axis is continuously tilted such that it always points towards a point that is at a certain distance above the centre of the earth.

moved, opposite to the sub-satellite velocity vector such that as the sub-satellite point travels through the arc length AB, the optical axis projection only travels through CD. Thus, a relative velocity reduction of CD/AB is achieved. The increase in dwell time not only allows a better signal-to-noise ratio, but also produces a lower data rate. However, this mode of operation has its own limitations. During a satellite pass, you can collect data only for a shorter strip compared to the classical mode of pushbroom operation. As the optical axis is tilted with respect to the satellite velocity vector, the ground projection of the pixel on the along-track and cross-track varies continuously from C to D. Since the projection of the detector on the ground from the image midpoint N increases to either side (NC and ND), both in the along-track and cross-track direction, the resolution is poorer on either sides of the nadir.

The Indian Technology Evaluation Satellite (TES), launched in 2001, successfully demonstrated this concept to generate 1 m spatial resolution imageries.

6.7.5.2   Using Faster Optics

A faster optics (lower F/#) can be realised by increasing the diameter D of the collecting optics or by reducing the focal length. However, since the IFOV is the required sensor parameter, if we reduce the focal length the detector pixel area also needs to be proportionally reduced to keep IFOV the same.

During IRS-1A/B, the CCD device used had a pixel size of 13 × 13 micron. The pixel sizes of successive generation of CCDs have decreased. Linear arrays of 2.5 micron pixel have been reported in the literature (Tatani et. al., 2006; Nixon et. al., 2007). Smaller size pixels lower the well capacity (that is, the maximum number of electrons a pixel can hold without saturation) which in turn limits the dynamic range. A smaller pixel size also requires the optics to operate at a higher spatial frequency. If we decide to increase the diameter of the collecting optics, since, as the size of the optics increases it brings about a number of design challenges for realising the mirror and associated mechanical system and thermal control. In practice, the system engineer considers all these aspects to arrive at an optical configuration for a particular mission requirement by a judicial choice of telescope aperture size, focal length, CCD choice, and so on.

The high resolution imaging systems in general has a smaller swath (12–15 km) to limit the data rate and reduce other engineering complexities. Therefore, to generate a larger swath in one pass, the camera optical axis is tilted (by manipulating the satellite attitude) to generate contiguous adjacent swath—generally referred to as the *paintbrush* mode. Such operations require a highly agile satellite to make quick movements in all three axes, yet regain attitude stability for imaging. Of course, such operations limit the geographical extent that can be imaged in a pass.

6.8 HYPER-SPECTRAL IMAGER

The cameras such as Landsat-MSS and TM, SPOT-HRV, IRS-LISS, and so on, acquire images either in one broad spectral band, usually covering the visible–near IR (known as the panchromatic band) or take imagery in a number of narrow spectral bands at specific thematic locations in the visible–IR region (referred to as multispectral imaging). Thus, in the case of IRS LISS-III, the data is collected in four spectral bands (0.52–0.59, 0.62–0.68, 0.77–0.86 and 1.55–1.70 μm) within the visible and shortwave–IR (SWIR) spectral region. Here we are only *sampling* the reflectance spectra which the multi-spectral instrument senses from the surface. For many applications, such as identifying the surface features and generating thematic information, this sampled information is adequate. However, when there are certain narrow spectral characteristics in the reflected spectra, the coarse spectral bandwidth (which averages the spectral response within the band) and the sampling at a few points do not bring out these characteristics. Figure 6.43 gives the reflectance spectra of the mineral halloysite [from the United States Geological Survey (USGS) spectral library] in the 0.3 to ~1.8 μm spectral region. Two specific absorption bands can be seen in the spectra. The dotted line in Fig. 6.43 shows how the reflectance spectra will look in the 0.52–1.7 μm region, if measured using the four bands of LISS-III. It is clear that the two absorption peaks are not brought out in this case. That is, multi-spectral sensors such as LISS and TM under-sample the spectral information content available from the reflectance spectra. Thus multi-spectral sensors measure the radiation reflected (and/or emitted) from the earth's surface at a few locations in the spectral region, with coarse spectral resolution, while hyper-spectral sensors make *contiguous* measurements in the spectral region of interest in *narrow* spectral bands. The above definition of a hyper-spectral sensor is still ambiguous, since it does not specify *how narrow the spectral band should be*. We may say that if a spectral feature has to be reproduced, the sampling bandwidth should be less than 1/4th of the spectral width of the feature under investigation. However, engineering considerations limit the spectral resolution achievable to provide an image with reasonable signal-to-noise ratio. For a space-borne hyper-spectral sensor with a few tens of metres spatial resolution, a spectral resolution of ~10 nanometres seems reasonable and feasible. It is not the number of bands that qualifies a sensor as hyper-spectral, but rather the narrowness and contiguous nature of the measurements (Shippert, 2004). Thus, hyper-spectral data reproduces the complete spectra for each pixel.

Laboratory studies have shown that a number of minerals have unique spectral characteristics due to electronic and vibrational transitional lines. Therefore, contiguous reflectance/emittance information in very narrow spectral bands, that is, spectroscopic information, can

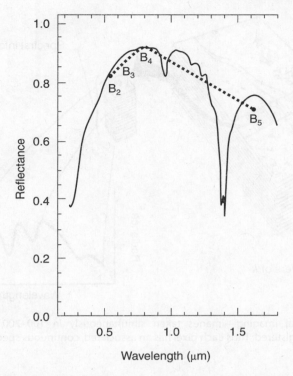

Fig. 6.43 Reflectance spectra of mineral halloysite. The solid curve gives the laboratory spectrometer data and the dotted curve shows what the spectrum will look like if taken through an IRS LISS-3.

identify those surface materials containing diagnostic spectral features. The spectroscopic information from vegetation shows many fine details (Thenkabail et. al., 2011), associated with morphological differences, biochemical changes occurring in the leaf, water/nutrient stress and others, which do not show up when observations are made in broad spectral bands. To study these and similar features hyperspectral imaging has emerged as a powerful tool.

The instrument for hyperspectral imaging called imaging spectrometer (more aptly imaging spectroradiometer), involves the convergence of two technologies – *spectroscopy* and *imaging* – from remote platforms to provide spatial and spectral information simultaneously. Hyperspectral data is generally represented as a data cube (that is, a three dimensional organisation) with spatial information represented in the *xy* plane and the spectral information in the *z* direction (Fig. 6.44). Some of the commonly used techniques for generating hyper-spectral imagery are given in the following sections.

6.8.1   The Scanner Approach

In this case, the projection of a pixel forms the entrance slit of the spectrometer. The dispersed energy falls on a linear detector array, wherein each detector responds to different wavelength regions (Fig. 6.45). A mirror scanning in the cross-track direction (as in the opto-mechanical scanner), provides successive pixel information. In actual practice, to increase the dwell time, the entrance slit to the spectrometer is the projection of an along-track array of pixels. In this case, the detector will be an area array giving the spatial information in one direction (along-track) and spectral information in the other direction.

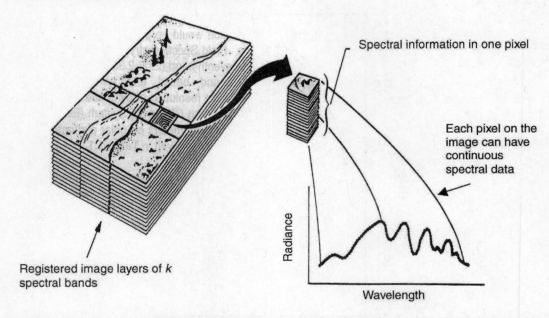

Fig. 6.44   Hyper-spectral imaging—images taken simultaneously in 100–200 narrow spectral bands, inherently registered. Thus each pixel has an associated, continuous spectrum. (NASA, 1987a)

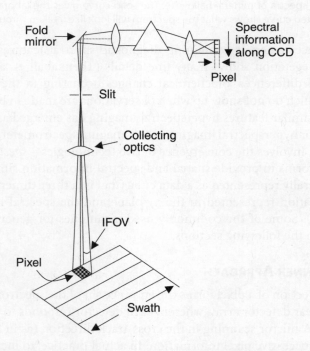

Fig. 6.45   Concept of imaging spectrometer in O–M scanner configuration. The scan mirror in object space is omitted for clarity.

6.8.2 PUSHBROOM APPROACH

Here the projection of a cross-track strip of one resolution element width and of length corresponding to the swath forms the entrance aperture of the spectrometer. The dispersing system spreads the spectral information across the array (along-track direction), thus producing spectral information of one strip of across-track scene. Pushbroom scanning technique produces contiguous image coverage (Fig. 6.46). As in the LISS camera, no scan mirror is required. However, pointing mirrors may be used for along-track and/or across-track pointing.

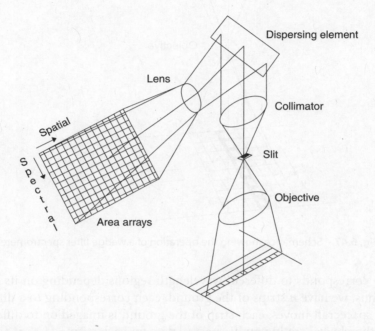

Fig. 6.46 Imaging spectrometer concept using pushbroom technique.

6.8.3 WEDGE IMAGING SPECTROMETER

Historically, hyper-spectral spectrometers have been built with dispersive optical systems using either prisms or diffraction gratings. Though such approaches can be realised to give high spectral resolution (a few nanometres), they generally require large re-imaging optics, which makes the instrument bulky. A recent approach, to have a compact spectrometer, is to use a wedge filter whose transmission wavelength varies along one dimension. These filters are essentially interference filters, wherein the thickness of the spacer layer (coating) is varied in one direction—along the length (hence the name 'wedge'). The rays passing through the wedge experience different path lengths and hence the spectral pass band changes with position along the filter. The wedge filter is placed in very close proximity to a two dimensional detector array, whose response matches with the wavelength region of interest. Here, an area of the ground is focussed on to a two dimensional detector array through the wedge filter (Fig. 6.47). At any instant, an image of each across-track strip from x_1 to x_n is generated such

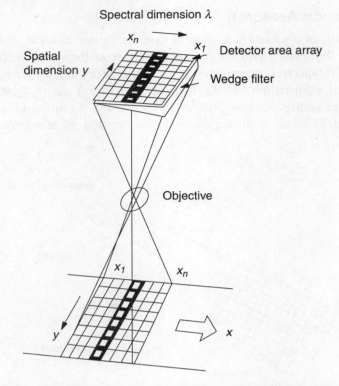

Fig. 6.47 Schematics showing the operation of a wedge filter spectrometer.

that each strip corresponds to different wavelength regions depending on its location at the wedge filter. Thus, we have n strips of the ground, each corresponding to a different spectral region. As the spacecraft moves, each strip of the ground is imaged on to different positions on the wedge, thereby generating multi-spectral data for each strip.

Such a system offers a substantial reduction in the complexity of the optical and mechanical assembly. The spatial resolution is primarily decided by the optics and size of the detector element. Even for applications not requiring continuous spectral information, suitable onboard processing can spectrally and spatially reconfigure (group) the pixels and transmit the data meeting the needs of spatial and spectral resolution. However, it should be remembered that different spectral bands are not inherently registered and hence the attitude stability/drift of the spacecraft will influence the band-to-band registration accuracy.

The Linear Etalon Imaging Spectral Array/Atmospheric Corrector (LEISA/AC) flown on NASA's EO-1 is based on this principle. In a single module, it uses 256×256 indium gallium arsenide arrays to cover a wavelength range of $0.8\text{–}1.6\,\mu m$.

6.9 HYBRID SCANNERS

Both, the whiskbroom and pushbroom imaging systems, on a low earth orbiting (LEO) satellite, generate image in one direction (along-track) due to spacecraft motion. However, from a geostationary orbit, the camera system has to produce scanning in two directions (E–W and N–S) to form a two dimensional image. It is possible to incorporate a linear CCD in one direction and a mechanical scanning in the other direction to form a two dimensional image from a geostationary orbit. That is a hybrid of O–M scanning and pushbroom (electronic) scanning. The first CCD-based imaging system from a geostationary orbit (GEO) was launched in 1999 on board the ISRO satellite INSAT-2E. The camera has three spectral bands (0.62–0.68 μm, 0.77–0.86 μm, and 1.55–1.69 μm), and each of the bands produces a 1 km IGFOV at the sub-satellite point (Iyengar et. al., 1996).

A new initiative is to achieve 'LEO earth observation capability from GEO'. Though a NASA study was conducted in 1974 to have a mission for earth resources survey from a geostationary orbit (Young, 1975; Oberheuser, 1975), no further work was carried out and GEO platforms currently are primarily designed for meteorological applications. This could be due to a technology gap. However, now there is a renewed interest to have a multispectral imaging system from GEO giving a spatial resolution close to that being achieved from LEO. The primary advantage of GEO imaging is fast responsiveness and short revisit times, of the order of minutes, not available from LEO missions. That is, the GEO system can reach a target region almost immediately, compared to the current LEO systems where it could be hours to days depending on where the satellite is. The higher temporal resolution substantially improves the data availability in periods of scattered clouds. These capabilities enhance the monitoring of earth's dynamic features and can also be effectively used for various types of disaster monitoring and relief operations.

From GEO, either linear array or area array can be used for imaging. Though area array requires more number of pixels, since the camera can be held stationary with respect to the scene imaged, there is no MTF degradation as in the case of linear array which has a image smear in the along-track direction.

6.10 MEASURING THE THIRD DIMENSION

The sensors hitherto discussed are primarily meant to produce two dimensional images. However, the third dimension – the height – is important for many applications such as geology and soil erosion studies. In this section, we shall briefly discuss imaging systems for generating height information in order to produce topographic maps. We have seen in Section 6.3.3, that relief displacement in a single photograph can be used to measure the height for features away from the principle point. If photographs are taken with the sun at an angle, by measuring the shadow, one can measure the height of objects from simple trigonometric relationships. However, these methodologies can be used only under specific conditions and have limited accuracy. The most optimal method to measure the third dimension is by stereoscopy. Stereoscopy is based on binocular vision, the same principle by which we perceive depth.

In binocular vision, each of the eyes (which are about 65 mm apart) produces images from different angles (view points), thereby generating slightly different spatial relationships between near and distant objects. The brain fuses these different views into a three dimensional impression. (The process of vision does not merely consist of 'seeing', but also of 'perceiving' and understanding through the central nervous system—perceiving is the process whereby sensory stimulation is translated into organised experience.)

The principles of binocular vision can be used to produce three dimensional data from images. This requires photographs taken from two locations. Conventionally, this is achieved by vertical photographs with an overlap (stereo pairs). The overlapped area is essentially

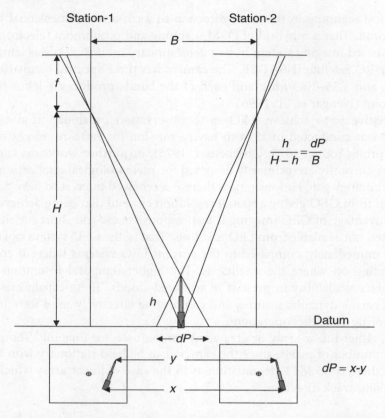

Fig. 6.48   Geometry of a stereoscopic pair of photographs. *B* — the base separation, *H* — the flight altitude, *f* — focal length of the lens, *h* — height of the object, *dP* is the difference in parallax from top and bottom of the object. (From Building Earth Observation Cameras by Joseph G, CRC press 2015. Reproduced with permission via Copyright Clearance Centre)

viewed by the same camera but displaced along the flight path. Due to the different view, there is a displacement of the object in the second photograph compared to the first (with respect to the principle point). This apparent shift due to the changed view angle is called *parallax*. From the stereo pairs, if the parallax difference between two points (*dP*) (Fig. 6.48) can be measured, then the height (*h*) is given as per the following equation.

$$h \simeq \frac{dp}{B/H}$$

where, *dp* = parallax difference between the points, *B* = length of airbase, and *H* = flight altitude.

The accuracy of height determination is dependant on the base to height ratio *B/H*. As the *B/H* ratio increases, the accuracy of height determination improves. Usually a *B/H* value of greater than 0.5 is used for stereoscopic imaging. The differential parallax *dP* from a photograph can be measured using standard optical techniques such as parallax bar, parallax wedge, and so on. There are many devices, which allow overlapping photographs to be viewed in stereo, that is, which allow only the left eye to see the left photo and right eye to see the right photo. The simplest one is the pocket stereoscope. For a detailed account on topographic mapping using aerial photographs, interested readers may refer to *Photogrammetry and Photo Interpretation,* Stephen H, Spurr Ronald Press Co., New York, 1966.

The need for a satellite-based imaging system for generating topographic maps of the global land area attracted the attention of various application scientists and space agencies. A number of proposals have also been made to develop such a mapping satellite system (Colvocoresses, 1979; Welch and Marko, 1981). From a space-based imaging system, stereo viewing (that is generating two images of the same point with different view angle) can be achieved in different ways. Broadly they are,

- generating stereo pairs by imaging from two different orbits—across-track stereoscopy, and
- viewing at different view angles along the same orbit—along-track stereoscopy.

Across-track stereoscopy is possible in two modes. In the case of LANDSAT MSS/TM, IRS LISS 1, 2, 3, images from two adjacent orbits have a certain common area—side lap. Since this area is looked at from two different imaging stations, the view angles are different and hence form a stereo pair. However, the B/H is only ~0.2 at the equator and progressively decreases as one goes to higher latitudes. In addition, the side lap covers only a very small area and hence cannot be used for full coverage of the earth.

SPOT 1 was the first mission for across-track stereoscopic viewing. Here, as mentioned earlier, a steering mirror in front of the collecting optics enables data to be collected ±26° across the track. The IRS-1C/1D PAN camera also can be steered across-track to ~ ±26°. Thus it is possible to generate stereo pairs of B/H up to ~1, depending on the cross-track steering (Fig. 6.49). However, such a scheme has the disadvantage that the stereo pairs are produced at different dates, which could be affected by varying atmospheric conditions including clouds and radiometric changes due to temporal variations between the observations. In

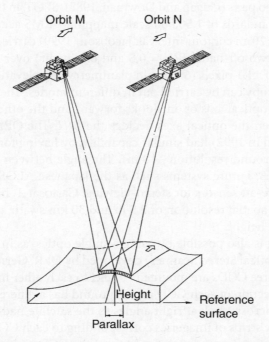

Fig. 6.49 Viewing geometry for generating stereo pairs by IRS-1C PAN.

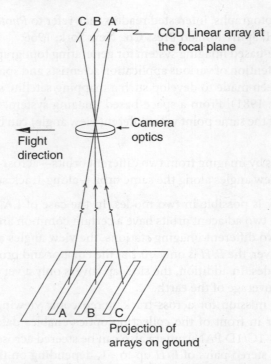

Fig. 6.50   Schematic of the MEOSS optical configuration.

addition, oblique viewing at different angles produces pairs with different spatial resolution. Notwithstanding the limitations, a number of software packages have been developed for restitution of SPOT stereo pairs (Gugan and Dowman, 1988). SPOT, in theory, can produce maps to meet the accuracy standards of 1:50,000 scale mapping—RMS accuracies of ±15 m in plan and 6 m in height, for a 20 m contour interval. Jacobson (1999) carried out investigations with three IRS-1C images (two off-nadir $B/H \simeq 0.8$ and one nadir) over Hanover, Germany and obtained an accuracy of ±1.1 pixels (6.5 m) in planimetry and elevation.

Along-track stereoscopy can be carried out in different modes. There could be two cameras mounted such that the optical axis of one looks forward and the other aft with respect to the nadir. The angle between the optical axes decides the B/H. The OPS sensor in the Japanese JERS Satellite (launched in 1992) had similar capability, by having forward and nadir looking linear array sensors, (ground resolution ~18 m). The angle between the optical axis was 15° giving a B/H ratio of 0.3. Future systems such as the Japanese ALOS and Indian Cartosat-1, will carry dedicated fore-aft sensors for stereo-viewing. Cartosat-1, has two cameras with 26° fore and –5° aft, with a spatial resolution of 2.5 m and 30 km swath, producing a B/H ratio of 0.64 from 617 km orbit height.

Fore and aft viewing is also possible by using a single optics, as in the instrument MEOSS (Monocular Electro-Optical Stereo Scanner) developed by DLR, German Aerospace Research Establishment. Here, three CCDs are mounted parallel to each other in the focal plane of a well corrected lens. The projection of each CCD on the ground has a different view angle (Fig. 6.50). The CCDs are aligned across-track at right angles to the satellite nadir track. Satellite motion generates three separate strips of imageries corresponding to each CCD array, thus generating stereo pairs between the imagery taken by any two of the CCDs.

Another method of having along-track stereoscopy is to have the sensor itself tilted in the along-track direction. This is being used in the high resolution (1 m) IKONOS satellites.

Other possible techniques for directly measuring the relative height is to use laser altimeters. There are aerial laser altimetry systems, which are commercially available for height measurements.

Photogrammetry techniques enable us to generate a Digital Elevation Model (DEM) or a Digital Terrain Model (DTM). (DTM are variants of DEM showing additional landscape attributes.) With today's computer technology, it is possible to 'drape' (co-register) an aerial or satellite image over the DEM to give a more realistic appearance. At first analogue plotters were used to generate DEM from stereo pairs. This is an opto-mechanical device, and the stereo matching was done manually. This was followed by the analytical plotter, in which a computer calculated the real world coordinates and stored them instead of mechanical plotting. Soft copy photogrammetry (SCP) is the most recent development in extracting physical dimensions from a photograph/image. Here, measurements are made not on hard copy (such as film prints) but on digital data (either obtained by digitising the photograph or from digital images) and hence the name soft copy photogrammetry. The soft copy workstation has no mechanical or optical moving parts, but requires a large image data storage capacity with fast data access. SCP uses a computer workstation and specialised software to replace almost all the laborious manual and analytical (optical) production processes normally required to create a 3-D model of an object from stereo (hard copy) aerial photography. Using SCP's computerised process, it is possible to perform much more intensive photogrammetric mapping, in a short time with less labour.

6.11   IMAGE QUALITY ASPECTS

Usually image quality is measured in terms of resolving power. However, in remote sensing, image quality encompasses much more than just the resolution or sharpness. The purpose of remote sensing is to identify the earth's features at a particular location by measuring the radiance. Thus, we are dealing with a *'reflectance (emittance) map'*, representing scene radiance at each 'location' on the ground. Thus, there are two parameters, which basically decide the image quality:

- geometric accuracy, which essentially ensures the accurate location of a picture element, and
- radiometric accuracy, which essentially ensures that the grey values are the true representation of the reflectance/emittance within the spectral band.

Hence, the extent of true reproduction of geometry and radiometry of the ground scene, both in absolute and relative terms determines the image quality. (The other parameters such as dynamic range, saturation radiance and IFOV in general contribute to the quality of the image; they are not considered here since they are considered as part of the sensor design parameters.) The image quality depends not only on the basic camera but also on the characteristic of the platform, intervening atmosphere and other parameters like data processing, map projection, and so on.

6.11.1   RADIOMETRIC CONSIDERATIONS

In computer classification of the features from the remotely sensed data, one normally looks at the statistical difference in the reflected value measured by the instruments. In this context, the absolute value of the reflectance (or radiance) is not important since one compares the relative reflectance value among the pixels. However, when one is interested in using two date data for classification or combining information from two different sensors to find out how the reflectance changed with time, it is necessary to have the absolute radiance value.

Most of the electro-optical imaging systems use more than one detector per band (LANDSAT TM has 16 detectors/band). Since all the detectors will not have the same responsivity, it is necessary to adjust the electronic gain in each channel so that the output voltage (the digital number in digital transmission systems) is same for equal radiance input. This is carried out by elaborate ground calibration. During the ground calibration, normally an integrating sphere, which fills the aperture of the collecting telescope, is used to illuminate all the detectors. The calibration data so generated is used to normalise the residual detector response variations present even after detector/amplifier gain adjustments. The data is normally stored as a look up file and corrections are done during the time of preprocessing. Even less than 1% detector-to-detector response variation can show striping in a photographic product, especially over low reflectance uniform target (Chapter 9). In the case of opto-mechanical scanners, since the scanning is done across the sub-satellite track, the response mismatch produces horizontal (across-track) stripes. In the case of CCD camera, the detector normalisation problem is more severe since we have a large number of pixels per band, whose responses are not identical. The problem gets compounded since the field of view of a CCD camera is normally quite large compared to opto-mechanical scanners and therefore the problem of generating a uniform source over a large field of view is to be tackled first. In this case, response non-uniformity will show as vertical (along-track) stripes. The calibration procedure can also be utilised to generate absolute radiometric transfer equations so that the output digital number can be expressed in terms of radiometric units (usually milliwatts/cm^2/sr/μm). To carry out absolute calibration, the integrating sphere output is first calibrated using radiometers, which are accurately calibrated against secondary standards.

Apart from the response variations of the detectors, other possible radiometric errors are due to the Modulation Transfer Function (MTF) of the camera system. The MTF essentially shows the contrast reduction from object space to the image plane. Because of this, the radiance measured by the instrument does not represent the actual reflectance of the pixel since the signals from the adjacent pixels spill over. Thus the measured reflectance value is dependent on the surrounding pixels and the MTF of the instrument. An account of the MTF effect on the radiance accuracy is given by Norwood (1974) and has been discussed in Chapter 5.

One of the major contributions to radiometric error is due to atmosphere, since the atmosphere corrupts the actual reflectance reaching the sensor. The atmospheric effect is given in Appendix 1, where we see that the path radiance reduces the contrast and also adds to the actual reflectance value. The atmospheric effect of nearby pixels on the radiance of a given pixel (adjacency effect) makes the atmospheric contribution evaluation more complex (Kaufman and Fraser, 1983).

Radiometric errors generally lead to poor classification accuracy.

6.11.2   GEOMETRIC QUALITY

The fundamental to geometric accuracy is the pixel level data registration to both standard maps (geodetic accuracy) and between successive scenes (temporal registration accuracy). The geometric accuracy primarily depends on:

- the basic camera characteristics including imaging geometry,
- platform (aircraft or satellite) characteristics, and
- the preprocessing accuracy.

The nature of the camera generated geometric distortion depends on the type of sensor. The scale variation at the edge of the film in a photographic camera due to lens distortion is well known. In the case of an opto-mechanical scanner, the major cause of distortion is due to the geometry of scanning.

Apart from these scan geometry related distortions, inherent sensor design inadequacy such as non-linearity of scan mirror velocity also produces geometric distortion. Since data samples are taken at regular intervals of time (expecting equal angular increment), the varying mirror rate produces across-track geometric distortion. The geometric errors produced by platform characteristics such as altitude variation, attitude (roll, pitch and yaw) disturbance and orbit drift all produce various geometric distortions.

Finally the information collected on each pixel has to be referred to a point on earth, which requires transferring the information of a spherical surface to a plane surface generally referred to as map projection. This can be achieved in a number of ways (Appendix 4). However, in all these transformations, some of the geometric relationships of the spherical surface get modified, thereby producing distortions in distance/direction/area measurements from region to region, in the picture frame depending on the type of projections (Robinson et. al., 1978).

These aspects are further discussed in Chapter 10.

The important parameters, which quantify the intrinsic image geometric quality, are given below (Boissin and Gardelle, 1987).

- *Length distortion* This is the root mean square (rms) value of the relative error in the distance between two points (separated by more than 500 m on the ground) as estimated from an image, assuming the sampling interval to be nominal.
- *Anisomorphism* For a given point, one can determine the length distortion in a given direction. Theoretically, the direction in which this parameter is minimal and maximal is perpendicular. The anisomorphism at a point is the difference between the length distortions in these two directions.
- *Location accuracy* The accuracy with which the scene centre is defined with respect to map coordinates (longitude, latitude).
- *Relief accuracy*, in the case of stereo imaging.

The errors are usually estimated by using well-distributed GCPs.

6.12 ON-ORBIT PERFORMANCE EVALUATION

Before a camera is put on-board a satellite, extensive pre-launch performance validation is carried out. Though cameras are well characterised in the laboratory, its performance can vary in orbit due to various reasons such as misalignment due to launch load, gradual component degradation due to on orbit environment and so on. Therefore it is essential to periodically monitor the in orbit camera performance. To monitor the radiometric sensitivity the cameras usually carry an in-flight calibration scheme as part of the sensor system. The on-board calibration system essentially monitors the stability of the radiometric response of the sensor. There are different designs to accomplish this task such as using lamps, provision to bring in the field of view diffused solar radiation. Though on board calibration systems have been used in almost all earth observation cameras, the stability of the calibration system itself is at times doubtful, thus defeating the whole purpose of using them. An alternative approach to monitor the post-launch radiometric stability is to use external stable calibration sources, whose radiances are known (Slater et. al., 1996). These sources could be bright targets such as snow, ice, desert, dark targets such as ocean, manmade artificial targets of precisely known characteristics, or celestial objects like the moon. In situ measurement of natural or artificial sites on the surface of the earth along with models is widely adopted to provide an independent method to establish the performance of the earth observation cameras. This methodology is known as vicarious calibration. The reflected radiance from the test site is measured at the time of over pass of the sensor under test. Along with surface measurements, concurrently various atmospheric parameters such as watervapour, ozone, optical depth and so on are also measured/derived. The surface reflectance data and the atmospheric information are used in a radiative transfer model to calculate the top of the atmospheric radiance value at the sensor.

Another sensor performance to be assessed is its spatial response, which is inferred through MTF. The MTF is evaluated by imaging natural objects which can be represented as points, lines and edges. It can also be calculated by imaging stars as point source which gives a point spread function. For more details readers may refer to Joseph (2015) and the references therein.

FOR FURTHER READING

1. *Remote Sensing: Optics and Optical Systems*, Slater P N, 1980, Addison-Wesley Publishing Company, Chapters 6, 7, 11, 12, 13 and 14.
2. *Remote Sensing and Image Interpretation*, Lillesand T M and Kiefer R W, 1979, John Wiley & Sons, Chapters 2, 5 and 6.
3. *Manual of Remote Sensing* Vol-1, Ed. Colwell, Chapter 6.
4. *Space Remote Sensing Systems: An Introduction*, Chen HS, Academic Press, 1985.
5. *http://www.its.caltech.edu/~ee157/lecture_note/Imaging%20geometries.pdf*
6. *https://engineering.purdue.edu/~bethel/eros_orbit3.pdf*
7. *http://nptel.ac.in/courses/105108077/module2/lecture10.pdf*
8. *https://landsat.usgs.gov/landsat-8-l8-data-users-handbook-section-2*
9. *https://nrsc.gov.in/uim_2014_proceedings/infolets/Resourcesat2_Handbook.pdf*
10. *https://pdfs.semanticscholar.org/ee00/151c7404e5384ffce40ee23e298bc023b8e7.pdf*
11. *http://www2.ph.ed.ac.uk/~wjh/teaching/dia/documents/stereo.pdf*
12. *http://depts.washington.edu/mictech/optics/sensors/detector.pdf*
13. *https://www.nasa.gov/content/landsat-8-instruments*
14. *"http://www.mdpi.com/2072-4292/6/11/10286/pdf" www.mdpi.com/2072-4292/6/11/10286/pdf*
15. *https://landsat.usgs.gov/sites/default/files/documents/Landsat8DataUsersHandbook.pdf*
16. *http://www.ugpti.org/smartse/research/citations/downloads/Pearlman-Hyperion_IEEE-2001.pdf*
17. *https://www.microsoft.com/en-us/research/wp-content/uploads/2016/02/CCD.pdf*
18. *http://www.specinst.com/What_Is_A_CCD.html*

7 | Microwave Sensors

The microwave region that is of interest to remote sensing covers the electromagnetic radiation of wavelength extending from a few millimetres to metres. The sensors operating in the microwave region, as in the case of the OIR region, can be broadly classified as active and passive sensors. However here, unlike in the OIR region, the radiation from the sun does not play any direct part. Thus, the microwave sensors can operate during day as well as night. Depending on the wavelength, the atmosphere is more transparent to microwaves than to optical rays, thus providing an all-weather monitoring capability.

The microwave spectrum is used for many applications other than remote sensing. The communication satellites as well as a number of terrestrial radars use microwave frequencies. The microwave energy emitted from the earth is very weak. Similarly, the signals the radio astronomers want to pick up from stars and galaxies are extremely weak (10^{-12} W). Thus passive sensing either of the earth or of celestial bodies is vulnerable to interference from active sensor emission not only due to their transmission frequency, but also due to out-of-band emissions. In order to avoid such conflicts, the allocation of frequency spectrum for various uses are coordinated by international bodies like the World Administrative Radio Conference (WARC). The microwave frequencies allocated for remote sensing is given in Table 7.1.

Though both light and microwaves are electromagnetic radiation, because of the large difference in the wavelength, the basic technique involved in realising the receiving and transmitting system in the two cases is different. One of the most important components in any remote sensor is the radiation collection system. In the OIR region, this is generally accomplished by lenses and mirrors. In the microwave region, this is accomplished by an *antenna*. However, there is a basic difference between the function of a lens (mirror) and an antenna. The lens just collects the EM radiation and concentrates it onto a detector or produces a collimated beam from a source at the focus. While the antenna can also perform a similar function, in addition it acts as a transducer—it converts an electrical signal to EM radiation and vice versa. In the following section, we shall try to provide some basic information on the antenna, in order to understand the functioning of microwave sensors.

Table 7.1 Microwave frequency allocation for active and passive remote sensing

Frequency (GHz)	Active	Passive
1.215–1.3	*	
1.427–1.429		*
2.690–2.700		*
3.100–3.300	*	
5.250–5.460	*	
8.550–8.650	*	
9.500–9.800	*	
10.6–10.7		*
13.25–13.75	*	*
15.35–15.4		*
17.2–17.3		*
18.6–18.8		*
21.2–21.4		*
22.21–22.5		*
23.6–24.0		*
24.05–24.25	*	
31.3–31.80		*
35.5–36	*	
36–37		*
50.2–50.4		*
52.6–55.78		*
55.78–59.3		*
65–66		*
86–92		*
94–94.1	*	
100–126		*
164–168		*
174.5–176.5		*
182–185		*
200–202		*

Source: Radio Regulation, 1998, International Telecommunication Union.

7.1 ANTENNA

The concept of an antenna for transmitting electromagnetic waves was developed in 1897 by Guglielmo Marconi. In a transmitting antenna, the signal from an electrical circuit causes electrons in the antenna to oscillate. These moving electric charges generate electromagnetic radiation, which propagates in space. Hence an antenna can be any conductive structure that can carry an electrical current. If it carries a time varying electrical current, it will radiate an electromagnetic field (by rule of reciprocity, whatever is true for transmission is also true for reception, that is, a conductor intercepting an EM field will carry an electrical current).

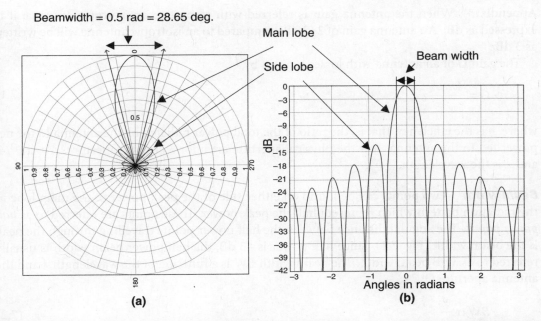

Fig. 7.1 Schematics showing radiation pattern for antenna aperture $D = 2\lambda$. (a) is a polar plot, the radius vector gives the relative voltage level. Since power is proportional to the square of the amplitude, the 3 dB (power) points are given at $1/\sqrt{2} = 0.707$. (b) The pattern is plotted in rectangular coordinates; here the plot is for power. The beam width is calculated with respect to 3 dB power points in the distribution.

However, such a structure may not radiate efficiently with the desired characteristics. Different types of antennae have been designed such that the spatial distribution of energy radiated by the antenna meets our requirement with minimum losses. Before we consider the realisation of antennae, let us familiarise ourselves with some of the terms used in antenna engineering.

Radiation pattern The radiation pattern or antenna pattern describes the relative strength of the radiated field with the angle, at a fixed distance (the radiation pattern also describes the receiving property of the antenna, when it receives). Radiation patterns are three dimensional. However, they are usually measured in two orthogonal principal planes. The pattern is plotted either in polar or rectangular coordinates. The patterns are normalised to the maximum value at 0 dB. In general, for any practical antenna for remote sensing, the pattern has a main lobe, where most of the energy is concentrated and sidelobes (Fig. 7.1), which are undesirable.

Antenna gain It is a measure of the ability of the antenna to 'focus' the radiation in a particular direction. Unless otherwise specified, the gain refers to the direction of maximum radiation. But how does an antenna, which is usually a passive device, generate gain? We cannot change the total power of the antenna; we just redistribute the energy in a particular direction of our interest. In other words, we reduce the power in the direction we do not want and redirect them in the direction where we want more power.

It is expressed relative to the performance of an ideal (theoretical) antenna, which radiates equally in all directions (isotropic antenna) and is usually expressed in decibels, dB (see

Appendix 3). When the antenna gain is referred with respect to an isotropic antenna, it is expressed as dB_i. An antenna gain of 2 (3 dB) compared to an isotropic antenna will be written as $3\,dB_i$.

The gain G of an antenna with losses is given by,

$$G = \frac{4\pi\eta A}{\lambda^2} \tag{7.1}$$

where, η is the efficiency, that is, the ratio of the total power radiated by the antenna to the net power fed to the antenna, A is the physical aperture area; for a circular aperture, $A = \pi D^2/4$, and λ is the wavelength.

Beam width   Two points can be found on either side of the peak power of the main lobe in the radiation pattern which represent half the peak power. These points are referred to as *half power points*. The angular distance between the half power points travelling through the peak is the beam width (Fig. 7.1). Since half power is –3 dB, the half power beam width is usually referred to as 3 dB beam width. The beam width BW is a function of the wavelength λ and the antenna aperture D.

$$BW \alpha \frac{\lambda}{D} \tag{7.2}$$

That is, for a larger antenna dimension compared to the wavelength, we have a narrower beam width. We have seen that a larger antenna has higher gain. Thus, higher gain antennae feature narrow beam widths.

There are other characteristics of the antenna, like impedance and Voltage Standing Wave Rate (VSWR), which an antenna designer should consider. However, to understand microwave sensors, these details are not very important and hence are not considered here. We shall now consider some typical antenna configurations, which are commonly used for microwave remote sensors. The purpose here is only to familiarise the readers with various concepts and not to give an in-depth analysis or design to realise them.

7.1.1 PARABOLOID ANTENNA

One of the most commonly used antennae, especially for microwave radiometers is the paraboloid antenna. This consists of a reflector (dish), which is a section of a surface formed by rotating a parabola about its axis. The reflector is illuminated by a feed, usually a horn, which is suitably located at the focal point of the reflector (Fig. 7.2). The parabolic antenna, depending on the design, gives good directionality. A variant of this is possible by using another sub-reflector near the focus. A commonly used dual reflector antenna is called the Cassegrain antenna (conceptually this is similar to the Cassegrain telescope, explained in Chapter 6). When used for receiving, the dish collects RF from a source and focusses it at the feed. While transmitting, the feed radiates RF that is collimated by the reflector for transmission in a specific direction.

7.1.2 HORN ANTENNA

It consists of a waveguide section in which the cross sectional area increases towards an open end, which is the aperture. It derives its name from the characteristic 'flared' appearance. The

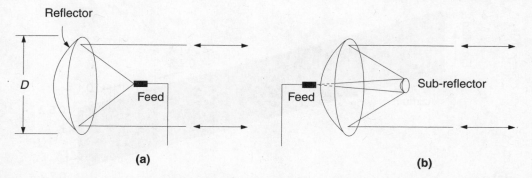

Fig. 7.2 Schematics of a parabolic reflector. (a) Prime focus feed. (b) Cassegranian feed. Indicates that the system can be used either for transmission or reception.

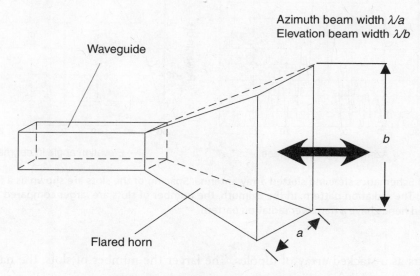

Fig. 7.3 Schematics of a horn antenna.

flared portion can be square, rectangular or conical. The maximum response is along the axis of the horn. With a rectangular cross section, the beam width in the azimuth and elevation can be adjusted by suitably choosing the dimensions (Fig. 7.3). Though horn antennae are commonly used as the feed to a reflector, such as the parabolic reflector, horn antennae can also be used all by themselves. The first Indian Satellite Microwave Radiometer (SAMIR) had horn antennae as the front end for receiving the radiation (Raju and Calla, 1985).

7.1.3 SLOTTED ANTENNA

A slotted waveguide antenna (Fig. 7.4) works by radiating energy from the inside of a waveguide through a number of slots cut in the waveguide. Each slot can be considered as a dipole. The back surface reflects the radiation in order to have a directional pattern. The waveguide with

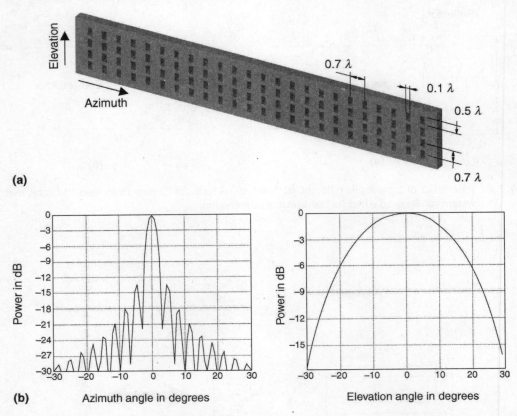

Fig. 7.4 (a) Schematics showing slotted array antenna. Spacing of the slots are shown as a fraction of λ. (b) The radiation pattern. In the azimuth, the number of slots are larger compared to elevation and hence have a narrower radiation pattern.

its slots acts as a stacked array of dipoles. The larger the number of slots, the narrower the beam width (more gain).

7.1.4 Phased Arrays

When two or more simple antennae are brought together and driven from the same source, the resultant radiation pattern is dependent on the interference between the signals transmitted separately from each of the individual elements. At some points, the interference may be constructive, causing the transmitted signal to be increased. Where destructive interference takes place, the signal will be minimum. The direction in which the interference takes place depends on the phase difference between the signals fed to the array element. If all the elements are fed in phase, the maximum radiation occurs at right angles to the array. This also can be explained as follows. The field at any point is equal to the vector sum of the fields from the individual elements at that point. By changing the phase between the elements, the direction of the beam also changes, thus, in effect, producing a scanning beam (Fig. 7.5). This is achieved by using special electronic devices called *phase shifters*. This is much simpler than

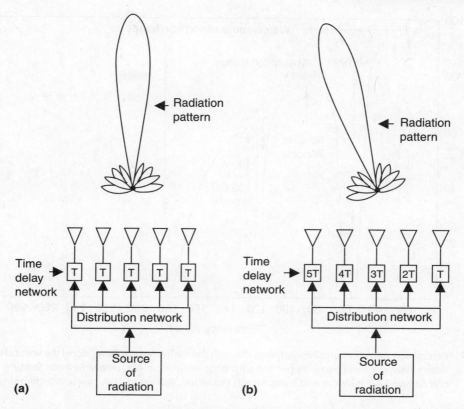

Fig. 7.5 Schematics showing beam scanning using phased arrays. (a) All elements are in phase. (b) Phases of elements modified resulting in off-broad side radiation. (After Gorijk R D, unpublished)

mechanically moving the antenna. This principle is used in a number of SAR instruments for beam switching.

There are a number of types of antennae used in microwave remote sensors and those interested can refer to Collin, 1985.

7.2   PASSIVE MICROWAVE SENSORS

Passive sensors detect the natural radiation emanating from the earth. In the OIR region, we have seen that this could be solar reflected radiation or self-emission of the body. However, in the microwave region, there are no strong natural sources illuminating the earth, which can be easily detected. Therefore, passive microwave sensors sense only the self-emission of the earth. Passive microwave sensors are generally known as microwave radiometers. The emission could be either from the surface of earth – land, ocean, ice – or from atmospheric constituents—the emission of the atmosphere itself. Sensing the emission of the atmosphere is called *atmospheric sounding*. Atmospheric sounders provide vertical profiles of the temperature and molecular constituents in the atmosphere by making measurements near the molecular resonance frequencies. This is dealt with in detail in Appendix 2.

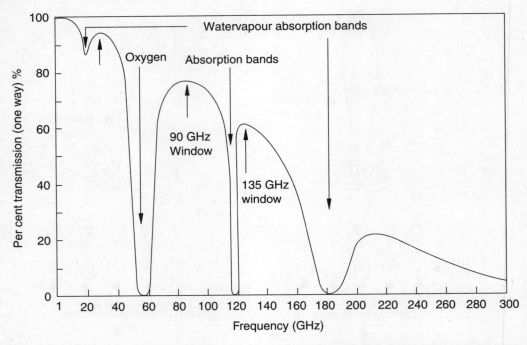

Fig. 7.6 Percentage transmission of microwaves through the earth's atmosphere, along the vertical direction, under clear sky conditions. (Reprinted with permission from Microwave Remote Sensing — *Active and Passive*, Ulaby, Moore and Fung, Artech House Inc., Norwood, USA., *www. artechhouse.com*)

Though microwaves are less affected by the atmosphere, even in this region there are preferred windows for observation, especially for passive sensing. Figure 7.6 gives the transparency of atmosphere for microwaves. From the figure it is clear that at 1–40 GHz, the atmosphere is fairly transparent under clear sky conditions. Other possible windows are around 90 GHz and 135 GHz. Thus the surface sensing frequencies are generally chosen below 40 GHz. Even measurement at window frequencies are affected to some extent by clouds or water vapour especially at higher frequencies (Fig. 7.7) and hence accurate estimation of surface radiance needs correction for these absorptions and emissions from the atmosphere. Most surface sensing radiometers include frequency channels also sensitive to water vapour and liquid water—mainly to correct for their effects. For observation of atmospheric parameters, frequencies are selected in the vicinity of the absorption peaks of atmospheric gases, which generally fall above 50 GHz. Table 7.2 gives the frequency bands and bandwidths used for satellite passive sensing in the microwave region.

7.2.1 PRINCIPLE OF MICROWAVE RADIOMETRY

We have seen in Chapter 2 that all bodies above absolute zero, emit electromagnetic radiation as per Planck's Law. At microwave frequencies, the Planck's equation can be approximated to

$$M_\lambda = \left[\frac{2\pi ck}{\lambda^4}\right] Te_\lambda(\theta, \phi) \, \text{wm}^{-2}\mu^{-1} \qquad (7.3)$$

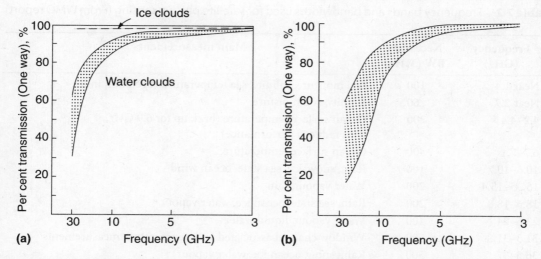

Fig. 7.7 Effect of cloud and rain on transmission of microwaves. (a) Effect of clouds on microwave transmission from space to ground. (b) Effect of rain on microwave transmission from space to ground. (Reprinted with permission from *Microwave Remote Sensing — Active and Passive*, Ulaby, Moore and Fung, Artech House Inc., Norwood, USA., *www.artechhouse.com*)

where $e_\lambda(\theta, \Phi)$ is the emissivity of the body at the absolute temperature T and wavelength λ. In the above equation, all the quantities in brackets are constant at a particular wavelength. Hence, at microwave frequencies, the emission from a body is proportional to the product of the temperature T and emissivity, which is called the *brightness temperature* (T_B) (see Section 4.3.1 for more details).

7.2.2 RADIOMETER PERFORMANCE PARAMETERS

A radiometer can be considered as a receiver designed to measure noise. The received signal is represented as an equivalent temperature, that is the temperature of a black body source, which would produce the same amount of signal in the bandwidth of the system. The noise power measured is the sum of the noise received by the antenna and the noise generated by the receiver system. The noise received by the antenna consists of

(i)   radiation from the actual object (earth surface) in the main lobe,
(ii) radiation emitted by the molecules in the path,
(iii) radiation from other objects received through the side lobe,
(vi) noise produced by the antenna itself due to its own temperature, and
(v)   noise produced by the receiver and other circuits.

Of the above, (i) or (ii), depending on the purpose of the mission is the real signal. The contribution from other sources have to be separated by calibration/modelling. The power delivered by the antenna to the receiver can be represented in terms of antenna temperature T_A (i to iii).

The receiver noise can also be represented by the receiver noise temperature T_R referred at the antenna input. Thus the total system noise T_{sys} is given by

Table 7.2 Frequency bands and bandwidths used for satellite passive sensing (From WMO report)

Frequency (GHz)	Necessary BW (MHz)	Main measurements
Near 1.4	100	Soil moisture, salinity, sea temperature, vegetation index
Near 2.7	60	Salinity, soil moisture
4.2–4.4	200	Ocean surface temperature (back up for 6.9 GHz, with reduced performance)
6.7–7.1	400	Ocean surface temperature
10.6–10.7	100	Rain, snow, ice, sea state, ocean wind
15.35–15.4	200	Water vapour, rain
18.6–18.8	200	Rain, sea state, ocean ice, water vapour
23.6–24	400	Water vapour, liquid water
31.3–31.8	500	Window channel associated with temperature measurements
36.5–37	500	Rain, snow, ocean ice, water vapour
50.2–50.4	200	O_2 (Temperature profiling)
52.6–59.3	6700(1)	O_2 (Temperature profiling)
86–92	6000	Clouds, oil spills, ice, snow
100–102	2000	N_2O
109.8–111.8	2000	O_3
115.25–122.25	7000(1)	O_2 (Temperature profiling), CO
148.5–151.5	3000	Window channel
156–158	2000	Window channel (temporarily needed)
164–167	3000	Window channel
174.8–191.8	17000(1)	H_2O (Moisture profiling), N_2O O_3
200–209	9000(2)	H_2O O_3 N_2O
226–232	6000(2)	Clouds, CO
235–238	3000(2)	O_3
250–252	2000(2)	N_2O
294–306	12000(2)	O_2 Nitrous oxide
316–326	10000(2)	Nitrous oxide
342–349	7000(2)	O_2 H_2O
497–506	9000(2)	Carbon monoxide, N_2O
624–629	5000(2)	O_3
952–955	3000(2)	H_2O

1. This bandwidth is occupied by multiple channels.
2. This bandwidth is occupied by multiple sensors.

$$T_{sys} = T_A + T_R$$

The function of the radiometer is to measure the antenna radiometric temperature T_A. Therefore, T_R has to be eliminated. Different types of radiometer are distinguished by the method of elimination of the receiver noise T_R from the above equation.

Any measuring instrument is characterised by its accuracy and precision. Laboratory calibration is carried out to convert the output voltage of the radiometer to antenna temperature values. Most radiometers employ square law detection (that is, the detector output is the square of the effective value of the applied signal voltage). Since power is proportional to the square of the voltage, the output voltage of the radiometer is linearly related to the noise temperature of the input source (ambient temperature is held constant). Therefore, two point calibration will uniquely define the calibration curve. However, more points are used in the laboratory and a least square fit is made through the points. This curve is then used to convert the output voltage to antenna temperature values. Here the accuracy of the radiometer is dictated by the accuracy with which the calibration noise temperature is known.

The measurement precision or the radiometric sensitivity (radiometric resolution $NE\Delta T$), is the smallest change in T_A that can be detected by the instrument. Generally, the detectable change is equated to the standard deviation of the DC level of the output voltage. Depending on the type of radiometer, the sensitivity ΔT varies. Two types of radiometers which are generally used are discussed below.

7.2.3 TOTAL POWER RADIOMETER

Any instrument, which measures the total noise power from the antenna (and from the receiver) can be considered as a total power radiometer (TPR). A simple schematic of a TPR is shown in Fig. 7.8. It essentially consists of a linear receiver with a well-defined bandwidth B (pre-detection bandwidth) and stable gain characteristics, connected to the antenna. This is followed by a square law detector, a video amplifier and an integrator. The output voltage V_o generated is given by,

$$V_o = aGB\,(T_A + T_R) \tag{7.4}$$

where G is the overall gain and a is the constant of proportionality, which includes the detection sensitivity. We shall now consider the radiometer sensitivity under two cases.

Case 1 For the radiometer having a stable gain, the fluctuation is dependant only on the random signal fluctuation and is given by

$$\Delta T_{sys} = \frac{T_{sys}}{\sqrt{B\tau}} = \frac{T_A + T_R}{\sqrt{B\tau}} \tag{7.5}$$

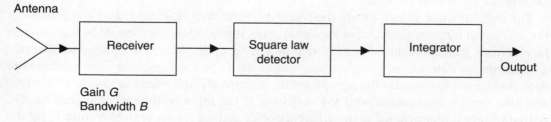

Fig. 7.8 Schematic showing the basic functional block of a TPR.

where τ is the integration time. ΔT_{sys} is the standard deviation of the measured value of T_{sys}. Therefore, ΔT_{sys} gives the minimum change in T_{sys} that can be measured. It is reasonable to assume that the receiver input noise temperature T_R is independent of the radiation incident upon the antenna. Therefore, the minimum detectable change in the radiometric antenna temperature ΔT is close to ΔT_{sys} (Ulaby et. al., 1981),

$$\Delta T \cong \Delta T_{sys} = \frac{T_A + T_R}{\sqrt{B\tau}} \tag{7.6}$$

Thus to have a higher sensitivity (lower ΔT value) we should use a receiver with as low a noise temperature as possible. The bandwidth generally depends on the specific mission and allocation by WARC. For example, a radiometer for vertical profiling needs a narrow bandwidth to have a better vertical resolution (Appendix 2). The integration time depends on the size of the pixel, sub-satellite velocity, scan efficiency (see Chapter 6), and so on.

Case 2   Equation 7.6 gives the radiometric sensitivity (or resolution) of an ideal total power radiometer with no gain fluctuations. However, for a real receiver, the gain varies with time. In such a case, the sensitivity of a TPR incorporating the effects of both noise and gain variation is given by (Ulaby, et. al., 1981),

$$\Delta T = (T_A + T_R)\left[\frac{1}{B\tau} + \left(\frac{\Delta G}{G}\right)^2\right]^{\frac{1}{2}} \tag{7.7}$$

where G is the system average power gain, and ΔG is the rms of the detected power gain variation.

Thus stabilising the gains of the system is an important design consideration for the total power radiometer.

7.2.4   DICKE RADIOMETER

A solution to the gain instability in radiometers was invented by Robert H Dicke, a Princeton University Physicist. It is now known as the *Dicke radiometer* (Fig. 7.9). Dicke radiometers reduce to some extent, the gain instability problem, by measuring the difference between the antenna temperature and a known reference temperature, instead of measuring only the antenna temperature. Here the input to the receiver is switched between the antenna and a load, which has a well-defined temperature. The switch, called the *Dicke switch*, is placed as close to the antenna as possible.

The switching rate should satisfy the Nyquist criteria, that is, should sample at least twice the maximum frequency content of the signal. Also, the switching rate should be high enough to eliminate gain fluctuations during one switching cycle. After the square law detector, a synchronous detector is placed, whose output feeds to the integrator. The synchronous detector essentially connects the signal from the antenna and the reference load to a difference amplifier, in synchronisation with the switching at the input to the receiver. Thus the DC output voltage is proportional to the difference of T_A and the reference temperature T_{ref} and is independent of receiver noise temperature T_R (here T_R is referred at the input of Dicke switch.

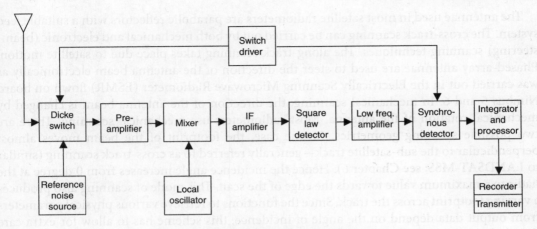

Fig. 7.9 Schematics of a Dicke radiometer.

The antenna contribution included in T_A is corrected using ground and on-board calibration). The general equation for the sensitivity of a Dicke radiometer is

$$\Delta T = \left[\frac{2(T_A + T_R)^2 = 2(T_{ref} + T_R)^2}{B\tau} + \left(\frac{\Delta G}{G} \right)^2 (T_A - T_{ref})^2 \right]^{\frac{1}{2}} \tag{7.8}$$

From the above equation it is clear that the sensitivity is still dependent on gain fluctuations except in the case of $T_A = T_{ref}$. In such a case, the above equation reduces to,

$$\Delta T = 2 \frac{T_A + T_R}{\sqrt{B\tau}} \tag{7.9}$$

That is, the sensitivity of the 'balanced' ($T_A = T_{ref}$) Dicke radiometer is poorer than the ideal TPR by a factor of 2. There are a number of schemes in order make $T_{ref} = T_A$, to eliminate the gain variation effect.

Another important parameter is the spatial resolution. The spatial resolution is determined by the 3 dB beam width (λ/D). For any reasonable aperture this is quite large especially at lower frequencies. Therefore, spatial resolution of satellite-borne radiometers is quite coarse—10 s of kilometres.

7.2.5 SATELLITE-BORNE MICROWAVE RADIOMETERS

An imaging microwave radiometer essentially consists of

- an antenna, which receives the incoming radiation,
- a scanning mechanism—mechanical or electrical,
- a receiver and associated electronics, which detects and amplifies the received radiation and produce a voltage output,
- in-flight calibration systems—hot body, sky horn, and so on,
- auxiliary logic systems providing signals for timing, multiplexing data and formatting, and
- house-keeping systems, which monitor various temperatures and voltages.

The antennae used in most satellite radiometers are parabolic reflectors with a suitable feed system. The cross-track scanning can be carried out by both mechanical and electronic (beam-steering) scanning techniques. The along-track scanning takes place due to satellite motion. Phased-array antennae are used to steer the direction of the antenna beam electronically as was carried out in the Electrically Scanning Microwave Radiometer (ESMR) flown on board Nimbus 5 and 6. In mechanical scanning, the direction of the antenna beam is changed by mechanical rotation of the antenna. Most radiometers use mechanical scanning. There are two possible scanning geometrics. In one case, the footprint of the beam moves almost perpendicular to the sub-satellite track—generally referred to as cross-track scanning (similar to LANDSAT-MSS; see Chapter 6). Hence the incidence angle increases from 0 degree at the nadir to a maximum value towards the edge of the scan. This mode of scanning also produces a varying footprint across the track. Since the functions to retrieve various physical parameters from output data depend on the angle of incidence, this scheme has to allow for extra care during data processing. The Advanced Microwave Sounding Unit (AMSU) flown in the TIROS series operates in this mode (Jarrett and Charlton, 1993).

The other viewing geometry is conical scanning, in which the beam is pointed ahead of the radiometer at a constant tilt angle and scans such that the incidence angle remains constant over the swath (Fig. 7.10). The Scanning Multi-channel Microwave Radiometer (SMMR) flown onboard SEASAT (Njoku, et. al., 1980) and Multi-channel Scanning Microwave Radiometer (MSMR) (Misra, et. al., 2002) onboard the Indian remote sensing satellite IRS-P4 operate in

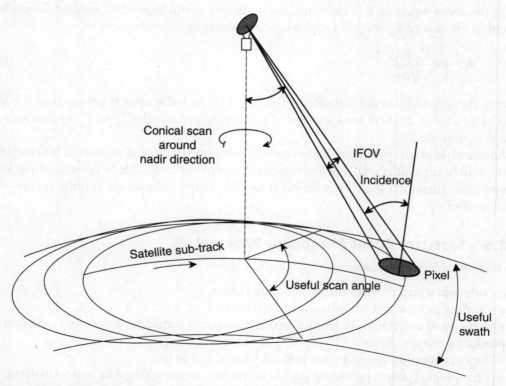

Fig. 7.10 Typical geometry of conically-scanned passive microwave radiometers. (From WMO report)

Table 7.3 MSMR sensor characteristics

Frequency	6.6 GHz	10.65 GHz	18 GHz	21 GHz
Polarisation	V and H	V and H	V and H	V and H
Antenna diameter	80 cm	80 cm	80 cm	80 cm
Beam width	3.7°	2.4°	1.4°	1.4°
Offset angle/ incidence angle	43.3°/49.8°	43.3°/49.8°	43.3°/49.8°	43.3°/49.8°
Pre-detection bandwidth	100 MHz	100 MHz	150 MHz	150 MHz
Quantisation	12 bits/sample	12 bits/sample	12 bits/sample	12 bits/sample
Data rate	5.6 kbps	5.6 kbps	5.6 kbps	5.6 kbps
Gridded T_B data Product cell size	150 km × 150 km	75 km × 75 km	50 km × 50 km	50 km × 50 km

this mode. Note that to have a reliable temperature measurement, on ground and on board calibration is very essential. In addition, the performance of each sub-system of the radiometer has to be modelled and should be taken into account at the final algorithm development. Interested readers may refer to Ulaby, et. al., 1982 for more details. We shall now describe the functioning of a multi-frequency Dicke radiometer, taking MSMR as an example.

Multi-frequency Scanning Microwave Radiometer (MSMR) is one of the two payloads that has been flown onboard Oceansat-I (IRS-P4) satellite, which has been configured primarily for oceanographic applications. The MSMR is a four-frequency (6.6, 10.65, 18.0 and 21.0 GHz), dual-polarised scanning microwave radiometer used to measure brightness temperatures of the earth surface. Brightness temperatures are used to derive parameters such as sea surface temperature, wind speed and water vapour content. MSMR is configured as a typical Dicke radiometer with fixed feed and reflector scanning configuration. The broad specifications of MSMR are given in Table 7.3. The radiometer consists of front end Precision Baseband Processing Subsystem (PBPS) and Data Acquisition and Control Subsystem (DACS). The antenna system of the MSMR consists of an offset parabolic reflector of 80 cm diameter and multi-frequency feed assembly for all the four frequencies. The reflector is rotated at a constant angular scan speed of 11.173 rpm, which corresponds to a scan time of 5.37 s. There are six receiver chains in the system. Two of them cater to 6.6 and 10.65 GHz each, with V and H polarisation data acquisition in alternate scan cycles. Dedicated channels were used for 18 GHz (V), 18 GHz (H), 21 GHz (V) and 21 GHz (H). For the purpose of onboard calibration, two sky horns are used as a cold source. One of them is for 6.6 and 10.65 GHz frequencies and the other for 18.0 and 21.0 GHz. All the six receiver chains along with two sky horns are clustered around the main feed in a compact assembly called Front End Feed Assembly (FEFA). The basic aim of this clustering was to minimise RF path losses prior to low noise amplification. The receiver input is switched at 1 kHz rate between the antenna and a reference noise source at ambient temperature. The FEFA and reflector assembly including the scan motor are mounted on a CFRP support structure in order to maintain rigid alignment.

The receiver assembly on the FEFA carries out low noise amplification, down conversion to IF and square law detection. High gain baseband amplification and synchronous detection

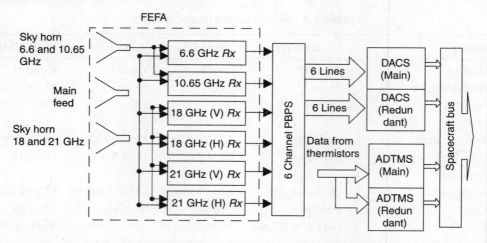

Fig. 7.11   A simplified schematics of MSMR Payload R_x-Receiver; PBPS: Precision Base band Processing System; DACS: Data Acquisition and Control System; ADTMS: Analog and Digital Telemetry System.

are carried out in the Precision Baseband Processing System (PBPS) (Fig. 7.11). All the inter payload control operation, timing sequence generation and digitisation are carried out in the Data Acquisition and Control System (DACS). The onboard integration time implemented in PBPS is 18 ms and 12 bit digitisation is carried out at a sampling interval of 9 ms to avoid aliasing effect so that further interpolations and averaging can be carried out in the ground processor. The scan cycle window consists of data collection in the first half cycle and calibration data acquisition in the form of two hot and cold calibration sequences in the other half. The radiometer data and the house-keeping information such as temperatures at various points and voltage levels are transmitted via a data transmission system for reception at the ground station.

7.2.6   Pushbroom and Synthetic Aperture Radiometer

One of the major constraints of current radiometers is their poor spatial resolution. In the case of a microwave radiometer, the IFOV is defined by the 3 dB beam width, which is approximately λ/D. Thus, if we want a 10 km resolution from a 700 km orbit at L band ($\lambda = 21$ cm), the antenna diameter has to be 15 m [$(21 \times 700)/10 = 1470$ cm] which is a tall order for a spacecraft mission, especially when one has to mechanically scan. The Japanese Advanced Microwave Scanning Radiometer (AMSR) employs a 2 m antenna operating in the TPR mode. The reflector sizes for mechanically scanned radiometers are limited to approximately 2 m for several reasons (NASA, 1994). An alternative solution to the problem of obtaining high spatial resolution without any mechanical scanning is a pushbroom radiometer. In a conical pushbroom, a suitably designed array of radiators (as feed elements) is placed at the focus of an offset paraboloid reflector, in order to produce a number of simultaneous circular footprints to cover the desired swath, in a circular arc, such that the same incidence angle is maintained (Fig. 7.12). It is essentially a single reflector with multiple feeds. Here one can deploy large antennae since no scanning is involved. A 14.7 m inflatable parabolic structure is being developed at NASA laboratories to develop a radiometer operating in the pushbroom mode.

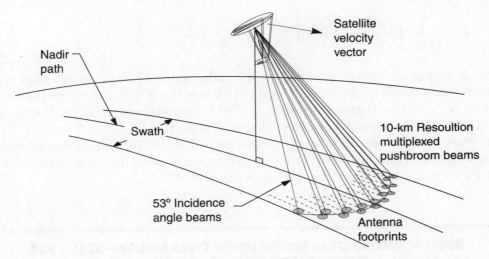

Nadir
path

Swath

53° Incidence
angle beams

Satellite
velocity
vector

10-km Resolution
multiplexed
pushroom beams

Antenna
footprints

Fig. 7.12 Conical pushbroom microwave radiometer scangeometry. (From NASA , 1994)

Another technique to generate high resolution microwave radiometers is interferometric aperture synthesis (Swift et. al., 1991; Le Vine et. al., 1994). Aperture synthesis was first applied in radio astronomy as a means to achieve a high resolving power with an array of antennae. The basic principle is that a pair of small antennae measures the scene to be imaged and the output of the radiometers are cross-correlated. With involved signal processing, the image can be reconstructed. Thus instead of a full aperture, we have a number of small apertures distributed within the same aperture area to produce a high resolution image. Radiometers using this concept are under development for space use. (Camps et. al., 1997; *http://www.esa. int/esapub/bulletin/bullet92/b92marti.htm*)

7.3 ACTIVE MICROWAVE SENSORS

As discussed earlier, active sensors carry their own source of electromagnetic radiation to illuminate the target. The active sensors used for remote sensing is basically one form of RADAR (Radio Detection And Ranging), that is, the sensor sends short microwave pulses and measures the backscattered energy and the time taken for the round trip travel (source to target and back). The time measurement gives the distance of the target from the sensor and hence gives the location of the target and the amount of energy backscattered depends on the target properties and hence gives a measure of some of the target characteristics. Depending on the radar source–receiver configuration and analysis techniques, different types of sensors can be realised. When separate antennae are used for transmitting and receiving, it is called a *bistatic radar*. For remote sensing, the same antenna is generally used for transmitting and receiving (alongwith suitable switches) and such systems are called *monostatic radars*.

The fundamental relation between the radar parameters, the target characteristics and the received signal is expressed by the radar equation. The form widely used for remote sensing radars (monostatic) is given below (Ulaby et. al., 1982).

$$P_r = \frac{\lambda^2}{(4\pi)^3} \int \frac{P_t G^2 \sigma^0}{R^4} dA \qquad\qquad (7.10)$$

where, P_r = average power returned to the radar antenna from an *extended* target, P_t = power transmitted by the radar, G = gain of the antenna, R = distance from the antenna to the target, λ = wavelength of the radar, and σ^0 = the radar scattering coefficient of the target (see box). The integral is over the illuminated area, A.

The above equation does not take into account the path losses. The radar system parameters, such as wavelength, transmit power, gain, polarisation, are constant during an observation and hence the average return power strength varies only with σ^0.

Radar Scattering Cross Section (Radar Cross Section—RCS), σ and Differential Scattering Coefficient σ^0

The strength of the radar signal reflected from an object is conventionally represented by the radar cross-section (RCS) σ. It is expressed in terms of the physical size of an isotropic radiator, that would give rise to the same level of reflection as that observed from the sample target. The RCS, σ is essentially a measure of a target's ability to reflect radar signals in the direction of the radar receiver and has units of area (m^2), or when expressed in decibels as dBm^2.

Experimentally, RCS is measured by comparing the radar return reflected from a target to the radar return reflected from a sphere, which has an area of 1 sq. m (or normalised if smaller area is used) (RCS of a sphere is independent of frequency if operating at sufficiently high frequencies, where $\lambda <$ range and $\lambda <$ radius of the sphere). The RCS of a sphere is πr^2, while that of a flat plate is $4\pi A^2/\lambda^2$, where A is the area of the plate. When an object has, say RCS 4 m^2, it implies that the radar return from that object is the same as that would have been produced by a sphere of cross sectional area 4 m^2. RCS is thus a convenient way to compare reflectance strength of various objects.

RCS is usually used for point targets or targets comparable to the resolution cell. In remote sensing, applications involve extended targets that usually are much larger than a resolution cell of the radar. Therefore, it is appropriate to define a differential scattering coefficient as the radar cross section per unit area. The differential scattering coefficient, σ^0 (generally referred to as just scattering coefficient) is defined as the average value of scattering cross section per unit area

$$\sigma^0 = \left\langle \frac{\sigma}{\Delta A} \right\rangle$$

where ΔA is the area on the ground having a radar cross section of σ.

In general, σ^0 has a significant variation with incidence angle, wavelength, polarisation and the properties of the scattering surface itself.

σ^0 is expressed in decibel (10 $\log_{10}$ of the ratio).

Radars used for remote sensing can be broadly classified as

- nadir looking, wherein the antenna sends a pulse straight down at the nadir below the platform. Altimeters are generally realised in this way, and
- side looking, wherein the sensor sends pulses away from the nadir—side looking. Side Looking Airborne Radar (SLAR) and Synthetic Aperture Radar (SAR) fall in this category.

We shall now discuss the principle of operation of these sensors and how they are realised, without getting into too many engineering details.

7.3.1 ALTIMETERS

The basic principle of an altimeter is illustrated in Fig. 7.13. Here, a short duration pulse of known power is transmitted towards the nadir of the satellite (platform). This is reflected at the earth's surface and then received back at the satellite. If t is the time taken for the two-way trip of the pulse, and h the height of the satellite above the surface of the earth (scattering surface), then

$$2h = ct; \; h = \tfrac{1}{2}\,ct$$

where c is the speed of light. Knowing the location of the satellite in space relative to the centre of the earth, the height of the surface in geodetic coordinates can be determined.

Satellite-borne microwave altimeters for earth observation are generally used for oceanographic studies; thus, they measure sea surface elevation, from which surface geostrophic currents can be inferred. In addition, near-surface wind speed and significant wave height can be determined from the power and shape of the returned signal. We have explained how these are achieved in Chapter 4. We shall now briefly discuss how some of the altimeter parameters are chosen.

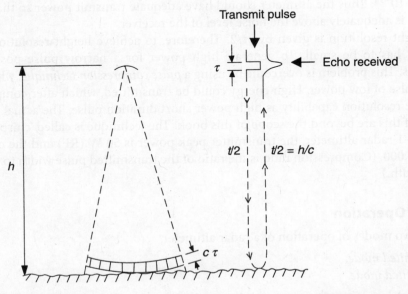

Fig. 7.13 Schematics showing altimeter operation. τ is the pulse width. The radar pulse takes h/c time at each swing. Thus, the total time for the round trip is $2\,h/c$. c is the velocity of light.

- *Operating frequency* selection is based on a number of requirements some of which are conflicting.

— Atmospheric absorption: above ~15 GHz, the atmosphere introduces significant signal loss (refer Fig. 7.7).

— The ionosphere introduces a time delay in the arrival of the pulse. The magnitude of correction for time delay increases as the frequency is reduced.

— Higher the frequency, in general, lower the size of the antenna.

— Interaction with other instruments onboard the satellite.

Apart from the technical considerations, the frequency and bandwidth have to be consistent with international agreement on the frequency allotted for remote sensing. Altimeters currently use the Ku band ~ 13–14 GHz (in some altimeters, a second lower frequency is used to carry out accurate correction due to the influence of ionosphere).

- *The pulse width* τ should be kept minimum to permit the height to be measured precisely. The constraint on the minimum value of τ is set by the maximum allowable bandwidth B ($B = 1/\tau$). A value close to 3×10^{-9} s is used in the present systems.
- *A high repetition rate* (~ 1000 pulses per second) is used to average the values to improve the accuracy, especially when the sea is rough.
- The *time measurement accuracy* (and hence the onboard clock stability) should be consistent with the height measuremet precision required. Suppose we want a measurement accuracy of Δh of 3 cm, then the timing stability $\Delta t = 2(3 \times 10^{-2})/3 \times 10^{-8} < 2 \times 10^{-10}$ s. Thus the uncertainty in timing should be less than or equal to 0.2 ns.
- The *antenna size* depends on the mode of operation (dealt with later).
- *Transmitted power* is an important parameter to be judiciously chosen for any active sensor. For an ERS-1 type altimeter, the typical ratio of received to transmitted power is of the order of 10^{-14}. Thus the altimeter should have adequate transmit power so that the power received is adequately above the noise level of the receiver.
- The height resolution is given by $c\tau/2$. Therefore, to achieve height resolution, the *pulse duration* has to be small. To generate high power for a narrow pulse poses technical problems. This problem is overcome by using a *pulse compression technique*, which allows a wider pulse of low power. High energy could be transmitted, which after compression has the same resolution capability as high power short duration pulse. The actual engineering details of this are beyond the scope of this book. The technique is called 'chirp' (Fig. 7.23). For ERS-1 radar altimeter, the transmitter peak power is 50 W (RF) and the compression ratio is 8,000. (Compression ratio is the ratio of the transmitted pulse width to compressed pulse width.)

Modes of Operation

There are two modes of operation of a radar altimeter.

- *beam-limited mode,*
- *pulse-limited mode.*

Though all the current altimeters are designed in the pulse-limited mode, we shall briefly discuss the principle of both modes of operation.

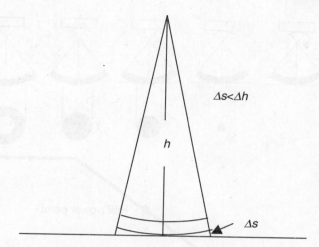

Fig. 7.14 Schematics showing conditions for beam-limited operation.

Beam-limited Mode

The antenna beam width defines footprint and the beam-limited operation requires that the entire footprint is illuminated by the transmit pulse simultaneously. Intuitively, we know that for this to happen we should have a very narrow beam. To be more quantitative, we may set a limit on how far the edge of the wave front can deviate from the middle (Δs) (Fig. 7.14) compared to the minimum rms surface roughness Δh to be resolved. We may set a condition that $\Delta s < \Delta h$ be close to the beam-limited condition. The beam aperture which is proportional to λ/D, should not exceed a minimum value for beam-limited operations. That is, the antenna diameter D should not be less than a certain minimum value. It can be shown that in order to resolve a minimum surface roughness (Δh) of 0.5 m, the ERS-1 type altimeter requires an antenna of ~10 m diameter to operate in this mode. In order to correct the measured range for off-pointing from the nadir direction, one should have an accurate knowledge of the pointing direction of the antenna. In the above case, it works out to be about ~57 arc second. Thus, beam-limited operations have stringent requirements on hardware. No wonder it is not widely used.

Pulse-limited Mode

Here, a broad beam is used. The reflected energy at any instant is proportional to the area of the surface illuminated by the antenna footprint. The pulse of the microwave energy propagates away from the antenna as an expanding spherical wave. For the present, let us assume a flat sea surface. The leading edge of the transmitted pulse first strikes the sea surface ($t = 0$), then the footprint becomes an expanded circle. The area of the circular footprint increases linearly with time until the trailing edge touches the sea. The maximum uniformly illuminated circle will have a radius of $(h\,c\,\tau)^{1/2}$. This is referred to as the footprint radius. The illuminated area, after the initial duration of one pulse width τ, forms an annulus of increasing radius, but constant area. Thus, with each increment of time, we have non-overlapping regions of a constant area being illuminated. The return radar power has three separate regions (Zieger et. al., 1991),

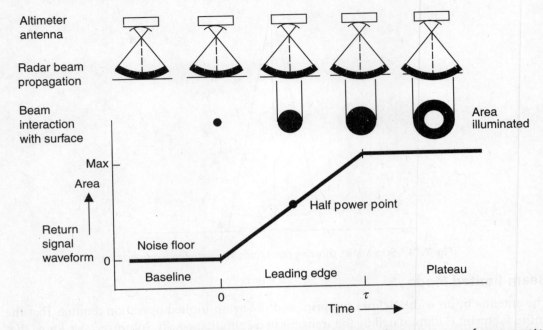

Fig. 7.15 Altimeter pulse interaction with the sea surface and the characteristic return waveform generated by the altimeter electronics. (Reprinted from 'NASA Radar Altimeter for the TOPEX POSEIDON Project', Alfred R Zieger, et. al., *Proceedings of IEEE*, Vol.79, No.6, June 1991, with permission)

- baseline, before any surface illumination, $t < 0$,
- leading-edge, with power increasing linearly with time, that is, as illuminated footprint grows from 0 to the maximum value $2 (h c\tau)^{1/2}$. This happens between time 0 to τ, and
- the plateau, when the surface illuminated is the annulus (at time $> \tau$), the power received as a function of time has a rapid rise reaching a maximum value (Fig. 7.15).

The rise time of the received power is a function of sea state (waves and swell). For a calm sea surface, the rise time is equal to the pulse duration τ. For a rough sea surface with significant wave height $H_{1/3}$, this rise time increases by $2c^{-1}H_{1/3}$ (Chelton, 1988). The position of the rising edge centre corresponds to the (average) distance of the sea surface. The range (height) measurement is made with respect to the rising edge centre (Section 4.3.2).

Altimeters have been generally used for characterising ocean surface and sea ice. Its application for non-ocean surfaces are difficult, since the height distribution of scatterers cannot be described by statistical or analytical models. From such surfaces, the form of echo is determined by the range of the various reflectors within the footprint and their reflectivity. This results in ambiguity for height determination.

The first spaceborne altimeter experiment was conducted during the 1973 Skylab mission (McGoogan, et. al., 1974). This was followed by a number of missions, which have the radar altimeter as one of its instruments (Stanley, 1979; Zieger et. al., 1991). With each mission, the accuracy of observation has improved. Table 7.4 gives some of the important characteristics of the satellite altimeters, carried during various missions. The future trend includes improving the horizontal resolution (footprint) by synthetic apertures, and/or interferometric techniques (Elachi et. al., 1990; Rodriguez and Martin, 1992).

Table 7.4   Characteristics of some of the spaceborne altimeters

	Skylab	GEOS3	Seasat	Geosat	ERS-1	TOPEX/ Poseidon	ERS-2	Envisat-1
Frequency (GHz)	13.9	13.9	13.5	13.5	13.5	13.6/5.3*	13.5	13.6/3.2*
Pulse width (ns)	100	12.5	3	3	3	3	3	3
PRF (Hz)	100	100	1020	1020	1020	4000/1700	1020	1800
RF Power (w)	200	2000	2000	20	50	20/5	50	50
Beam width (deg)	1.5	2.6	1.6	2.1	1.3	1.1	1.3	1.3
Footprint (km)	8	3.6	1.7	1.7	1.7	2.2	1.7	1.7
Altitude (km)	435	840	800	800	800	1300	800	800
Launch	1973	1974	1978	1984	1991	1992	1995	2002

Second frequency.

7.4   SIDE LOOKING RADAR

Vertically downward-looking radar illuminates a circular patch. All the points on the periphery of the circular patch are at the same distance from the radar and hence the backscattered signals from the periphery reach the radar at the same time. This poses uncertainty in resolving from where the signal has arrived. This 'right–left' ambiguity can be overcome if the radar illuminates to one side of the nadir off the platform (aircraft or spacecraft). Thus, imaging radar data is collected looking off to the side of aircraft or spacecraft. For remote sensing, side-looking imaging radars can be broadly classified into two categories:

(i) Real aperture radar—usually referred to as SLAR (Side-Looking Airborne Radar) or SLR (Side-Looking Radar),
(ii) Synthetic Aperture Radar (SAR).

We shall now discuss the principle of operation of these systems.

7.4.1   REAL APERTURE RADAR

Side-Looking Airborne Radar (SLAR) was the first active sensor to produce imagery of the terrain from backscattered microwave radiation. Here the antenna is mounted underneath the aircraft to produce a fan beam (which is wide vertically and narrow horizontally) pointed to the side of the flight track (Fig. 7.16). That is, the antenna beam produces a narrow beam width in the along-track (azimuth) direction, while the beam width in the cross-track (range) direction is broad and defines the swath. A short pulse is transmitted by the radar, which when strikes the ground, a part is backscattered to the antenna. The time delay associated with the received signal gives the distance of the target from the antenna and hence the location. The backscattered intensity which depends on the sensor and terrain characteristics is also measured by the radar. When the aircraft has moved one beamwidth forward, the backscattered signals come from a different strip on the ground. Thus the radar beam pattern produces an image (which represents the $\sigma°$) of the strip across-track and the aircraft motion produces a successive image strip along-track, thus building up a contiguous two dimensional image. A simplified block diagram of the operation of a radar is given in Fig. 7.17. The timing

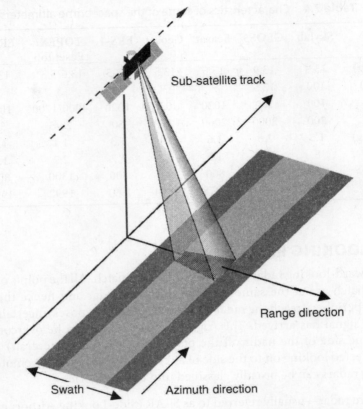

Fig. 7.16 Schematics showing the projection of the side-looking radar beam on ground.

and frequency control module generates a trigger to produce a pulse by the pulse generation module, which gates the transmitter like the Travelling Wave Tube Amplifier (TWTA). The transmitter output is coupled to the antenna through a Transmit/Receive (T/R) switch (which toggles between the transmitter and the receiver). The return signal is connected to a low noise RF amplifier by a T/R switch. After demodulation, the envelope and phase of the return are separated from the carrier frequency, the return signal is amplified, digitised and transmitted to the ground (or recorded onboard) for further processing. The signal transmitted and received could be either vertical polarised (V) or horizontal polarised (H). Depending on the transmit and receive polarisation, four possibilities exist,

   (i)   Transmit H, Receive H; HH,
  (ii)   Transmit V, Receive V; VV,
 (iii)   Transmit H, Receive V, HV, and
  (iv)   Transmit V, Receive H, VH.

(i) and (ii) mode of operation is called a like-polarised system; (iii) and (iv) operation is called a cross-polarised system.

Let us now familiarise ourselves with some of the terms used in describing an imaging radar system (Fig. 7.18).

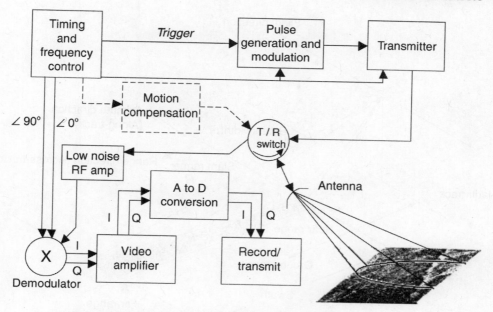

Fig. 7.17 Radar hardware block diagram. (Adapted from David, 1999)

Range: Across-track direction.

Azimuth: Along-track direction.

Near range: Portion of the image swath closest to the nadir track.

Far range: Portion of the image swath farthest from the nadir track.

Slant range: The line of sight distance measured from the antenna to the terrain target.

Ground range: The horizontal distance measured along the surface from the nadir track to the target.

Depression angle: The angle of the radar beam to the target (that is, line of sight from the antenna to the target) measured from a horizontal plane (η) (Fig. 7.19).

Look angle: The angle of the radar beam to the target measured from a vertical plane (θ).

The depression angle and look angle are complementary ($\eta + \theta = 90°$) and hence only one of them needs to be known. These can be considered as the 'illumination angles'. This value is dependent on, where the target is and hence varies across the image. υ is least at the near range and maximum at the far range.

Incidence angle: The angle between the radar beam to the target and the perpendicular to the ground surface, where the beam strikes (Φ). When the surface is horizontal, the incidence angle and the look angle are the same. When the surface is not horizontal, the terrain slope affects the local incidence angle [Fig. 7.19(b)]. For a horizontal surface, the incidence angle is least at near range and maximum at far range.

Spatial Resolution

One of the important parameters in any imaging system is spatial resolution. We define radar image resolution as the separation between two objects of equal reflectivity, which

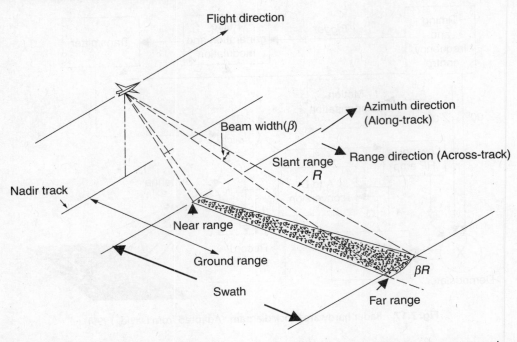

Fig. 7.18 Schematics explaining the terms used for a side-looking radar projection on ground.

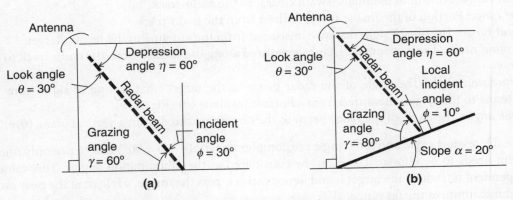

Fig. 7.19 Radar angle nomenclature. (Adapted from David, 1999)

will appear individually in the processed radar image. Let us consider two targets A and B [Fig. 7.20(a)]. The radar pulse will be reflected first from B (since it is closer) and then from A. If we have to separate A and B, the leading edge of pulse from A should not reach the antenna until the energy from the trailing edge of B has reached the antenna [Fig. 7.20(b)]. For this to happen, the *round trip* time from B and A should differ at least by the pulse width.

$$\frac{2R_a}{c} - \frac{2R_b}{c} = \tau \text{ (the pulse duration)}$$

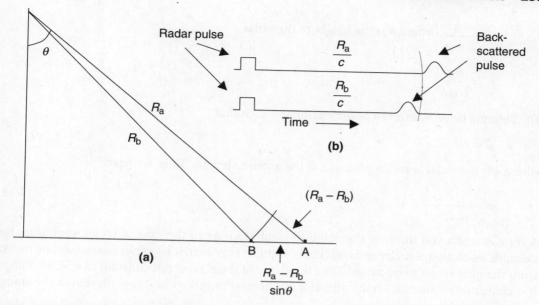

Fig. 7.20   (a) Schematics explaining the concept of spatial resolution in the range direction. (b) The pulse return time relationship for just resolving the targets A and B. Time for one way travel R_a/c and R_b/c is also shown.

$$(R_a - R_b) = \frac{\tau c}{2}.$$

$R_a - R_b$ gives the slant range resolution. The slant range resolution is constant throughout the image and is dependent only on the pulse duration.

However, one is interested in knowing the resolution with respect to the ground distances. For this, we should project the slant range resolution on to the ground. If θ is the off-nadir look angle [Fig. 7.20(a)], by simple trigonometric relation, the ground range resolution r_g is given by

$$r_g = \frac{c\tau}{2\sin\theta} \tag{7.11}$$

From the above equation, we find that the range resolution (across-track resolution) depends on two radar parameters, the pulse length and the look angle. Since θ increases as the ground range increases, the range resolution is better in the far range than in the near range. The resolution can be improved by shortening the pulse length. However, as the pulse length is reduced, the energy content of the pulse decreases and depending on receiver sensitivity, there is a lower limit of pulse length below which the return pulse cannot be detected.

For a real aperture radar to separate two objects in the along-track direction, it is necessary that their separation on the ground should be greater than the footprint of the radar beam in the direction of flight. The azimuth resolution r_a is given by

$r_a = \beta R$, where R is the slant range and β is the azimuth beam width

$$R = \frac{h}{\cos \theta} \quad \text{where } h \text{ is the height of the radar}$$

$$r_a = \frac{h\beta}{\cos \theta}$$

The antenna beam width can be approximated such that

$$\beta = \lambda / L$$

where λ is the radar wavelength and L is the antenna length. Thus, we have

$$r_a = \frac{h\lambda}{L\cos \theta} \tag{7.12}$$

A long antenna will improve the azimuth resolution. As in the case of range resolution, the azimuth resolution also depends on the look angle. However, it becomes coarser as one moves from the near range to far range. Thus the shape of the pixel is not constant in a SLAR image. It is elongated in the cross-track direction in the near range, while it is elongated in the along-track direction in the far range.

The azimuth resolution becomes poorer as the observation height (h) increases. This is a serious limitation in real aperture radar using satellites. Nevertheless, a Side-Looking Real Aperture Radar was flown by USSR on COSMOS 1500. The instrument operated at 9.5 GHz in V polarisation providing 0.8×2.5 km resolution and a swath width of 425 km. This resolution is very poor for many applications. Let us find out the implications of having an ERS-1 SAR, if implemented using RAR. The parameters are $\lambda = 3$ cm, $h = 785$ km, look angle at mid swath 23°. For an azimuth resolution of 25 m, from the above equation, the antenna length L works out to be about 1 km, an impossible task. Thus RAR cannot produce fine resolution radar imagery from satellite altitudes. The solution to the problem is Synthetic Aperture Radar (SAR).

7.4.2 Synthetic Aperture Radar

As seen above, azimuth resolution from SLAR deteriorates as the platform height increases. While this is not a serious problem for aircraft surveys, it limits the use of imaging radars from spacecraft for any worthwhile applications. In 1951, it was first realised that the Doppler spread of echo signal could be used to synthesise a much longer aperture (and hence the name Synthetic Aperture Radar, SAR) to greatly improve the resolutions of a side-looking radar. Thus, SAR is based on the generation of an effective long antenna by means of signal processing instead of the actual long physical antenna. In such a system, a side looking antenna mounted on a moving vehicle emits a series of coherent pulses. The echoes are stored as they are received, maintaining the overall coherent phase relationships. Subsequently, they are coherently integrated and the return so generated would appear as if they have been produced by an array of elements which simultaneously transmitted a pulse.

To illustrate the idea of SAR, consider Fig. 7.21. The antenna is carried on a platform moving with a constant velocity v and the antenna beam axis is oriented at right angles to the platform velocity vector. When the antenna is at A, the target P is just illuminated. It continues to illuminate the target for a distance L_s, until it reaches C, when the beam just leaves the

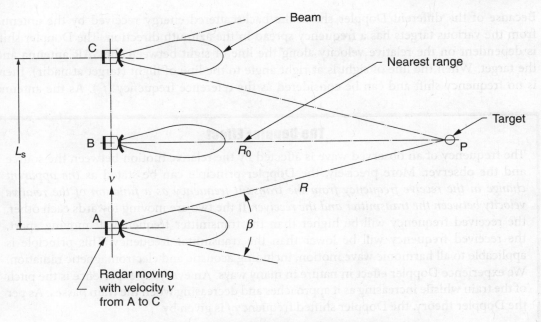

Fig. 7.21 Schematics illustrating the synthetic aperture concept.

target. Thus the target P is continuously in the 'view' of the antenna for the entire length L_s, which is called the *synthetic aperture* and is simply the total width of the real aperture beam on ground:

$$L_s = \beta R_0 = \frac{\lambda}{L} R_0 \tag{7.13}$$

where, L is the real aperture length and R_0 is the slant range distance. Thus L_s is the real aperture radar azimuth slant range resolution. Let us consider a SAR with $L_s = 3$ km, $v = 7$ km/s and pulse repetition frequency 1150 Hz (these are close to Radarsat parameters). The target P is actually illuminated by about 500 consecutive pulses ($3/7 \times 1150 \sim 500$). That is, the information from P is contained in the received 500 pulses. By suitable processing of the received signal, the information appears to have come from an aperture of length equal to the path length over which the radar return is collected, that is, the synthetic aperture. Thus the synthesised antenna can be thought of as a number of independently radiating elements (real aperture), whose separation is decided by the PRF and platform velocity. However, each pulse illuminates the total footprint, each received pulse also contains information on adjacent targets within the footprint. Deciphering this jumbled information is carried out by processing of the received signal—both amplitude and phase. In fact, what distinguishes a SAR from a RAR is the complex signal processing. There are different ways in which one can understand the principle of signal processing of a SAR. We shall try to give a basic idea of how the received signal is processed to generate azimuth information on the basis of the Doppler effect (see box).

When two targets on the ground are separated in the azimuth direction, they are at different angles from the antenna with respect to the line of flight. Therefore, they have different speeds at any given instant with respect to the antenna and hence different Doppler-shifted frequency.

Because of the different Doppler shifts, the backscattered energy received by the antenna from the various targets has a frequency spread in the azimuth direction. The Doppler shift is dependent on the relative velocity along the line of sight between the SAR antenna and the target. When the line of sight is at right angle to the line of flight (target at nadir), there is no frequency shift and can be considered as the reference frequency (f_o). As the antenna

---

The Doppler Effect

The frequency of an observed wave is affected by the relative motion between the source and the observer. More precisely, the Doppler principle can be stated as *the apparent change in the receive frequency from the transmit frequency as a function of the relative velocity between the transmitter and the receiver.* If the two are moving towards each other, the received frequency will be higher than the transmitter frequency. If moving apart, the received frequency will be lower than the transmitter frequency. This principle is applicable to all harmonic wave motion, including acoustic and electromagnetic radiation. We experience Doppler effect in nature in many ways. An everyday experience is the pitch of the train whistle increasing as it approaches and decreasing when the train passes. As per the Doppler theory, the Doppler shifted frequency f is given by

$$f = \left(1 \pm \frac{v}{c}\right) f_0, \text{ for } v \ll c$$

where, f_o is the transmitter frequency and +/− sign corresponds to whether the source is approaching the receiver or receding from the receiver.

The Doppler frequency shift $(f_o - f)$ is therefore $= v/c\, f_o$

In the case of SAR, the target experiences this shift in frequency and the return is also Doppler shifted, thus producing a total Doppler shift to the return pulse $f_d = 2v/c\, f_o$.

It can be shown that with a Doppler frequency shift of f_d, the azimuth coordinate x is

$$x = \frac{f_d \lambda R}{2 v_{\text{rel}}}$$

Thus even if another target is at range R and within the beam at the same time, its Doppler shift frequency allows us to associate with its azimuth coordinate.

(http://www.geo.uzh.ch/~fpaul/sar_theory.html)

Apart from SAR, the Doppler principle is used in wind measurement, using the Doppler shift from rain drops or clouds as tracers moving along with the wind. In astronomy, the measurement of the frequency shift of light received from distant stars/galaxies (known as the red shift) enables their recession velocities to be found.

---

is approaching the target, the backscatter frequency increases and after crossing the nadir point, the backscattered frequency is down shifted. Thus as the antenna moves from A to C, the backscattered frequency varies from $f_o + \Delta f$, to $f_o - \Delta f$, where Δf is the Doppler shift. The two dimensional SAR image is generated from the knowledge of the range for each scatterer (from the round trip time of the pulse) and its Doppler history. At any given range, a scatterer

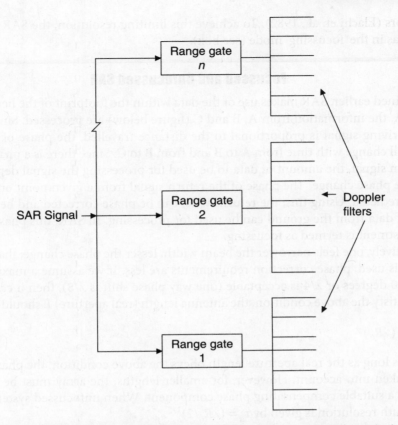

Fig. 7.22 Schematics showing electronic processing of SAR signal. The range gates decide the return time. (Reprinted with permission from *Introduction to Synthetic array and Imaging radars*, Hovanessian S A, Artech House Inc., Norwood, USA, *www.artechhouse.com*)

is mapped at its zero Doppler position. Thus, conceptually signal processing of SAR can be accomplished by a set of range 'gates' for the cross-track direction. Each range gate is followed by a set of Doppler filters for the along-track direction resolution (Fig. 7.22). The output of the Doppler filter essentially gives the difference between the received frequency with respect to a reference signal which is the transmitted pulse frequency.

Thus the output gives the Doppler frequency changes and the amplitude of the returns from each target within the antenna beam. It can be shown that the Doppler frequency shifts essentially give the phase history. Thus the received signal is a complex quantity having both amplitude and phase. The actual processing of the signal to generate an image with good geometric fidelity and radiometric accuracy is quite involved and beyond the scope of this book.

Range and Azimuth Resolution of SAR

The theoretical limit of along-track (azimuth) resolution r_a is given by $L/2$, where L is the real aperture of the antenna. However, this does not mean, we can optimise the resolution by using a very small antenna. Other aspects of image and processing – SNR, swath width, PRF – depends on antenna size and hence the antenna size is chosen by optimising many other factors (Elachi et. al., 1982). To achieve this limiting resolution, the SAR data has to be processed as in the 'focussing' mode (see box).

Focussed and Unfocussed SAR

As explained earlier, SAR makes use of the data within the footprint of the beam. Thus for a point A, the information from A, B and C (figure below) are processed. Since the phase of the arriving signal is proportional to the distance travelled, the phase of the arriving signal will change with time from A to B and from B to C. Since there is a phase change of the return signal, the amount of data to be used for processing the signal depends on the allowable phase change. The phase of the return signal from a given point on the ground can be predicted. Using this, the return signal can be phase corrected and hence a longer length of data from the ground can be used for processing. In SAR, this phase correction and adjustment is termed as focussing.

Intitutively, one feels narrower the beam width, lesser the phase change; that is, if a long antenna is used, phase correction requirements are less. If we assume a maximum phase shift of 90 degrees or $\lambda/4$ is acceptable (one way phase shift is $\lambda/8$), then it can be shown, that to satisfy the above condition, the antenna length (real aperture) L should be such that

$$L > (\lambda R_0)^{\frac{1}{2}}$$

That is, as long as the real aperture length obeys the above condition, the phase shift need not be taken into account. However, for smaller lengths, the array must be focussed by inserting a suitable compensating phase component. When unfocussed systems are used, the azimuth resolution is given by $r_a = (\lambda R_0/2)^{1/2}$.

(For more details refer to *Manual of Remote Sensing*, Vol. 1, Chapter 10, 1980)

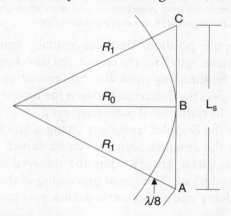

The ground range resolution r_g is the same as that for real aperture radar:

$$r_g = \frac{c\tau}{2\sin\theta}$$

It may appear surprising that the azimuth resolution is independent of the range, and improves with a smaller antenna length (aperture). Let us try to understand the physical reason behind it.

The construction of the synthetic aperture can proceed, and information about a target can be obtained, so long as the target is illuminated by the real beam. A decrease of L increases the real beam width and hence increases the time for which a target is illuminated thereby improving the azimuth resolution produced by synthesising the aperture. Similarly as R increases, the along-track footprint on the ground also increases, increasing the time for which a target is illuminated and this offsets the deteriorating effects of a more distant target. The lower limit on the size of the aperture is controlled by the need to generate adequate gain and effective transmitted power.

The best azimuth resolution is achieved when the Doppler information from the full synthetic antenna length L_s is used. However, from the available Doppler phase history, one can synthesise an antenna aperture less than the maximum synthetic antenna length, by dividing L_s into n equal parts. A smaller antenna can also be synthesised but the resolution degrades proportionately due to the simple reason that synthetic antenna length is reduced. Such a process of generating a smaller length of antenna is called *multilook* and each of such antennae is called a 'look'. For n independent looks, the resolution will be degrading (that is, $nL/2$). However, the speckle noise (see Section 7.4.3) inherent in the SAR imagery can be reduced by incoherently adding the imagery from n different looks.

Range resolution is dependent on pulse durations—shorter the pulse, higher the range resolution. However, shorter the pulse width, lower the transmitted energy (for a fixed peak power) and hence poorer signal-to-noise ratio. This problem is discussed in Section 7.3.1 while dealing with altimetry. The same technique is used in the case of SAR also—to generate a longer pulse with frequency modulation (chirp). Upon reception of the pulse, it is compressed to separate adjacent resolution cell as demonstrated in Fig. 7.23. Thus signal processing permits the use of an extended pulse at lower peak power.

Pulse Repetition Frequency (PRF) – the interval between the successive radar pulses – needs to be chosen carefully to meet the system requirements and avoid 'ambiguities'. In the first place the interval between the pulses should be long enough, so that the return from farthest range is received before the next pulse is sent. For example, if the maximum slant range is 300 km, then the round trip time taken for the pulse from this range to reach the receiver is 2 ms ($2 \times 300 \times 10^3/3 \times 10^8 = 2 \times 10^{-3}$). That is, the total time from a transmitter to the target at a slant range of 300 km and back to the receiver is 2 ms. If the interval between the pulses is less than 2 ms, the radar return pulse from two successive pulses can overlap and the receiver will be confused about where the returns have arrived from. This is referred to as range ambiguity. For example, if the pulse interval is 1.5 ms, the second pulse could return to the receiver, at the same time as the return from the first pulse from a target at 300 km, after reflection from

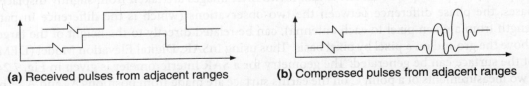

(a) Received pulses from adjacent ranges   (b) Compressed pulses from adjacent ranges

Fig. 7.23 Schematics showing how pulse compression can help discriminate adjacent pixels. Though the two expanded pulses overlap (a) after compression (b) they are time separated. (Reprinted with permission from *Introduction to Synthetic array and Imaging radars*, Hovanessian S A, Artech House Inc., Norwood, USA., *www.artechhouse.com*)

a target at 75 km slant range (2.0 − 1.5 = 0.5 ms round time is possible from a target $3 \times 10^8 \times$ ½ $\times 0.5 \times 10^{-3}$).

In short, range ambiguities occur when portions of the radar return from a previous pulse overlap with the return from the present pulse. The condition for this not to happen is

$$PRF \ll \frac{c}{2R_{max}}$$

Thus there is an upper frequency limit.

What is the lower limit of PRF? The greater the number of pulses reflected from a target, the greater the probability of distinguishing it from the noise. More importantly, the frequency of sampling of a scene should follow the Shannon criteria to avoid aliasing, which produces azimuth ambiguities (Li and Johnson, 1983). To satisfy these criteria, the PRF has to be greater than $2V/L$, where V is the satellite velocity and L the antenna length (real aperture).

Thus, the PRF should lie between the limits,

$$\frac{2V}{L} \leq PRF \leq \frac{c}{2R_{max}} \tag{7.14}$$

However for spaceborne SAR, the upper limit of PRF as given above cannot be applied, due to the long distances involved. In this case, the ground return may come after several pulses have been transmitted and has to be taken care of in the design of the SAR, called the Staggered PRF Operation. In short, these ambiguities pose severe constraints on the system design of spaceborne SARs. The effect of these ambiguities are given in terms of ratio of power received due to ambiguity to that of the signal received and expressed in dB.

In all our earlier discussions we have assumed that the SAR platform is travelling in a straight line, however, attitude and orbit perturbations produce motion errors, which should be compensated in the processing of the data. The signal-to-noise ratio of a radar primarily depends on the transmit power. However, there are a number of other factors influencing the S/N such as Doppler centroid error, azimuth ambiguity ratio, impulse response function and so on.

Interferometric SAR (InSAR)

SAR interferometry is one of the powerful emerging applications of radar observation of the earth's surface (Massonnet, 1997). As mentioned earlier SAR is a coherent imaging system, that is, during data acquisition and further data processing of the received radar echo, the amplitude and phase information is retained. SAR interferometry makes use of this coherence property. The principle of InSAR is that if two SAR images are taken from slightly displaced bases, the phase difference between the two observations (which is the difference in path length from a given pixel to each antenna), can be related directly to the height of the target above the ground on a pixel by pixel basis. Thus using InSAR, Digital Elevation Model (DEM) of the surface can be generated. The geometry for a SAR Interferometer is given in Fig. 7.24. Two measurements of a point C on the earth's surface are made from positions A_1 and A_2. The difference between these two positions is called the interferometric baseline, B. As mentioned before, the phase difference between the measurements from these two positions can be mathematically demonstrated to have the information regarding the topography, $z(y)$, of the

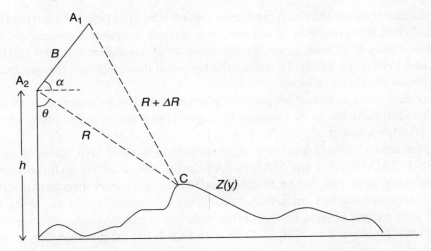

Fig. 7.24 Schematic of an interferometric mode of SAR operation.

earth's surface. The phase difference depends on the baseline distance (B), baseline angle (α), range (R), look angle (θ), and height of point $z(y)$.

The requirement of dual observation to form a baseline can be realised in two ways. In one approach, the baseline is produced by two physical antennae, which are mounted on a platform. The first antenna sends and receives the radar returns, while the second antenna solely receives the backscattered radiation. Thus it is possible to capture the data in a single pass. This is usually the arrangement for aircraft radar interferometer like NASA/JPL TOPSAR (Zebker and Goldstein, 1986; Zebeker et. al., 1992). The antennae could be mounted perpendicular to the flight path (across-track interferometry) or parallel to the flight direction (along-track interferometry). Along-track interferometry is used for mapping of ocean currents and moving targets such as glaciers and ice sheets.

In the second case, a SAR interferometer is realised with a single satellite instrument in a nearly exact repeating orbit (referred to as repeat pass interferometry). Though this technique is ideal for satellite-borne SAR systems, it has certain limitations, which should be taken into account while processing data. The derived terrain height accuracy is dependant on the accuracy with which the orbital parameters (and hence baseline) and altitude can be determined. The basic interferometric product is an interferogram. A precise knowledge of the length and position of the baseline is essential to generate a good interferogram. If the baseline is too short, the sensitivity to signal phase differences will be undetectable, while if the baseline is too long, additional noise due to spatial decorrelation corrupts the signal (Li and Goldstein, 1990). There is a critical baseline dependant on the SAR parameters, beyond which the phases of the two images cannot be compared interferometrically, because they are uncorrelated. The critical baseline for ERS-1/2 is 1100 metres, while the optimum baseline for DEM generation is considered to be around 200 m.

Another problem is that the features themselves may change in the scale of wavelength (for example, tilling, soil moisture, agricultural cover change), which produces phase change though the height remains essentially the same. That is, for generating interferograms, radar-scattering characteristics within each pixel must remain similar in time between the two-image acquisition. When this condition is not met, it is termed *temporal decorrelation*. Temporal decorrelation makes it difficult to assign the cause of phase difference seen in the images (Zeberker and Vellasanor, 1992). To reduce the temporal decorrelation, the gap between the successive passes should be reduced.

The phase difference as in any interference phenomenon has an uncertainty of $2n\pi$ (n, an integer). This ambiguity has to be removed by a special processing called phase unwrapping. (Hartl and Wu, 1993; Just et. al., 1995).

Repeat pass interferometry has been experimented in various SAR missions like ERS-1/ ERS-2, JERS-1, RADARSAT-1 and SIR C/X-SAR. In the case of ERS-1 SAR using an array of 19 corner reflectors deployed along a 20 km spread in the across-track direction, it was possible to detect a change as small as 1 cm in one of the corner reflectors (Prati et. al., 1993). However, for terrains with natural objects, the rms error of height is much coarser. Werner (1992) has shown that with 8 looks and an SNR of 20 db with ERS-1, the height resolution is better than 2.5 m for a wide range of correlation values. A dedicated interferometric SAR mission was carried out by NASA called the Shuttle Radar Topography Mission (SRTM). It carried two antennae separated by a distance (after deployment in orbit) of 60 m. The mission carried out in March, 2000 has acquired data of about 80% of the earth's surface, thus enabling the creation of topographical maps over large areas of earth.

7.4.3   IMAGE QUALITY IN RADAR IMAGERY

There are two aspects to the image quality, radiometric and geometric. These issues are more complex compared to VNIR/TIR imagery, due to the very nature of radar signal generation and acquisition process.

Radiometric Issues

If we have one class of object (say, wheat field), we expect the same grey value wherever the same class of object is in the image. However, this does not happen because of various reasons such as, the distance from the radar to the target varies depending on the look angle, and the scattering coefficient itself varies with incidence angle (which varies across the track).

Antenna pattern   The antenna transmits more power in the mid-range portion of the illuminated swath than at the near and far ranges. Correction to such effects can be incorporated in the instrument itself or can be modelled and implemented on the ground. On board improvements include shaping the antenna beam (cosec-squared pattern), modelling $\sigma°$ variation and incorporating a variable gain (sensitivity time control, STC) and so on (Ulaby et. al., 1982). Modelling for the $\sigma°$ variation with the incidence angle, which holds good for a variety of targets is difficult. Thus the problem of producing an image which has close grey tones for targets of the same class over full swath is a complex problem.

Speckle   Radar imagery has a characteristic noise, which is not present in OIR images. This is called speckle, which appears as a grainy 'salt and pepper' texture in an image. We shall now try to understand why this noise arises. Each radar resolution cell (pixel) on ground contains a number of scatterers, which can independently scatter the radar signal. Even for very high resolution imagery of say, 10 m × 10 m, the resolution cell is coarser than the radar wavelength. Therefore, the EM wavelength of only a few centimetres can interact with individual scatterers. Though the radar signal is coherent, after reflection from the individual scatterers these signals have a random path in the resolution cell which produce arbitrary phase differences, which when combined produce constructive or destructive interference. Constructive interference results in a strong return signal and hence a bright pixel in the image, while destructive interference produces a dark pixel. Speckle makes radar image interpretation difficult and suitable processing techniques are used to reduce speckle. Multi-look processing discussed earlier is one such technique. Suitable filtering of the image is also used for reducing speckle. The filter function should be carefully chosen to preserve spatial variability (textural information) of the scene.

One positive aspect of radiometry of radar images compared to optical is its large dynamic range. While optical systems like LANDSAT MSS have 8 bits, most of the imaging radars process the data as 16 bits.

Geometric Distortions

Side-looking radar geometry and the return pulse time measurement, results in geometric distortion in the imagery.

Range Distortion

A side-looking radar measures the slant range, but an analyst is interested in the ground range. Since the slant range depends on the look angle, an image based purely on return pulse timing (slant-range imagery), will show scale variation across the image. The near range imagery will be more compressed than the far range image, that is, for two objects of the same length, the one at near range will show a shorter length than the one which is at far range (Fig. 7.25).

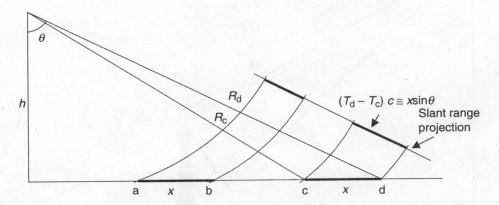

Fig. 7.25 Schematics showing range distortion in radar imaging. In slant projection, two objects ab and cd of equal length show different lengths. T_d and T_c are the return pulse timing from the points d and c. Knowing platform altitude h, slant range R can be converted to ground range as $(R^2 - h^2)^{1/2}$ for a flat terrain.

The scale distortion in the slant range imagery does not permit its use for any planimetric mapping. The ground range map could be generated for a flat terrain knowing the platform height. However, even if the DEM is known, this becomes more complex for undulated terrain due to other effects, which are given next.

Relief Displacement

In radar imagery, a vertical structure has relief displacement, that is, the top is displaced with respect to the bottom. We have seen in Chapter 6, that the photographic image also has relief displacement. However, the relief displacement in radar imagery is in the opposite direction compared to optical imagery, that is, the camera sees the relief displayed away from the nadir point, while the radar sees the relief towards the nadir line. We shall explain this phenomenon for a 'tower' as shown in Fig. 7.26. From simple geometry you find that the slant range R_T of the top of the tower 'a' is shorter than the slant range R_B from the base and consequently the radar pulse reaches the top of the tower before the base. Therefore, the radar return from the top reaches the antenna first compared to return from the base. Hence, in the radar image, the top of the tower will appear closer to the flight line than the bottom. Here the top of the feature 'lays over' the base and is referred to as the *lay over* effect. The amount of lay over is a function of look angle; it is maximum near the nadir and smallest out in the far range. (Note that this is the opposite to relief displacement in photography.) There is a region on the side of the tower further from the nadir, where the radar pulse cannot reach and hence no return is received and will appear black in the image. This portion is called the shadow, and is based on the same principle as geometric optics.

Another effect of the range measurement is the confusion between two targets horizontally separated and at different heights as in Fig. 7.26 (towers a and b). The top of both the towers a and b have the same slant range and their return will be mapped to a single resolution cell. As

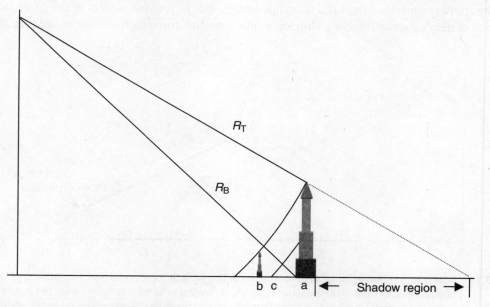

Fig. 7.26   Schematics showing the cause of 'lay over' in radar imagery. The radar return from the top reaches earlier than the return from the base since $R_T < R_B$. Thus the top is 'seen' ahead of the base.

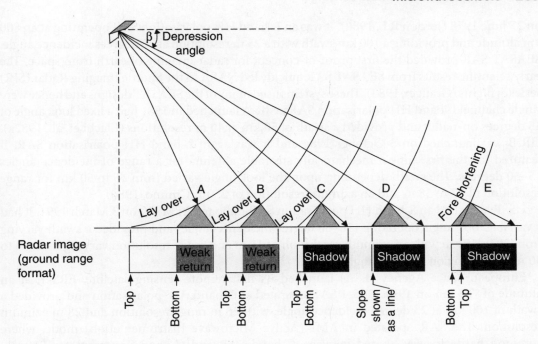

Fig. 7.27 Effects of terrain relief on side-looking radar images. (Adopted from David, 1999)

the wave front moves further away towards the tower, it makes a simultaneous return from the foreground and the radar facing side of the tower (c). In general, the land surface in front of a tall 'object' having the same range as that of any portion of the 'object' structure is affected. In most cases, the radar facing structure of the tower produces the stronger backscatter of the two and as a result, information about foreground landscape is obliterated (David, 1999).

In the images of a sloping terrain as a mountain region, the lay over and shadow characteristics depend on the nature of the slope, and the look angle (which together also determine the local incidence angle). Five different conditions are shown in Fig. 7.27. If the inclination of the terrain slope facing away from the antenna is less steep than the depression angle, the radar pulse can illuminate the surface. However, the illumination will be very weak because of the large local incidence angle (A, B). When the slope is not at all illuminated (C, D and E), the area of non-illumination extends beyond the slope, making the shadow masking the features beyond the slope. In Fig. 7.27, D shows an interesting case, when the local incidence angle is zero. The return reaches at the same time the from the base and the top, and the slope is shown as a line. At large look angle, the lay over ceases and a new distortion takes place. Here the radar pulse reaches the base of the feature before the top (E). However, the slopes of the surfaces will not be shown in true size. Here the slope appears to as compressed and referred to as *foreshortening*.

7.4.4 SPACEBORNE SAR SYSTEMS

The Apollo Lunar Sounder Experiment (ALSE) sensor was the first spaceborne SAR system, flown around the moon on the Apollo-17 spacecraft Lunar Orbiter in 1972 (Porcello L J et. al., 1974). NASA launched the first civilian satellite-based Remote Sensing SAR on SEASAT on 27 June 1978 (Jordon R L, 1980). It was an L-band HH polarisation SAR operating at an 800 km altitude and providing a 100 km swath with a 25 m resolution at 23 degrees incidence angle. SEASAT SAR provided the first proof-of-concept for radar imaging of earth from space. The early scientific results from SEASAT SAR quickly led NASA to the Shuttle Imaging Radar (SIR) series of flights (Granger, 1983). These systems used many of the SEASAT designs and hence were single channel L-band HH polarisation SARs. SIR-A launched in 1981 had a fixed look angle of 45 degrees off-nadir, and provided a swath of 50 km at 40 m resolutions (Elachi et. al., 1982a). SIR-B was launched on 5 October 1984 and it was again L-band HH polarisation SAR. It featured for the first time a mechanically steerable antenna for a range of incidence angles 15–60 degrees. The swath depending upon the look angle varied from 15 to 50 km for range resolution of 17 to 58 m and an azimuth resolution of 25 m (Cimino, 1986).

USSR launched an S-band HH polarisation SAR onboard ALMAZ, on 3 March 1991. It had a variable look angle operation (30–60 degree incidence angle) and provided a swath varying from 20 to 45 km with an azimuth resolution of 15 m and range resolution varying from 15 to 30 m depending on the look angle.

European Space Agency (ESA) launched its first remote sensing satellite, ERS-1, at an altitude of 785 km on 1991. ERS-1 SAR operated at C-band, VV polarisation and provided a swath of 100 km at 23 degree incidence angle, with 26 m range resolution and 28 m azimuth resolution. The SAR operated in AMI (Active Microwave Instrumentation) mode, where common hardware was shared between C-band SAR and C-band Scatterometer (Attena, 1991). As a follow-on, ESA launched ERS-2, an exact copy of ERS-1 in April, 1995.

The Japanese Earth Resources Satellite (JERS-1) carrying a SAR on board was launched on 22 February 1992. It was an L-band HH polarisation SAR having a swath width of 75 km with a resolution of 18 m in range and azimuth direction (Nemoto et. al., 1991). Japanese Advanced Land Observing Satellite (ALOS) launched in 2006 carried a Phased Array type L-band Synthetic Aperture Radar (PALSAR) (Wakabayashi et. al., 1996).

Shuttle Imaging Radar SIR/C/X-SAR, a joint venture of US/German/Italian groups was successfully launched in 1994 (Jordan et. al., 1995). This was the first multi-frequency spaceborne mission operating at L, C and X-bands. It provided the first polarimetric SAR operations in L and C-band. X-band was in VV polarisation. It utilised for the first time the active array antenna utilising distributed transmit-receive (T/R) modules for electronically beam steering in L and C-band. A wide look angle of 15 to 60 degrees was obtained by electronically beam steering in L and C-band and mechanical beam steering in X-band.

RADARSAT-1 was the first sophisticated resource survey remote sensing satellite of Canada (Raney et. al., 1991; Parashar et. al., 1993), which was launched in 1995 at an altitude of 800 km for a mission life of 5 years. It carried a C-band SAR in HH polarisation with a number of imaging features. It utilised the programmed phased array antenna capability to electronically steer the antenna to cover the look angles 20 to 49 degrees in various beam configurations. It had seven operating modes providing various swaths and resolution combinations. Way and Smith, 1991, have summarised the evolution of SAR system. The major SAR missions carried out over the last three decades operating from L to X bands have covered significant grounds in SAR applications. To meet the application needs the SAR system configuration has also seen substantial improvements from single-beam fixed resolution system to multiple resolution and swath systems, and from single polarisation configuration to multi-polarisation/polarimetric configuration. Consequently, SAR technology also witnessed a transformation from a passive antenna-based system to an active phased array antenna with T/R (transmit/ receive) modules distributed over the antenna aperture to provide beam steering capability electronically. Table 7.5 gives major system parameters of some of the past, space borne SAR systems (the list is not exhaustive). The launch of Radar Imaging Satellite (RISAT-1), on 26 April 2012 carrying a multi-mode C-band SAR system has opened a new chapter in Indian Space Research Organisation's Earth Observation (EO) programme—indigenous capability of developing, launching and operation of a state of the art microwave imaging sensor. We shall now briefly describe the RISAT-1 system.

7.4.4.1 Radar Imaging Satellite (RISAT-1)

RISAT-1 is the first indigenously developed imaging radar sensor system of ISRO, complementing its optical IRS series of earth observation missions. RISAT-1 operates from a sun-synchronous orbit at 536 km height. The synthetic aperture radar onboard RISAT-1 operates at C-band (5.35 GHz) in different modes of polarisation, incidence angle and resolution. The SAR consists of two broad segments—deployable active antenna, and RF and baseband systems housed on the satellite deck. The earth-facing side of the active antenna is a broadband dual polarised microstrip radiating aperture, consisting of three deployable panels, each of 2 m × 2 m size (Fig. 7.28). In order to achieve all polarimetric modes, separate tansmit–receive (TR) modules with independent transmit and receive chains are provided for H and V polarisation (Misra et. al., 2013). Two separate chains of receiver and data acquisition and compression systems cater to simultaneous operation in two polarisations. With this architecture, when the H and V polarised beam is transmitted simultaneously with 90° relative phase shift, the SAR generates circularly polarised transmit signals and can receive linearly polarised H and V signals—this mode of operation is referred to as hybrid polarimetric operation. RISAT-1 SAR is the first payload to use this mode for earth observation. Various polarisation transmit–receive combinations in which data can be collected is given in Table 7.6. Apart from these, there is a Quad Pol. mode where for part of the synthetic aperture time (the time for a target to cross the azimuth antenna beam), the beam polarisation is switched from H-transmit to V-transmit and vice versa, and data for both the polarisations are received simultaneously (HH + HV, VH + VV).

The instrument can collect data in different resolutions and swath. The basic imaging modes, incorporated in the payload, are as follows:

- Coarse Resolution ScanSAR Mode (CRS): 50 m resolution, 223 km swath,
- Medium Resolution ScanSAR Mode (MRS): 25 m resolution, 115 km swath,
- Fine Resolution Stripmap Mode-1 (FRS-I): 3 m resolution, 25 km swath,
- Fine Resolution Stripmap Mode-2 (FRS-2): 9 m resolution, 25 km swath, and
- High Resolution Spotlight Mode (HRS): 1 m resolution, 10 km swath, 10–100 km azimuth extent.

We shall briefly discuss the features of different modes of imaging. *Stripmap imaging* is the conventional mode of SAR in which the orientation of the antenna beam is fixed with respect to flight path so that a strip of constant swath is illuminated (Fig. 7.18). The Stripmap SAR image dimension is limited in swath but not in length dimension, total scene length will depend on storage capacity. [The data rate is greater than 640 Mbps which is too high for real-time transmission and the data is recorded in Solid State Recorder (SSR) with a capacity of 300 Gbits.]

Table 7.5 Summary of characteristics of spaceborne SAR

	Freq. Band	Pol.	Altitude (in km)	Resolution (in m)	Swath (in km)	Incidence angle (in deg)
SEASAT-SAR (June 1978)	L	HH	800	25 × 25	100	23
SIR-A Nov. 1981	L	HH	259	40 × 40	50	50
SIR-B Oct. 1984	L	HH	225	Range 17–58 Az .25	15–50	15–60
ALMAZ SAR (March 1991)	L	HH	280	Range 15–30 KM Az 15	25–50	30–60
ERS-1 SAR (July 1991)	C	VV	785	26 × 28	100	23
JERS-1 SAR Feb. 1992	L	HH	568	18 × 18	75	38
SIR C/XSAR April, Oct. 1994	L,C,X	Single/dual Multi pol (L and C) VV in X Band	225	Range 10–60 Az 30	15–100	15–60
ERS-2 SAR April 1995	C	VV	785	26 × 28	100	23
RADARSAT-1 SAR Nov. 1995	C	HH	798	Standard 25–35	100–150	20–49
				Fine resl. 9	50	37–47
				SCANSAR 50	300	20–46
				100	500	20–50
				Extended low 25 m × 28 m	75	10–20
				Extended high 25 m × 28 m	75	50–60
ENVISAT ASAR 2002	C	HH/VV HH + VV VV + VH HH + HV	790	30	56–105	15–45
				30	56–106	15–46
		HH/VV		150	405	17–42
		HH/VV		1000	405	17–42
RADARSAT-2 SAR 2007	C	HH/VV	798	25–40	70–170	10–60
				10	50	37–48
				50 / 100	300/500	20–50
		HH, VV, HV, VH		11 / 25	25	20–44
				3	10/20	30–40
PALSAR (ALOS) 2006	L	HH / HV or VV + VH HH+ VV	700	7–44	40–70	8–60
				14–88		
				24–88	20–65	8–30
		HH / VV		100	250/350	18–43

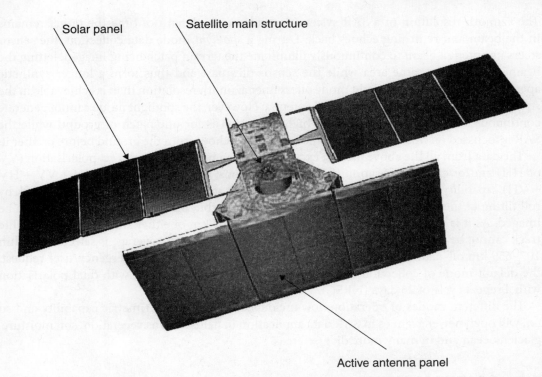

Solar panel

Satellite main structure

Active antenna panel

Fig. 7.28 Schematics showing on-orbit configuration of RISAT-1. (Image credit: ISRO)

There are certain technical constraints to get a wider swath using the stripmap imaging mode. However to collect data at the regional/global scale and better revisit capability, it is necessary to realise wider swath. The *scanSAR* mode of operation enables us to achieve wider swath compared to the stripmap mode of operation. In the scanSAR mode of operation, the antenna beam is electronically stepped in elevation, and the data is collected from each beam position which forms a subswath. The antenna look angle is maneuvered to cover several overlapping parallel subswaths which are then subsequently combined together while processing to generate full swath imagery. Since the scanSAR mode shares the synthetic aperture time between subswaths, the wider swath is produced at the cost of having a coarser azimuth resolution.

Table 7.6 Possible polarisation combinations for generating RISAT-1 SAR data

Transmit polarisation	Receive polarisation	Terminology
Vertical	Vertical	VV
Vertical	Horizontal	VH
Horizontal	Vertical	HV
Horizontal	Horizontal	HH
Right circular	Horizontal + vertical	Circular

The azimuth resolution of a SAR system depends on the length of time the target remains in the beam and returning echoes back. During a *spotlight* mode data collection, the sensor steers its antenna beam to continuously illuminate the terrain patch being imaged, letting the beam dwell on the same area while the sensor flies past and thus form a longer synthetic aperture. Therefore, the spotlight mode offers finer azimuth resolution than is achievable in the stripmap mode using the same physical antenna. However, the spotlight mode cannot generate continuous along-track coverage—the high resolution is for one patch of ground while the SAR is focussed on this one patch; it is not acquiring echoes from the ground before or after it.

The data from all the above modes, except FRS-2 can be operated with co-polarisation (VV or HH) and/or cross polarisation (VH or HV) options. Quad polarisation (HH + VV + HV + VH) capability is incorporated in FRS-2. The SAR can image on either side of the track by roll tilting of the spacecraft by ±36°. However, in one orbit, only one side of the orbit can be imaged. As it is a side looking active sensor, around 107 km of either side of the sub-satellite track cannot be imaged for the orbit under consideration. Swath coverage is selectable within 107–659 km off-nadir distance on either side. In the absence of the emergency/user request, the default mode of collection will be MRS descending, left looking, with dual polarisation with a repeat cycle of 25 days (NRSC).

The different modes of operation, low incidence angle, full polarimetric capability and so on, will open newer avenues in SAR data application in fields such as vegetation, soil moisture, glacier, ocean and in many more diverse areas.

7.5 SCATTEROMETER

Scatterometer is a calibrated radar specifically designed to measure accurately the scattering coefficient $\sigma°$. The principle of a scatterometer is basically the same as that of a radar; that is, the scatterometer transmits microwave pulses, the backscattered intensity and the round trip time is measured. The intensity gives a measure of the scattering coefficient, and the time information gives the target location. Three basic considerations are important in all scattering measurements—calibration, determination of area covered and obtaining sufficient independent samples to make a precise measurement (Ulaby et. al., 1982). Absolute calibration leading to accurate measurements is needed for comparing results from different systems.

The scattering coefficient $\sigma°$ is related to other instrument parameters as follows (Ulaby et. al., 1982)

$$\sigma^0 \approx \frac{(4\pi)^3 R^4}{G_0^2 \lambda^2 A_w} \left[\frac{P_r}{P_t} \right] \qquad\qquad 7.14$$

where, G_o = the maximum gain of the antenna, λ = wavelength, R = range, P_t = transmit power, P_r = received power, A_w = weighted area A_w, which takes into account the radiation pattern $\int A_i g^2 (\theta, \phi)\, dA$, $g\,(\theta, \Phi)$ = normalised antenna gain (radiation pattern) such that the antenna gain $G = G_o g\,(\theta, \Phi)$, and A_i = area of illumination, that is, the integration over the illuminated area.

The antenna gain G is dependent on the radiation pattern and is the most difficult part of quantifying to generate absolute calibration. It may be noted that $\sigma°$ is proportional to (P_r/P_t), and so only this ratio need be measured for relative calibration, provided the range is known accurately. However, the received power in practice is the sum of the power from the resolution cell and the contribution from the natural emissivity from earth's atmosphere and the instrument noise. Therefore, these later quantities should be estimated and subtracted from the received power in order to get the backscattered power and estimate $\sigma°$ from the radar equation.

In an operational environment, the stability of various subsystems of the instrument such as transmitter stability, receiver gain drifts and so on, affect the overall accuracy of the instrument. Internal calibration of a system permits determination of relative scattering coefficients with the precision dependent on the calibration scheme, while external calibration permits determination of the absolute value of the scattering coefficient. The internal calibration could be to use a sample of transmitted signals to calibrate the receiver, so that the ratio of (P_r/P_t) can be directly determined. For external calibration, a 'homogeneous' extended target of known scattering coefficient may be viewed during the flight. The dimensions of the calibration target should be much larger than the resolution cell so that sufficient averaging can be done (for details of different concepts and systems for internal and external calibration, the reader may refer to Ulaby et. al., 1982).

Ground-based scatterometers are designed to provide backscattering cross-section as a function of incidence angle for the area under observation. However the motivation to have a space-based scatterometer was to measure the ocean surface backscatter as a means to derive the surface wind vector. Though the Skylab Mission in 1973 carried the first spaceborne scatterometer (S-193), the instrument specifically designed for sea surface wind measurement is the SESAT-A, Satellite Scatterometer (SASS) instrument launched in 1978. The estimation of wind velocity from scatterometers require multiple co-located measurements of backscatter from different azimuth angles. Though multiple azimuth viewing can be met using either fan beam antennae or scanning spot beams, the earlier instruments relied on fan beam antennae. The fan beam antenna configuration is essentially a side looking radar, with a footprint wide in the cross-track direction and narrow in the along-track direction. However, since the measurements have to be made at different zenith angles, multiple antennae oriented at different angles, to the cross-track direction is used. We shall discuss some of the details of SASS to get some insight into the realisation of a fan beam scatterometer.

SASS uses four fan beam antennae—two on either sides of the sub-satellite track (Grantham et. al., 1977). The two antennae on each side are aligned so that they are pointed 45° and 135° relative to the spacecraft flight direction. Thus, the footprint of the four antenna beam produces an X-shaped illumination pattern on the earth (Fig. 7.29). In this way, a given surface location is first viewed by the forward antenna and later by the aft antenna, near orthogonally. Thus $\sigma°$ measurement of the same region is provided by two azimuth angles separated by approximately 90°.

The two values of $\sigma°$ (from two azimuth angles) are insufficient to get a unique wind speed measurement. In fact, it gives four solutions (Fig. 7.30) This four-fold ambiguity in wind direction resulting from $\sigma°$ measurement at only two orthogonal azimuth angles severely limited the sue of SASS. Keeping this in mind, for the NASA scatterometer NSCAT flown onboard Japanese Satellite ADEOS, an additional antenna was added between the fore and aft beam to both sides of the swath (Fig. 7.31) (Naderi et. al., 1991).

The polarisation of the microwave radiation emitted and received by the mid beam was both vertical (VV) and horizontal (HH). For the other antenna and instruments only VV

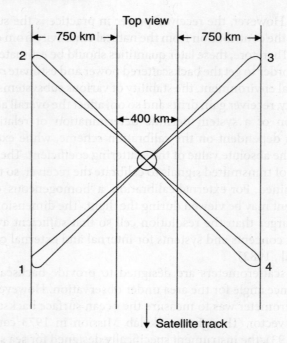

Fig. 7.29 Projection of antenna beam pattern 1, 2, 3 and 4 of Seasat-A scatterometer.

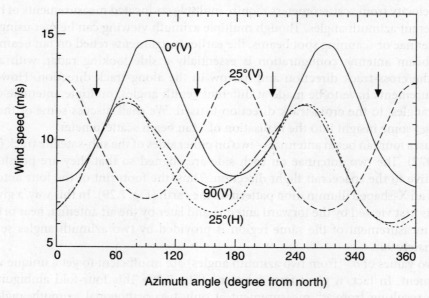

Fig. 7.30 Justification for making measurements at various azimuth to reduce wind direction, ambiguity. Loci of possible vector winds associated with colocated noise-free $\sigma°$ measurements obtained from antennae at various azimuth angles. Heavy solid line: antenna angle of 0° (V-pol); dashed line: angle of 90° (V-pol); light solid line: angle of 25° (V-pol); dotted line: angle of 25° (H-pol). Arrows indicate solutions obtained using only the antennas at 0° and 90°. (Reprinted from 'Spaceborne Radar Measurement of Wind Velocity over the Ocean – An overview of the NSCAT Scatterometer System', Naderi F M, et. al., *Proceedings of IEEE*, Vol. 79, No. 6, June 1991, with permission)

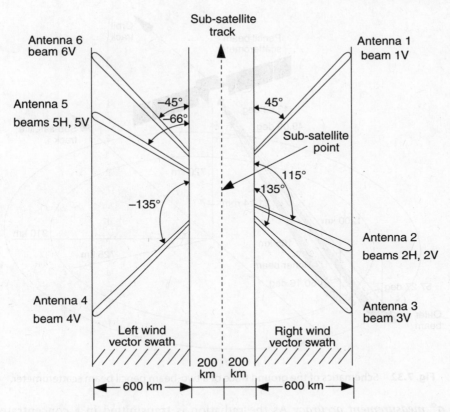

Fig. 7.31   NSCAT Antenna illumination pattern. There are two sets of antennae covering both sides of the sub-satellite track; each set has three antennae covering the swath of 800 km.

polarisation is used. For HH polarisation, the relationship between backscatter and wind differs from VV, and the HH polarisation provides useful complementary information, in particular on wind direction. The addition of an antenna with two polarisations makes it possible for four independent measurements at each location in the swath. The two additional measurements help to resolve wind vector directional ambiguity (Fig. 7.30). Although conceptually simple, the fan beam design introduces several complexities in practice: the incidence angle θ varies as a function of cross-swath (along-beam) position, and thus the geophysical model function must be known for a wide range of incidence angles; received power P_r decreases dramatically across the swath (even for fixed $\sigma°$) owing to the (R^4/A) term in the radar equation.

We shall now consider the pencil beam scatterometer. The instrument essentially consists of two off-nadir beams—inner and outer. (Fig. 7.32). These beams are generally realised by having two offset feeds along with a parabolic reflector, which is mechanically spun about the yaw axis of the satellite. Each point in the inner swath is viewed twice by the inner beam and similarly twice by the outer beam. These four $\sigma°$ measurements enable retrieval of wind velocities with a better accuracy.

A scanning pencil beam scatterometer offers some specific advantage over a fan beam system, which are given below:

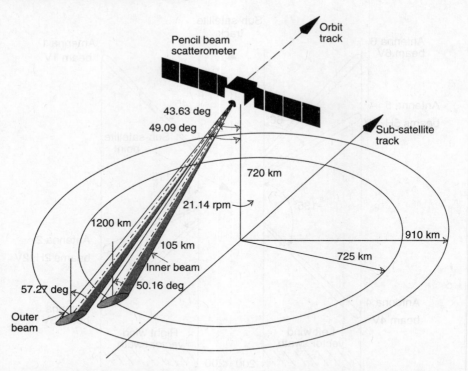

Fig. 7.32 Schematics of the ground trace of a two-beam pencil beam scatterometer.

- *High $\sigma°$ measurement accuracy* As the radiation is transmitted in a concentrated pencil beam, the signal-to-noise ratio (SNR) values are significantly higher than those for fan beam systems at similar incidence angles. This improves the measurement accuracy of low wind speeds where radar backscattering coefficient ($\sigma°$) values are very small.
- *High directional accuracy* Directional accuracy is increased because most of the points on the surface are viewed from four azimuth angles (twice by the inner beam and twice by the outer beam) as opposed to thrice in traditional fan beam systems.
- *No nadir gaps* The pencil beam system uses a conical scan mechanism and so the incidence angle is constant for each scan, independent of the cross-track distance. Thus, the swath obtained is continuous with no nadir gaps unlike a fan beam design.
- *Simplified model design* For a traditional fan beam system, the empirical model function relating $\sigma°$ to winds needs to be known for a broad range of incidence angles; whereas in a pencil beam system, this is simplified in view of only two incidence angles.
- *Easier signal processing* A pencil beam scatterometer necessitates less complex onboard signal processing scheme, which also reduces the processed data rate.
- *Smaller in size* The pencil beam configuration results in a smaller and lighter instrument. Only a single parabolic antenna is required which does not need any onboard deployment mechanism. Hence it is more easily accommodated on the spacecraft than a fan beam system.

One prominent disadvantage of a pencil beam scatterometer is the shorter dwell time. In a fan beam system, the entire swath is illuminated simultaneously and hence a relatively longer

Table 7.7   Characteristics of some of the spaceborne scatterometers

Instrument	Launch date	Spatial resolution	Scan characteristics	Operational frequency
SeaSAT-A Scatterometer	1978	50 km with 100 km spacing	Two-sided, double swath	Ku band (14.6 GHz)
ERS-1/2 Scatterometer	1991/1997	50 km	One-sided, single swath	C band (5.3 GHz)
NSCAT	1996	25 km and 50 km	Two-sided, double swath	Ku band (13.995 GHz)
Seawinds on QuickSCAT	1999	25 km	Conical scan, one wide swath	Ku band (13.4 GHz)
SeaWinds on ADEOS II	–	25 × 6 km	Conical scan, one wide swath	Ku band (13.4 GHz)

integration time is available and thereby, more independent samples are possible. This is not possible in a pencil beam system, as the antenna footprint is quickly scanned from one location to another. (Compare with pushbroom and cross-track scanners in the OIR region, Chapter 6.)

Seawinds is the first satellite-borne scanning scatterometer featuring a pencil beam radar (Wu et. al., 1994). The instrument was launched on a dedicated Polar Satellite QUICKSCAT in 1999. The instrument has a one metre parabolic reflector antenna rotating at 18 revolutions per minute, scanning two pencil beam footprint paths in a circular pattern at incidence angle 46° and 54°. The instrument operates at the K_u band. Seawinds on QUICKSCAT mission was a 'quick recovery' mission to fill the gap created by the loss of data from NSCAT when ADEOS failed. This was a really quick mission—realised in just 12 months!

Though the primary use of a scatterometer is for the determination of wind speed and direction over the oceans, it is increasingly acknowledged that, despite their coarse resolution, various geophysical parameters can be measured and monitored over land surfaces. One of the most promising areas is soil moisture estimation, especially as input for weather prediction models. Table 7.7 gives the major characteristics of some of the satellite-borne scatterometers.

7.6   GROUND PENETRATING RADAR

Ground penetrating radar (GPR) is a technique of obtaining information about sub-surface features by using electromagnetic radiation (EMR) which propagates into the medium under investigation to provide the location, size and depth of buried objects and information on the presence/ discontinuity of natural sub-surface strata. GPR is being successfully used in many areas such as civil engineering, geology, archaeology, forensic investigation, soil studies and others. Another important use of GPR is for the detection of buried landmines because of its potential in being able to detect of plastic encased mines which contain no metal.

The propagation of electromagnetic radiation in a medium is determined by permittivity (ε), permeability (μ) and electrical conductivity (σ) of the medium (Annan, 2003). All these three macroscopic parameters are in general a function of frequency. In a medium, the permittivity and permeability are expressed with respect to value in vacuum that is, relative permittivity (called dielectric constant) and relative permeability (see Section 2.1). Earth materials are mostly non-magnetic materials, having a relative magnetic permeability of 1 and can be neglected when dealing with a non-magnetic medium. The conductivity primarily affects absorption of the radar signal by the medium. Consider an electromagnetic wave radiated from a transmitting antenna falling onto a loss less isotropic homogenous (same electrical properties in all directions) medium. The wave spreads out and propagates through the medium without any deviation from the original direction at a velocity which is determined primarily by the permittivity of the material. But, in a lossy medium, as the wave propagates, the wave amplitude (and hence the intensity) gets progressively reduced at a rate depending on the penetration depth of the medium (see Eq. 2.13) until it finally dissipates with depth. However, when the radiation encounters a medium of different dielectric constant, then part of the wave's energy is 'reflected' back, while part of its energy continues to travel forward. If the interface is a smooth (in relation to wavelength, Eq. 4.8) flat surface, then we have Fresnel reflection (Fig. 2.7). The reflected value increases with increasing difference of the dielectric constant of the two media.

In actual GPR measurements, the targets we encounter are not infinitely large, but have finite size. The reflection of an isolated target is measured by the Radar Cross Section (RCS) (Section 7.3). When size of the target is smaller than the wavelength, the RCS is proportional to the size of the object (a larger target reflects stronger signals). In such cases, the amplitude of the reflected wave is a good measure of the size of the radar target. On the other hand, reflection from linear objects such as pipes, strongly depends on the EM wave polarisation. When the direction of the pipe is collinear to the polarisation of incident EM wave (electric field is parallel to the pipe), then even if the diameter of the pipe is very small compared to the wavelength, the reflectivity is very large. When the incident polarisation is perpendicular, even a metallic pipe does not reflect the EM wave (Sato, 2001). Therefore, GPR polarisation is very important in applications such as pipe and cable detection.

To summarise, in a GPR, the electromagnetic radiation generated by a transmitting antenna launched into a medium when encountered by an electrical discontinuity gets scattered back which is received by the receiver antenna. By measuring the time taken by the pulse to reach from the transmitter to receiver (two-way transit time) and knowing the velocity in the medium, the depth information of the scattering object can be deduced. The system scans the ground to collect the data at various locations. Then a GPR profile can be constructed by plotting the received signals as a function of the two-way transit time and position of the instrument representing a vertical slice of the sub-surface. The GPR can produce two or three-dimensional images by moving the antennas on a line or a two dimensional grid.

7.6.1 GPR INSTRUMENT

Based on the technology used in realising GPR, they can be classified into two groups—time domain and frequency domain (Fig. 7.33). GPR systems that transmit an impulse and receive the reflected signal from the target are in general called *pulsed radar*. They operate in the time domain. That is, a time domain GPR sends out a short pulse and records reflections as a function of time. The time domain GPR can be operated either as carrier-based or carrier-free mode. In the carrier-based mode, the pulse is sent such that a carrier frequency is modulated by a square envelope. In order to achieve a good depth resolution, it is important that the duration of the pulse is as short as possible. Therefore, only one cycle of the wave is used (mono- cycle). In the

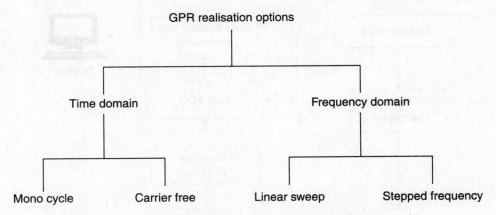

Fig. 7.33 Schematics showing GPR realisation techniques.

second category, the pulse sent by the GPR has no carrier. The width of the carrier-free pulse is kept very short (less than a nano second) to have a large bandwidth. The carrier-free radar is also called Ultra-Wave Band (UWB) GPR, because of the large bandwidth.

GPR systems operating in the frequency domain transmits individual frequencies in a sequential manner over a fixed bandwidth and the reflected signal from the target is measured as a function of frequency. Commonly used GPR systems usually use frequencies between 10 MHz and 1 GHz. In the frequency domain also two configurations are possible. In one scheme, a continuous wave is frequency modulated with a linear sweep and is, named FMCW GPR. In the other scheme, the frequency of the continuous wave changes in fixed steps and is, called stepped frequency GPR (SFGPR). The received signal is mixed with a sample of the transmitted waveform and results in a difference frequency which is related to the phase of the received signal from which the time delay between the transmitted and received signal can be estimated and hence range of the target.

The majority of surface penetrating radars are based on the time domain impulse design (Daniel, 2005) and they dominate in the commercial market place. We shall briefly describe its operation. A simplified block diagram of a time domain GPR is given in Fig. 7.34 (Scheers, 2001). The time domain GPR has four major parts:

- transmitter,
- timing circuit,
- receiver unit, and
- the data processing and display system.

The transmitter consists of a pulse generator, producing short transient pulses with a certain pulse repetition frequency (PRF) which is coupled to a wide bandwidth antenna. The characteristics of the antenna determine the central frequency of the radiated EM wave and the associated bandwidth is determined by the pulse width (Jol, 2009). The centre frequency is refereed as its operational frequency and plays a crucial role in achieving the objective of the survey, since it determines the penetrating depth as well as both vertical and horizontal resolutions. (The frequency around which most of the pulses' energy is concentrated is called the centre frequency, f_c.) Lower frequency in general has higher penetration in the media, but

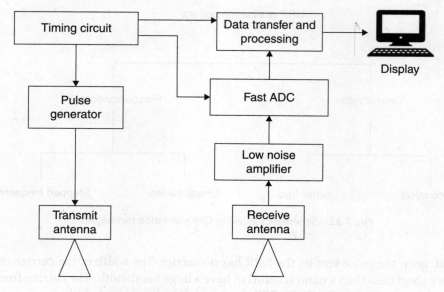

Fig. 7.34 Simplified block diagram of a Time Domain GPR.

poor vertical resolution compared to higher frequency, since vertical resolution is generally accepted to be one fourth of the wavelength (Jol, 2009).

The receiver antenna gets the signal from three paths (Fig. 7.35). The signal picked up by the receiver antenna goes through a low noise amplifier (LNA), a sample and hold circuit (S/H) and an analog-to-digital converter (A/D converter). A very stable and precise timing circuit synchronises the work between the different parts in the system. The digital output goes to a microprocessor for further processing of the data and display. The simplest form is to display the radar return signal as a function of time on an oscilloscope screen with the X-axis showing the time line, and the Y-axis the amplitude of the received echo signals (Fig. 7.36).

7.6.2 GPR OPERATION

There are two methods of collecting data using a GPR—namely Common Midpoint (CMP) and Common Offset (CO). In CMP, the antennae are kept side by side and the spacing between them is incrementally increased relative to a fixed location, that is, the midpoint. In the common offset mode, the transmitter and receiving antennae are kept apart at a fixed distance and moved together at fixed increments along the survey line. The majority of GPR surveys designed for near surface survey use the common offset method (Jol, 2009). We shall briefly describe the operation of a common offset mode operation. The GPR system is mounted on a wheeled trolley to enable it to be moved smoothly for the exploration of the sub-surface. In order to couple the EM energy into the ground efficiently, the antennae are located on or just above the ground. The system is moved in steps along a line to different 'stations' to collect data. The location of each station is recorded for accurate placement of all reflections within a surveyed grid for future display. At each station, the measurement is repeated many times to improve the signal quality. To illustrate data collection, consider a single object within the soil. Due to the beam width of the antennae, a target in the ground is already 'seen' by the

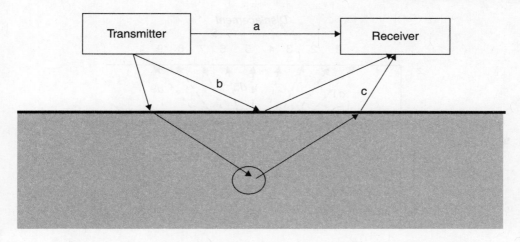

Fig. 7.35 Typical signal path in a GPR. (a) Air wave, (b) Ground wave, (c) Target reflection.

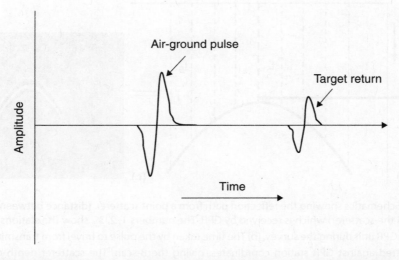

Fig. 7.36 Amplitude–time record of a single measurement over a target with the antennae at a given fixed position: referred to as an A-scan.

GPR system even when it is not exactly under the antenna. As the radar moves closer to the target position, the reflections get stronger and take place at an earlier time due to shorter physical distances between the radar and the target. The reflections become more attenuated and take a longer time to reach receiver as the radar carrier moves away from the target (Fig. 7.37). Thus, when the antenna is above the target, the time taken for a pulse to travel to and from the target is minimum. This time can be used to estimate the depth of the target. If t is the minimum time taken for the two way travel of the pulse (that is, from the transmitter to the target and the target to the receiver) then the depth d is given by $d = \frac{c_m \times t}{2}$, where c_m is the velocity of the transmitted radiation in the medium. At each station we get an A-scan profile.

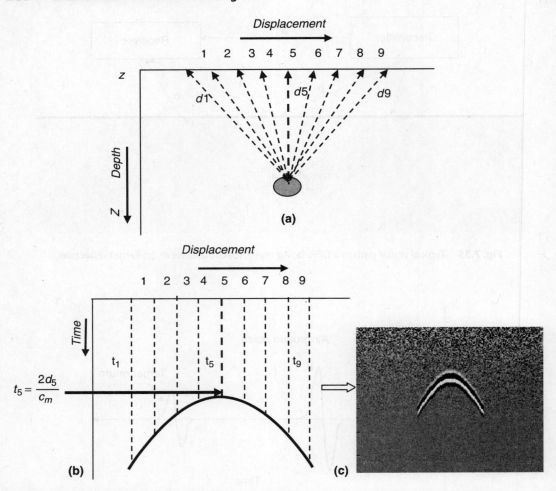

Fig. 7.37 (a) Schematics showing the reflection path from a point scatterer (distance between the radar unit and the scatterer) which is received by GPR. The numbers 1, 2, 3... show the stations (positions) of the GPR unit during the survey. (b) The time taken by the pulse to travel from transmitter to receiver plotted against GPR station coordinates, giving the B-scan. The scatterer depth d_5 is given by $c_m \times \frac{t_5}{2}$, where c_m is the velocity of the operating EM radiation in the medium. (c) Representation of a typical B-scan radargram.

By keeping all the scan profiles side by side with station position along the X-axis and echo receive time on the Y-axis, we get a radar map having the shape of a hyperbola (referred to as the B-scan). The actual depth of the target can be estimated from the position of the apex of the hyperbola, if the propagation velocity of EM waves in the soil is known. This gives a two dimensional profile, which approximates a vertical 'slice' through the earth. For visualisation, the amplitude of the echo signals are represented by grey scales or by colour schemes on this surface. Thus discrete buried objects typically appear as hyperbolic reflections in the raw data, with the limbs of the hyperbolae projected downwards like an inverted U, while sub-surface layers appear as continuous reflectors on the radargram (Yelf, 2007). Finally, when collecting multiple parallel B-scans, that is, when moving the antenna over a (regular) grid in a fixed xy-plane, a three dimensional data set (x, y, t) can be recorded, called a C-scan.

The actual data from the GPR survey is more complex than what we considered when only one target is present. The dielectric constant changes in the medium (apart from the target) such as, inhomogeneous moisture in the soil, small stones and gravel included in the soil. These also get reflected along with the target reflection. That is, we have reflections from targets which we are not interested in—referred to as clutter. The clutter cannot be removed by the time-averaging method since it is not a random signal. A number of clutter removal algorithms have been developed to reduce the effect of clutter on data interpretation (Solimene et. al., 2014).

7.6.3 PERFORMANCE CRITERIA

The performance of a GPR is evaluated by the maximum detectable range and radar resolution. The maximum detectable range is defined by the maximum depth at which the radar can detect the object. This depends on the attenuation of the medium in which the object under investigation resides.

The attenuation increases as electrical conductivity increases due to various factors such as increase in water content, clay content and conductive contaminants. They are in general frequency dependent. As mentioned earlier, lower the frequency lesser is the attenuation but at the cost of poor resolution. Attenuation also occurs due to scattering of the EM energy in unwanted directions by inhomogeneities in the sub-surface. If the scale of inhomogeneity is comparable to the wavelength of EM energy, scattering may be significant. The GPR user has no control over the above factors since these are site specific characteristics. However, the GPR designer has control over increase in transmitter power and increase in receiver sensitivity to achieve a greater depth. Thus, we can say that the maximum detectable depth from the instrument is determined by the ratio of the transmitter power and the minimum detectable signal level, which is normally the noise level of the receiver (Katsuhisa and Ishikawa, 2009). For a given instrument the signal can be improved by increasing the *Pulse Repetition Frequency* (PRF). Increasing the PRF increases the number of data collected from a single station and by averaging all the data collected from the station, the signal-to-noise-ratio (SNR) can be improved. The improvement in SNR helps to improve the detection limit thereby increasing the penetration depth.

Here, the concept of resolution is similar to any radar system we discussed earlier—the ability to distinguish between two targets by the measurement. Two types of resolutions to be considered are the depth (vertical, range) resolution (Δd) and horizontal (lateral) resolution (Δh) (Fig. 7.38). These resolution limits are imposed by the constraints in bandwidth and antenna beam width and are similar in concepts to the real aperture radar we discussed in Section 7.4.1.

Vertical resolution Δd, is the minimum separation between two reflectors that still allows the reflectors to be distinguished by GPR. For this to happen the round trip time from the two targets should differ by at least pulse width, as discussed under RAR.

$$\Delta d = \frac{\tau c_m}{2}$$

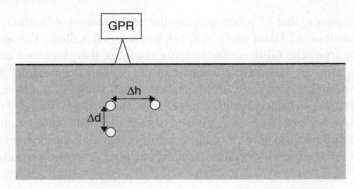

Fig. 7.38 Schematics showing the concept of depth and horizontal resolution.

where τ is pulse duration and c_m is the velocity of the electromagnetic radiation in the medium.

In a non-magnetic medium, referring to Eq. 2.2 $c_m = \frac{c}{\sqrt{\varepsilon_r}}$, where c is the velocity of EM radiation in vacuum and ε_r is the dielectric constant of the medium, the pulse duration is related to band width B as B $= \frac{1}{\tau}$ (Cogdell,1999). A more conservative value for vertical resolution is to take twice as much as the theoretical value (Alvarez, 2007).

The horizontal resolution is the minimum distance between two objects in the same horizontal plane parallel to the surface which the radar 'sees' both objects as separate ones. That is, it is the minimum horizontal distance between two targets at the same depth before the radar smears them out into one single event. Therefore, the horizontal resolution of a GPR is important when two targets at the same depth need to be distinguished. The horizontal resolution mainly depends on the number of traces (observation) per metre, the antenna beam width (see Eq. 7.2), the radar cross section of the target and the depth at which the target is located. The antenna beam illuminates a surface in the medium which is called antenna footprint. If the targets are within the footprint it will not be resolved. Therefore a narrower beam gives a better horizontal resolution. The antenna footprint increases with depth (Reynolds, 1997) and hence horizontal resolution decreases with depth.

Horizontal and vertical resolution are dependent upon the wavelength, such that the smaller the wavelength (higher frequency), the better the resolution. Although higher frequency sources will yield better resolution, the higher frequency signals will not penetrate as deep as lower frequencies. Therefore a careful choice must be made regarding the GPR frequency choice based on expected project goals.

Thus, the quality of performance of a GPR is closely linked with various parameters such as electrical property of the site under investigation, transmitter power, receiver sensitivity and frequency of operation. The frequency is selected as per the investigation objective. Some commonly used frequencies for specific applications are given below (Doolittle, 2012). For soil investigations in general, centre frequencies between 100 and 500 MHz are used. For organic soils, where greater depths of penetration are often desired to profile the organic/ mineral soil interface, lower frequency (70–200 MHz) antennae are preferred. Frequencies in the range of 100–300 MHz are commonly used for water table, lithological, and stratigraphic studies, and for investigations in areas of more conductive and attenuating soil materials. Higher-frequency antennae (400–500 MHz) provide better results in relatively dry, electrically resistive soils.

Antennae with frequencies of 900 MHz to 1.5 GHz have been used for shallow investigations in some coarser-textured soils.

FOR FURTHER READING

1. *Remote Sensing and Image Interpretation,* Lilesand T M and Kiefer, 1994, Chapter 8.
2. *Manual of Remote Sensing,* Vol. 1, Ed. Colwell R N, Chapters 10, 11 and 13.
3. *Microwave Remote Sensing – Active and Passive,* Ulaby et. al., 1981, Vol. 1: Chapter 6, Vol. 2: Chapters 8 and 9.
4. *Introduction to Synthetic Array and Imaging Radars,* Hovanessian, 1980.
5. *Satellite Oceanography,* Robinson I S, Chapter 12.
6. *Tutorial Review of Synthetic Aperture Rada, Kiyo Tomiysu, Proceedings of IEEE,* Vol. 66, No. 5, May, 1978, pp. 563–583.
7. *http://faculty.nps.edu/jenn/Seminars/RadarFundamentals.pdf*
8. *http://spot.colorado.edu/~zhaoc/radiometer.html*
9. *https://www.asf.alaska.edu/asf-tutorials/sar-faq/*
10. *http://www.jars1974.net/pdf/04_Chapter03.pdf*
11. *http://www.ece.uah.edu/courses/material/EE710-Merv/SARPart1_11.pdf*
12. *www.ee.ubc.ca/sar/SARintro/SAR.html*
13. *http://authors.library.caltech.edu/61818/1/01457498.pdf*
14. *http://www.usradar.com/about-ground-penetrating-radar-gpr/faq/*
15. *www.gb.nrao.edu/140foot/subpages/radio.html*
16. Daniels D J, Gunton D J and Scott H F, 1988, Introduction to subsurface radar, *IEE Proceedings,* F-Radar and Signal Processing, Vol. 135, No. 4, pp. 278-320.
17. Martin R, Bristow C, McKinley J and Ruffell A, 2013, Ground Penetrating Radar, *http://www.geomorphology.org.uk/sites/default/files/geom_tech_chapters/1.5.5_GPR.pdf*
18. Scheers B, 2001, Ultra-Wideband Ground Penetrating Radar, with Application to the Detection of Anti Personnel Landmines, PhD dissertation. *http://www.sic.rma.ac.be/~scheers/phd.html*
19. Baker G S, Jordan T E and Talley J, 2007, An introduction to ground penetrating radar (GPR), in Baker G S and Jol H M, Eds, Stratigraphic Analyses Using GPR: *Geological Society of America,* Special Paper 432, pp. 1–18. *https://www.researchgate.net/publication/279869961_An_introduction_to_ground_penetrating_radar_GPR*
20. *http://geo-sense.com/index.php/methods/ground-penetrating-radar-gpr-surveys/ground-penetrating-radar-gpr/*
21. *http://utter.chaos.org.uk/~eddy/cv/speckle.htm*
22. *https://nature.berkeley.edu/~penggong/textbook/*
23. *http://web.pdx.edu/~emch/ip2/RADAR.pdf*

8 | Platforms

Remote sensors have to be supported on suitable platforms to carry out measurements. The platform could be as simple as a tripod stand to hold a field radiometer or a complex spacecraft. For the same instrument, in general, the spatial resolution decreases as the observation height is increased, while the observational area increases. Thus, the higher the instrument is carried, the larger is the synoptic view but with coarser spatial resolution. Remote sensors are designed taking into account the platform on which the instrument is to be mounted. That is, an instrument designed for an aircraft platform, in general, cannot be accommodated in a spacecraft and vice versa. Though aircrafts and satellites are the platforms commonly used at present, balloons and rockets were also used to carry remote sensors. In India, free-floating balloons were used on an experimental basis to collect multi-band photography (Joseph, 1977).

The payload used for the Indian balloon experiment consisted of three Hasselblad cameras with different film filter combinations, in order to provide photography in panchromatic black and white, infrared black and white and infrared false colour. The three cameras were mounted on a platform, which was servo-controlled to maintain a fixed direction in azimuth irrespective of balloon rotation. An electronic programmer onboard provided automatic command signals at regular time intervals for operating the cameras. The instrument was kept inside a cane cage with proper shock absorbers to protect the cameras from landing shocks. The payload was flown by a 6840 m3 polyethylene zero pressure balloon. The balloon floated at a constant height of about 30 km and took photographs for about 4 hours. Because of the higher flight altitude, compared to a normally instrumented aircraft for aerial survey, the balloon imagery gives a larger synoptic view and is also economical for per sq. km coverage. However, it should be admitted, that taking an image of a specific target on an operational basis is very difficult as the course of the balloon is governed by the wind at the floating altitude.

Rockets carrying photographic cameras to take oblique photographs for reconnaissance purpose has also been reported in the literature. However, their use for resources survey is very limited.

Aircraft were traditionally used for taking aerial photographs. Generally, aircraft have a provision to carry multiple instruments. Depending on the mission, specific instruments can be activated. Aerial flights have the advantage that the data can be collected over a specified area at short notice, dependant only on the availability of the instrumented aircraft (unlike in the case of a low orbit satellite mission, wherein we have to wait for a favourable satellite orbit to view the site of interest). Depending on the photographic scale requirements, it is possible to make observations at various heights or use lenses with suitable focal length. However, a major drawback is the high cost of making repetitive observations over large areas. Repetitive global observation to study phenomena, such as vegetation dynamics, is too expensive using aircraft. Thus, the use of aircraft for the survey of resources is generally limited to making observations to derive high resolution data for specific areas.

Another platform gaining popularity is Unmanned Aerial Vehicles (UAVs)-aircraft remotely operated from the ground-especially to cover small geographic areas. UAVs can acquire data over a specific site more rapidly and low-altitude flight allows sensors to observe the ground from a height much lower than a piloted aircraft and hence can collect finer spatial resolution data. The operating cost is also lower than for piloted aerial vehicles. UAV can provide 'ground truth' image data for a large area much faster in comparison to a field visit.

Space-borne remote sensing is the ideal choice for repetitive global coverage. Satellites can take different paths around the earth, referred to as orbits. The type of orbit is very important for a specific observation. We shall now try to understand the basic principle involved in the motion of a satellite and the characteristics of different orbits.

8.1 PRINCIPLES OF SATELLITE MOTION

The word 'satellite' originally came from a French word, which means a guard or attendant. Johannes Kepler (1571–1630) gave a new meaning to the word. While studying the planet Jupiter, Kepler discovered several objects moving around Jupiter, which Kepler called satellites of Jupiter—maybe he thought of them as 'guardians' of Jupiter. Astronomers use the term 'satellite' to denote objects moving around a planet. Thus, the moon is the natural satellite of earth. With the launch of Sputnik in 1957, several artificial satellites have been launched and are orbiting around the earth. In general, we can talk of satellites as those moving around the gravitational force of a central mass (Ha! the earth is a 'satellite' of the sun!!).

Kepler's Law

Kepler used Tycho Brahe's (1546–1601) data on the movements of planets and realised that the motion of celestial bodies is very organised and follows certain rules, which are now known as Kepler's Laws.

Kepler's first law   *The path followed by each planet is an ellipse, with the sun at one of the foci.*

An ellipse has two foci; in the case of earth satellites, the earth is at one of the foci. As mentioned earlier, the path followed by a satellite is called an orbit. The point on the orbit closest to the earth is called *perigee* and the point farthest is called *apogee* (Fig. 8.1). The straight

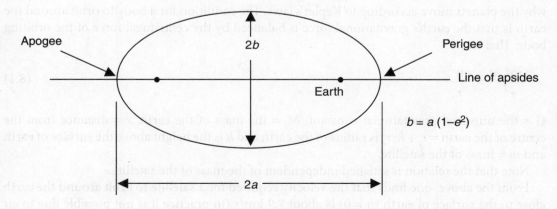

Fig. 8.1   Schematics of the orbit of a satellite. The earth is at one of the foci.

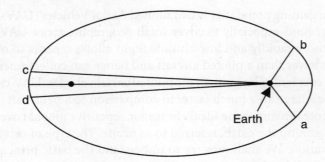

Fig. 8.2 Schematics showing the concept of Kepler's 2nd law. During the time interval t, the satellite at the perigee moves through a longer arc (ab) compared to that of the apogee (cd) to keep the area swept by the earth satellite line the same.

line drawn from the perigee to the apogee is called the *line of apsides*. The distance between the perigee and the apogee is twice the semi-major axis and is a measure of the size of the orbit. The distance between the two foci decides the shape of the orbit. When the foci come together, we have the special case of a circular orbit. How far the orbit has deviated from the circular shape is given by a term called *eccentricity* (*e*). For a circular orbit $e = 0$.

Kepler's second law *The line joining the planet to the sun sweeps out equal areas in equal times.*

The second law describes the relationship of the speed of the satellite to its orbit's size and shape. Since the line joining the earth and the satellite is least at the perigee, the satellite moves faster at the perigee compared to the apogee to generate the same area in a given time (Fig. 8.2).

Kepler's third law *The square of the period of the planet is proportional to the cube of the semi-major axis.*

The period of a satellite (*T*) is the time taken by the satellite to go around the earth once. As per Kepler's third law,

$$T^2 \propto a^3$$

While Kepler's laws describe how planets move, it is Newton's laws of motion which describe why the planets move according to Kepler's laws. The condition for a body to orbit around the earth is that the earth's gravitational force is balanced by the centrifugal force of the orbiting body. That is,

$$\frac{GM_e m}{r^2} = \frac{mv^2}{r} \tag{8.1}$$

G = the universal gravitational constant, M_e = the mass of the earth, r = distance from the centre of the earth = $r_e + h$; r_e is radius of the earth and h is the height above the surface of earth and m = mass of the satellite.

Note that the relation is satisfied independent of the mass of the satellite.

From the above, one finds that the velocity required for a satellite to orbit around the earth close to the surface of earth ($h = 0$) is about 7.9 km/s (in practice it is not possible due to air drag). At this speed, we have a circular orbit. This is called the *first astronautical velocity*. As the velocity is increased, the satellite's orbit becomes elliptical and at about 11.2 km/s, the satellite escapes the influence of earth's gravity and leaves its orbit. This is called the *second astronautical velocity* (or *escape velocity*).

From Eq. 8.1, the orbital period (time to complete one revolution) for a circular orbit (*T*) can be deduced as

$$T = \frac{2\pi}{\sqrt{GM_e}} (r_e + h)^{3/2} \tag{8.2}$$

As a thumb rule, a convenient, easy to remember relationship for a circular orbit is, $T = 10^{-2}$ $(r_e + h)^{3/2}$, when r_e and h are expressed in kilometres and T is in seconds.

The velocity of the satellite in a circular orbit can be derived from Eq. 8.2. During the period *T*, the satellite travels through a distance of $2\pi (r_e + h)$, that is, the circumference of the orbit. The satellite velocity v_s is given by $2\pi (r_e + h)/T$.

$$v_s = \left(\frac{GM_e}{r_e + h} \right)^{1/2} \tag{8.3}$$

During the same time duration, the sub-satellite point moves through a smaller distance compared to the satellite movement, due to the arc length difference at r_e and $r_e + h$. Hence the sub-satellite velocity at the ground v_g will be less than v_s in proportion to the radius vector ratio.

$$v_g = v_s \left(\frac{r_e}{r_e + h} \right) \tag{8.4}$$

Let us now calculate these values for an IRS-1A/B orbit of $h = 904$ km.

$$V_S = \left(\frac{398601}{6378 + 904} \right)^{1/2} = 7.4 \text{ km/s}$$

$$V_g = V_s \left(\frac{6378}{6378 + 904} \right) = 6.5 \text{ km/s}$$

$$T = 103.2 \text{ min}$$

One obvious observation from Eq. 8.2 is that as the orbital height increases, the orbital period increases. We shall discuss the interesting possibilities of this characteristic for earth observation later. Table 8.1 gives the satellite velocity (*v*) and orbital period (for circular orbit) for a few satellite altitudes (*h*).

8.2 LOCATING A SATELLITE IN SPACE

To describe a satellite's orbit and to locate the satellite on its orbit at a particular time, we require a set of parameters called *orbital elements* or *Keplerian elements*. To do so, the first task is to develop an *inertial coordinate* system. The coordinate system adopted is as follows:

Table 8.1   Satellite velocity and orbital period for different satellite altitude

Altitude (km)	Speed (km/s)	Orbital period		
h	v_s	H	M	S
500	7.61	1	34	37
700	7.50	1	38	47
1000	7.35	1	45	08
5000	5.92	3	21	19
10000	4.93	5	47	40
30000	3.31	19	10	51
35786	3.08	23	56	04
40000	2.93	27	36	39

- The z-axis is aligned with the earth's spin axis.
- The x-axis points from the centre of the earth to the sun at the moment of *vernal equinox*, that is, when the sun is crossing the equatorial plane from the southern to the northern hemisphere.
- The y-axis is then chosen to make a right handed coordinate system (Fig. 8.3).

A sphere centered on these coordinates is called a *celestial sphere*. If you sit on the top of the sphere and look down at the earth, you will see it rotating counter-clockwise on the z-axis. We shall now explain various orbital elements with respect to this coordinate system.

Inclination (i)   The orbital plane always goes through the centre of the earth. The angle between the satellite orbital plane and the plane containing the earth's equator (equatorial plane) is defined as the *inclination*. By convention, inclination is a number between 0 and 180°. An orbit aligned with the equatorial plane has an inclination of 0° if the satellite rotates in the same direction as the earth, while if the satellite were rotating in the opposite direction to the earth's rotation, its inclination would be 180°. Orbits with inclination 0° to < 90° are called *prograde* and with 90° to 180° are called *retrograde* orbits.

Right ascension of ascending node (RAAN) (Ω)   The point where the satellite crosses the equator from the southern hemisphere to the northern hemisphere is called the *ascending node* and the point where it crosses the equator from the northern hemisphere to the southern hemisphere is called the *descending node*. The line joining the nodes is called the *line of nodes*. RAAN is the angle between the x-axis (vernal equinox) and the ascending node measured in the anti-clockwise direction from the x-axis. By convention, RAAN is a number between 0° and 360°.

Argument of perigee (ARGP) (ω)   It is the angle between the line of nodes and the major axis of the orbit (line of apsides) measured along the orbital plane from the ascending node to the perigee. By convention, ARGP lies between 0° and 360°. When ARGP = 0, the perigee occurs at the same place as the ascending node.

   i, Ω and ω *define the orbit in inertial space.*

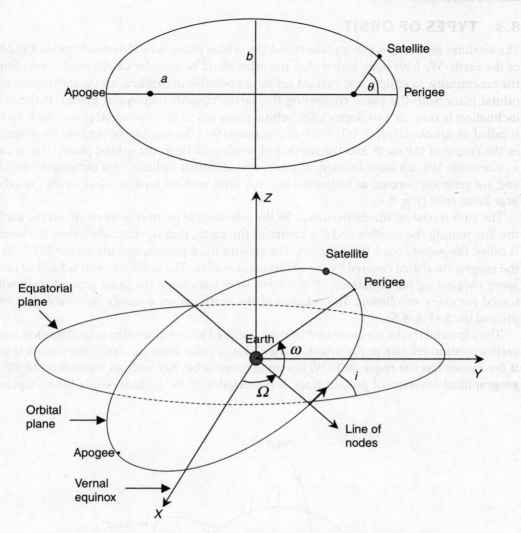

Fig. 8.3 Schematics showing the coordinate system to locate a satellite in space.

Eccentricity (e)   gives the shape of the orbit. When $e = 0$, the orbit is a circle.

Semi-major axis (a)   gives the size of the orbit.
 e and a decide the shape and size of the orbit.

True anomaly (θ)   It is the angle made by the line joining the satellite and the centre of the earth with the major axis measured counter-clockwise from the perigee along the orbital plane, that is, the actual angle that a satellite has moved since the last passing perigee. $\theta = 0$ at perigee and 180° at apogee. θ lies from 0° to 360°.
 θ defines the position of the satellite on the orbit at any instant. The above six parameters at any instant (epoch) define the satellite in space.

8.3 TYPES OF ORBIT

The satellites always move in a plane called the *orbital plane*, which passes through the centre of the earth. We have seen earlier that the orbit could be circular or elliptical depending on the eccentricity. In either case, various orbits are possible depending on the inclination of the orbital plane with the plane containing the earth's equator (equatorial plane). If the orbital inclination is zero (or 180 degree), the orbital plane lies in the equatorial plane. Such an orbit is called an *equatorial orbit*. When the inclination is 90°, the satellite moves over the poles, that is, the centre of the earth and the north and south pole lie in the orbital plane. This is called a *polar orbit*. We can have a variety of orbits whose orbital inclination is between 0° and 180° and are generally termed as *inclined orbits*. An orbit with inclination close to 90°, is called a *near polar orbit* (Fig. 8.4).

The path traced on the earth surface by the sub-satellite point (the intercept on the earth by the line joining the satellite and the centre of the earth, that is, vertically below the satellite) is called the *ground track* (*nadir trace*). The ground track pattern and the sensor FOV decides the geographical area covered by the observation system. The satellite's orbit is fixed in inertial space (neglecting perturbations). If the earth were stationary, the same ground track will be traced for every revolution. The rotation of the earth causes a steady westward shift of the ground track (Fig. 8.5).

Thus, ground tracks are generated by the combined action of satellite orbital motion and the earth's rotation relative to the orbital plane. Thus, a polar orbit can cover the complete globe if the sensor has the requisite FOV. For an inclined orbit, say with an inclination of 30°, the geographical coverage of ground track is restricted to ± 30° latitude, while for an equatorial

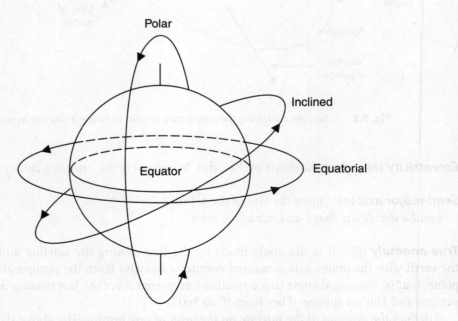

Fig. 8.4 Schematics showing different types of orbits.

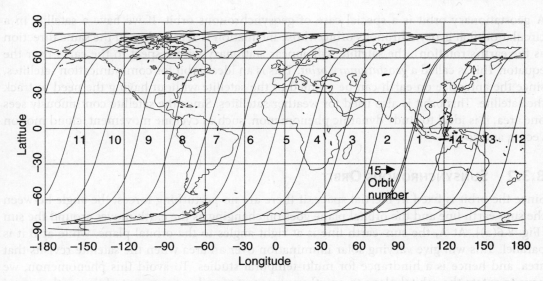

Fig. 8.5 Descending ground traces of IRS-1A/1B for one day. The satellite crosses the equator after every 103.192 minutes. During this time earth rotates a distance of 2871.8 km at the equator causing a westward drift for the ground track (1, 2, 3, ...). In 24 hours the satellite makes 13.9545 revolutions around the earth. The orbit on the second day (15th orbit) is shifted westward from orbit No.1 by about 130 km.The ground traces repeat after every 307 orbits in 22 days.

orbit the coverage will be around the equator, depending on the FOV of the sensor. When the spacecraft moves from north to south, the orbit crossing the equator is called a *descending node crossing* and when the orbit crosses south to north it is called an *ascending node crossing*. A satellite in the inclined orbit will cross the equator two times during each orbit, once each in their ascending mode and in their descending mode.

We shall now discuss some special orbits.

8.3.1 Geosynchronous and Geostationary Orbits

We have seen in Table 8.1, that as the satellite height increases, the time taken for one revolution (period) also increases. At about 35,786 km height, the period is equal to one siderial day, that is, 23 hours, 56 minutes, 4.091 seconds. This orbit is called a *geosynchronous orbit*, that is, the orbital period is synchronised with the rotational period of the earth.

Siderial vs Solar Day

We measure time according to the position of the sun in the sky. Our day is noon (sun overhead) to noon, which takes 24 hours (solar day).

A siderial day refers to the time taken (relative to stars) by the earth to rotate 360° and is equal to 23 hours, 56 minutes and 4.019 seconds.

Thus the solar day is longer than the true rotation period of the earth (siderial day) by about 4 minutes. The difference between the two 'days' arises due to the fact that during the day, the earth also travels nearly a degree further on its yearly 'voyage' around the sun.

A geostationary orbit is a special case of geosynchronous orbit. If we have a satellite in a circular orbit at geosynchronous orbit, whose inclination is zero (orbits in the same direction as the earth's rotation), the satellite will appear stationary with respect to the earth over the equator. This is called a *geostationary orbit*. This is an ideal orbit for communication satellites, since the antennae on earth can be pointed to the satellite without having the need to track the satellite. This orbit is also used for weather satellites. Since the satellite continuously sees one area, it is ideal to study dynamic phenomenon, such as cyclone movement, cloud motion vector, and so on.

8.3.2 SUNSYNCHRONOUS ORBIT

Since the orbit is fixed in inertial space, if there are no perturbing forces, the angle between the sun–earth line and the orbital plane goes on changing as the earth moves around the sun [Fig. 8.6(a)]. At A, the sun–earth line is at right angles to the orbital plane, while at B it is parallel. This will give varying solar illumination over an area when the satellite revisits that area, and hence is a hindrance for multi-temporal studies. To avoid this phenomenon, we have to rotate the orbital plane to exactly compensate for the movement of the earth around the sun. In Fig. 8.6(a), if the orbital plane can be rotated through 90°, as the earth moves from A to B, we have the same angle between the sun–earth direction and the orbital plane both at A and B [Fig. 8.6(b)]. That is, we want the orbital plane to precess continuously at the rate of 360°/365.25° per day. How can we make the satellite orbit itself to rotate (or technically referred as to 'regress') around the earth at the rate of 0.9856°/day? Fortunately, a natural phenomenon makes it happen. The earth is not a perfect sphere, but an 'oblate spheroid', with an average polar radius of about 6356 km and an equatorial radius of 6378 km. This mass imbalance makes the orbital plane rotate about the axis of the earth except in the case of an

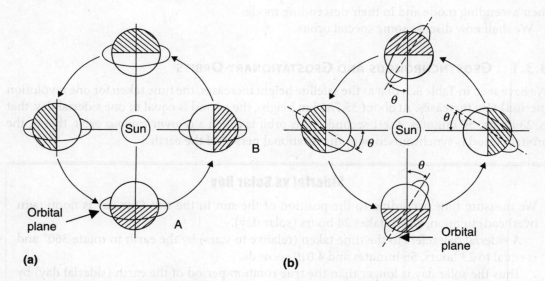

Fig. 8.6   (a) Represents a non-sunsynchronous orbit, while (b) represents a sunsynchronous orbit. Note that in the case of (b), the sun–earth line makes a constant angle θ with respect to the orbitalplane as the earth moves around the sun.

exact polar orbit. This precession rate of the orbit is a function of the satellite altitude and the orbital inclination. Thus by choosing these two parameters appropriately, the precession rate can be made to exactly compensate the mean rate of the earth about the sun. In this way, the satellite always 'sees' the point on the earth, when the sun is shining on the earth from the same angle—the same sun time [Fig. 8.6(b)]. Such an orbit is called a *sunsynchronous orbit* and is always near polar. For IRS-1C, the parameters for the sunsynchronous orbit are: height 817 km and inclination 98.69°. In a sunsynchronous orbit, the satellite crosses the equator at the same local time everyday. Local time (LT) is defined as

$$LT = t_u + LONG/15°$$

where, t_u is the coordinated universal time and LONG is the longitude of the sub-satellite point at the equator.

It should be noted that solar illumination condition changes due to seasonal variations (due to solar elevation angle change) even in the case of sunsynchronous orbits.

Choosing the Right Orbit for Remote Sensing

The orbit is fixed in the inertial space. Due to earth rotation, there is a westward displacement of the sub-satellite point. The earth rotates at a rate of (360/24) degree per hour, therefore during a period of T minutes, the longitudinal displacement $\Delta\lambda$ between consecutive orbits is given by

$$\Delta\lambda = \left(\frac{360}{60 \times 24}\right)T = 0.25 \times T \text{ deg } (T \text{ in minutes})$$

For the IRS-1A/1B orbit, $\Delta\lambda = 0.25 \times 103.192$
$$= 25.798°$$

At the equator, 1° longitude corresponds to 111.32 km, the amount of displacement at the equator is given by $25.798 \times 111.32 = 2872$ km. That is, the successive orbits will be displaced by 2872 km at the equator. The shift in the orbit on successive days (which is adjusted based on the swath of the sensor), decides the minimum number of days required for imaging without any gap.

If x km is the westward shift on successive days, for the example worked out, a minimum of $2872/x$ days are required to obtain complete coverage of the earth. The basic requirement for periodic coverage is that the sub-satellite track (nadir trace) return, after completing certain number of orbits (R), to a previously traversed track, after some definite number of days (N). That is, the satellite makes R complete orbits in N days, and on the $(N + 1)^{th}$ day repeats the cycle, that is, starts with day 1 track (Fig. 8.7). Both N and R must be integers. The coverage pattern can be described in terms of an orbit repetition parameter Q, such that

$$Q = I + \frac{K}{N}$$

The corresponding orbital period is

$$T = \frac{24 \times 60}{I + K/N} \, \text{min}$$

where I, K and N are integers, I is the integer number of complete satellite revolutions per day. The fraction K/N determines the swathing pattern, independent of I (Light, 1990). If K/N is zero, the orbit is called 'resonant', that is, the resonant orbit makes integral number of revolutions per day. In this case, the satellite passes over the same location everyday. Approximate satellite altitudes for 13, 14 and 15 integer orbits are 1257 km, 888 km and 561 km, respectively. For an orbit with 14 integer orbits, the shift between successive orbits will be $2 \pi r_e/14$, which works out to be about 2860 km. Therefore, to get a global coverage from a 14 integer orbit, without any gaps, the imaging system should have a swath of at least 2860 km. In principle it is possible to have such wide swath imaging, but produces high distortion towards the edge of the image due to the earth's curvature and there are complexities in realising a sensor with such a wide swath. Therefore, resonant orbits are seldom used for remote sensing applications.

As mentioned earlier the ratio K/N decides the drift of the orbit in successive days. The mission design procedure begins by selecting K/N fraction to give the desired ground trace shift pattern and then selecting I, corresponding to the altitude range that is desired (Light, 1990). IRS-1A/1B, LISS-1 camera has a swath of about 145 km. In order to have adequate side lap, the longitudinal shift for successive day equatorial crossing is chosen as ~130.54 km, that is, 1.1726 degrees. The amount of side lap increases for images taken at higher latitudes, since the longitudes converge at the poles. The orbit height is trimmed to have a K/N to achieve this drift. In the case of IRS-1A/B it takes 22 days (N) and 307 orbits (R) for the full coverage of earth (Fig. 8.7). Since in 22×24 hours, the satellite completes 307 orbits, the orbital period is 103.192 min $[(22 \times 24 \times 60)/307]$. The corresponding orbital height can be calculated from Eq. 8.2.

As discussed earlier, the precession of the orbit is dependent on the orbit height and inclination. The inclination i required for a circular sunsynchronous orbit can be expressed as (Light, 1990):

$$\cos i = -0.09896 \left(\frac{r_e + h}{r_e} \right)^{3.5}$$

For the IRS-1A/B orbit we considered, with $h = 904$, and assumed to be circular, the inclination angle i works out to be 99.09 degree. The values worked out here for IRS-1A/B will not match exactly with the actual values due to the assumption of a perfect circular orbit and spherical earth. The actual parameters of IRS-1A/B are given in Table 8.2.

8.3.3   VIEWING GEOMETRY FROM ORBIT

From any orbit, the maximum visibility of the earth is from horizon to horizon (that is, the line from the satellite is tangential to the earth's surface) [Fig. 8.8(a)]. The relationship between half angle of earth view (ϕ_v) and the satellite altitude h is given by Eq. 8.5.

$$\phi_v = \sin^{-1} \left(\frac{r_e}{r_e + h} \right) \qquad\qquad (8.5)$$

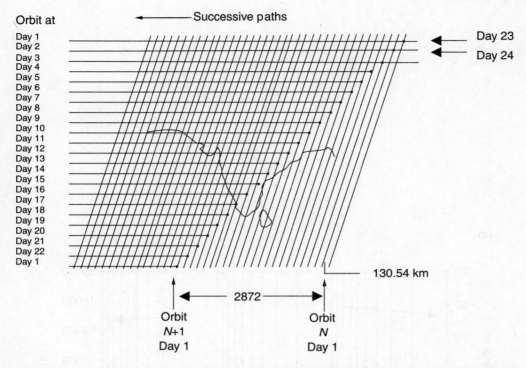

Fig. 8.7 IRS-1A/B Swathing pattern. Everyday the sub-satellite track shifts westward. One coverage cycle takes 22 days. On the 23rd day, the satellite retraces, the day-1 sub-satellite track and begins the second cycle.

Table 8.2 Details of IRS-1A/B parameters

S. No.	Parameter	Value	Units
1.	Semi major axis	7282.277	Kilometres
2.	Eccentricity	0.002	
3.	Inclination	99.028	Degrees
4.	Period	103.192	Minutes
5.	Westward longitudinal shift of successive orbits	25.798	Degrees
6.	Longitudinal shift in successive days	1.17264	Degrees
		(130.54)	Kilometres
7.	Number of orbits per day	14	
8.	Number of orbits per cycle	307	
9.	Repetivity	22	Days

As the height increases, ϕ_v decreases but the maximum distance on earth (horizon to horizon) that can be seen by the satellite increases. Figure 8.8(b) gives ϕ_v and the maximum ground coverage distance. However, resolution substantially degrades as one observes points close to the horizon, due to the curvature of the earth and viewing geometry (refer Section 9.3.1).

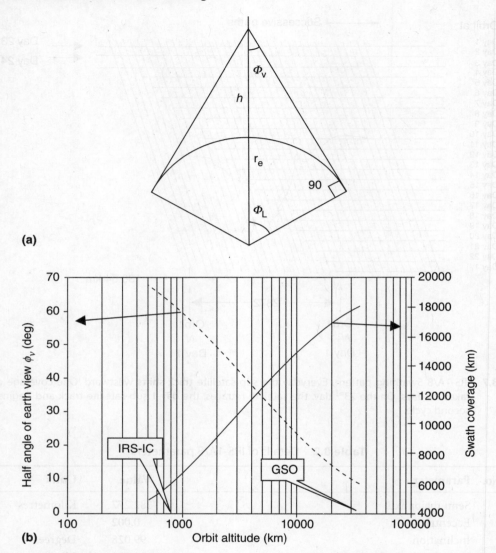

Fig. 8.8   (a) Geometry for calculating maximum visibility area from an orbit (b) Half angle for viewing earth from horizon to horizon and the corresponding distance over the surface of the earth for different altitudes. (Mathew, 2002)

Therefore, in order to avoid large resolution degradation, we have to limit the observation over a distance from the nadir which is less than theoretically possible. As an example, Table 8.3 gives the distance over which observations can be made for which IGFOV degradation is not more than 2 times compared to the nadir view. The table also gives the maximum values, for horizon-to-horizon coverage. In the case of pushbroom scanner, the IGFOV degradation is primarily due to the earth's curvature effect; while both viewing geometry and earth curvature affect the whiskbroom type opto-mechanical scanner (see Section 9.3.1).

From a geosynchronous orbit, the maximum (horizon-to-horizon) earth area covered is about 42% of the earth's surface, covering a latitude of about ±81°. However, as explained

Table 8.3   Effect of sensor viewing geometry and curvature of earth on spatial resolution (Mathew, 2002)

Altitude (km)	For horizon-to-horizon coverage		Swath coverage for which edge IGFOV is twice that of the nadir IGFOV	
	ϕ_v	Swath	Whiskbroom scanner	Pushbroom scanner
	Deg	km	km	km
500	68.01	4894	928	2415
700	64.30	5721	1262	2839
1000	59.82	6719	1729	3363
5000	34.09	12447	5648	6740
30000	10.09	17789	10841	10989
35786	8.70	18100	11074	11282
40000	7.90	18278	11362	11457

earlier, due to the poor resolution near the horizon limits, the usable data is limited to regions less than ±81° latitude. Nevertheless by positioning 3–4 satellites at suitable longitudes in the geostationary orbit, one can have global coverage continuously except around the poles.

8.4   ORBITAL PERTURBATIONS

There are several external forces, which influence the satellite orbit and make the orbital elements vary. Major sources of disturbance for near earth orbit is the drag due to residual atmosphere. If not corrected, the satellite will start losing orbit and will start 'spiraling inward' and will either burn out in the atmosphere or finally crash to earth. Other forces which cause orbital perturbation include the non-spherical shape of the earth, gravitational force from other celestial bodies, such as the moon, planets, radiative pressure from solar radiation, solar wind (particle flux), influence of earth's magnetic field, and so on. However, during the operational period we would like to keep the orbital parameters constant and hence 'orbit maintenance' has to be carried out. The orbital corrections are carried out by a suitable operation of 'thrusters' on board.

8.5   THE SPACECRAFT

Satellite systems could be broadly separated into two main blocks.

 (i)   A service module (satellite bus), and
(ii)   a payload module.

(The payload refers to a package of sensors that performs the mission of the satellite, such as, cameras, SAR, MSS, communication transponders, and so on.)

   The payload module carries actual instruments for the specific mission such as the cameras, SAR and altimeter, along with the payload specific subsystems. The service module or the satellite main bus provides all the support needed to realise the mission. Though the basic functioning of the satellite bus is similar, individual spacecraft can be very different from one another. Different technologies/ approaches could be adopted to achieve the same end result. The newer satellites are smaller and less massive than their predecessors, yet they function like their predecessors or better.

A detailed account of the design and functioning of a satellite is beyond the scope of this book. Here the purpose is to familiarise the reader with the basic functions of the various subsystems that make a remote sensing satellite. An exploded view of an IRS-1C/1D satellite is given in Fig. 8.9.

The major subsystems of the satellite bus are briefly described below

Structure All the subsystems are mounted on a suitable structure. The structure provides the overall mechanical integrity to the spacecraft. The structure could have different shapes— cylinder, hexagon, rectangular, and so on. The structure provides a place to attach the various subsystems internally and externally. It must have the required strength and stiffness to support all the subsystems, and withstand the launch loads, yet be light enough to reduce the overall weight. A good design keeps structural weight less than 10% of the overall weight of the satellite.

Power system For all satellites, the main source of power is from solar cells. These are photovoltaic devices, which convert light energy to electricity. Silicon and gallium arsenide are typical materials used for solar cells. The latter has a higher efficiency to convert light to electricity but is more expensive. These cells are cemented on to a substrate to form panels.

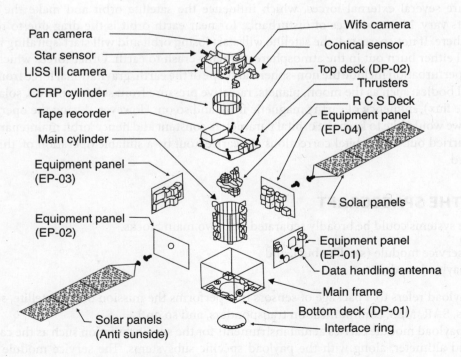

Fig. 8.9 Exploded view of IRS-1D spacecraft.

Electrical connections are made in series and parallel to generate the required output voltage and currents. The area of the panel is dependant on the power requirements. The panels are folded and anchored during the launch phase and are deployed in the orbit. Suitable drive mechanisms (Solar Array Drive Assembly, SADA) ensure that the solar panel is sun pointed to get maximum power. Electrical power is brought from the panel via the slip rings of the SADA for further conditioning and distribution. To supplement peak power requirements during payload operations, as well as to support critical satellite systems during satellite eclipse (sun not visible), batteries are used. These batteries are recharged during the sunlit portion of the orbit.

The output of the solar panel/battery goes to a number of power conditioners – DC to DC converters – which produce the required voltage, current and stability as required for each subsystem.

Attitude and orbit control system (AOCS)   A satellite must maintain a certain attitude to allow the observational instrument to point to the desired direction, like pointing the camera optical axis and communication antenna to the earth, and so on. Various factors, such as magnetic field, earth's non-uniform gravitational field and solar wind disturb the satellite orbit and attitude which have to be continuously adjusted. The first task is to know the attitude. This is achieved by using various sensors, which use the earth/sun/stars as reference points to define the orientation of the satellite axes. In addition, gyroscopes are used to find out the perturbations on the attitude and drift. Mechanical gyros are generally used. Fibre optic gyros (FOG) are preferred for long duration missions as they are more reliable, due to the absence of moving parts.

There are two basic techniques generally employed to stabilise the satellite. The whole body of the satellite is rotated in order to provide a powerful gyroscopic action by which the spin axis is maintained in a specified direction. The weather observational satellite METEOSAT, uses this principle for stabilisation by rotating the body to about 100 revolutions per minute. However, the communication antenna has to be continuously earth pointed. This is achieved by attaching the antenna to a 'despun' platform. For high resolution imaging, especially from a low earth orbit, this is not optimal. Instead, we should have the camera always pointed towards the earth, this is called three-axis stabilisation. To achieve this, generally, three rotating discs – momentum wheels – are mounted on three mutually perpendicular axes. A change in the speed of the momentum wheel produces a reaction on the satellite in the opposite direction. The error signals from the attitude sensor can be used to suitably modulate the wheel speed to maintain the attitude.

We have seen earlier that the orbit perturbation takes place due to various reasons, which causes a change in altitude and inclination. The orbit parameters are measured by tracking the satellite. Orbit correction is done by the propulsion carried in the spacecraft. Suitable combination of thrusters (can be thought of as micro rockets, which gives a thrust in the opposite direction as the propulsion is expelled through the nozzle) are located on the various faces of the satellite.

Thermal control   Free space temperature is about 4 K. The subsystems consuming power generate heat. It is essential to keep the temperature of different subsystems within a specified temperature limit. Sensitive optical components such as lenses and telescope assembly, have to be maintained within close tolerance. In addition, detectors may be required to be controlled within a tight tolerance of ±0.1°C or better. Temperature management is carried out by a combination of passive and active (using heaters) techniques. A conspicuous appearance of a spacecraft ready for launch is the golden coloured blanket covering most part of the external surface. These are multi-layer insulation (MLI) blankets, which are efficient IR reflectors protecting the spacecraft from overheating due to solar radiation. It also helps to retain the heat generated within the spacecraft to prevent too much cooling. Optical Solar Reflectors (OSR) which are quartz mirror tiles are used to radiate heat from the spacecraft. Thermal paints and special thermal tapes, which control the ratio of emissivity to absorptivity are also used in passive thermal control of the subsystems. Other passive temperature control systems include heat pipes (wherein a fluid is circulated to remove heat). Thermal detectors are usually cooled to about 100 K using radiative coolers. Closed cycle sterling coolers can also be used for cooling detectors, but are not preferred due to their limited life and lower reliability.

Active thermal control includes thermostatically controlled heaters, as well as electric heaters that can be commanded on and off from the ground.

Propulsion subsystems   Propulsion subsystems enable attitude correction and maintenance of orbit within a certain altitude and inclination range by producing the required thrust in the desired direction.

The subsystem consists of propellant tanks, plumbing systems with valves and helium tanks to provide pressurisation for the propellant, and the nozzle through which the propellant is expelled. Hydrazine is one of the commonly used propellants.

Telemetry, tracking and command (TT & C)   Telemetry systems collect data on the 'health' of the various subsystems and send it down through a communication link to the satellite control station. The data includes the voltages of different power modules, temperature of different subsystems, satellite attitude data, and so on. Telemetry is the only means for the spacecraft controller to know how the satellite is functioning. A secure and reliable command system is very essential for successful operation of any satellite. Commands are generated from a control console at the ground station and transmitted to the satellite. At the satellite, the received signal is decoded and stored in memory. The command code is sent back to the ground station via telemetry links to check the validity. If the command word is found correct, an execute command is sent for actual execution of the function. The command is used to select/shut off certain subsystems, change gain, and so on.

Communication subsystem   The EM radiation transmitted from earth to the satellite is known as *uplink* and the radiation transmitted from the satellite to earth is known as *downlink*. The RF carrier is modulated with information to be carried in each direction—command signals on the uplink and telemetry on the down link. Command and telemetry carrier are usually different from data communication links. Currently, the sensor data is sent via X band for IRS satellites.

The RF signal for transmission from the spacecraft is generated by a *transmitter*. This subsystem consists of an electronic circuit, which generates the RF tone. The tone is further modulated and amplified to the final power level, generally by a microwave device called the Travelling Wave Tube Amplifier (TWTA). Data transmission (or reception) is achieved through a set of antennae. Telemetry and telecommand antenna provides wide angle coverage, while the payload data transmission is carried out by high gain antennae.

The satellites generally carry an extremely stable RF source called a beacon, which is tracked by the ground station antenna to establish orbital parameters. A number of ground stations with adequate separation are required to get correct orbital data.

Reliability is an important consideration in satellite design and realisation. Special 'space qualified' components are used. The basic design includes adequate redundancy so that a single point failure does not totally jeopardise the mission objectives.

The amount of time a satellite is in view of a ground station depends on the satellite altitude and the orbit location with respect to ground station. At 1000 km orbit, one can have a maximum contact time of about 19 minutes. The ground station can receive data through the communication link only when the satellite can be 'seen' by the ground station. This depends on the height of the satellite. As the altitude increases, the satellite can be seen farther away from the ground station. Thus, for each satellite, the ground station can receive the imagery within a limited area around it usually referred to as the visibility circle (Fig. 8. 10). So to have global coverage, geographically distributed ground stations, or adequate onboard storage facility is required, such that when the satellite is not within the visibility of the ground stations, tape recorders/solid state recorders can record the data, and the recorded data can be sent to a ground station, when the satellite is within its visibility.

8.6 GLOBAL NAVIGATION SATELLITE SYSTEM (GNSS)

Many times when a ground observation is made, one would like to know its exact location on earth—longitude, latitude, and height from the mean sea level. A satellite navigation system that provides autonomous geo-spatial positioning with global coverage is termed a global navigation satellite system or GNSS. The GPS was the first GNSS introduced by USA. Subsequently other countries also launched GNSS: GLONASS by Russia, GALILEO by Europe, BEIDOU (Compass) by China and QZSS by Japan. India has a Regional Navigational System (IRNSS) to provide accurate position information service to users in India as well as the region extending up to 1500 km from its boundary, which is its primary service area. We shall describe the operation of a satellite navigation system using GPS as an example. The satellite-based position fixing is based on the principle of trilateration. Trilateration is a basic geometric principle that allows one to find a location if its distance is known from atleast three other already known stations. Let us try to understand this in two dimensional space.

Let us assume a man lost his way in a jungle. He has a map of the area, with the location of three magic radio stations marked on it. The station's magic is that if anyone dials it, it is able to tell the distance of the caller from the station. The man calls the first station. The station gives the distance as x_1. Then he could be anywhere on the periphery of a circle with the station No.1 as centre and radius x_1 [Fig. 8.11(a)]. Next he calls station No.2 and it gives the distance as x_2. If he now draws a circle with station No.2 as centre and x_2 as radius, it intersects the previous circle at two points [Fig. 8.11(b)], one of which should be his bearing. The third station gives a distance x_3 and a circle drawn with station No.3 as centre and x_3 as radius will uniquely decide the location [Fig. 8.11(c)] (assuming no error and is everything perfect!). Satellite-based navigation is the three dimensional extension of this principle.

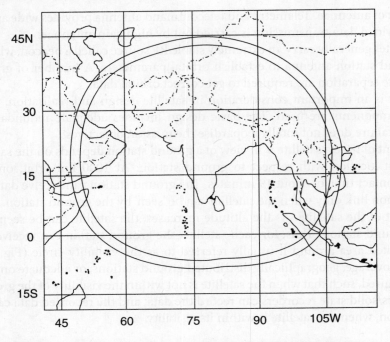

Fig. 8.10 Visibility circle for IRS-IA from NRSA ground station, Hyderabad.

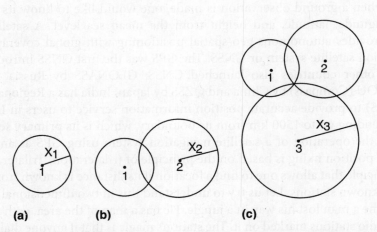

Fig. 8.11 Schematics showing the principle of operation of a GPS in two dimensional space.

If the man is ranging the satellite, he could be anywhere on the sphere, centred on the satellite, with the distance from him and the satellite as the radius. By ranging two satellites, the intersections of two spheres, establishes a circle. By ranging three satellites, he has the intersection of three spheres, thereby just narrowing down the position to two points in space and usually one location will be ridiculous (very odd unrealistic coordinates) and hence his correct location is known. Thus, we are essentially using satellites in space as reference points to establish locations on earth. Now, we shall discuss how exactly this is realised.

The GPS consists of a space segment (the satellites), a control segment (ground station to maintain the satellite) and the user segment (GPS receiver). The space segment consists of 24 satellites (NAVigation Satellite Timing And Ranging, NAVSTAR) at a nominal altitude of about 20,200 km (period 12 h), with a 55° inclination, placed in six different orbital planes, with four satellites in each plane. Each satellite transmits two L band signals (L_1 with 1575.42 MHz and L_2 with 1227.60 MHz). These signals are modulated by pseudorandom binary codes (PN). Each satellite has a specific code, thus when the GPS receiver reads the code, it knows which satellite the signal is from, though all the satellites transmit in the same frequency. The PN code is also fundamental to determine the time taken by the signal to reach the receiver, and hence the distance. Two types of codes are used.

Coarse acquisition code (C/A code) This consists of 1023 bits, which repeats itself every millisecond. If the timing is converted into distance, the code length is ~300 km with each bit ~300 m. The positioning service using C/A code ranging data is referred to as the *Standard Positioning Service* (SPS).

Precise code (P code) It is a long binary code, which repeats only once a week. The bit is equivalent to 30 m of length and the code length is 181.44×10^7 km. In order to guard against fake transmission of this code, it is encrypted and the resulting code is termed the Y code (the process of encryption is called anti-spoofing, AS). The positioning service based on P code ranging data is known as *Precise Position Service* (PPS).

The L_1 signal is modulated by both C/A and P codes and L_2 is generally modulated by P code. The satellite also broadcasts navigation information modulated on L_1. Each satellite sends a full description of its own orbit data necessary to establish its location in space at any instant and an approximate guide to orbits of other satellites. The other information transmitted include health of the satellite, parameters for propagation, error correction, and so on. To sum up, in simple terms, when the GPS receiver decodes the message it essentially conveys:

'I am satellite A, my position is currently B and this message is sent at a time T!'

Now the most critical issue is how the receiver evaluates the distance between the receiver and the satellite. This is done by measuring the time taken by the signal to reach the receiver. Let us assume we are using a very accurate and stable clock in the satellite and the receiver and they are synchronised. If the PN code is transmitted at a time T by the satellite and at the same instant, the receiver also runs the same code, then the PN code received from the satellite can be compared with the receiver PN sequence to find out the delay in arrival. To implement this requires clocks of high level accuracies found only in atomic clocks (stability better than 1 s in 3×10^6 years). Satellites carry stable atomic clocks. But using them as receivers would have made the cost of the receiver very high and would not have been cost-effective for many end users. Therefore, GPS uses inexpensive quartz clocks as reference and use other ingenious techniques to achieve the same result. In one of the possible modes, the GPS receiver determines the travel time of a signal from the satellite by comparing the *pseudorandom code* it is generating with an identical code in the signal from the satellite. To explain this conceptually, the receiver slides its codes backwards (later and later in time, since the satellite signals arrives late at the receiver and it has to travel through a distance) until it synchronises with the satellite codes. From the amount it has to slide, the signal arrival time can be established after correcting for tropospheric and ionospheric delays. However, since the receiver clock is not perfectly synchronised with the satellite clock, the time measure has a constant bias. Therefore, the range measured using this time is not correct and hence called pseudo-range. Three measurements will of course intersect to give a position. However a fourth measurement made as a crosscheck will not intersect with the first three. The receiver then looks for a single correction factor which can be added/subtracted to the time measurement of all the observations in order that they intersect at a single point. Thus with an extra measurement, the receiver, though not synchronised with the satellite clock can give reliable position coordinates. A more accurate position fixing can be achieved by a technique called *carrier phase measurement*. This can give *centimetre accuracies* (Remondi, 1986). However, code based receivers, though less accurate than the carrier phase system, have gained widespread applications for GPS, vehicle tracking and land navigation due to its very low cost. To improve the accuracy of the position fix, it is also important that the satellites chosen for position fixing should be widely separated and well distributed.

To use the satellite as a reference for ranging, we should know its position accurately at any instant. Satellite orbit parameters are transmitted by the satellite. Due to the perturbation of the orbit, this needs to be frequently updated. The GPS control segment estimates the satellite orbit based on measurements carried out by its five ground stations spread worldwide, along with necessary corrections. The updated orbit parameters are uploaded to the satellite to correct the orbit information it transmits.

The system directly interfacing with the user is the GPS receiver. The receiver detects and decodes the GPS signal and carries out processing using the built-in computer to generate an output to the user in a format usable for his end use. It could be LCD displays, RS-232 digital output, and so on. There are different types of receivers. The choice depends on the end use in terms of accuracy, size and auxiliary information availability, and of course, the cost.

As seen earlier, the time taken by the satellite signal to reach the receiver can be estimated by the code correlation technique or the carrier phase measurement technique. Based on the architecture, GPS receivers may be classified as continuous receivers or switching receivers. A continuous tracking receiver has dedicated hardware channels and each channel tracks a single satellite. There should be a minimum of four receiver channels and depending on the cost may even contain up to 12 channels. These receivers have a better accuracy and inherent redundancy as provision if one of the hardware channels fails.

The basic functional subsystems of a GPS receiver consists of the following.

Antenna and preamplifier   The task is to receive the electromagnetic radiation coming from the satellites and amplify them for further processing. The antennae should have broad beam characteristics so that they do not have to be pointed to the source. There are several types of antennae used with GPS. The microstrip antenna is one of the widely used systems.

Radiofrequency section and computer processor   The RF section of a GPS receiver converts the incoming signal after preamplification to an intermediate frequency (IF) for further processing.

The modulated signal extracted from the carrier is processed by a powerful microprocessor. There are different signal processing techniques – conventional and proprietary – to generate the position fix.

Input/output device   This enables operators to interact with the microprocessor, and the measured data is stored/displayed. It will also have a standard interface to transfer the digital data outside.

Power supply   Transportable and handheld GPS being very common, internal battery packs form a part of the receiver.

Errors in Measurement

The GPS was designed to provide two levels of accuracy, with highest accuracy for military users via Precision Positioning Service and the other for civilian use. With C/A code, the accuracy was thought to be about 100 m. However, in actual practice, it was noticed that the standard positioning service (SPS) for a civilian user gives an accuracy of ~40 m. In order to limit the accuracy for civilian use, the US government in 1990 deliberately introduced an error in the orbit data and clock accuracy (dither) for L1 signals. This is called *selective availability* (SA). SA used to be the single largest error source for SPS. Fortunately, due to the wide civilian applications of GPS, the SA has been discontinued since May, 2000.

The type of errors which influence GPS accuracy involve random errors and unmodelled residual biases. The biases are generally of three classes. Satellite-dependant biases are due to uncertainty in the orbital parameters of the satellite or even the computation procedure itself. There could be receiver-dependant biases due to clock stability with time. Signal propagation biases include delays due to ionosphere and troposphere propagation. Though this can be modelled, there could be biases due to the parameters used in the model and the mathematical model itself. GPS measurement errors include multi-path effects (interference of the direct signal and that reflected from the nearby objects), receiver noise, and so on. GPS accuracy is also dependant on other parameters such as mode of operation and algorithm used. For example, if the user is stationary, repeat observation is possible and averaging can reduce random errors, which is not possible in the case of a moving observer. If post-processing of data is possible, more complex algorithms which are computation intensive is possible compared to a real-time requirement. Currently the SPS gives a positional accuracy of ~25 m in plane and ~30 m in height using C/A code tracking technique. To get better accuracy, a technique called Differential GPS (DGPS) is used.

DGPS is based on the concept that bias errors in the position of one location are similar to those for all locations within a given local area (say within ~100 km). The first one establishes a 'reference station', whose location is very accurately known. The GPS receiver at the reference station, after receiving the satellite data computes its location and calculates the difference between its known position and the position received from the satellites. These error data are transmitted to the second receiver (whose location is to be established, rover station), which uses this information to correct the data it has received. DGPS removes those errors common to both reference and rover receivers (not multi-path or receiver noise of a random nature). For the DGPS to be effective, it is necessary that both the base and rover stations should use the same satellites for position computation. DGPS can provide positional accuracies ~1–2 m even using C/A codes, when the rover is less than 1–2 km from the reference station.

For the remote sensing community, GPS has been widely recognised as an accurate, fast and cost-effective method for collecting geographic coordinate data that can be used in GIS. Surveying applications, which would normally take months using conventional techniques can be done in a few days using GPS. GPS also finds extensive use in areas like navigation, precise orbit and attitude determination of low earth orbiting satellites, and so on. The number of applications of GPS systems have been continuously increasing and is likely to increase, limited only by our imagination.

FOR FURTHER READING

1. *Manual of Remote Sensing*, Colwell R J, Ed., ASP, Chapter 12 and 16.
2. *https://solarsystem.nasa.gov/basics/*
3. *http://www.trimble.com/gps_tutorial/*
4. *https://www.ja-gps.com.au/what-is-gps.aspx*
5. *https://earthobservatory.nasa.gov/Features/OrbitsCatalog/*
6. *https://www.princeton.edu/~alaink/Orf467F07/GNSS.pdf*
7. *https://www.amacad.org/publications/Section_4.pdf*
8. *http://www.au.af.mil/au/awc/space/au-18-2009/au-18_chap06.pdf*
9. *http://www.its.caltech.edu/~ee157/lecture_note/orbits.pdf*
10. http://www.ioccg.org/training/turkey/DrLynch_lectures2.pdf

Data Reception and Data Products

The output from all sensors except the photographic camera is in the form of electrical signals. The electrical output from the sensors may have a direct relationship with the reflectance/emittance from the surface of earth, as in the case of opto-mechanical sensors like MSS, or could be a complex function like the Doppler history as in the case of SAR which requires involved processing to generate an image. In addition, the data has various errors/distortions introduced by the sensor, platform, atmosphere, and so on. The data from various sensors have to be presented in a form and format with specified radiometric and geometric accuracy which can be readily used by various application scientists for specific themes of their interest. This may be in the form of photographic output or in a digital format amenable for further computer processing. The data thus presented is called *data products*. In this chapter, we shall cover, in a very general way, the various steps involved in generating a data product, starting from the electrical signal sent by the sensor.

9.1 DATA FORMATS

Electrical signals produced by sensors will be recorded on board the aircraft/spacecraft and/or transmitted to the ground using suitable communication systems. Let us first consider how the signals are formatted before they are recorded/transmitted. We will explain the image data formatting for recording/transmission taking the example of a single band CCD camera. Consider a CCD with n elements as the detector, thus generating the image data for n pixels. Each pixel gives an output voltage proportional to the energy falling on the respective detector element. By suitable electronics, the output voltage is digitised, thus providing a 'word' of say, m bits. The number of bits depends on the radiometric accuracy requirement, saturation radiance level settings and so on. Thus, we have a string of binary data of n words (corresponding to n pixels), each with m bits. In addition, one could add other auxiliary information related to spacecraft or payloads, such as temperature of critical subsystems, orbit and attitude data, and others. This could form one line of data to be transmitted. To find out the start of the line, we have a 'unique word' (sync word) preceding each line data. The length and pattern of the unique word is so chosen that on a statistical basis, the probability of a set of image data mimicking the unique word is very low. Thus, one frame of telemetry data represents one cross-track image and successive image lines produce successive telemetry frames (Fig. 9.1). At the receiving end, if we can locate the position of the unique word, then it is possible to strip out the video information and auxiliary data. If there is more than one band (multi-spectral information), then the additional bands can be suitably included (formatted)

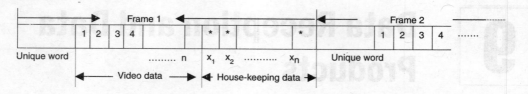

Fig. 9.1   Schematics of a single band CCD telemetry format.

in the telemetry frame. The telemetry system described above is a very simple system to explain the concept. However, in actual practice, as the length of one telemetry frame becomes too long, it is split into sub-frames; each word may have parity bits to detect any error picked up during transmission and reception.

Each line of video information of n words placed one below the other making a two dimensional array gives a digital image. In the present example of single band CCD imaging, the image rows give information across the sub-satellite track (swath) and the columns gives along-track information [Fig. 9.2(a)]. Images in which the pixels are arranged in rows and columns are called *raster* images. Each element of the two dimensional array has a digital number representative of the intensity value received by the sensor. Thus a single band image data consists of, say, p rows and n columns, with a 'brightness' value at each pixel location usually referred to as DN (digital number) value. To summarise, a digital image consists of a two dimensional array of individual picture elements (pixel), arranged in rows and columns. Each pixel represents a specific area on the earth's surface and the digital value (DN) is a measure of the reflectance/emittance of that area on the earth. When we have multi-spectral imaging of k bands, we have k 'layers' of images [Fig. 9.2(b)]. Data product generation primarily involve assigning each pixel to the correct geographic location from

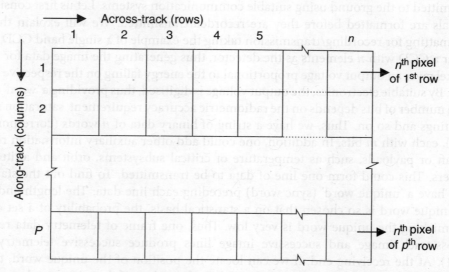

Fig. 9.2(a)   Schematic representation of a digital image, consisting of n pixels in the cross-track direction and p scan lines.

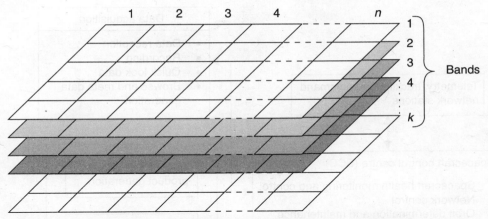

Fig. 9.2(b)   Schematic representation of the multi-spectral digital image of *k* bands.

which the sensor received the data, and keeping as close to the true radiance (emission/reflection) value as possible.

In the case of satellite missions, the formatted serial data as discussed above, is suitably modulated to a carrier frequency, (usually S or X band of the electromagnetic spectrum, see Chapter 2) which are allocated for remote sensing data transmission. At the ground station the data is received by an antenna and recorded on a high density digital tape recorder (HDDTR) or other suitable recording medium like digital linear tape (DLT), and so on. The details of the ground segment is given below.

9.2   GROUND SEGMENT ORGANISATION

The ground segment function for a remote sensing satellite system can be broadly classified into three categories:

- spacecraft control centre,
- data acquisition station, and
- data processing, product generation and distribution centre.

This is schematically shown in Fig. 9.3.

The main task of the spacecraft control centre (SCC) is to monitor various parameters of the satellite by analysing the telemetry data and keeping the satellite in good 'health' by scheduling necessary commands, orbit determination and schedule payload operations as per the user needs. In order to support these activities, there will be a network of telemetry, tracking and command (TTC) stations. The TTC network ensures telemetry data reception, recording, conditioning and transmission to a centralised location such as SCC, transmits commands to the satellite as determined by the spacecraft control centre and tracks the satellite in order to accurately determine the orbit. Orbit determination is very important to generate data products. Spacecraft control centre has a very crucial role to play in ensuring that the satellite functions properly. This becomes particularly important during the failure of some subsystems and/or when the spacecraft shows an anomalous behaviour, compared to a normally predicted one. The telemetry data which provides information about various subsystems have to be analysed

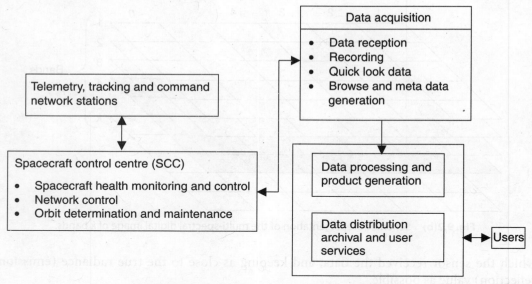

Fig. 9.3   Typical ground segment functions.

and studied and corrective measures taken so that the spacecraft is maintained properly. The image data is received at the data reception centre, which is usually not co-located with the SCC. The RF signal from the satellite carrying the image data is received by an antenna mounted on a compact tracking pedestal. The antenna continuously tracks the satellites as it moves. The signals received by the antenna are down converted to a suitable lower frequency and the down converted signals are demodulated suitably and the base band data are recorded on suitable recorders (HDDT, DLT).

The supply of data products to users, in response to their requests, is carried out at the data processing, product generation and distribution facility. Data processing and data product generation comprises transferring the raw data from the medium on which the raw data is recorded to the computer for data correction and formatting and finally to the required medium – photographic or digital – and data product quality checking. The details of some of these are discussed in the following sections. In addition to product generation, the centre has facilities for browsing and archiving.

A browsing facility is a pre-requisite for the generation of data products. It enables a user to select the area of interest for product generation, based on factors such as distribution of cloud cover over the scene, percentage of cloud cover and data quality. Browsing facility archives sub-sampled and compressed browse images, on mass data storage devices along with corresponding catalogue information. Browsing can be carried out at the user's work place, through Internet/LAN network/Dial-up-lines, depending on the scheme adopted by the concerned centre. The raw data and photo master films are archived to cater to any future back-dated requests. How long the raw data will be archived depends on the data policy of each satellite operator.

What is discussed above gives the basic configuration and function of a data reception and processing and distribution system. We shall now briefly describe the current system at the National Remote Sensing Centre (NRSC) for data reception and dissemination.

9.2.1 REMOTE SENSING SATELLITE DATA RECEPTION STATION AT NRSC

National Remote Sensing Centre (NRSC), one of the prime centres of the Indian Space Research Organisation (ISRO), is the focal point for the distribution of remote sensing satellite data products in India and its neighbouring countries. NRSC earth station and associated facilities for data product generation are located at Shadnagar, about 55 km from Hyderabad. As per the data policy of the Government of India, NRSC is entrusted with the authority to acquire and disseminate all satellite remote sensing data in India, both from Indian and foreign satellites.

In the initial phase, the data reception subsystems at the Shadnagar campus were configured manually with satellite specific parameters and actual data products were generated at the Balanagar campus of NRSC on a mission specific data processing system. As the number of remote sensing missions has increased as has the scope of supporting emergency requirements and disaster monitoring, the earlier mission specific model was found inadequate. In order to improve the turn around time from data acquisition to product delivery to the user in near real time, the entire chain of operations at the Shadnagar and Balanagar campuses were re-engineered to adopt an *Integrated Multi-mission Ground segment for Earth Observation Satellites* (IMGEOS), located at the Shadnagar campus. The main objective of IMGEOS is to realise a multi-mission system environment, adaptable to new EO missions. IMGEOS is configured to provide faster processing and dissemination of data products to users in order to meet disaster and other emergency applications. The system provides web based online data selection/ordering by users and online delivery of data products all over the world.

The data reception facility currently comprises four 7.5 m diameter parabolic antenna with dual polarisation S/X band signal reception and tracking capability. These ground stations are configured to track and receive data in S and X-bands from several national and international satellites. The planning of data acquisition is accomplished through *Pass Planning System*, which translates the user request into a format required for programming the satellite payload and scheduling a satellite pass over the ground station, after resolving the clashes with respect to different users and various missions. Based on the pass information /details available in the pass schedule file, the station control computer generates the satellite trajectory /antenna look angles and configures the tracking and receive chain subsystems such as down converters and data demodulators for mission specific parameters such as carrier frequency, modulation scheme, data rate and encoding. The X and S-band signals received by the antenna are down converted to suitable intermediate frequency (IF). The IF signals are then fed to the high data rate digital demodulators for extracting the baseband data signals. The data down converters and demodulators are configurable through remote control interface via ethernet to facilitate automatic programming as per the scheduled mission. The scheduling and antenna assignments for any satellite pass are carried out by the station control computer, based on the work order generated by the station workflow manager.

The data received is directly archived on to a storage medium, referred to as *Data Ingest system*. One ingest system is configured for each antenna system along with one additional backup system. The ingested data is processed (Level-0) by Ancillary data processing (ADP) systems connected through Storage Area Network (SAN) fabric network. The pre-processing functionalities such as ancillary data processing, browse image generation and raw data formatting are carried out at this stage. After this preprocessing, the data is moved to the main SAN disk for archival and further processing. All the data acquired from the satellites is transferred to a three tier *Data Storage Archival System* for further use as and when required. Tier-1 contains recent data and most frequently used data. Tier-2 will have data acquired in the last 15 months and off-the shelf products.Tier-3 will hold all the acquired data on tapes (Lakshmi et. al., 2014).

Data quality checking for parameters and metadata information is done automatically with reference to user data request. After quality checking, the data is moved to the web portal or media writing centres for dispatch to the user as specified in the user request. Customised products with improved geometry (location accuracy) and radiometry are value added products. Some of the special products are, precision corrected, image fusion products and mosaic products. The product delivery is online through the internet via a secure web portal. For supply in physical media – CD/DVD – there is a separate media generation workstation.

All the data acquisition and processing activities of the ground station (IMGEOS) are controlled and monitored by a station workflow manager (a customised computer program) which coordinates all activities/operations in an automated environment, starting from data ordering, planning, pass scheduling, data acquisition, processing and product generation till data dissemination on a 24 × 7 basis. The IMGEOS network architecture ensures efficient data transfers free from congestion, no single point failure, high availability, scalable and robust enough to handle network centric satellite data acquisition, archival, processing and dissemination. The data and information transfer to and from the IMGEOS system is carried out through fully secured data exchange gateways.

9.3 DATA PRE-PROCESSING

The remote sensing data given to users should faithfully represent the geometric and radiometric properties of the ground scene. However, the raw data received at the ground station has a number of errors/artifacts produced due to the sensor itself, platform, intervening atmosphere and the data transmission and reception system. Therefore, one has to 'restore' the distorted image data to a more faithful representation of the original scene. The data products are produced after correcting for geometric and radiometric errors (correction for atmospheric effect is usually not carried out). We shall discuss the source of these errors and how they are corrected. The errors can be broadly classified as systematic errors and random errors. Systematic errors are those which are constant or can be modelled so that they can be eliminated by suitable operation on the data (example, earth's rotation, panoramic distortion, detector offset and so on). Random errors are difficult to eliminate totally (detector noise, transmission/reception noise and jitter of spacecraft).

9.3.1 SOURCES OF ERRORS IN RECEIVED DATA

Radiometric Errors

The radiance value recorded for each pixel should be, ideally, a faithful representation of the reflectance/emittance property of the corresponding resolution element on the ground. Radiometric errors are introduced due to sensor characteristics, intervening atmosphere and noise introduced during signal generation, transmission/reception. A common radiometric error in a photographic camera is that, even for uniform Lambertian surfaces, the intensity at the edge of the field falls compared to the on-axis intensity. The photo cathode of a vidicon is not equally sensitive at all locations, producing an image in which equal input intensity produces different grey levels. This is referred to as 'shading'. In the case of opto-mechanical scanners, when more than one detector is used per band (as in LANDSAT MSS), then each detector will have a response slightly different from the other. For example, in the case of LANDSAT MSS which has six detectors per band, the output of the six detectors will be different for a constant uniform source due to the response characteristic of the detector, and variation of gain and offset of the amplifier chain. If not suitably corrected, this effect will result in some kind of 'striping' in the across-track direction. In the case of a CCD camera, a similar effect can be seen, since all the CCD pixels do not have exactly the same light transfer function. Figure 9.4 shows the variation of response of one band of the IRS LISS camera for a uniform light input. The x-axis gives the CCD pixel position and the y-axis, the video output digital value. In the case of a linear CCD camera, such detector inequalities if not corrected, produce striping in the along-track direction. In addition, the detector output itself may be a non-linear function of the input radiance. Radiometric correction is aimed at relating the sensor output to the input radiance, so that after correction, all the CCD elements give the same digital number for the same radiance input.

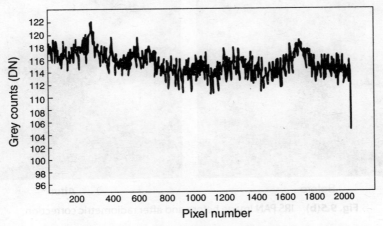

Fig. 9.4 The response variation of Band 4 of an IRS LISS-2 camera.

Radiometric errors are corrected by using a light transfer function evaluated by elaborate calibration on the ground. A very uniform source produced by an integrating sphere is placed in front of the optics so that the total input aperture of the sensor is covered by the source. The output readings are taken for varying light intensity, thereby generating a transfer characteristic from the input light level to the output electrical signal level. This information is stored in the computer as look up tables and are used in correcting the data received from the satellite. Figure 9.5(a) gives the histogram of the output digital value of a CCD camera, before and after correction for a uniform light input. Figure 9.5(b) gives the IRS-1D PAN image before and after radiometric correction. It may be remembered that the radiometric errors produced

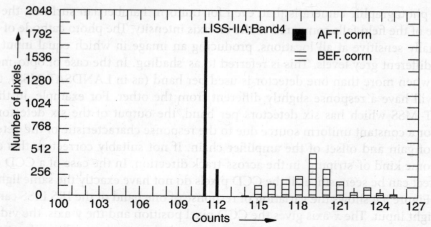

Fig. 9.5(a) Histogram of a CCD camera output before and after radiometric normalisation correction. Note that after correction, most of the pixels show 111 counts. Spill over to 112 counts is due to quantisation.

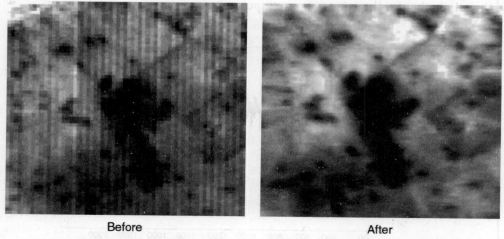

Before   After

Fig. 9.5(b) IRS PAN image before and after radiometric correction.

due to MTF (point spread function) is not corrected in this process. In addition to laboratory calibration, various in-flight calibration techniques are employed to evaluate the degradation of the sensor during its orbit life.

Apart from detector response variation, striping could also be produced by coherent noise produced due to electrical coupling between various signals. These periodic noises often manifest as a two dimensional pattern, which will be visible particularly at low intensity and under contrast enhancement. Suitable filtering can be performed to reduce the noise. However, such filters could also affect the information content of the image. There could be detector degradation during the operational life of the satellite, which may not be fully correctable by in-flight and laboratory calibration. There are special algorithms, based on the distribution of data for each pixel to correct such errors.

Another issue is the loss of data due to the noise introduced while transmission/reception causing telemetry frame synchronisation loss, thereby causing the loss of one line. If the line losses are very few then they may be replaced by the previous line or interpolated between the previous and the subsequent correct line. Atmospheric errors are not generally corrected in the data products because it is highly model-dependent. This is carried out by end users depending on their need. Similarly, variation in solar illumination is also not generally corrected. However, information on sun angle is available on the photographic product and on the header of the file of the digital product.

Geometric Errors

Due to various geometric errors, the imaging system does not faithfully reproduce the image of a grid on the earth. The geometric errors are either intrinsic to the sensor or due to the platform. The scale variation at the edge of the film in a photographic camera due to lens distortion is well known. In the case of an opto-mechanical scanner, the major cause of distortion is due to the geometry of scanning. For example, for LANDSAT MSS or TM, the data samples are taken at regular intervals of time, which means that each data value is for equal angular interval increments. However, the ground distance swept by the sensor IFOV is proportional to $\sec^2\theta$, where θ is the angle of scan measured from the nadir (Fig. 9.6). This produces scale variation along the scan direction, such that the details are compressed towards the edge of the scan and a straight line feature will be curved (Fig. 9.7). Due to this intrinsic scan geometry, the off-nadir resolution is degraded. The problem is compounded due to the curvature of the earth. Figure 9.8 gives the relative resolution degradation with scan angle for an opto-mechanical scanner, in the along-track and across-track direction from a satellite altitude of 900 km. In the case of a pushbroom camera, in an ideal case, there is no across-track

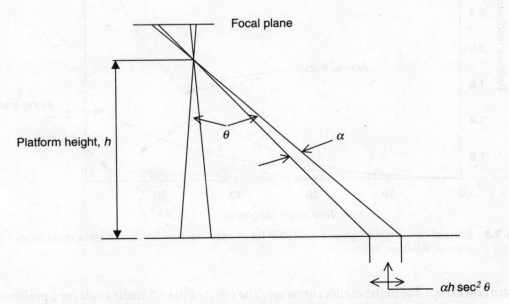

Fig. 9.6 Effect of scan geometry on ground resolution for an opto-mechanical scanner.

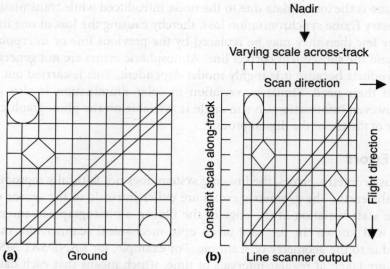

Fig. 9.7   Schematics showing distortion in a line scanner. (Reprinted from *Remote Sensing and Image Interpretation*, 1st Ed., Lillesand & Kieffer, 1979, with permission of John Wiley & Sons, Inc.)

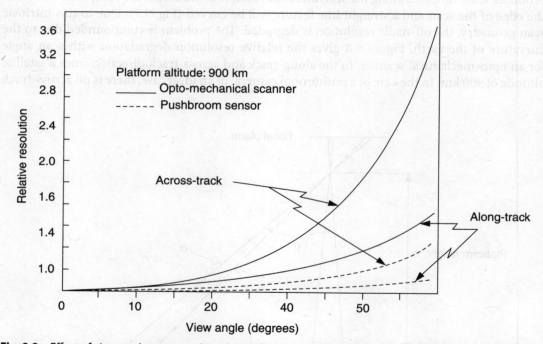

Fig. 9.8   Effect of view angle on ground resolution for an opto-mechanical scanner and a pushbroom scanner. (Mathew, 2002)

distortion except due to the earth's curvature. The effect of the off-nadir angle for a pushbroom sensor, taking into account the earth's curvature is also shown in Fig. 9.8.

Another effect due to scan geometry is scan skew distortion. During the time the scan mirror completes one active scan, as in an MSS, the satellite moves along the ground track. Therefore, scanning is not at right angles to the satellite velocity vector (ground track) but is slightly skewed, which produces along-track geometric distortion, if not corrected.

Rotation of the earth is another effect which should be considered while generating data products of data from a satellite platform. The satellite orbit is fixed in the inertial space. Therefore as successive across-track imaging is carried out, the earth rotates beneath the sensor, thus imaging a skewed area, which has to be taken into account during generation of a geometrically corrected image.

Apart from these scan geometry related distortions, inherent sensor design inadequacy such as non-linearity of the scan mirror velocity also produces geometric distortion. Since data samples are taken at regular intervals of time (expecting equal angular increment), the varying mirror rate produces along-scan geometric distortion. The distortions of the lens system also produces geometric distortions.

The distortions discussed above – scan skew, mirror scan velocity non-linearities, panoramic distortion, earth rotation, optics distortion – are 'systematic' errors and can be corrected through sensor characterisation data, ephemeris and imaging geometry by using suitable algorithms. However, the geometric errors produced by platform characteristics such as altitude variation, attitude (roll, pitch and yaw) disturbance and orbit drift all produce various geometric distortions, random in nature (Fig. 9.9), and cannot be easily modelled to produce images with a high degree of geometric precision.

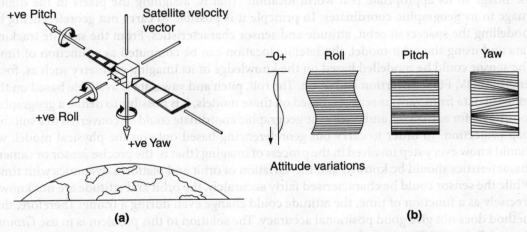

Fig. 9.9(a) (a) Roll, pitch, yaw definition for a spacecraft (b) Effect of attitude rates on imagery. (Adapted from Kasturirangan *et. al.*, 1991)

9.3.2 GEOREFERENCING

To effectively use the remote sensing data, it is necessary to identify the location on the ground where a feature is seen on the image. In other words, the user should be able to relate each pixel to the corresponding longitude and latitude on the earth. For this purpose, it is necessary to transform the image coordinate system to one of the map projections coordinate system

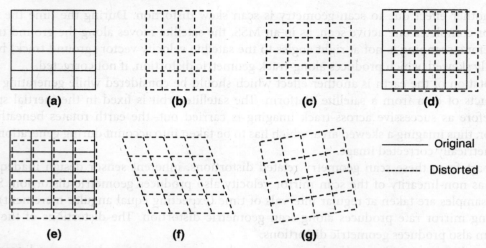

Fig. 9.9(b) The distortions of an image that can be corrected by a first-order (linear) equation. The above examples show (a) the original image, (b) and (c) a scale change in x and y, (d) and (e) linear shift in x and y, (f) skew and (g) rotation.

(Appendix 4). This image to map registration is referred to as georeferencing or geocoding. Basically, georeferencing is the process of taking a digital image-satellite image (or could be a scanned geologic map) and adding geographic coordinates to the image so that one can 'place' the image in its appropriate real world location. That is, assigning the pixels in the digital image to its geographic coordinates. In princple it is possible to carry out georeferencing by modelling the spacecraft orbit, attitude and sensor characteristics. From the satellite tracking data and using the orbit model, the satellite location can be computed as a function of time. The sensor could be modelled based on the knowledge of its imaging geometry such as, focal length, IFOV, FOV, distortion and so on. The roll, pitch and yaw data is available based on the onboard data from various sensors. Based on these models, it is possible to define a geographic coordinate for each pixel, and finally the geographic coordinate could be converted to a suitable map projection. In order to carry out georeferencing based only on the physical model, we should know every step involved in the process of imaging (that is, the precise sensor or camera characteristics should be known) and the variation of orbit and platform dynamics with time. While the sensor could be characterised fairly accurately, the orbit and attitude are not known precisely as a function of time; the attitude could change even during a frame. Therefore, this method does not give good positional accuracy. The solution to this problem is to use *Ground Control Points* (GCPs) in order to generate an accurate transformation model (sometimes referred to as mapping function) to relate the image coordinates to a map coordinate.

A GCP is a feature which can be uniquely identified in the image and whose map coordinates (or geographic coordinates) are known or can be determined. The GCPs chosen should be stable, so that its appearance is unambiguous. The usually selected GCPs include features such as road intersections, airport runway intersections, river confluence and prominent coastline features. The coordinates of the GCPs can be found out from existing maps or from GPS surveys. The coordinate system of the raw image is expressed in terms of pixels and lines (columns and rows). The map coordinate systems are usually oriented in a Cartesian form in terms of x and y coordinates corresponding to a latitude and longitude. Thus, we have two Cartesian coordinate systems, one describing the location of GCPs in the reference map (x, y) and the other defining the GCPs in the input image (u, v). These two coordinate systems can be related by a pair of mapping functions such that

$$u = f(x, y)$$

$$v = g(x, y)$$

The mapping function could be a polynomial. A first degree polynomial can model six kinds of distortion, including translation in x and y, scale changes in x and y, skew and rotation (Billingsley, 1983) [Fig. 9.9(b)]. This can be expressed by a 1st degree polynomial (a linear equation) such that

$$u = a_o + a_1 x + a_2 y$$

$$v = b_o + b_1 x + b_2 y$$

The equation essentially tries to find out which point in the output image (corrected) should come from (or corresponds) which point in the image (yes, it is working backwards—that is, to determine the distorted image position corresponding to map position).

We have to evaluate the coefficients a_i and b_i using the GCPs. The minimum number of GCPs required depends on the degree of polynomial (n) used in the mapping function and is given by $(n + 1)(n + 2)/2$. Thus for a 1st degree, one should have a minimum of three GCPs, for a 2nd degree, six GCPs and so on. However in practice, a larger number of GCPs than the minimum mentioned are required for applying the least square method to solve the equations. For moderate distortions in a relatively small area of an image (quarter of a TM or IRS-LISS scene), a linear transformation is sufficient for image to map registration. For corrections of larger area, a higher degree polynomial will be required. However, higher degree polynomials (greater than 3) could produce errors in areas devoid of GCPs. Higher degree polynomials can be used to make the image 'warped' on to the map (sometimes referred to as 'rubber sheeting'). The accuracy of the corrected product depends on the quality of GCPs. The GCPs should be distributed evenly throughout the image. In general, registration error decreases with an increase in the number of GCPs. The next task is to assign DN values for each pixel in the new, transformed image. The image to map registration is like laying a new rectified image in its correct orientation on top of the old (distorted) image (Fig. 9.10). The new coordinates (x, y) may not have a one-to-one relationship with the (rows, columns) of the original image. The process of determining what DN value is to be assigned to the new pixels (or how to estimate the new pixel DN values) is known as resampling. Some form of interpolation of the original pixel DN values is used to assign the pixel values to the output image.

A number of resampling schemes are possible to assign a DN to the output image. We shall briefly describe three generally used methods.

(i) *Nearest-neighbour interpolation*   Figure 9.11(a) gives the original distorted input image and Fig. 9.11(b), the rectified output image. By applying the mapping function, the pixel (5, 6) in the output image lie, say, at 3.2 and 4.8 in the input image. In the nearest-neighbour

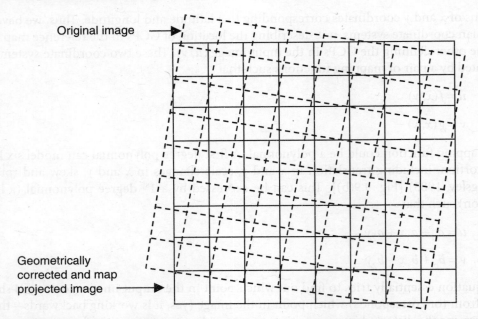

Original image

Geometrically
corrected and map
projected image

Fig. 9.10   Schematics showing the pixel misalignment between the original image and the corrected image, necessitating resampling.

interpolation, the pixel (5, 6) in the output is assigned the DN value corresponding to the nearest pixel to the computed position in the raw images, in this case (3, 5). This has the advantage that the radiometric values are not altered and are computationally efficient. However, this produces a geometric discontinuity of ± 0.5 pixel, thus giving a 'patchy' appearance especially at the edges and in linear features.

(ii) *Bilinear interpolation*   In this case, find four pixels on the input grid (raw image) closest to the computed value [in this example, (3, 4), (4, 4), (4, 5) and (3, 5)] and find out the weighted DN value according to the distance from the four points (the point nearest has the maximum weight). This is computationally more demanding than the earlier method, but produces a smoother appearing resampled image. However, the DN value is altered.

(iii) *Cubic convolution interpolation*   This uses the weighted average of sixteen input values closest to the computed point. This gives a much smoother appearance and sharper edges but is computationaly most intensive (about 20 times of that of the nearest-neighbour interpolation), (Bernstein, 1983).

Any interpolation is basically a low pass filtering operation, thus producing a loss of higher frequencies depending on the interpolation method used. Another aspect to be kept in mind is that although higher order interpolation improves the visual appearance of the images, multi-spectral classification can be sensitive to the interpolation technique used, due to alteration of radiometric values.

Error modelling and correction can be done on a scene basis as well as on a satellite pass basis (this is referred in IRS data processing as swath modelling, however, the term path modelling

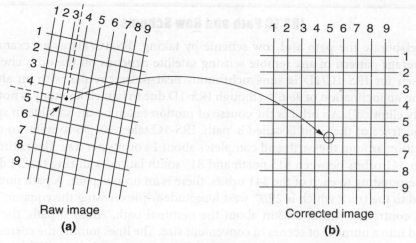

Raw image
(a)

Corrected image
(b)

Fig. 9.11 Illustration of resampling technique of nearest neighbour.

is more appropriate and is used here). In error modelling on a scene basis, one scene at a time is considered. This modelling has a simple mathematical form and computational procedure but requires more number of control points, to correct all the scenes in a pass. Therefore, a scene cannot be corrected if there are not adequate ground control points in that scene. In path modelling, the model is constructed from control points located in several contiguous scenes (full pass). This, though requiring a large computer memory, has the advantage of using only a few GCPs. However, the geometric accuracy achieved is less than the scene-based correction using well distributed GCPs.

What is discussed above, is the transformation of the remotely sensed image such that it has the location and scale properties of the desired map projection. The procedure employed has a wider application in other areas of digital processing of remote sensing images, besides georeferencing of the image. For example, registering between images of different bands, and of multiple dates, multiple resolution, all use coordinate transformation and resampling techniques discussed above. We shall discuss this in detail Section 10.2.2.

9.4 REFERENCING SCHEME

The photographic cameras and TV cameras used for remote sensing generally produce pictures frame by frame, such that each frame can be identified to a scene on the ground with certain length and breadth. However other sensors like opto-mechanical scanners (like MSS), CCD cameras, SAR and so on, produce a continuous strip of imagery along the satellite track of a width defined by sensor parameters and orbit height. Such a long strip of data is difficult to handle for various preprocessing and also will not be useful to many users, since they have to handle a large amount of data outside their area of interest. Therefore, the contiguous data is split into a number of scenes. The successive scenes will have a certain amount of overlap.

For the convenience of identifying a region of interest, suitable schemes can be used to refer a geographic point to a scene. One of the ways is to designate a scene in terms of a path number and row number, which defines the scene centre in terms of latitude and longitude.

IRS 1C Path and Row Scheme

We shall elaborate the path and row scheme by taking IRS-1C/1D as an example. The image coverage pattern of any remote sensing satellite depends on the orbit chosen. The orbit chosen for IRS-1C/1D is sunsynchronous near-polar circular with an altitude of 817 km and an inclination of 98.69° (though IRS-1D due to launch anomaly is not circular but slightly elliptical). An orbit is the course of motion taken by the satellite in space and the ground trace of the orbit is called a 'path'. IRS-1C takes 101.35 minutes to complete one revolution around the earth and completes about 14 orbits per day. The entire globe is covered in 341 orbits between 81° north and 81° south latitudes during the 24 day cycle. Thus corresponding to each of the 341 orbits, there is an unique path. A path number one is assigned to the track which is 29.7° west longitude while crossing the equator. The path pattern is controlled within ±5 km about the nominal path. Along a path, the data are segmented into a number of scenes of convenient size. The lines joining the corresponding scene centres of different paths are parallel to the equator and are called 'rows'. While framing the scenes, the equator is taken as the reference line for segmentation. The scenes are framed in such a manner that one of the scene's centre lies on the equator. For example, a LISS-III scene, consisting of 6000 lines, is framed such that the centre of the scene lies on the equator. The next scene is defined such that its centre lies exactly 5,703 lines from the equator. The centre of the next scene is then defined 5,703 lines northwards and so on. This is continued up to 81° north latitude. The path–row referencing scheme eliminates the usage of latitude and longitudes and facilitates convenient and unique identification of a geographic location. It is useful in preparing accession and product catalogues and reduces the complexity of data product generation. Since the various sensors of IRS-1C have different swaths, it is required to have a different referencing scheme for each sensor.

The swath of LISS-III is 141 km in visible and near-infra red bands and 148 km in short wave infrared (SWIR) band. Since the swath of LISS-III in all the four bands is greater than the inter-path distance (117.5 km), the sensor scans the entire globe once in every cycle without gaps. The referencing scheme of LISS-III consists of 341 paths numbered from west to east. Each path consists of 149 rows. Consecutive paths are covered with a separation of five days. If path 1 is covered on day one, path 2 will be covered on day six (Fig. 9.12). For the chosen path, the ground track repeats every 24 days after 341 orbits. The deviations of orbit and attitude parameters are controlled within limits such that the coverage pattern remains almost constant throughout the mission. Therefore, on any given day, it is possible to determine the orbit which will trace a designated path. Once the path is known, with the help of a referencing scheme, it is possible to find out the region covered by that path. Therefore, an orbital calendar, giving the details of paths, covered on different days will be helpful to users to plan their procurement of satellite data products.

9.5 DATA PRODUCTS GENERATION

The digital data received from the satellite camera undergoes different processing steps. The degree of data processing applied is referred to as 'level of processing'. The minimum level of processing is 'Level 0'. Level 0 data are unprocessed instrument/payload data at full resolution.

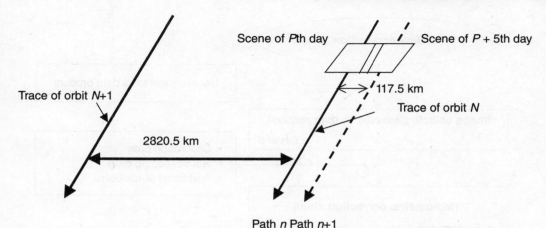

Fig. 9.12 IRS-1C LISS-III coverage pattern. Contiguous imaging of LISS-III with side lap happens every fifth day.

Any artifacts introduced during the data transmission from the spacecraft to the ground station and on the reception at the ground station (such as synchronisation frame losses) are removed in this step. Using this basic data, higher level data products are generated which are readily usable at the user end. There is no universally accepted definition of processing levels and could vary depending on data product provider and even the type of payload (NASA, 2003).

A broad outline of the data product available from the National Remote Sensing Centre (NRSC) IMGOES is given. The various processing levels of products generated for any remote sensing mission is categorised depending on the level of processing /correction (Table 9.1), in which the sublevels (A, B, C...) may vary from agency to agency. Figure 9.13 gives the schematic chart showing workflow of data product Level 1 generation for a space borne remote sensing camera.

Table 9.1 Broad classification of various processing levels of products generated at IMGEOS

Level	Correction
Level 0	Raw data of pass in FRED format along with ancillary data information and browse image (no correction)
Level 1A	Radiometrically calibrated*
Level 1B	Radiometrically corrected**
Level 1C	Radiometrically and geometrically corrected (level 1B + geometric correction)
Level 1D	Orthorectified product (level 1C + terrain corrections)
Level 1E	Atmospheric correction applied (input could be level 1C or level 1D
Level 2	Geophysical products

*Only radiometric normalisation applied. Generally used for internal assessment of system performance.
**Corrected for other radiometric degradation such as blur, noise and so on.
For details of geophysical products refer to http://www.nrsc.gov.in/Geophysical_Products

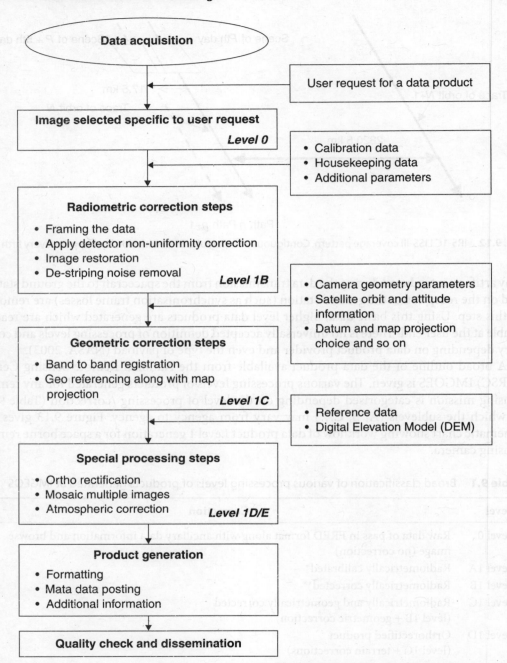

Fig. 9.13 A schematic chart showing Data Product Level-I generation work flow for a space-borne remote sensing camera (Moorthi and Garg, 2016).

The raw data is corrected for both geometric and radiometric distortions. Radiometric distortions arising due to the following factors are corrected.

- Non-uniform response of the detectors.
- Specific detector element failure.
- Data losses during communication or archival/retrieval.
- Blur in the image arising due to combined effect of optics, detector, atmosphere turbulence and scattering, and attitude variation.
- Noise in the image occurring from various sources.
- Narrow dynamic range.
- Image to image variations, wherever applicable.

A radiometric correction is applied through a *Look Up Table* (LUT) based on the image intensity levels, prepared for normalising the responses of all detector elements using the ground calibration data. The same calibration can be used for the conversion of radiometrically corrected digital number (DN) values to radiance values at the user end. Correction for major frame synchronisation losses (scan line losses) will be carried out using appropriate averaging of the neighbouring pixel values. If data losses occur in more than two consecutive scan lines, they will be replaced by a line consisting of all dark (minimum DN value) pixels. The failed detector pixel values (if any), will be replaced with the average of the adjacent pixels on the same scan line. Blur in the image is corrected by estimating the point spread function (PSF) from laboratory calibration data or using in-orbit stellar data. It is also possible to estimate PSF directly from the image if a suitable target for extracting PSF is available in the imagery. After a proper estimation of the PSF, image deconvolution can be performed to get a sharp image. The deconvolution process increases some amount of noise in the image. Generally after deconvolution, a noise filtering operation is performed to get a noise free image without degrading image sharpness.

Geometric distortions arising due to the following reasons are corrected.

(i) Scene related
  - earth rotation effect,
  - earth shape (ellipsoid and geoid) induced distortions,
(ii) Sensor related
  - sensor focal plane detector geometry,
  - alignment of optical axis with respect to spacecraft attitude reference,
  - multi-band and multi-array mis-registration,
  - off-nadir pointing (if exercised as in PAN/LISS IV) induced distortions.
(iii) Spacecraft related
  - image orientation with respect to spacecraft heading,
  - altitude and velocity variations affecting image scale,
  - attitude variations in roll, pitch and yaw directions.
(iv) Measurement/calibration errors
  - estimation of spacecraft state vectors,
  - attitude and pointing angles measurement,
  - attitude change rate measurements,
  - calibration of various alignment angles involved,
  - synchronisation of onboard and ground reception times.
(v) Multi-image variations in geometric distortion
  - image to image variations in geometric distortion.

(vi)   Map projection, boundary overlay and resampling options.

(vii) Geocoded correction—true north rotation.

Geometric corrections are performed through a dynamic model, which represents the imaging geometry. For precision products, ground control points (GCP) are used additionally for improving the geolocation accuracy. The grey values for all the output points transformed by the geometric model will be obtained by resampling the input image samples. Map projection and the image orientation are incorporated at the time of fixing the output grid. Finally, the data is formatted for generating the photographic or digital products in the required format.

9.5.1   PRODUCT OPTIONS

The user can order for a product of their interest based on the following choices.

(i)   *Path/row based products*: These products will be generated based on the referencing scheme of each sensor.

(ii) *Shift along track products*: If a user's area of interest is less than the dimensions of a full scene and falls in two successive rows of the same path, then the data will be supplied by sliding the scene in the forward (along the path) direction. These are called *Shift Along Track* (SAT) products. This way, the required area can be accommodated in a single product. The percentage of shift along the path has to be specified between 10% and 90% in multiples of 10%.

(iii) *Quadrant products*: Each LISS-III scene is divided into four nominal and twelve derived quadrants to generate a quadrant of the scene.

(iv) *Stereo products*: The oblique viewing capability of PAN sensors can be used to acquire stereo pairs. A stereo pair comprises two images of the same area acquired on different dates and at different angles.

(v)   *Geocoded products*: Geocoding corrects the imagery to a source-independent format, whereby multi-date and multi-satellite data can be handled with ease. Geocoded products are generated after applying radiometric and geometric corrections, orienting the image to the true north and generating the products with an output resolution, appropriate to the map scale. The advantage of a geocoded product is that it can be overlaid on a *Survey Of India* (SOI) toposheet map.

Geocoded products are generated based upon the SOI map sheets attributes of scale and extent, for PAN on a 1: 25,000 scale and for LISS-III on 1: 50,000 scale. The inputs required to be specified by the user, in addition to those provided in case of path/row based products, is the SOI Map sheet number. In addition, LISS-III district geocoded products are generated at 1:500,000 for districts having an area of 400 km × 400 km or more and at 1: 250,000 for smaller districts.

(vi) *Special products*: Value added products are generated after further processing of standard products, by extracting a specific area, mosaicking, merging and enhancing the data. These products include

  • PAN + LISS-III merged products: In order to exploit the dual advantage of the spectral resolution of LISS-III and the spatial resolution of PAN, PAN + LISS-III merged product is generated in PAN resolution. Other types of merged products available from IMGEOS include LISS IV data merged with high resolution panchromatic data from Cartosat (for details of image fusion refer 9.7.5).

- Ortho rectified image: Orthorectification is the process of removing the effects of image tilt and terrain relief effects thereby creating a planimetrically correct image. The orthorectified image has a constant scale wherein features are represented in their 'true' positions. This allows for the accurate direct measurement of distances, angles and areas.
- Template registered product: Here, one image is registered to a reference image (template), without the use of GCPs. *Tie points* are identified on both images and the image is spatially mapped on to the reference image. The templates used may already have the desired geometric characteristics. This technique caters to the need of registering multi-temporal data (for more details refer 10.2.2).
- Mosaic products: Two or more satellite images with an overlapping area can be stitched together to generate an imagery covering a larger geographic area.

More details on various products available from NRSC can be seen in Resourcesat data user's handbook (NRSC, 2011)

9.5.2 PRODUCT REQUEST

The user can request or order any Indian remote sensing satellite data through a web-based tool named *User Order Processing System* (UOPS), through which the user can define/select data based on various parameters such as, type of sensors—optical/microwave, resolution, swath, bands of interest, repetivity, area of interest, emergency or normal, digital media or FTP output, and so on. The first step to access the UOPS application is through user registration with an authentication from NRSC/ISRO. The user can define the requirements/specify the data product through this application software/tool. If the requested data is readily available in the NRSC archives, it is delivered to the user as per the request. If the data is not available in the NRSC archives, NRSC can acquire it on a nearest possible future date /available satellite pass over the ground station, process and supply it to the user.

9.6 DATA PRODUCTS OUTPUT MEDIUM

9.6.1 PHOTOPRODUCT

To generate a photographic product, the electrical information is converted to light energy, which is written on a photosensitive film or paper. The simplest way of doing this is to modulate the output intensity of a light emitting diode (LED) according to the DN value. The LED carrier moves across producing optical data corresponding to the scan lines. At the end, the film carrier is stepped to produce successive lines. The basic first derivative product is called 'master'. Masters of most IRS photographic products will be 240 mm films. For some of the special products, the master will be a 960 mm film.

The output data is supplied either as a paper print or as positive film transparency. Both black and white (B/W) and FCC products are available. Positive transparency has the advantage that by using suitable optical magnifiers, the image can be enlarged to match suitable scale reference maps for generating interpreted maps. However, paper prints are very convenient to

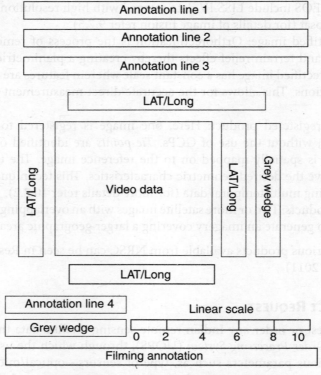

Fig. 9.14 IRS-1C photographic product layout.

carry during field checks, ground truth collection etc. The photoproduct also carries a number of other information useful to the interpreter. This is called product annotation. Figure 9.14 gives the layout of an IRS photographic product.

The annotation format has three lines on the top of the image data and one annotation line at the bottom of the data (NRSA, 1995). The first annotation line 1 on the top gives details regarding the satellite, and the type of product including the type of projection and resampling technique used.

The second annotation line 2 on the top gives details regarding the date of acquisition with time, path/row details, sensor sub-scene details, quadrant number, look angle information, the corrected scene centre and information on the sun elevation and azimuth in degrees.

The third annotation line 3 on the top has the same information content as that of annotation line 2 (top), if the generation of the data involves more than one scene.

The fourth annotation line 4 (bottom) at the bottom of the image data gives details regarding the generation—ID, date of generation with time, the type of enhancement used, details about which data product system (DPS) generated the product, place of generation and information about the product generation agency. This annotation line is for internal use only. Figure 9.15 gives the annotation information.

Each band produces a black and white photograph. Because of the limited dynamic range, it is difficult to easily discern more than about 16 grey shades in a black and white photograph. Any three bands can be combined to produce a colour photograph. Here, each band is assigned

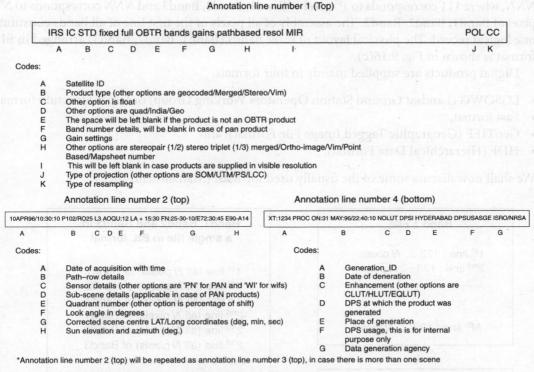

Fig. 9.15   Information of photographic products of IRS-1C LISS-III given in the annotation.

one of the three primary colours (blue, green, red) and the resultant image gives colour in various hues. Usually green, red and NIR bands are assigned blue, green and red colours respectively to produce false colour composites (FCC).

9.6.2   DIGITAL PRODUCTS

In order to carry out computer processing/classification, the image has to be retained in its digital form. The digital output is provided on a suitable medium such as CD-ROMs, DAT, and so on, depending on user requests. The data may be arranged in band sequential (BSQ), band interleaved by line (BIL) or band interleaved pixel (BIP) formats. To understand BSQ, BIL and BIP layout, let us consider a 3-band image, say, band-1(B1), band-2 (B2) and band-3 (B3), having M number of rows (scan lines) and N number of columns (pixels) each. In the BSQ layout, data in one band for the *whole scene* is written continuously, followed by the 2nd band and so on. That is B1, B2 and B3 are written as separate files on to the medium [Fig. 9.16(a)]. In BIL, one line for band 1 is followed by the data of the same line in the 2nd band till all the bands are over, then the 2nd line with band 1 starts. This is repeated for the *whole scene* and the Mth line of B1, B2 and B3 represents the last record [Fig. 9.16(b)].

In the case of BIP, a single image file in pixel interleaved order is generated. Actually in BIP, pixels are interleaved, that is, (1st pixel of Band1, 1st pixel of Band2, 1st pixel of Band3) constitute a single pixel group. Similarly N pixels of one scan line are written as 111222333...

NNN, where 111 corresponds to 1st pixel of Band1, Band2, Band3 and *NNN* corresponds to *N*th pixel of Band1, Band2, Band3. The assembly of all pixels of the first line of all bands constitute one logical record. The physical layout of three bands (Band1, Band2, Band3) arranged in BIP format is shown in Fig. 9.16(c).

Digital products are supplied mainly in four formats:

- LGSOWG (Landsat Ground Station Operators Working Group) or Super Structure format,
- Fast format,
- GeoTIFF (Geographic Tagged Image File Format), and
- HDF (Hierarchical Data Format).

We shall now discuss some of the usually used formats. (Mahammad, 2002)

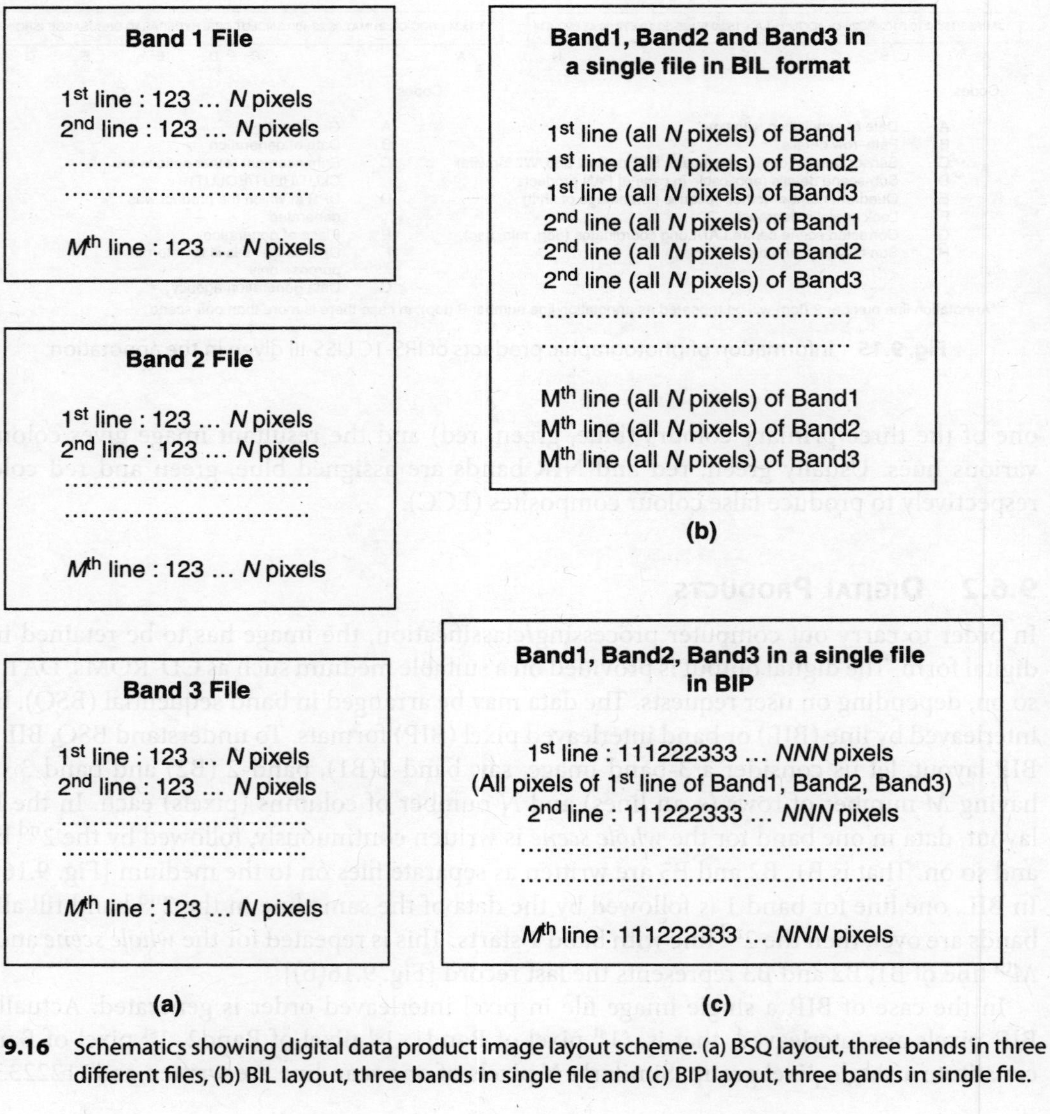

Band 1 File

1st line : 123 … *N* pixels
2nd line : 123 … *N* pixels
……………………………
……………………………
*M*th line : 123 … *N* pixels

Band 2 File

1st line : 123 … *N* pixels
2nd line : 123 … *N* pixels
……………………………
……………………………
*M*th line : 123 … *N* pixels

Band 3 File

1st line : 123 … *N* pixels
2nd line : 123 … *N* pixels
……………………………
……………………………
*M*th line : 123 … *N* pixels

(a)

Band1, Band2 and Band3 in a single file in BIL format

1st line (all *N* pixels) of Band1
1st line (all *N* pixels) of Band2
1st line (all *N* pixels) of Band3
2nd line (all *N* pixels) of Band1
2nd line (all *N* pixels) of Band2
2nd line (all *N* pixels) of Band3
……………………………………
……………………………………
*M*th line (all *N* pixels) of Band1
*M*th line (all *N* pixels) of Band2
*M*th line (all *N* pixels) of Band3

(b)

Band1, Band2, Band3 in a single file in BIP

1st line : 111222333 … *NNN* pixels
(All pixels of 1st line of Band1, Band2, Band3)
2nd line : 111222333 … *NNN* pixels
……………………………………
……………………………………
*M*th line : 111222333 … *NNN* pixels

(c)

Fig. 9.16 Schematics showing digital data product image layout scheme. (a) BSQ layout, three bands in three different files, (b) BIL layout, three bands in single file and (c) BIP layout, three bands in single file.

Super Structure Format

This is a very exhaustive data products format suitable for Level-0 (RAW, that is, no correction applied), Level-1(RAD, that is, Radiometric Correction Applied) and Level-2 (GEO, that is, both Radiometric and Geometric correction applied) products. Though all categories of products can be supplied in this format, Level-0 and Level-1 are the most preferred.

Super structure digital data file format consists of five files namely,

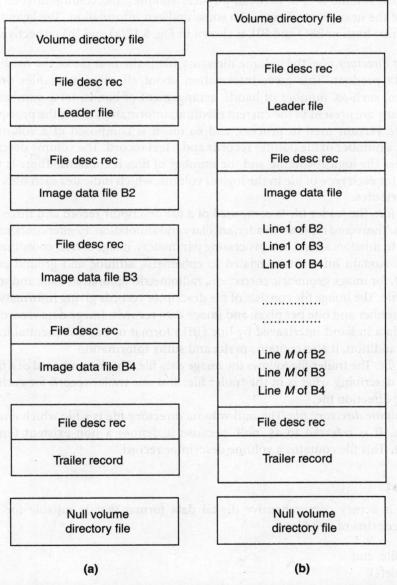

Fig. 9.17   (a) Physical layout of three band image data (for example, IRS-1C/1D LISS-3 B2, B3, B4) in the super structure BSQ. (b) Super structure in BIL format. File desc rec file descriptor record.

  (i)   volume directory file,
  (ii)   leader file,
 (iii)   image file (either in BSQ or BIL) format,
 (iv)   trailer file, and
  (v)   null volume directory file.

A logical volume is a logical collection of one or more files recorded consecutively. All logical volumes have a volume directory as the first file and null volume directory as the last file. When a logical volume is split between physical volumes, the volume directory is repeated at the start of the next physical tape with some updated information. The layout of the super structure format both in BSQ and BIL is shown in Fig. 9.17(a) and (b) respectively.

  (i)   *Volume directory file*: The volume directory file is the first file of the media containing the data product. This gives information about all subsequent files present in the medium, such as, number of bands, arrangement of bands, total number of files and how many are present in the current medium, information about the processing station, software version used to process, and so on. It is composed of a volume descriptor record, a number of file pointer records and a text record. The volume descriptor record identifies the logical volume and the number of files it contains. There is a file pointer record for each type of file in the logical volume, which indicates each file's class, format and attributes.

  (ii)   *Leader file*: The leader file is composed of a file descriptor record and three types of data records. The record types are header, ancillary and annotation. Header contains information related to mission: sensor and processing parameters, image corner coordinates. Ancillary records contain information related to ephemeris, attitude and ground control points (GCPs), for image geometric correction, radiometric calibration data, and so on.

 (iii)   *Image file*: The image file consists of file descriptor records giving information regarding band number and bite per pixel, and image data records. Image data record contains the video data in band interleaved by line (BIL) format or band sequential format (BSQ), and in addition, it also contains prefix and suffix information.

 (iv)   *Trailer file*: The trailer file follows the image data file. This is composed of a file descriptor record describing what is in the trailer file, and one trailer record for each band in the volume direction file.

  (v)   *Null volume directory file*: The null volume directory file is a file which ends the logical volume. It is referred to as 'null' because it defines a non-existent (empty) logical volume. This file contains a volume descriptor record.

Fast Format

Fast format is a very comprehensive digital data format that is suitable for Level-2 data products. It consists of two files:

  (i)   header file, and
  (ii)   image file(s).

The physical layout of fast format is shown in Fig. 9.18.

(i) *Header file*: The first file on each volume, a Read-Me-First file, contains header data. It is in American Standard Code for Information Interchange (ASCII) format.

The header file contains three 1536-byte ASCII records. The first record is the **Administrative Record** which contains information that identifies the product, the scene and the data specifically needed to read the imagery from the digital media (CDROM, DAT or DISK). In order to retrieve the image data, it is necessary to read entries in the Administrative Record.

The second record is the **Radiometric Record**, which contains the coefficients needed to convert the scene digital values into at-satellite spectral radiance.

The third record is the **Geometric Record** which contains the scene geographic location (for example, latitude, longitude and so on) information. In order to align the imagery to other data sources, it will be necessary to read entries in the Geometric Record.

(ii) *Image files*: Image files are written into CDROM, DAT or DISK in Band Sequential (BSQ) order, that is, each image file contains one band of image data. There are no header records within the image file, nor are there prefix and/or suffix data in the individual image record or scan lines.

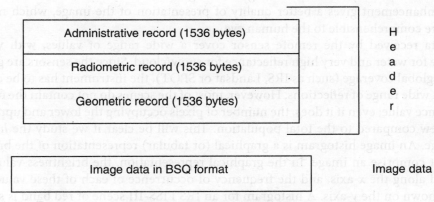

Fig. 9.18 Fast format physical layout.

GeoTIFF (Geographic Tagged Image File Format)

Although currently various data formats (PGM, GIF, BMP, TIFF) are in use for storage of raster image data, they have a common limitation in cartographic applications. The main problem is that, it is almost impossible to store any geographic information together with image data in a unified and well-defined way in the above mentioned formats.

GeoTIFF is based on the original TIFF (Tagged Image File Format) format, with additional geographic information. The GeoTIFF specification defines a set of TIFF tags provided to describe all 'cartographic' information associated with TIFF imagery that originates from satellite imaging systems, scanned aerial photography, scanned maps, or as a result of geographic analysis. Its aim is to allow for tying a image to a known model space or map projection. This is a platform-independent format which is used by a wide range of GIS (Geographical Information System) and Image Processing Packages currently available in the market.

IRS-1C/1D data products are supplied in the GeoTIFF format in CDROM. The map projection information along with the geographic tie points (latitude/longitude) that are embedded in the image files in GeoTIFF format makes it user friendly and hence widely accepted among user community.

The details of GeoTIFF format can be obtained from *http://geotiff.maptools.org/faq.html*

9.7 SPECIAL PROCESSING

Certain manipulations can be performed on the digital data in order to have better visual presentation or for information extraction. Some of the commonly used image manipulation techniques are given below.

9.7.1 CONTRAST ENHANCEMENT

Contrast enhancement is an image manipulation technique to make the features contained in an image, stand out more clearly, by optimal use of the full grey scale of the instrument. Such manipulations improve the visual appearance of the objects in the image and enhance visual interpretation capability, thereby making the image easier to analyse and interpret. Thus, contrast enhancement gives a better quality of presentation of the image, which make the image more comprehensible to the human eye.

The data received by the remote sensor cover a wide range of values, with very low reflectance for water and very high reflectance for snow/cloud. Since the sensors are generally meant for global coverage (such as IRS, Landsat or SPOT), the instrument has to be designed to accept a wide range of reflections. However, most of the scenes do not contain the full range of reflectance value; even if it does, the number of pixels occupying the lower and upper range are very few compared to the total population. This will be clear if we study the *histogram* of an image. An image histogram is a graphical (or tabular) representation of the brightness values that comprise an image. In the graphical representation, the brightness values (DN) are plotted along the *x*-axis, and the frequency of occurrence of each of these values in the image is shown on the *y*-axis. A histogram for an IRS LISS-III scene of red band is shown in Fig. 9.18.

Though the instrument has a capability to cover 0–127 grey values, Fig. 9.19 shows that the grey values are confined to a small region between 20 and 60. In contrast enhancement, the DN values are manipulated to occupy the full range (though LISS data is 7 bit, the display and photowrite systems use a 0–255 range, the enhancement is carried out to cover this range). The DN value corresponding to each pixel in the image is assigned a new value, based on the type of enhancement. The process of changing the original data numbers to new values is called mapping. A mathematical description of the mapping is called a *mapping function*. The type of enhancement can be broadly classified into two categories:

  (i) linear contrast enhancement, and
 (ii) non-linear contrast enhancement.

In *linear contrast enhancement* (also called linear stretching), the original DN values are modified to the full range of possible DN values.

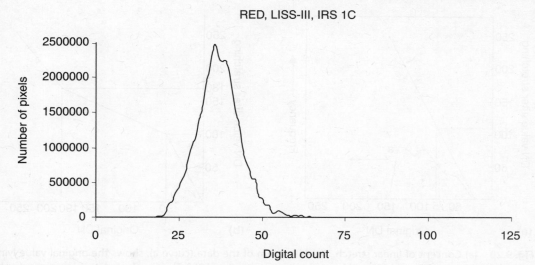

Fig. 9.19 Histogram of the IRS-1C LISS-III raw data for the red band. Note that all the data are confined to a small range between 20 and 60 DN values.

To do this, first we find out the histogram of the original data. Let the data lie between n_1 and n_2 and if 0 to 255 is the dynamic range of the output device, then the histogram is modified such that the values lying between n_1 and n_2 occupy the range between 0–255.

The transformation equation is

$$N_{out} = \frac{(N - n_1)}{(n_2 - n_1)} 255$$

where N_{out} is the transformed DN value and N, the original DN value [Fig. 9.20(a)]. There are a number of other possible variants of the linear contrast enhancement. If the information content at the low and high end is not much, instead of transforming the whole data from 0–255, we may stretch only those lying between an upper and lower threshold level. That is, all pixel values below the lower threshold is forced to zero and all pixel values above the higher threshold is forced to 255. In this case, the slope of the linear contrast is very much increased compared to a simple min–max stretch. When the histogram of an image has multiple modes or not Gaussian, it is preferable to have piecewise linear contrast stretch to the imagery [Fig. 9.20(b)]. Here each mode can be expanded independently and hence the slope of the linear contrast enhancement changes within the dynamic range. Figure 9.20(c) shows a practical example of linear stretch of IRS-1C PAN data.

Apart from linear contrast stretching, various types of *non-linear contrast enhancement* are also used. For example, contrast enhancement can be achieved by modification of the histogram of the DN values. One of the commonly used technique is histogram equalisation; that is, the original histogram will be redistributed to produce a uniform population density of pixels. Here one attempts to match the original cumulative histogram F_{C1} to a new cumulative histogram F_{C2} (Fig. 9.21). Here more DN values are assigned to the frequently occurring portions of the histogram.

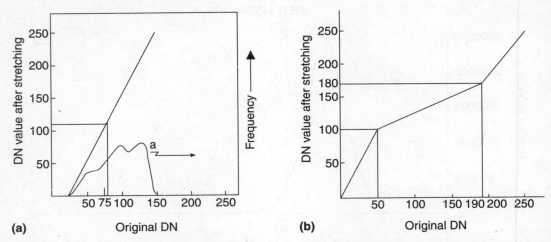

Fig. 9.20 (a) Concept of linear stretch. The histogram of the data (curve a), shows the original value lying between 25 and 150, transformed to lie between 0 and 250. The transfer function is represented by the straight line. The modified DN value for the original DN value *N* is (*N* – 25) 250/125. Thus DN 5 25 will be zero, while 75 will be transformed to 100. (b) Concept of piece-wise linear stretch. The three regions, namely, 0–50, 50–190, 190–250 have different transfer functions.

Fig. 9.20(c) IRS-1C PAN over Ahmedabad region. (i) Original (ii) After linear stretching.

This redistribution reduces the contrast in the very light (higher DN value) and dark (lower DN value) of the image and the maximum contrast enhancement happens to the most populated range of the brightness (DN) values in the image. On the other hand, if contrast at the tail of the distribution has to be emphasised, then the Gaussian stretch technique can be used wherein the histogram is made to fit a Gaussian distribution. There are other transfer functions possible (such as cube root and logarithmic). to enhance the features, each having its own advantages and limitations (Frei, 1977; Maul and Qualset, 1974; Gillispe et. al., 1986).

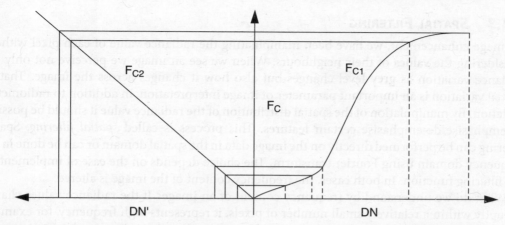

Fig. 9.21 Schematics showing histogram equalisation. F_{C1} is the original cumulative histogram. F_{C2} is the transformed new cumulative histogram. F_{C1} is equally partitioned so that each piece will correspond to one digital number in the equalised image. (Adapted from University of California, Berkeley Website Section 6.1)

What we considered hitherto was to apply the same technique throughout the image. However, when the scene has significantly varying features (like a coastal region), a more optimum enhancement can be achieved by using an adaptive algorithm, whose parameters change from pixel to pixel according to the local image contrast (Fahnestock and Schowengerdt, 1983).

Bear in mind that the type of enhancement used is dependent on the scene and the image analyst's interest for a specific feature, since contrast enhancement is applied primarily to improve or enhance the visual image analysis. Highlighting one feature could be at the cost of another feature and hence different techniques may be experimented with before choosing the right one for the study. It is rather evident that contrast enhancement only increases the detectability of a feature for visual observation and does not increase the information content.

9.7.2 ENHANCEMENT BY COLOUR CODING

The human visual system can discriminate between about 20 shades of grey under a given adaptation condition. Under the same condition, it is able to discriminate a much larger number of colour hues (Moik, 1980). Small gray scale differences in a black and white image that cannot be distinguished by the eye, if mapped into different colours, can provide more information to a visual interpreter (this should not be confused with colour images composed with different spectral bands wherein the information extraction is enhanced due to the reflectance (or DN value) difference in each band, depending on the surface characteristics). A single band black and white image can be converted to a colour image by certain pseudocolour transformations. One simple technique is by density slicing. Here the grey levels in the image are converted to a series of grey level (density) intervals, or slices, each corresponding to a specified grey level range. Each sliced range can then be assigned a separate colour. This is used extensively for the display of thermal IR images in order to highlight temperature differences and is usually carried out by suitable look up tables (LUT). The data is stored as a one dimensional array of integers, wherein for each original DN value, a new value (here colour) is given.

9.7.3 Spatial Filtering

In image enhancement, we have been manipulating the radiance value of each pixel without considering the values of their neighbours. When we see an image we perceive not only the radiance variation as grey level changes but also how it changes across the image. That is, spatial variation is an important parameter of image interpretation, in addition to radiometric variation. By manipulation of the spatial distribution of the radiance value it should be possible to emphasise/de-emphasise certain features. This process is called *spatial filtering*. Spatial filtering can be performed directly on the image data in the spatial domain or can be done in the frequency domain using Fourier transform. The choice depends on the ease of implementing the filtering function. In both cases, the frequency content of the image is altered.

What do we understand by frequency content of an image? If the radiance values change abruptly within a relatively small number of pixels, it represents high frequency, for example, roads, field boundaries, coast line and so on. However, when the radiance value changes very slowly over a large part of the image, the area has predominantly low frequency content. Images with mainly low frequency components will appear 'smooth', for example, large monocropped agriculture fields, large water bodies, snow cover area and so on. In tune with electrical engineering, the filtering techniques applied are high pass filters, which emphasise the high frequency component thus sharpening the edge; low pass filters, which suppress the high frequency component thereby 'smoothing' the image and notch filter, wherein a band of frequency can be eliminated, as in the case of elimination of certain coherent noise. The implementation of spatial filtering can be conceived as a process of modifying the grey value of a pixel on the basis of the grey levels of the neighbouring pixels. The relative weightage given to the pixel grey level values will depend on the type of filtering function to be established. In the spatial domain, this is achieved by first establishing a window of an $N \times N$ array containing the weighting functions. The array called operator or (kernel) is usually a matrix of an odd number of pixels (3×3, 5×5, and so on). The kernel is then convoluted with the image to get the filtered output. The convolution is essentially the sum of the products of the elements in the window of the operator and the corresponding image pixel grey level divided by suitable normalising factor. The window is moved along the row and column of the image, one pixel (one line) at a time and the operation is repeated to produce the filtered image.

Low Pass Filter

In the case of a low frequency filter, the operator can have a form given below.

$$
\begin{array}{ccc}
1 & 1 & 1 \\
1 & 1 & 1 \\
1 & 1 & 1
\end{array}
$$

The window is kept on one corner of the image and the convoluted value is calculated. It is divided by 9 (that is the sum of the elements of the mask) to normalise it. In this case, it is simply the average of the nine pixels for the central pixel. The window is moved to the right by one pixel and the process repeated till the window reaches the end of the line. Then the window is stepped to the next line and the process continued till the total image is covered.

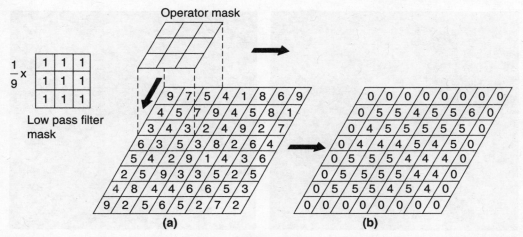

Fig. 9.22 Concept of moving window averaging. (a) Original image; (b) Low pass filtered Image. The difference between the adjacent pixels in the filtered image is much smaller than in the original image.

This is called a *moving average filter* which can be considered as a special case of a general class of filter called *box filters* (McDonnell, 1981). In this case, the signal-to-noise ratio is improved by the window size (3 times in the case considered). Increasing the window size is equivalent to decreasing the band width of the filter. Figure 9.22 gives a worked out example of low pass filtering.

Since the low pass filter suppresses the high frequency component, it blurs the image, that is, sharpness of the edges is lost, though it reduces the noise (Fig. 9.23). Blurring becomes more pronounced as the window size increases because more of the high frequency component is removed. Thus though low pass filtering is a good technique to reduce noise, it also reduces the sharpness of the image. There are techniques to reduce noise without blurring the image (Chin and Yeh, 1983; Wang et. al., 1983). They are sometimes referred to as edge preserving smoothing methods. Instead of having the same operator function throughout the image, it is possible to have the weights of the operator calculated for each window position, based on the mean and variance of the grey level of the area of the image underlying the window. This is called an *adaptive filter* and has been used successfully to remove the speckle noise in SAR imagery (Lee, 1981; Frost et. al., 1982).

High Pass Filter

In this case, higher frequency components are retained, while suppressing the lower frequencies. High frequency filtered images show sharper edges. A simple procedure to implement high pass filtering is to subtract the low pass filtered image from the original image. The resulting image (or a part of it) can be added to the original image thus effectively increasing the high frequency content. This can be represented as (Mather, 1987):

$$N_H = N - fN_L + C$$

where N is the original DN value, N_H and N_L are the high pass and low pass filtered DN values, f is a fraction less than 1 and C is a constant to ensure N_H is always positive. Another

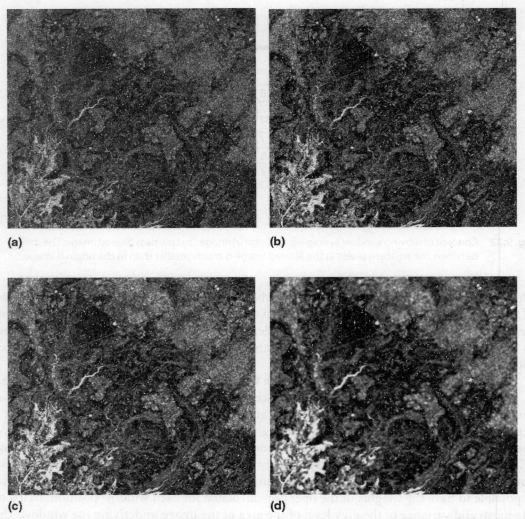

Fig. 9.23 (a) The imagery generated by the shuttle imaging Radar in the X band over Bhavnagar, Gujarat State. (b) After applying low pass filter of 3 × 3 window. (c) After applying low pass filter of 5 × 5 window. (d) After applying low pass filter of 9 × 9 window. As the window size increases there is a general noise (speckle) reduction. However, sharpness of linear features is reduced.

way to implement it is to have a moving window operator (as in the case of low pass filter), with positive weight for central pixels, and negative weight for surrounding pixels. One such possible operator is

$$
\begin{matrix}
-1 & -1 & -1 \\
-1 & 9 & -1 \\
-1 & -1 & -1
\end{matrix}
$$

Since such an operator can give negative values as well, the output data should be suitably stretched to all positive grey levels before display. In this case as the window size increases, more higher frequency components are retained (Schowengerdt, 1997). Figure 9.24 shows a practical example using IRS-1C PAN data.

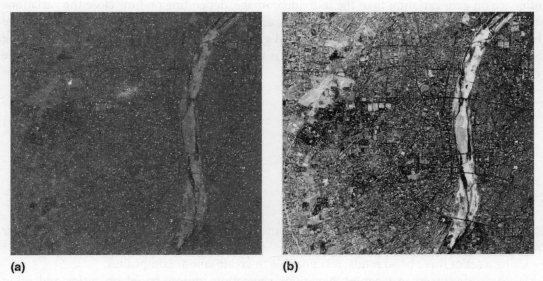

(a)   **(b)**

Fig. 9.24   IRS–1C PAN image over Ahmedabad. (a) Original (b) After high pass filter.

The grey level profile of an ideal edge is a step function. This does not happen in practice due to the point spread function of the sensor, image motion and so on, and the grey level gradually changes such that grey level of the edge of an object is reduced and that of its neighbouring background is increased, thereby reducing the contrast at the edge. The edge enhancement technique is used to increase the grey level difference between the edge pixel of the object and its neighbouring background. As mentioned earlier, high pass filter acts as an edge enhancement filter.

Though high pass filtering sharpens the edges, it also enhances the noise and produce a 'rough' appearance. A compromise filter called a *high frequency emphasise* (HFE) filter has been proposed, wherein the low frequency is unchanged and exaggerates the high frequency (Duda and Hart, 1973). In many applications, it is useful to detect the edges and provide a map of them. For example, a lineament map in geological studies. Edge detection is the process of identifying a picture element which has the likelihood of an 'edge element'. Details of various edge detection algorithms can be found from Davis (1975), Peli and Malah (1982).

9.7.4   IMAGE TRANSFORMS

Till now we have been considering various manipulations which can be carried on a single band imagery. In image transformation, two or more images from a multi-spectral or multi-temporal image of the same area is manipulated to generate a 'new' image. The transformed image may bring out features not discernable in the original images or preserve the features of the original images in reduced dimensions. The simplest form of image transformation is ratio imaging. The ratio of two bands can eliminate any multiplication error (gain variation) which are identical in both bands—for example, solar illumination angle variation with terrain relief change. Even if the gain variations are not identical in both bands, the ratio image shows lesser influence on gain variation than the individual image, depending on how close the variations are in the two bands. If there are three bands, and all the three bands have identical additive (bias) and multiplication errors, both bias and gain errors can be removed by computing the ratio of difference between the three bands. If ρ and R are the measured and actual reflectance respectively

$$R_1 = a + b\rho_1$$

$$R_2 = a + b\rho_2$$

$$R_3 = a + b\rho_3$$

$$\frac{R_1 - R_2}{R_1 - R_3} = \frac{\rho_1 - \rho_2}{\rho_1 - \rho_3} = \frac{1 - \rho_2/\rho_1}{1 - \rho_3/\rho_1}$$

Ratio image also helps in certain cases to enhance the spectral signature differences, if proper bands are chosen, like the vegetation indices.

Using a set of three band ratios, it is possible to create colour composites.

We have discussed in Chapter 4, various vegetation indices based on ratios and other transforms which are useful in vegetation studies. There are a number of other transforms of general interest. We shall discuss in detail one of them—principal component transform.

Principal Component Transforms

Multi-spectral images often exhibit a high correlation between the spectral bands. When two data sets are perfectly correlated, then the same information content in one set is available in the other set and hence the second data set becomes redundant. Thus if there are n correlated spectral bands, the PC transformation tries to reduce such redundancy in multi-spectral data. That is, to transform all the information contained in n data sets into a fewer than n new sets of data and use this transformed data sets in lieu of the original n sets for analysis/classification and so on.

Let us consider the reflectance in spectral bands λ_1 and λ_2 and plotted along the x and y axis. This is called a two dimensional feature space. Figure 9.24 shows the schematics of such a plot, wherein most of the information is contained along the line AB. Though there are two spectral bands, we say that the dimensionality of the data sets is one, since most of the variance is along only one direction. The dimensionality of LANDSAT 4 band MSS is only two. A worked out example to carry out the PC transformation is given in Jensen (1986). The concept can be explained for a two dimensional feature space (Fig. 9.25).

(i) The coordinate system can be rotated such that one axis lies along the maximum variance AB in Fig. 9.25. This new axis is called the principal component (PC1).

(ii) If m_1 and m_2 are the means of the two bands in the xy coordinates, a second axis through (m_1, m_2) perpendicular to PC1 gives the second principal component (PC2). The variance

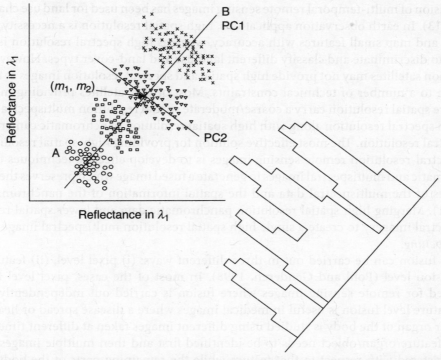

Fig. 9.25 Concept of a principal component transform. The histogram shown is for PCI. All the five classes are separated in the histogram.

in PC2 will be less than PC1. The original values (x,y) can now be projected to the new set of axes PC1 and PC2.

(iii) When you have n bands, we have PC3, PC4 … , each component having monotonically decreasing amount of variance. The sum of the variances of the transformed PCs is the same as the sum of the variances in the original band. But the variances of the transformed PCs are ordered such that each PC has variance less than the previous bands.

9.7.5 IMAGE FUSION

Image fusion refers to the process of combining two or more images of the same scene captured at different spatial or spectral resolutions/ranges or at different time periods to form a new image through some mathematical procedure. The resulting image will provide more information than any one of the input images alone. Image fusion has a wide range of applications in various fields such as military, medical imaging, security and surveillance. Remote sensing satellites provide data covering different portions of the electromagnetic spectrum at diverse spatial, temporal and spectral resolutions. For many practical real-life problems/applications, information captured in a single imagery from earth observation satellites is always not adequate. Therefore, combining complimentary/supplementary information enhances the utilisation of the data. Thus combining optical and SAR data gives more information which are not available from analysing the data separately (Hong et. al.,

2009). Fusion of multi-temporal remote sensing images has been used for land use change (Du et. al., 2013). In earth observation applications, high spatial resolution is a necessity in order to detect and map small features with accuracy, whereas high spectral resolution is needed in order to discriminate and classify different land use and land-cover types. However, earth observation satellites may not provide high spatial and spectral resolution images at the same time, due to a number of technical constraints. Most of the satellites providing metre and sub-metre spatial resolution carry a coarse/moderate spatial resolution multispectral camera with high spectral resolution along with high spatial resolution panchromatic camera having low spectral resolution. The most effective solution for providing high-spatial resolution and high spectral-resolution remote sensing images is to develop effective techniques to merge panchromatic and multispectral images to generate a fused image which preserves the spectral properties of the multispectral data and the spatial information of the panchromatic data (Plate 9.1). Merging high spatial resolution panchromatic data and lower spatial resolution multispectral imagery to create a single high spatial resolution multispectral image is called *pan sharpening*.

Image fusion can be carried out in three different ways: (i) pixel level, (ii) feature level, (iii) decision level (Pohl and Genderen, 1998). In most of the cases, pixel level fusion is considered for remote sensing images where fusion is carried out independently at each pixel. Feature level fusion is useful in medical images where a disease spread or healing at a particular organ of the body is studied using different images taken at different time periods where a feature/organ/object needs to be identified first and then multiple images need to be co-registered with respect to that feature while the remaining parts of the body are not highlighted. In decision level based fusion, information from each of the input images is extracted separately, and then combined together through decision rules for coherent interpretation and to establish correct/better understanding of the observed objects (Shen, 1990; Pohl and Genderen, 1998), and such methods would be useful for robotic applications. In this section we will only focus on pixel based image fusion as it is widely used in many remote sensing applications. Since a number of applications need both high spectral and high spatial resolution, many studies have paid attention towards generating pan sharpened multispectral imagery using diverse techniques. We shall now discuss details of some of the techniques used for generating pan sharpened imagery by fusing panchromatic data and lower resolution multispectral data.

One of the early efforts of image fusion techniques was to combine Landsat RBV and MSS data for land cover mapping (Lauer and Todd, 1981). The SPOT-1 satellite launched in 1986 generated for the first time multi-resolution imagery from the same instrument— multispectral imagery with 20 m spatial resolution and panchromatic imagery covering a broad spectral region with 10 m resolution. Since then a number of satellites have been flown which can generate high spectral resolution multispectral data along with high spatial resolution broad band panchromatic data from the same instrument. As discussed earlier, panchromatic image (PAN) reveals high geometric/spatial details but their spectral bandwidth is coarse and hence, though objects were detected they could not be differentiated spectrally (that is, different features had similar grey shades or same feature had diverse shades). On the other hand multispectral bands (MS) with narrow spectral bandwidth provide differentiable colour details about various land cover features but not accurate geometric details. Therefore, if MS and PAN images are combined, it is possible to get geometric details (spatial) from PAN and colour details (spectral) from MS together. Thus pan sharpened image increases the spatial resolution of multispectral images, ideally without distorting the spectral information of original MS data.

For a data fusion model to be successful, the merged product should preserve the high spatial resolution information of the panchromatic data while retaining the spectral information of the original multispectral data. There are many different methods employing pixel level fusion— Intensity Hue Saturation (IHS), Principal Component Analysis (PCA), Brovey transform (BT), Intensity Modulation (low pass and high pass), Synthetic Variable Ratio (SVR), Ratio Enhancement (RE), pyramid based, wavelet, curvelet and many more (Toet, 1989; Carper et. al., 1990; Chavez et. al., 1991; Yocky 1996; Liu, 2000; Barron et. al., 2009). According to their efficiency of implementation, IHS, PCA and BT are the most commonly used algorithms by the remote sensing community (Tu et. al., 2001). We shall see a few of these techniques in this section. In remote sensing image fusion, it is mandatory that the input images are radiometerically and geometrically corrected and the low-resolution multispectral image is resampled to match the ground sample interval of the higher resolution PAN image. The higher resolution PAN image is used as the reference, to which the lower resolution MS image is geometrically registered (Section 10.2.2).

9.7.5.1 IHS Based Fusion

IHS is the short form for *Intensity Hue Saturation* and it is also referred to as HSI. The term *intensity* refers to brightness (shades of grey: black to white shades); *hue* refers to the dominant colour (in other words it refers to the visible range wavelength at which the energy output from the pixel is dominant); and *saturation* refers to purity of the colour (whether light shade or dark shade of the colour) (Gillespie et. al., 1986; Carper et. al., 1990) (Fig. 9.26; detailed explanation is given in the box on p. 347).

In remote sensing, the false colour composite (FCC) is made using any three of the available bands, and substituting those bands to each of the display guns (red, green and blue). This produces different colour combinations. If the input bands are less correlated, then separability of the feature will be better. If there are more than three bands available, at first we need to select 3 bands which are optimal for information extraction or visualisation. For this purpose, Optimum Index Factor (OIF), which weighs band combination on the basis of histogram distribution (quantified in terms of standard deviation) and correlation (quantified in terms of correlation coefficient), that is, the wider the distribution more the information and the lesser the correlation more the information (refer Section 10.2.1), is calculated for each of the possible 3-band combinations from the given list of bands. Once a particular set of three bands is chosen, then these bands are transformed from the RGB space into the IHS space. There are a number of algorithms available to carry out this transform; one of the methods is shown in the accompanying box. The IHS transform helps to separate spatial and spectral details from a given RGB image and human vision related to colour perception operates in a similar fashion as the IHS space (Pohl and Genderen, 1998). The IHS transformation results in three new bands representing *I, H, S*. The PAN band is assigned the intensity information. The PAN data, in some cases, is contrast stretched so that it has approximately the same variance and average as the intensity component

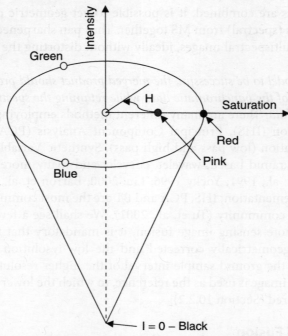

Fig. 9.26 HIS colour model. The vertical axis specifies the intensity of the beam, from black at the bottom through grey to some maximum value at the top corresponding to the brightest possible white and is measured in per cent from black (0) to white (100). The points on the circumference denote different hue (saturated). The hue (H) of the point is determined by an angle from some reference point usually red (that is, for red hue is zero) and the hue increases counter clockwise from red. The primary colors are separated by 120°. Saturation is the radial distance from the vertical axis measured in per cent from the centre of the cone (0) to the surface (100).

data (Chavez et. al., 1991). The stretched, higher spatial resolution PAN data replaces the intensity component of the transformed IHS space and H and S are kept the same. Finally, the new set of I, H, S bands are transformed back into the RGB space. There are a number of algorithms to convert RGB to IHS and vice versa. Readers interested in the details may refer to Gonzalez and Woods (2008). Now the final RGB image is the PAN sharpened image which would reveal enhanced spatial details along with spectral information. Figure 9.27 provides operational steps involved in the IHS based fusion. The fused image provides geometric (spatial) details of the PAN image, but introduces some colour distortion because of the low correlation between the PAN image and the intensity component. A high correlation is possible only if the bandwidth of the PAN image covers the entire range of bandwidths of all the MS original bands (El-Samie et. al., 2013). Unlike the PAN images of SPOT and IRS sensors, IKONOS and QuickBird PAN images cover wavelengths from the visible to near-infrared (NIR) which is not covered in their MS data. Therefore, when IHS-like fusion methods are used with IKONOS or QuickBird imagery, there is a significant colour distortion, due primarily to the difference in the range of wavelengths in an IKONOS or QuickBird covered in MS and PAN Image (El-Mezouar et. al., 2010).

IHS Colour Model

We have seen in Chapter 6 that any colour can be generated by adding different proportions of the three primary colours—Red (R), Green (G) and Blue (B). However the RGB model does not describe all the properties of a colour. When we view a coloured object we do not ascribe the percentage of different primary colours present instead we describe it by its hue (H), saturation (S) and brightness—intensity (I). We shall now try to understand each of these terms.

When we analyse the spectral content from an object it is never a single wavelength, instead it contains energy over a band of wavelengths. *Hue* is the wavelength within the visible light spectrum at which the energy output from the object under consideration is greatest. Hue represents the dominant colour as perceived by an observer. Thus, when we call an object red, blue or green, we are specifying its hue.

Saturation is the relative purity or the amount of white light mixed with a hue. The concept can be understood by referring to the accompanying figure, which gives a plot of the spectral response of a pixel with respect to wavelength. Here all the three curves have maximum response at the same wavelength—same hue. However, curve 1 has the narrowest response compared to the other two curves. Curve 3 is the broadest indicating that it has maximum contribution from wavelengths outside the peak wavelength. In the example shown, curve 3 represents a colour with low saturation and curve 1 represents a colour with fairly high saturation compared to the other two. Thus, saturation

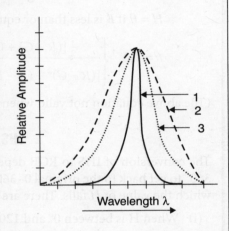

is related to the width of the plot of intensity vs wavelength as described above. As saturation increases, colours appear more 'pure'. As saturation decreases, colours appear more 'washed-out'.

Intensity (brightness value) is an attribute of visual perception in which a source appears to emit a given amount of light. The intensity is related to the 'strength' of the light beam (http://whatis.techtarget.com/definition/hue-saturation-and-brightness). There are a number of ways in which HIS model can be represented. Figure 9.26 gives the *cone representation* of IHS. The HIS colour model decouples the intensity component from the colour-carrying information (hue and saturation) in a colour image. As a result, the IHS model is an ideal tool for developing image processing algorithms based on colour descriptions that are natural and intuitive to humans (Gonzalez and Woods, 2008).

RGB to IHS Conversion

There are a number of algorithms to convert RGB to HIS and the reverse. One method given by Gonzalez and Woods, 2008, is discussed. First RGB values are normalised 0 to 1. The intensity I is given by:

$$I = \frac{R + G + B}{3}$$

Now let m be the minimum value among R, G and B. The IHS saturation value of a colour is given by the equation

$$S = 1 - \frac{m}{I} \quad \text{if} \quad I > 0, \text{ or } S = 0 \quad \text{if} \quad I = 0.$$

To convert the hue H, to an angle measure, the following equations are used:

$H = \theta$ if B is less than or equal to G; if B is $> G$, $H = 360 - \theta$

$$\theta = \cos^{-1}\left\{ \frac{\frac{1}{2}[(R-G) + (R-B)]}{[(R-G)^2 + (R-B)(G-B)]^{\frac{1}{2}}} \right\}$$

(The above equation not valid when $R = G = B$.)

IHS to RGB Conversion

The conversion of IHS to RGB depends on the value of H. First the hue is multiplied by 360° to get back to the original 0–360 range. The conversion value depends on the range in which the value of H falls. There are three cases.

(i) When H is between 0° and 120° (R–G sector)

$$B = I(1 - S)$$

$$G = 3I - (R + B)$$

$$R = I\left[1 + \frac{S \cos H}{\cos(60 - H)} \right]$$

(ii) When H is between 120° and 240° (GB region)
First subtract 120 from the H value obtained to get a new H value for this sector. Then,

$$R = I(1 - S)$$

$$G = I\left[1 + \frac{S \cos H}{\cos(60° - H)} \right] \quad B = 3I - (R + G)$$

(iii) When H is between 240° and 360° (BR region)
First subtract 240 from the original H value to get the new H value for the sector. Then,

$$G = I(1 - S)$$

$$B = I\left[1 + \frac{S \cos H}{\cos(60° - H)} \right] \quad R = 3I - (G + B)$$

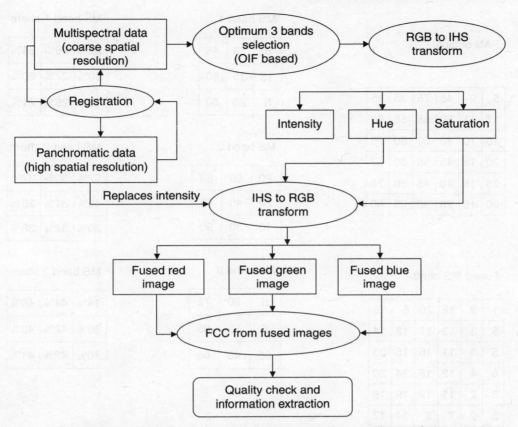

Fig. 9.27 Schematics showing processing steps for HSI-based image fusion.

9.7.5.2 Brovey Transform Based Fusion

Fusion of multiple images is possible using band arithmetic operations. Such arithmetic based fusion techniques are simple to execute and less complex. Brovey is one of the arithmetic based transformation techniques (Vrabel, 1996) in which high resolution information is proportionately shared with each of the low resolution images based on their individual contribution in the spectral profile.

$$\text{fusedimag } e_j = \frac{DN_j}{\Sigma_{i=1}^{n} DN_i} * DN_{\text{pan}} \tag{9.1}$$

where j refers to band number of the low spatial resolution image which is to be converted into high spatial resolution after fusion, *pan* refers to high spatial resolution panchromatic image, n refers to number of low resolution bands in the input. For example, if a pixel in a low resolution band1 has a DN value of 50, and the total sum of DN values from all the bands at that pixel is 238, then the share of band1 is only 21%. Hence 21% of the DN value from PAN is allocated to band1 in the fused image (Eq. 9.1). A simple pixel level example is provided in Fig. 9.28 for easy understanding.

PAN original

5	9	45	75	35	65
17	11	50	65	55	60
15	10	40	60	50	75
20	12	45	55	80	67
25	18	40	45	90	75
30	15	25	30	65	80

MS band 1

10	53	45
15	35	60
5	25	50

MS band 1 share

29%	26%	24%
30%	27%	30%
10%	26%	21%

MS band 2

20	60	69
20	40	55
10	30	90

MS band 2 share

57%	30%	37%
40%	31%	28%
20%	32%	38%

MS band 3

5	90	72
5	55	85
35	40	98

MS band 3 share

14%	44%	40%
30%	42%	43%
70%	42%	41%

Fused MS band 1

1	3	12	20	8	15
5	3	13	17	13	14
5	3	11	16	15	23
6	4	12	15	24	20
3	2	11	12	19	16
3	2	7	8	14	17

Fused MS band 2

3	5	13	22	13	24
10	6	15	19	20	22
6	4	12	18	14	21
8	5	14	17	22	18
5	4	13	14	34	28
6	3	8	9	25	30

Fused MS band 3

1	1	20	33	14	26
2	2	22	29	22	24
5	3	17	25	21	32
6	4	19	23	34	28
18	13	17	19	37	31
21	11	11	13	27	33

Fig. 9.28 Brovey transform based fusion of multispectral (MS) and panchromatic (PAN) images—an implementation example. Pixel 1 of all bands are added (10 + 20 + 5 = 35). Fused MS band 1 share for pixel 1 is 10/35 = 29% of PAN. Since each MS pixel covers 4 pixels in PAN, corresponding PAN values are multiplied by the percentage of share to generate fused MS pixels.

9.7.5.3 Principal Component Based Fusion

The concept of Principal Component Analysis (PCA) has been discussed in Section 9.7.4. PCA helps to transform a correlated multi-variate data set into an uncorrelated reduced data set called *principal components* (PC) which is a linear combination of input variables. In other words PCA extracts information from all the bands and tries to represent them through a few bands. The first three principal components represent nearly 98% of information in the original data. In PCA based fusion, the first component (PC1) is replaced with PAN data, and then inverse PCA is carried out to derive fused images (Chavez et. al., 1991), (Fig. 9.29). Importantly, the PAN data which is used to replace PC1 must be histogram matched with PC1 in order to have similar mean and variance. It is also possible to layer-stack all the images from multiple resolutions together first (that is, both MS and PAN in one single file) and then do PCA and inverse PCA to get fused images (Yesou et. al., 1993). In IHS based fusion only three bands can be used, but in PCA based fusion multiple bands can be used, and hence much more information can be obtained in the latter approach. However, since PCA fusion adopts a statistical procedure it is sensitive to the area to be sharpened and produces fusion results that may vary depending on the selected image subsets (Ehlers et. al., 2010).

Recent years have seen an increase in the number of earth observation systems, especially operating in the metre and sub-metre class spatial resolution, capable of providing concurrently low spatial resolution multispectral data along with high spatial resolution panchromatic data. Because of the spurt of such data, pan sharpening is receiving a lot of attention from the remote sensing community. What is discussed here is intended to provide the fundamental aspects of image fusion commonly used in remote sensing applications. However, note that this is an active research area wherein many advanced techniques have been developed in the recent past to further improve spatial and spectral qualities of the final fused image. Some of these advanced techniques include the Ehlers fusion approach based on an IHS transform coupled with a selective Fourier domain filtering (Klonus and Ehlers, 2007); Gram-Schmidt spectral merging approach (Maurer, 2013); wavelet-based methods (Otazu et. al., 2005).

9.7.5.4 Quality Evaluation

Ideally the fused PAN sharpened image is expected to have a higher resolution (sharper edges) compared to the original colour image without additional changes to the spectral data. However, during the process of merging MS and PAN images, fusion algorithm may introduce spectral distortion and spatial distortion which affect the quality of the fused image. Assessing the quality of the fused image is important before using them for remote sensing applications. In pan sharpening, the end user is interested in assessing the preservation of spectral characteristics and the improvement of spatial resolution. Different quality metrics have been evolved to assess the fusion technique that gives best spatial and spectral information in the fused image. Image fusion quality evaluation approaches can be considered based on two main categories:

(i) Qualitative approaches, which involve visual comparison of the tonal details between original multispectral (MS) and fused images, and the spatial detail between original pan and fused images by an experienced photo interpreter.

(ii) Quantitative approaches, which involve a set of predefined quality indicators for measuring the spectral and spatial similarities between the fused image and the original MS and/or pan images.

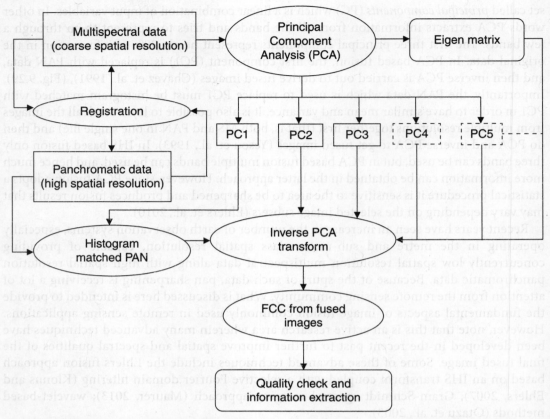

Fig. 9.29 The schematics showing the processing steps to carry out image fusion based on PCA.

In the qualitative approach, human observers with expertise are asked to view a series of fused images and rate them. Although the subjective tests are generally accurate, qualitative approach is likely to contain subjective factors and may be influenced by personal experience. In addition they are inconvenient, expensive and time consuming (Blum and Liu, 2005). Therefore quantitative approaches are often required to prove the efficacy of the fusion technique adopted. Objective image quality assessment helps to quantitatively compare the effectiveness of different fusion algorithms—which fusion procedure maximally preserves the spectral and spatial information of the original multispectral and PAN data in the fused image. For quantitative evaluation of the quality of fused image, a number of statistical methods have been introduced by different researchers. Statistical evaluation procedures have the advantage that they are objective, quantitative and repeatable.

Quantitative analysis is carried out by two approaches—comparing with a reference image and without a reference image. Generally, it is not possible to get an ideal reference image at fused resolution. Some statistical criteria have been used to compare the fused image with original data without the help of a reference image. One example is the use of the histograms (Garguet-Duport et. al., 1996). The principle behind this approach is that the histograms of the original multispectral and the fused product should be similar. The standard deviation gives information about the spread of the histogram. For comparison, the change in the standard deviation of the distribution is considered in addition to the shift in the mean. A combination of these two metrics quantifies the changes in the histogram of each band. Thus, the comparison of histograms is a fairly good estimator of image quality, and is easy to handle (Thomas and Wald, 2005). It is reasonable to assume that the mean and standard deviation (SD) of the histogram of the original and fused image will be very close if the spectral distortion is minimal. Wald (2002) expressed this as RMS Error (RMSE) to compare the standard deviation and mean of the histogram of the fused and original multispectral data (as given below).

$$\text{RMSE} = \sqrt{\text{bias}^2 + \sigma^2}$$

where $\quad \sigma = S_o - S_f$

$$bias = X_o - X_f$$

S is the standard deviation and X is the mean; o and f refer to the original and fused image.

Since a reference image of the same resolution as that of the fused image is generally not available, one has to synthetically generate a reference image so that the fused multispectral image can be compared statistically with the reference image to generate quality metrics. If one is interested only in comparing different fusion algorithms, one technique adopted is to first degrade the original PAN and MS images to an inferior spatial resolution level by the ratio of the spatial resolution of the pan and MS images. For example, if one is using SPOT panchromatic (10 m) and multispectral (20 m), the PAN data is resampled to 20 m and MS to 40 m. These lower resolution data are used for fusion and the original MS data is treated as the reference image to compare with the experimental fused results (Thomas and Wald, 2004; Zhang et. al., 2012).

How do we generate a reference image synthetically? One of the common approaches found in literature (Liu, 2000) consists in resampling original MS bands to a higher resolution equivalent to the fused image, and this new resampled image is used as reference. To get best result from comparison, the synthetically produced image should be as identical as possible to an image from a sensor having an inherent higher resolution would have produced. Another approach is to degrade the fused image to the spatial resolution of the original image and compare with original MS data which is taken as reference. There are a number of mathematically defined statistical indicators for quantitative comparison of the reference image and the fused image. One of the commonly used protocols is Root Mean Square Error (RMSE) which is based on the difference between the reference and fused images by directly computing the variation in pixel values. If F_R (x_i,y_j,k) represents the reference MS image of band k, (created by resampling the original MS data to the same resolution as the PAN image) and F_F (x_i, y_j, k) the fused image having $(m.n)$ pixels, the RMSE is expressed as

$$\text{RMSE}(k) = \sqrt{\frac{1}{mn} \sum_{i=1}^{m} \sum_{j=1}^{n} [F_R(x_i, y_j, k) - F_F(x_i, y_j, k)]^2}$$

The combined image is close to the reference image when the RMSE value is zero. RMSE is a good indicator of the spectral quality of the fused image (Zoran, 2009).

Another quality indicator is *mean per pixel deviation*. For this method, it is necessary to degrade the fused image to the spatial resolution of the original image. This image is then subtracted from the original image on a per pixel basis (Klonus and Ehlers, 2009). The absolute values of the subtraction are summed and divided by the pixel count to obtain the average deviation, which when there is no spectral distortion, is ideally zero.

Correlation function can be used to compute the similarity of spectral features between the reference and fused images. The correlation coefficient (CC) quantifies the closeness between the reference image and the fusion result. It ranges from −1 to +1. Coefficients near 1 indicate that the images are highly correlated and similar.

There are a number of quality indicators developed by various researchers. Jagalingam and Hegde (2015) give a compilation of various quality metrics available in the literature. What we have discussed so far was, how to evaluate colour distortion while carrying out fusion between low spatial resolution multispectral data and high resolution panchromatic data. Another important quality parameter is how well the high resolution capability is embedded in the fused image—spatial quality assessment. However, a literature survey shows that most researchers have concentrated on spectral consistency with very little emphasis on spatial improvement.

It is reasonable to assume that the process of pan sharpening of MS data 'injects' high frequency from PAN data to the fused image. Therefore, spatial information unique in panchromatic images should be mostly concentrated in the high frequency domain. Thus the correlation coefficient between the high-pass filtered fusion image and the high-pass filtered panchromatic image can be used as an index of the spatial quality. Another criterion is based on the comparison of edges. In this method, first the edges of the panchromatic and fused image are detected by a suitable operator. The spatial quality is then assessed based on how closely the edge data of the fused image matches with the edge data of the panchromatic image (Yakhdani and Azizi, 2010).

Many studies have compared different fusion techniques (apart from what is discussed in this section) through various quality measures, and interestingly there is no single superior technique which was consistently recommended by all (Wang and Bovic, 2002; Wang et. al., 2005; Karathanassi et. al., 2007; Naidu and Rao, 2008; Kumar and Singh, 2010; Jagalingam and Hegde, 2015). The user should keep in mind that different techniques may be useful for different applications: some demand more detail in colour for interpretation and mapping; some demand higher classification accuracy and some prefer a beautiful fused colour image just for visualisation purposes (Zhang, 2004).

The intention here is to present the basic concepts of some of the representative techniques which are popularly used in PAN sharpening. Readers interested in getting more details may refer to books and review articles such as Alparone, 2015; Stathaki, 2011; Mitchell, 2010; Zoran, 2009; Pohl and Genderen, 1998, and the references therein.

FOR FURTHER READING

1. *Introductory Digital Image Processing* , Jensen J R, Prentice-Hall, NJ 1986.
2. *Remote Sensing Digital Image Analysis*: *An introduction*, Springer, Richards J A and Jia Xiuping, Chapters 2, 4, 5 and 6.
3. *Remote Sensing Models and Methods for Image Processing*, Schowengerdt R A, Academic Press, Chapters 5 and 8.
4. *www.cnr.berkeley.edu/~gong/textbook/*
5. *http://u.cs.biu.ac.il/~nathan/IR_book/Ch3.pdf*
6. *http://www.gdmc.nl/oosterom/PoRSHyperlinked.pdf*
7. *http://www.cs.otago.ac.nz/cosc453/student_tutorials/principal_components.pdf*
8. *http://fusion.isif.org/proceedings/fusion09CD/data/papers/0136.pdf*
9. *http://www.intechopen.com/books/new-advances-in-image-fusion/investigation-of-image-fusion-for-remote-sensing-application*

10 Data Analysis

The data generated by remote sensing sensors have to be interpreted/analysed to generate meaningful information. Since most remote sensing data generates images, we shall discuss the principles involved in image analysis. The primary purpose of image analysis in remote sensing is to derive quantitative information about features observed in the image data collected, such as its type, location, extent (What is it?; Where is it?; How many objects are there?; How much of area has changed since the last N decades/years), and to understand the dynamics of the ground processes in the long run. Interpretation can be carried out visually by a human analyst (as in the case of photographic products) or by using a computer (for digital data). Both techniques draw upon the fundamental concept of human perception. Perception in its very broad sense is the ability to discriminate between different kinds of objects 'seen' by humans. Thus, the way we perceive objects and phenomena is fundamental to image analysis. Seeing is only a visual sensory stimulation (that is, data is generated), but perception is the integrated effect of our 'experience', which translates the data into a 'structured' understanding. Therefore, perception depends on our past learning, the object we see, its surroundings and various characteristics of the objects. For example, if a person who normally uses spectacles for long distance vision, looks without his glasses at a person coming towards him, though the face of the person is not very well defined (due to lack of spectacles), he will still be able to recognise him if that person is familiar to the observer, by his physical appearance, gait or other mannerisms. Thus, human perception takes into account a large amount of information about the object, integrates them (each of which forms a 'key') and makes deductions. For an accurate deduction, the analyst's experience is of paramount importance. In this chapter we shall first discuss the basics of visual interpretation and then discuss some of the computer based data analysis concepts in order to fully exploit the gamut of available satellite data. The satellite data used for analysis is the data products discussed in Chapter 9, which are generated after processing the image which includes radiometric and geometric correction, map projection and so on.

10.1 VISUAL IMAGE ANALYSIS

An image is a record of the features on the ground at the time of data collection. The image can be analysed at different levels of detail—a broad category (of least complexity for identification) could be waterbodies and land cover. Further classes of land can be sectorised by finding out more details of the land surface such as agricultural land, fallow land, and so on. The detail to which an image can be analysed also depends on the scale of the photograph. A photographic interpreter undertakes at least some of the tasks such as detection, recognition and identification, further leading to classification and deduction. Each term mentioned above is subtly different from the other. Let us illustrate this. We may detect the presence of an object from the background. At a better spatial resolution or higher scale, we may recognise this as, say an aircraft. But at a suitable scale of photograph, we may be able to identify the type of aircraft, say, transport, fighter, or others. Classification in a broad sense arranges the targets identified into a systematic orderly manner, in the form of maps, tables or graphs, based on which users can make deductions to meet their goals. For example, the classified image as a land use map may be used by the planner to find out areas suitable for afforestation.

Visual interpretation makes use of the following basic characteristics and their variations:

- tone (colour),
- texture,
- shape,
- size,
- shadow,
- pattern,
- site,
- height, and
- association.

The process of visual interpretation is to associate these characteristics seen on the image with real features or phenomena on the ground. Our eyes can differentiate only about 16–20 grey levels in the black and white photograph, while more than a hundred colours can be distinguished in a colour photograph. Therefore, colour images are preferred over black and white for visual image interpretation. When multispectral data is obtained, the task is to identify the optimal three bands to generate the colour composite. False Colour Composite (FCC) using green, red, and NIR are the most preferred combination for visual interpretation. However, the analyst may initially experiment with different band combinations, ratios and suitable enhancement on sample imagery to assess which is best suitable for his analysis.

Tone is a measure of the intensity of electromagnetic radiation reflected (emitted) by the terrain. Areas of lower reflectance appear as dark grey tones, while higher reflectance areas appear as light tones in a black and white photograph. In a colour photograph, the colour can be associated with relative reflectances in the spectral region. IR colour images (or FCC generated from electro-optical sensors) show vegetation in varying hues of red, since healthy vegetation reflects highest in the NIR (in FCC, NIR data is used as red).

Texture is the frequency of tonal change on the image. The texture gives the 'rough' or 'smooth' appearance of the image. Though both the green grass of pastureland and tree crowns have similar overall tone, tree crowns will appear coarser or rougher compared to green grass. Texture is also dependent on the scale of imagery. A smooth texture may appear coarse at a larger scale.

Size and shape are representations of the geometric arrangements of tone or colour of the pixels. Size of an object in the image depends on the scale. However, for the same scale, the relative size helps interpretation. The shapes of some objects are so distinctive that they are easy to distinguish. For example, both highways and railway lines are linear, but railway lines can be easily distinguished on the basis of its long stretches, with slow curvature and absence of perpendicular crossing as in roads.

Pattern refers to the spatial arrangements of objects. Typically, an orderly repetition of similar tones and textures will produce a distinctive pattern. For example, in urban areas regularly spaced houses separated by streets give a specific distinguishable pattern. Natural occurrences such as lithological patterns, drainage or man-made objects like road networks, have specific patterns which enable their identification.

When stereopairs are available, height can be inferred, which helps in discriminating objects with a third dimension.

Shadows can adversely affect or enhance interpretation capability depending on the situation. Objects within shadows reflect less light and give a dark tone making the identification of objects within the shadow difficult. However, the presence of shadows enhances the photo interpreter's perception of shape and therefore helps in the identification of objects. Geological boundaries and terrain elevation variations are enhanced by shadows, which is especially highlighted in low sun angle photographs.

Site or location and association of a feature with respect to other objects or features helps to narrow down the possible option of classes to which that feature belongs. A very high reflectance feature in the Himalayan valley could be due to snow or cloud, while in Kerala (in south India), you cannot expect to image snow or glaciers and hence very high reflectance in the visible region could be only due to clouds. Clouds can be identified in association with the shadows they cast, if we know the solar elevation.

Of all these characteristics, tone (or colour) in a photograph is the most fundamental image property for visual analysis. All the rest can be considered as spatial arrangements of the tones.

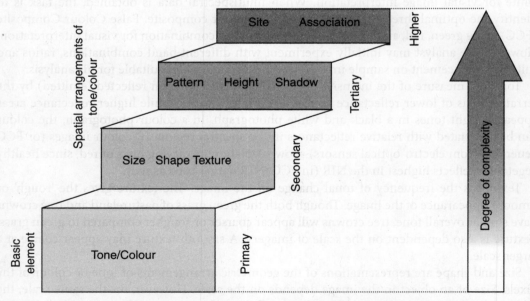

Fig. 10.1 Schematics showing the hierarchal relationship among the basic image characteristics for visual interpretation. The basic characteristics of importance are tone/colour. Spatial arrangements of tone/colour give characteristics of greater complexity.

In almost all cases, it is the difference in tone or colour between objects or between an object and its background that is important. Without such a difference in tone or colour between the background and the edge of an object, there can be no detectable feature. Primary ordering of image elements fundamental to the analysis process (Estes et. al., 1983) is shown in Fig. 10.1.

An image analyst, uses other collateral information along with the photographs to interpret the data. These include information from recorded data (books, reports) laboratory measurements, field survey records and so on. Since visual analysis is carried out by several individuals, it is necessary to lay down guidelines for proper procedure so that there is consistency in the image analysed by various interpreters. Therefore suitable interpretation *keys* are used as guidelines to interpret photographs. The key is organised by giving numerous examples of photographs and supporting text to which interpreter tries to associate the feature observed (selection key). In another form of key (*elimination key*) the 'interpreter' proceeds step by step through a series of choices such as light tone, dark tone, smooth texture, and so on, so that by successive elimination the object is identified. As a generalisation, keys are more reliably used for cultural feature identification (houses, bridges, roads) than for vegetation or land form identification (Lillesand and Kiefer, 1987). As an example, the interpretation key for two different scales are given in Appendix 5.

Temporal changes are important for the image analyst. For example, forest mapping imagery taken during a particular season enhances the discriminability. Therefore, imagery of the correct season is very important.

The level of detail one can infer from an image primarily depends on the scale and hence it is necessary to have list of interpretable classes at different scales (generally referred to as *levels of classification*). Anderson et. al. (1976) have suggested a four level classification system for land use and land cover mapping. Level 1 gives a very broad level classification (1:1 million scale). With an increasing scale of image, a higher level classification is possible. Table 10.1(a) gives level 1 and 2 for the land use and land cover classification system for use with remote sensing data according to Anderson et. al. (1976). Further categorisation of level 3 and level 4 can be made depending on the scale of the image and the details required by the interpreter. An example of level 3 classification of level 2 residential category is also shown in Table 10.1(a). Table 10.1(b) gives the landuse/land cover classification system adopted in India and Table 10.1(c) gives the urban land use/cover classification system for urban agglomeration adopted in India for the preparation of development plans in urban areas. Needless to say, the accuracy of image interpretation depends on the interpreter's understanding of how and why images show shapes, tone, shadow pattern, texture, association of various objects in a terrain, and so on.

The output format generated by various analysts also should be consistent. For example, while making land use maps, one should identify the legends, which gives specific names for a class and mode (colour or symbol) of its representation.

We shall now describe the procedure for generating land use/land cover maps by visual interpretation. The flow chart of activities for carrying out this task is given in Fig. 10.2.

Selection of satellite data is important for proper interpretation. Season(s), product/ format of satellite data is selected on the basis of the objective, scale of mapping and level of details required. For example, two seasons (*Rabi* and *Kharif*) data is required to discriminate scrub land and cropped area in dryland regions and also to provide cropped area statistics and distribution during the year. For small scale (1:250,000) mapping, coarse resolution data (LISS-I with 70 m resolution) is sufficient, but for 1:50,000 scale mapping, LISS-III type data

Table 10.1(a)   Land use and land cover classification system for use with remote sensor data

Level I	Level II	Level III
1. Urban or built-up land	11. Residential	111. Single family units
	12. Commercial and services	112. Multi-family units
	13. Industrial	113. Group quarters
	14. Transportation, communications and utilities	114. Residential hotels
	15. Industrial and commercial complexes	115. Mobile home parks
	16. Mixed urban or built-up land	116. Transient lodgings
	17. Other urban or built-up land	117. Other
2. Agricultural land	21. Cropland and pasture orchards, groves, vineyards,	
	22. Nurseries, and ornamental horticultural areas	
	23. Confined feeding operations	
	24. Other agricultural land	
3. Range land	31. Herbaceous range land	
	32. Shrub and brush range land	
	33. Mixed range land	
4. Forest land	41. Deciduous forest land	
	42. Evergreen forest land	
	43. Mixed forest land	
5. Water	51. Streams and canals	
	52. Lakes	
	53. Reservoirs	
	54. Bays and estuaries	
6. Wetland	61. Forested wetland	
	62. Non-forested wetland	
7. Barren land	71. Dry salt flats	
	72. Beaches	
	73. Sandy areas other than beaches	
	74. Bare exposed rock	
	75. Strip mines, quarries and gravel pits	
	76. Transitional areas	
	77. Mixed barren land	
8. Tundra	81. Shrub and brush tundra	
	82. Herbaceous tundra	
	83. Bare ground tundra	
	84. Wet tundra	
	85. Mixed tundra	
9. Perennial snow or ice	91. Perennial snow fields	
	92. Glaciers	

Source: Anderson et. al., 1976.

Table 10.1(b)   Land use/land cover classification system

Level I	Level II
1. Built-up land	1.1 Built-up land
2. Agricultural land	2.1 Crop land
	(i) *Kharif*
	(ii) *Rabi*
	(iii) *Kharif + Rabi*
	2.2 Fallow
	2.3 Plantation
3. Forest	3.1 Evergreen/semi-evergreen forest
	3.2 Deciduous forest
	3.3 Degraded or scrub land
	3.4 Forest blank
	3.5 Forest plantation
	3.6 Mangrove
4. Wastelands	4.1 Salt affected land
	4.2 Waterlogged land
	4.3 Marshy/swampy land
	4.4 Gullied/ravinous land
	4.5 Land with or without scrub
	4.6 Sandy area (coastal and desertic)
	4.7 Barren rocky/stony waste/sheet rock area
5. Water bodies	5.1 River/stream
	5.2 Lake/reservoir/tank/canal
6. Others	6.1 Shifting cultivation
	6.2 Grassland/grazing land
	6.3 Snow covered/glacial area

Source: NRSA 1989, Manual of land use/Land cover mapping.

(~23 m) is required. Diapositives are used when interpretation is done through enlargers whereas paper prints require a light table as an interpretation aid. Choice of the scale of mapping depends upon the level of information required and thus on the expected use of the map. For example, 1:250,000 scale maps are used for planning purpose at the district level, whereas 1:8000/4000 scale map is required for implementation of activities (say choosing a site for a check dam) at the field level.

After having decided the scale of the map and the classification system, one has to carry out a field survey to collect the 'ground truth'. Ground truth sites are selected after studying the imagery of interest and prior knowledge of the area. During the field visit, information about various land cover classes and their conditions are collected. The amount of field data required for a given remote sensing task depends upon various considerations such as the level of information to be derived, accuracy requirements, terrain conditions and area accessibility, existence of other ancillary information, and so on.

Table 10.1(c)   Urban land use/land cover classification system of urban agglomeration

| S. No. | Urban land use/cover category | | |
	Level I	Level II	Level III
1.	Urban or built-up land	Residential	High rise
			Medium rise, low rise
		Industrial	Heavy, light
		Recreational	Parks/gardens, stadia
			Playgrounds
		Transportational	Roads (bus stands)
			Railways (tracks/yards)
			Airport (runway and
			airport area)
		Public and semi-public	Educational institutes
			Cantonments
		Mixed built-up	
		Open/vacant land	
		Quarrying/mining area	
		Reclaimed land, slum areas	
2.	Agricultural land	Crop land, fallow land	
		Plantations	
3.	Forest	Evergreen, deciduous	
		Mixed forest, scrub/degraded	
4.	Wastelands	Salt affected land	
		Gullied/ravinous land	
		Water-logged area	
		Undulating land with or	
		without scrub	
		Sandy area, rock outcrops	
5.	Water bodies	Rivers/steam	
		Reservoirs/tanks/lakes	
		Canals/drains	

Source: SAC Technical Report 1999 : SAC/RESA/TR-03/July 1999.

A proforma used for recording ground truth information is given in Table 10.2. Nowadays, ground truth information is recorded as geo-tagged digital photographs (using GPS enabled digital cameras) which can be directly linked to satellite images on the screen while interpreting. Indian Space Research Organisation's online dissemination and visualisation platform Bhuvan based mobile applications are also being used for real-time updation/field data collection with the help of internet technology (*http://bhuvan.nrsc.gov.in/bhuvan_links.php#*). In addition to this, as stated earlier, other data in different forms (map, statistics, graphs) from many sources such as literature, measurements and analysis, ground and aerial photographs and so on, are used in remote sensing to aid and verify interpretation.

Information related to land use/land cover derived from remotely sensed data mostly provides polygons belonging to different categories. However, there is always a requirement to find the location of these units with respect to administrative boundary and transport network (road, railway) links. This is achieved by georeferencing the image or interpreted map with a topographical/reference map. To do so, the details about habitation, road/railway and water bodies are taken from Survey of India (SOI) maps on a 1:250,000 or 1:50,000 scale. A map providing these details is called a *base map*. Generally, the base map is on the same scale on

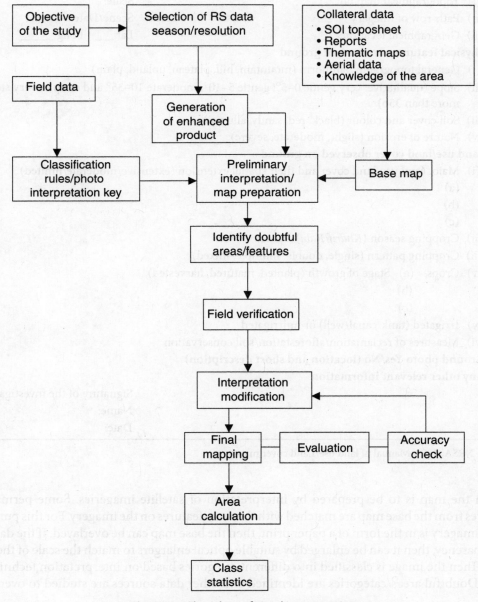

Fig. 10.2 Flow chart of visual interpretation.

Table 10.2 Proforma for collecting ground truth on land use/land cover

1. **Test site**
   State:
   District:
   Tehsil:
   Town/Village:

2. **Reference**
   (i) Topographical map no: Scale:
   (ii) Path-row of imagery   Scene/Date:
   (iii) Geographical location: Lat _____ Long _____

3. **Physical features observed on ground**
   (i) General topography/landform (mountain, hill, plateau, upland, plain)
   (ii) Slope (qualitative: very gentle 0–5°; gentle 5–10°; moderate 10–35° and steep to very steep, more than 35o)
   (iii) Soil cover and colour (black, red, sandy, alluvial)
   (iv) Nature of erosion (slight, moderate, severe)

4. **Land use/land cover observed on ground**
   (i) Major land use/land cover and their spatial extension (extensive/moderate/limited)
       (a)
       (b)
       (c)
   (ii) Cropping season (*Kharif/Rabi*)
   (iii) Cropping pattern (single, double, multiple, mixed)
   (iv) Crops   (a) Stage of growth (planted, matured, harvested)
             (b)
             (c)
   (v) Irrigated (tank/canal/well) or unirrigated
   (vi) Measures of reclamation/afforestation/soil conservation

5. **Ground photo Yes/No (location and short description)**

6. **Any other relevant information**

                                              Signature of the investigator:
                                              Name:
                                              Date:

Source: NRSA, 1989, Manual of land use/Land cover mapping.

which the map is to be prepared by interpretation of satellite imageries. Some permanent features from the base map are matched with the same features on the imagery. For this purpose, if the imagery is in the form of a paper print, then the base map can be overlayed. If the data is a transparency, then it can be enlarged by suitable optical enlargers to match the scale of the base map. Then the image is classified into different categories based on interpretation techniques/keys. Doubtful areas/categories are identified and other data sources are studied to overcome confusion. If doubt persists, the area is further visited on ground and the interpretation is verified. Accordingly, modifications are done and the final interpreted sheet is prepared. The details from the interpreted sheet are transferred to the base map directly by matching the features if the scales of both are the same. Some minor adjustments, if required, are done using optical enlargement/reduction aids. A flow chart of various activities for visual interpretation is given in Fig. 10.2.

Cartographic work is performed on these final interpreted sheets by providing reference/ legend, scale, standard symbols and colours to these classes. Point symbols can take the form of dots, circles, letters, icons, and so on, which specify a localised feature such as a school or an airport. Line symbols take the form of lines, dot strings, double hatching, dot patterns and lines with different colours; these are used to represent various thematic information such as agricultural land, fallow land, forested area, built-up land, and so on. Class-wise statistics for administrative units (or natural units like watersheds) is generated through measurement of the area from final maps. Area measuring aids used include plainimeters, dot grids and graph sheets.

Errors in a map prepared through interpretation of remotely sensed data may result due to various reasons such as inherent inaccuracy in location due to error in the data itself, limitations of cartography, printing, and wrong interpretation resulting in poor classification accuracy. Statistical methods are used to evaluate classification accuracy, which are discussed in detail later in this chapter.

10.2 DIGITAL CLASSIFICATION

We have till now discussed how remote sensing imagery is visually interpreted. Visual interpretation takes into account not only the tonal differences (grey level changes) but also many other factors such as texture, size, shape and context, all fused together with the expertise and experience of the human interpreter, to extract thematic informations. Even though visual analysis is extensively used even now for interpreting remote sensing data, it has the limitation of not being able to provide quantitative information, like for example, relating yield to reflectance values. In addition, when the volume of data is very large (a large number of scenes have to be interpreted), the throughput of information extraction through visual analysis is very low. Visual analysis also makes it difficult to effectively use all spectral bands. Thus computer processing of data is essential to take full advantage of the capabilities of remote sensing data to identify and quantify features.

We have seen in Chapter 4 that objects are discriminated based on the reflectance/emittence variation of their EM radiation (spectral signature) and/or other characteristic properties. A pixel is associated with a set of values, that is, a digital number (DN), for each spectral band. The task of digital classification is to assign or label each pixel of the remote sensing image to one of the several possible objects on earth – water, forest, snow – to a specific class. If this labelling is done for all the pixels in the scene, we get a thematic map (classified image) as in the case of visual interpretation (Fig. 10.3). We shall first consider conventional multispectral classification techniques, which perform class assignment based only on spectral signatures.

There is no unique value of reflectance/emittance associated with each class (object). Thus the spectral response pattern from various surface classes will generally have a mean value and

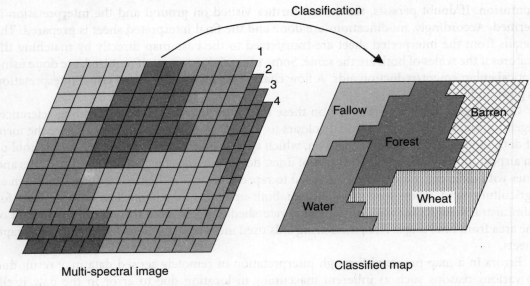

Fig. 10.3 Schematics showing the generation of a thematic map from a multispectral image.

a 'spread' around the mean (Chapter 4). A number of factors cause this spread or variability within a class, some of the major causes are atmospheric scattering, topography, illumination and view angles, class mixture and so on. It should be borne in mind that even without any of the external effects, even for a single class, there is a within-class variability. For example, the intrinsic reflectance of a wheat field cannot be unique since each plant which contributes to the reflected radiation is not identical with respect to its physiological characteristics, orientation, size, and so on. This within-class variability is referred to as *scene noise*. In addition to all these, noise in the data collection system also contributes to the variance. We have seen in Chapter 1, the need for multi-spectral imaging. How we select an optimum number of bands for classification is important to reduce cost and effort. We shall now familiarise ourselves with some basic aspects of band selection.

10.2.1 OPTIMUM BAND SELECTION FOR DIGITAL CLASSIFICATION

The data available from earth observation sensors vary in terms of number of spectral bands, central wavelength, band width, and so on. The first task in hand for the analyst is to choose the right combination of spectral bands for analysis. When you have a large number of bands, how do we select the best three or four bands which can give highest classification accuracy? If we generate a correlation matrix for these bands, one finds that some bands are highly correlated. When two bands are correlated, both contain similar information and use of any one of the bands should serve the purpose. Table 10.3 gives the correlation matrix derived from a Landsat-TM data (Justice et. al., 1983). As seen from the table, bands 1, 2 and 3 are highly correlated (> 0.9). Similarly bands 7 and 5 are also correlated to a great extent. The least correlated from this table are bands 3, 4, 5, 6 and 7. Though the correlation gives a handle to understand the redundancy of data if two correlated bands are used, it is highly scene

Table 10.3   Correlation matrix

Bands	1 (0.45–0.52)	2 (0.52–0.60)	3 (0.63–0.69)	4 (0.76–0.90)	5 (1.55–1.75)	6 (10.4–12.5)	7 (2.08–2.35)*
1	1						
2	0.943	1					
3	0.953	0.948	1				
4	−0.401	0.305	−0.485	1			
5	0.063	0.143	0.007	0.652	1		
6	0.355	0.405	0.341	0.390	0.497	1	
7	0.413	0.478	0.385	0.273	0.877	0.649	1

Landsat TM data of August 22, 1982, Source: Justice et. al., 1983.
The figures in brackets denote the spectral region of each band in micrometres.

dependent. So this alone cannot be the criterion for band selection. We have to understand the physical process involved in the spectral signature, to further finalise the bands.

The correlation matrix does not give an idea of the separability between various classes. Several statistical methods are available to quantify the separability between various classes. If we consider just two classes, then the two classes can be separated if the DN distributions of the two do not overlap, which depends on how close the mean values are and how broad the spread is. We can define a statistical separability criteria such that normalised distance between the means is beyond a certain value. The normalised distance d_{12} is given by

$$d_{12} = \left| \frac{\mu_1 - \mu_2}{\sigma_1 + \sigma_2} \right|$$

where μ_1 and μ_2 are the class means and σ_1 and σ_2 are the standard deviations. When $d_{12} > 2$, the two classes can be separated with a confidence level of 95%. A review of various separability indices are given in Swain and Davis, 1978.

The *separability between the classes depends more on the right combination of spectral bands than just the number of bands* used for classification. Figure 10.4 gives the minimum divergence (which is a measure of separability) between 4 classes for a number of band combinations of TM. It is clear that the addition of band 5 (shortwave IR) increases the separability substantially for the classes considered.

Optimum Index Factor (OIF) proposed by Chavez (Chavez et. al., 1982, 1984) is one of the common statistical methods which is applied in order to designate the most favourable three-band combinations from a set of spectral bands collected by the earth observation cameras. Though it was originally suggested to have the best combination to make the colour composite, it is useful in selecting the best combination of bands for classification as well. It is based on the standard deviation of the digital number (DN) values of the bands and correlation coefficient among bands. Higher standard deviation of the DN values is an indicator of more information content and lower the correlation coefficient between bands indicates lesser duplication (repetition) of information content.

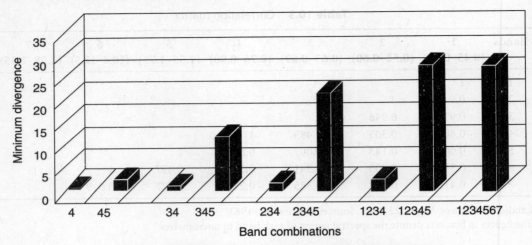

Fig. 10.4 Separability vs band combination. The numbers on the x-axis correspond to TM bands. (Adapted from Sharma et. al., 1995)

$$OIF = \frac{\sum_{i=1}^{3} \sigma_i}{\sum_{j=1}^{3} abs(r_j)}$$

where σ_i is the standard deviation of each of the three selected bands and $[abs(r_j)]$ is the absolute value of correlation coefficient between any pair formed by these bands.

The values of OIF, per se, are not comparable across scene /sensors but the order of OIF is critical. The OIF factor is evaluated for all possible combinations of groups with three bands. The number of possible combinations of three bands within the map list is given by N! / (3! * (N – 3)!) where, N is the total number of bands. Thus 4-band Resourcesat-LISS III data will have four three-band combinations. A high value of OIF indicates that the bands

Table 10.4 OIF ranking of LISS III data for four different scenes (Oza, 2016)

BAND	OIF (Rank)			
	Theme-1	Theme-2	Theme-3	Theme-4
2 3 4	157.968 (4)	46.745 (4)	36.865 (3)	16.666 (4)
2 3 5	295.978 (1)	55.096 (3)	17.110 (4)	17.736 (2)
2 4 5	293.191 (2)	93.304 (1)	47.148 (1)	17.518 (3)
3 4 5	284.306 (3)	62.139 (2)	42.992 (2)	18.507 (1)

Band numbering corresponds to LISS III; #2: 0.52–0.59 μm; #3: 0.62–68 μm;
#4: 0.77–0.86 μm; #5: 1.55–1.70 μm.
Themes #1: Glaciated region; #2: Coastal region; #3: Agriculture dominated scene
#4: Desert region.

contain much information (high standard deviation) with least duplication (low correlation between the bands). Many researchers have used OIF for selection of spectral band combination for classification of different themes (Patel and Kaushal, 2011; Kienast and Boettinger, 2010). However, the optimum band also depends on the contents in the scene. Table 10.4 gives ranking of the best three bands for three different types of scenes (Oza, 2016). It is seen that ranking is dependent on the scene content.

10.2.2 DATA REGISTRATION

Remote sensing application scientists use the global and repetitive measurements provided by a wide variety of remote sensing systems. To derive useful information from the data it is usually required that different data sets are used together—from different spectral bands, taken at different times, taken from different types of sensors and so forth. These data sets in general are not necessarily geometrically aligned on a pixel to pixel basis. The sets of data have to be *registered* before they can be subjected to digital data analysis. Thus, image registration is the first step before applying the digital analysis technique in all remote sensing applications that utilise multiple image inputs, including multi-sensor image fusion. Image registration is also required for mosaicking of images to cover a larger area in a single scene. Image registration is used in many application domains other than remote sensing, such as medical image analysis, computer vision, astrophysics, military applications, and so on.

In remote sensing, image registration is the process of overlaying two or more images that represent the same geographical area such that the corresponding pixels in all the sets of images that are registered belong to the same parcel on the ground. Georeferencing (discussed in Section 9.3.2) can also be called image-to-map registration and some of the concepts explained there are applicable to image registration also. In this section we shall describe various steps involved in image registration, that is, aligning two images—the *reference image* and the one which is to be matched to the reference image called the *sensed image*. To be mutually registered, two images should contain overlapping views of the same ground features. To achieve registration one image may need to be translated, or translated and rotated, to align it with the other. Thus the fundamental function of any image registration technique is to arrive at spatial transformation or mapping function needed to properly align two images. The general approach to registration can be covered under the following broad steps.

(i) *Feature identification*: The first step involves locating similar regions in the two images to be registered. Candidate features identifiable in an image include man-made or natural structures identifiable in the image—closed-boundary regions, edges, contours, line intersections, corners, and so on. One important requirement is that the features must be robust to changes in sensor geometry, wavelength and noise characteristics. For further processing, these features will be represented by their point representatives such as the centroid of the areas, line endings and line crossing. That is, each feature is identified with a pixel location in the image, and these corresponding points are usually referred to as *control points* (CPs), *tie-points*, or *reference points*. They should be distinct, spread all over the image and well detectable in both images. The CPs are selected either manually or automatically. In the manual mode, human operators select corresponding features in the images to be registered. In order to get reasonably good registration accuracy, a large number of control points must be selected across the whole image. Therefore, the manual procedure is very tedious, labour intensive, time consuming and with limited accuracy and hence automatic technique is adopted for faster throughput. (For details refer Guyon et. al., 2006 and Nixon 2008.)

(ii) *Feature matching*: Once the features are identified, the next step is to establish the correspondence between the features detected in the sensed image and those detected in the reference image. The matching can be performed either manually or automatically. In the case of manual procedure, correspondence is achieved along with the feature identification step itself. However, to bring in sub-pixel accuracy, the features have to be identified in the magnified images (for example, two times or four times zoom factor) rather than at the original resolution.

The automated registration procedure can be classified into two broad categories—area-based and feature-based. Area based (also referred to as correlation-like or template matching) methods deal with the images directly. They consider areas of the image as features without attempting to detect salient points and windows of pre-defined size are often used for matching. Thus the feature detection step and the matching part are carried out together. Here a number of sub-images (windows or pixels-chips) in the sensed image are compared statistically with windows of the same size as the reference image. The procedure starts with placing '$n \times n$' evenly spaced grids on the sensed image [Fig. 10.5(a)] and '$m \times m$' on the reference image [Fig. 10.5 (b)]. The sensed chip is moved within the reference image window (search area) to find out maximum correlation. The comparison uses certain statistical/

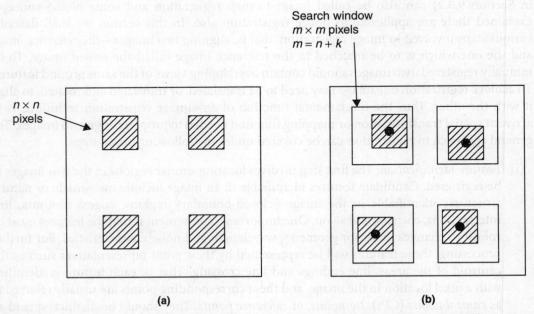

Fig. 10.5   Concept of area-based matching. A chip of $n \times n$ pixels in the sensed image (a) is moved over the window region of the reference image (b). Where the maximum correlation occurs, the centre of the chip is used as control point-shown as a dot.

mathematical techniques to measure the similarity between two given windows. All the digital correlation algorithms rely on some similarity criterion between the two images to be registered. One such technique used is termed Sequential Similarity Detection Algorithms (SSDA) (Barnea and Silverman, 1972).

The centres of the matched windows are treated as *control points* (*CP*), which can be used to solve for mapping function parameters between the reference and sensed images (Li et. al., 1995). The prerequisite of the area-based matching is that grey level distribution of the sensed image and reference image must be similar. Therefore, area-based methods are not well adapted to the problem of multi-sensor image registration since the grey-level characteristics of images to be matched can vary from sensor to sensor. The rectangular window, which is most often used, suits the registration of images which locally differ only by a translation. If images are deformed by more complex transformations, this type of window is not able to cover the same parts of the scene in the reference and sensed images. Another issue is the high probability that a window containing a smooth area without any prominent details will be matched incorrectly with other smooth areas in the images (Brown, 1992). Feature-based methods, on the other hand, tend to yield more accurate results, since features are derived properties of the original grey level images and are inherently unique. Secondly, similarity is based on the attributes and /or relations and thus, it is more invariant to illumination, reflectance and geometry.

In feature-based matching, features that are likely to be uniquely found in the reference and sensed images are selected. Feature matching establishes relationship between the features in the two images. Each feature in one image is compared with the potential corresponding feature in the other image. A pair of features with similar attributes is accepted as a match. In computing the mapping function, centroids of closed boundary regions, salient points along the contours or locations of maximum curvature can be used as control points. Thus in this step, the correspondence between the features detected in the sensed image and those detected in the reference image is established. Various feature descriptors and similarity measures along with spatial relationships among the features are used for that purpose. Instead of mapping each point individually, these techniques map the set of points in one image onto the corresponding set in the second image, that is, the matching solution uses the information from all points, thereby establishing a more robust correspondence between the two images.

(iii) *Spatial transformation*: Once the feature matching has been carried out, the next step is to establish a transformation function (also referred to as mapping function) to align the sensed image with the reference image. The mapping functions are computed using the coordinates of control points in the two images to establish the geometric relation between the two images. This is essentially a mathematical model which describes the allowable transformations. It is used to transform the geometry of one image to that of the other to spatially align them. The transformation should not change the overall geometric relationships between points after the transformation, that is, the triangle in the image should be mapped as similar triangle after transformation.

The parameters of the mapping functions are computed by means of the established feature correspondence of the *control points* acquired from the matching process. In general, the function should be flexible and general enough to handle all possible degradations which might appear in the sensed image. When the cause of some of the misregistrations is known (such as scale change due to height variation, scan non-linearity and so on) pre-correction for these deviations can be carried out before generating the mapping function. When the distortions producing the mismatch is fairly uniform, global models are possible which use all CPs for calculating one set of the mapping function parameters valid for the entire image. However, when the distortions vary across the image, then local mapping functions need to be generated treating the image as a composition of patches and the function parameters depend on the location in the image; the procedure is also known as *rubber-sheeting* or *spline transformation*.

(iv) *Resampling*: After the transformation, the corrected (transformed) image coordinates may not have a one on one relationship with the (rows, columns) of the original image. A procedure called resampling is used to determine the digital values to place in the new pixel locations of the corrected output image as discussed in Section 9.3.2.

What is presented here is the principle involved in image registration. The implementation strategy is beyond the scope of the book. Interested readers may refer to Zitova and Flusser, 2003; Moigne et. al., 2011; Alparone et. al., 2015; Brown, 1992.

10.2.3 CLASSIFICATION TECHNIQUES

We briefly discussed in Chapter 1, the concept of feature space. Let us revisit that for continuity. If we plot the reflectance values of one spectral band λ_1 in the x-axis and another band λ_2 in the y-axis, we have a two dimensional feature space (Fig. 10.6). With three bands, we can have a three dimensional feature space. In general, we can have an n-dimensional feature space with n bands data. However to explain the concept of classification, we shall restrict ourselves to two dimensions. For any class, the DN value has a mean and a spread around the mean. Therefore in the feature space, there will be a spread of points clustered around a mean value. In multispectral classification, the task is to decide how to partition the feature space into regions associated with each class so that a data point occurring in any part of the space can be uniquely assigned to a class. In practice, based on any one of the classification algorithms, the computer calculates to which cluster a pixel belongs. Thus, based on the decision rule, each pixel is assigned to a cluster. Pixels that do not fall within any class is called *unclassified*. Based on the prior knowledge of a spectral signature, each cluster can be assigned to a class such as, water, forest, urban, and so on. We shall discuss some of the algorithms used for classification in the subsequent sections.

Multispectral classification can be broadly clubbed under two broad categories,

(i) supervised classification, and
(ii) unsupervised classification.

In supervised classification, the analyst, based on the prior information (from ground truth) on the spectral characteristics of the classes, 'trains' the computer to generate boundaries in the feature space within which each class should lie. Then each pixel lying within a class boundary is assigned to that class. In contrast to this, in the unsupervised classification, the computer is asked to group (cluster) each pixel in the data into different spectral classes on the basis of natural spectral groupings present in the image grey values. Some statistically determined separability criterion is used for such clustering. Subsequently, the image analyst determines the land cover class associated with each 'spectral cluster' from the prior knowledge already available from ground reference data. Most application scientists use supervised classification. We shall now discuss the steps involved in supervised classification.

10.2.3.1 Supervised Classification Procedure

Typical supervised classification involves three steps (Lillesand and Kiefer, 1987):

(i) the training stage, wherein the multi-spectral parameters are extracted for various classes from the training sites identified by the user in the image,

(ii) the classification stage, wherein each pixel is assigned by the computer algorithm to a class to which it most probably belongs, and

(iii) the output stage—the presentation of the data is in the form of maps, tables, graphs, and so on. However, this is common for unsupervised classification also.

Training stage

In this step, pixels from the training samples are extracted to train the classifier to create discriminant functions which assign each pixel to a class in the feature space. The selection of training samples is very crucial to the accuracy of the classification. The first step is to locate in the image, representative areas of each class. These areas, called training sites, are selected based on ground surveys, studying aerial photographs, and so on. The analyst circumscribes the training sites with polygonal boundaries drawn (using the computer mouse) on the image display. The site chosen should be homogeneous and a typical representation of the class. In addition, the sample size (that is the number of pixels for a class in the training sites) should be large enough to reliably estimate the statistical properties of the class. If there are n bands there should be at least $(n + 1)$ pixels per class. In practice more than $10\,n$ training pixels per class are typically needed (Swain and Davis, 1978). It should also be borne in mind that, as within-class variability increases, the number of training pixel requirement also increases. For example, for the same crop, if the soil or climatic condition changes considerably from one region to another, the spectral signatures will have differences across the region. Therefore, one should be very careful in extending the signature on a large spatial scale. Differences in crop species also cause signature variation. When signatures are different due to environmental and species differences, it is desirable to treat them as different classes. For example, one may consider wheat crop as wheat 1, wheat 2, and so on, and to find the total area under the wheat crop, the results obtained under all the wheat categories can be added. This will give more accurate results, than combining the signatures of all categories of wheat. In actual practice, even for a uniform site, there could be some 'outliers' due to various reasons. These have to be eliminated before further processing. There are a number of statistical techniques to detect outlying values in a training sample (Campbell, 1980; Mather, 1999). In summary, the accuracy of the supervised classification of a multispectral image depends essentially on the number and quality of the training sites selected.

Equally important is the location of the training site since it should be easily identifiable in the image. On the whole, the skill and experience of the analyst goes a long way in choosing the correct training sites. The training site data for each class is used to calculate various statistical parameters such as mean, standard deviation, variance and covariance matrix for carrying out classification.

Classification stage

The classification algorithms can be broadly grouped into (i) parametric and (ii) non-parametric. Parametric classifiers assume that samples from each class belong to a population modelled by a probability density function, generally a Gaussian distribution is assumed and requires estimates of the distribution parameters, such as the mean vector and the covariance matrix. Non-parametric algorithms do not make such assumptions. Non-parametric techniques are sometimes termed 'robust', because they can be applied with a wide variety of class distribution, *if class signatures are distinct to begin with* (Schowengerdt, 1983). However, it may be noted that results with parametric algorithms also usually yield good results, even the population in the training site does not exactly follow the assumed class distribution. There are a number of algorithms under each group. We shall consider three of them.

Minimum distance to mean classifier

This classifier (also referred to as central classifier) is the simplest classifier. Here the analyst first computes the mean of each training class. Next the distance (Euclidian) of each pixel from the mean in the feature space is calculated. The pixel is assigned to that class whose distance is nearest to the mean (that is the Euclidian distance is minimum between the pixel and the mean). Figure 10.6 shows five hypothetical classes a, b, c, d and e. The mean of each class is designated by am, bm, cm, dm and em. Let us consider to which class pixel P belongs. We see that of the distances p_{am}, p_{bm}, p_{cm}, p_{dm} and p_{em}, p_{am} is the least and hence P belongs to class a. (Mathematically, the concept can be extended to *n*-dimensional space.) Using similar criteria, pixel Q should belong to class e, though considering the scatter of class d, it looks more appropriate if Q is assigned to d. This has happened since we have considered only the mean, but the variance of the training samples in a class has not been taken into account in making the decision boundary (Swain and Davis, 1978). The parallelopiped algorithm takes into account both mean and variance.

Parallelopiped classifier

Here the mean and standard deviation for each band of each class is calculated. The lower and higher threshold for the DN numbers in each band of a class may be selected based on the variance. For example, the range for each class may be defined as (mean ±1 standard deviation) for each spectral band. In the two dimensional feature space, this forms a rectangular box. We have as many boxes as the number of classes (Fig. 10.7). All the data points which fall within a box are labelled to that class. Problems arise, when the boxes overlap. The pixels in the overlap region may be labelled as unclassified or arbitrarily assigned to one of the classes. The overlap of decision boxes happens when the two bands are correlated for that class, thus producing an 'elongated' distribution. Unfortunately, a certain amount of correlation does happen in the spectral response of various bands.

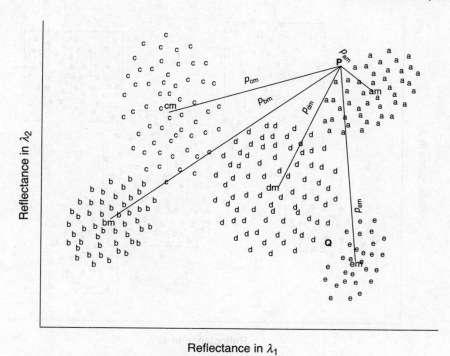

Fig. 10.6 Schematics showing minimum distance to mean classifier.

To solve the resulting problem, the analyst may 'taper' the boxes avoiding the overlap by interactively modifying the decision boundary into 'steps'. Resulting (Fig. 10.8). Thus though the parallelopiped classifier is simple to compute the value of the resulting sets its accuracy is limited. However, computationally it is very efficient.

Maximum likelihood classifier (MXL)

The earlier two classifiers to be discussed did not require that the actual values for each class have a Gaussian distribution. For a maximum likelihood for the mean (mean and standard deviation) can be computed by means of a maximum likelihood mean mean can be associated with a probability thus yielding a mean probability as that for any pixel, the computer calculates the probability for that class. The pixel is assigned to the class for which the probability is the maximum or if it is above a threshold specified by the analyst. If the probability of all classes are below the threshold it remains unclassified for a pixel if the probability of two classes happens to be exactly equal, decision making is not possible and additional conditions have to be imposed, for example, assigned to the class to which its neighbours belong. Since it is likely that most pixels close to a higher.

A pixel close to the mean of a class will have the maximum probability for that class and as it moves away from the mean the probability decreases in accordance with its distribution function. Thus we can have equiprobability contours around the mean in a feature space, with the probability declining away from the mean. In a two dimensional feature space the contours like the shape of an ellipse. The shape and orientation of the ellipse depend upon the scatter. Thus distance.

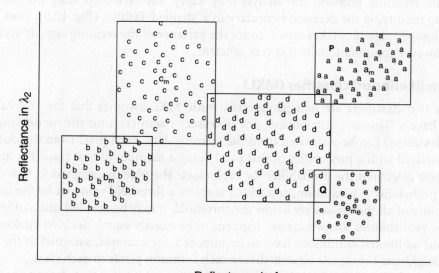

Fig. 10.7 Parallelopiped classifier scheme.

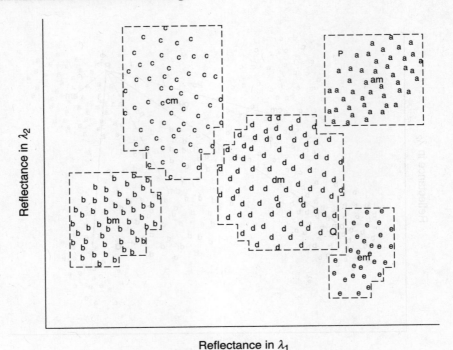

Fig. 10.8 Parallelopiped classifier scheme stepped boundary.

To solve the resulting problem the analyst may 'taper' the boxes avoiding the overlap by interactively modifying the decision boundary in a 'stepped' fashion (Fig. 10.8). Thus though the parallelopiped classifier takes into account the variance of the training sets, its accuracy is limited. However computationally it is very efficient.

Maximum likelihood classifier (MXL)

The earlier two classifiers are non-parametric, while MXL assumes that the DN values for each class have a Gaussian distribution. The necessary parameters for the model (mean and standard deviation) can be estimated from the training data. Each pixel from the class mean can be associated with a probability of that pixel being a member of that class. For any pixel, the computer calculates the probability for each class. The pixel is assigned to that class for which the probability is maximum, and which is above a threshold value set by the analyst. If the probability of all the classes are below the threshold, it may be labelled unclassified. For a pixel, if the probabilities for two classes happens to be exactly equal, decision-making is not possible and additional conditions have to be imposed, for example, assigned to the class to which its neighbour belongs or equally divide such common pixels to each class.

A pixel close to the mean of a class will have highest probability for that class and as it moves away from the mean, the probability will decrease depending on the distribution function. Thus we can have equiprobability contours around the mean in a feature space, with the probability declining away from the mean. In a two dimensional feature space, the contours take the shape of an ellipse. The shape and orientation of the ellipse depend upon the scatter. Thus distance from the mean centre alone is not the criterion for assigning the pixel to the class, but the shape of the probability contour also matters. Therefore, since the MXL classification takes into account the shape of the distribution, this method provides a better accuracy compared to the earlier two classifiers. The major drawback of the MXL classifier is the large number of computations to classify each pixel.

In the above discussion, we have assumed equal probability of occurrence for each class. Many times, some feature may be more in a scene. For example, in a scene of a predominantly urban region, the built-up area is more than the agricultural land. This *apriori* information can be used to enhance the classification accuracy, especially when probability distribution function overlaps. This is achieved by weighting each class probability by appropriate *apriori* probability (Strahler, 1980).

We were considering each vector made of different spectral bands. In place of different spectral bands, we can consider the same wavelength data at different days. For this purpose, the multi-temporal images are first registered and one of the classification techniques can be applied. Such multi-temporal analysis is especially suitable for features which are changing with time. For example, we have seen in Chapter 4 that the reflectance characteristics of crops vary with growing stages and hence multi-temporal images can discriminate better than using a single date data.

10.2.3.2 Unsupervised Classification

In supervised classification, the essential requirement is a set of training patterns, whose class membership is known. If such information is not available, unsupervised classification technique can be adopted. Unsupervised classification is based on the assumption that similar classes cluster in a feature space. Clustering is done by applying suitable algorithms on the basis of spectral signature, generating 'spectral classes'. By ground verification (or verifying with other maps), each spectral class is assigned to a class on the ground.

There are a number of statistical techniques for clustering. To carry out clustering, we should first define a measure of similarity between patterns and then how we partition a set of patterns into clusters. One criterion for similarity could be the distance between the data points in the feature space. Similar objects are expected to be 'closer' than the dissimilar object. We may start with arbitrary cluster centres and distances of each pixel from the centre computed and assign each point to the nearest cluster centre. Then find out a new mean value of the cluster centre and the procedure is continued until there is no change in cluster mean from one iteration to the next. A flow chart of basic clustering algorithm is given in Fig. 10.9. A simple worked out example is given by Jensen (1986).

10.2.3.3 Digital Classification Using Expert Systems

The classifiers discussed so far make use of only spectral information. In addition, the widely used maximum likelihood (MXL) classifier assumes that the grey level distribution data is Gaussian, which is not always true. As human beings, we identify an object not by its colour (spectral signature) alone. We also take into account the size, shape and texture which could be associated with a feature. In a visual interpretation of an FCC of a satellite imagery, the interpreter aggregates all information related to an image feature and uses his accumulated knowledge to identify the feature. That is, the process of visual interpretation is a complex

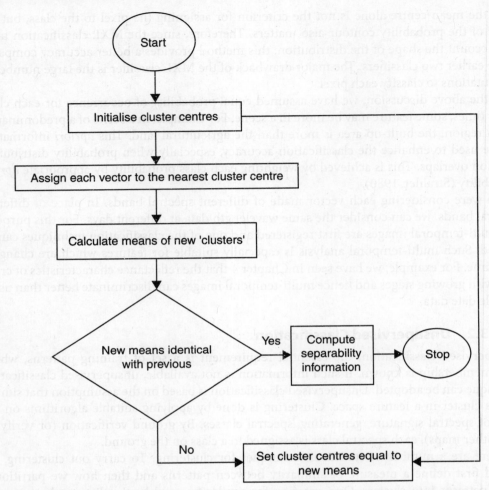

Fig. 10.9   A basic clustering algorithm for unsupervised classification. (Adapted from Swain and Davis, 1978)

intuitive process of combining information from various sources and heuristic at each stage. It does not depend on colour (spectral signature) alone as in the case of digital classification discussed earlier. For example, meadow and forest canopy may have a similar reddish tone in an FCC which could be misclassified in digital classification. But in a medium resolution imagery, the canopy texture of a forest is coarser compared to that of a meadow, which information the visual interpreter will use in addition to tone to identify the object. In this section, we shall give the basic concepts of newer techniques of classification, which can be broadly referred to as expert systems.

Scientists have been looking into the possibility of making computers do things which, at the moment, people do better—a field generally called *Artificial Intelligence* (*AI*). That is, can a computer mimic human skills in solving complex problems automatically? Broadly, AI uses computer programmes to manipulate a knowledge base, which can mimic the different ways people think and reason. The applications of AI cover a variety of fields from military

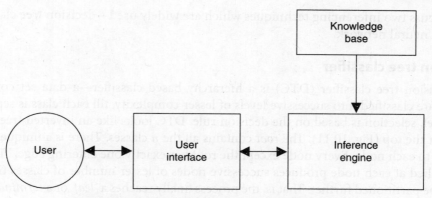

Fig. 10.10 General schematics of an expert system.

operations to the entertainment industry. The systems which perform AI are also called *expert systems*, since they take decisions on a real-life problem, in a way a human expert does. They are also referred to as *knowledge-based* (*KB*) systems.

An expert system broadly consists of three parts—a knowledge base, an inference engine and a user interface (Fig. 10.10). Creation of the knowledge base involves gathering knowledge from domain experts, or other existing sources for each domain, organising knowledge in a database and rule-biasing, that is, choosing a method for decision-making. Each domain requires a different knowledge base, for example the knowledge contents for land use classification is different from that required for environment analysis. The rule-base used to represent knowledge is in the form:

> if <condition> then <action>

For example,

> if <NDVI is greater than 0.5> then <label as vegetation>

Obviously, the quality of the data or knowledge base and the threshold setting (0.5 in the above example) will determine the accuracy of the classified output.

The manipulation of the knowledge base to exhibit human-like diagnostic abilities (in the limited area of the specific domain) is carried out by the inference engine. An inference engine is a software tool to execute an action (to take a decision) if the data supplied by the user satisfies the conditions allowed by the rules. The inference engine selects a rule from a set of available domain knowledge, and action based on the selected rule is executed. The inference engine then selects another rule and executes its actions and the process continues until all the data are analysed or no applicable rule remains (in which case the data will be labelled unclassified). There are two ways of doing it—*forward chaining and backward chaining*. Forward chaining is a 'top down' approach. Backward chaining is a 'bottom up' approach, which starts with an action and queries the information, which satisfies the conditions contained in the rules. It is a verification process of the result, whether it is as per the decision rules, that is, we try to explain the cause of what we observe. We shall later discuss in detail the forward chaining method which is a more popular technique. We shall now discuss two inferencing techniques which are widely used—decision tree classifier and artificial neural network.

Decision tree classifier

The decision tree classifier (DTC) is a hierarchy based classifier—a data set containing n themes are classified into successive levels of lesser complexity, till each class is separated. At each level, selection is based on the decision rule. DTC looks like an inverted tree where the root is at the top (Fig. 10.11). The *root* contains all the n classes. There is a unique path from the root to each node. Every node except the root has exactly one entering edge. The decision rule applied at each node produces successive nodes of lesser number of classes till the class cannot be partitioned further. That is, the process finally reaches a '*leaf* or a *terminal* (Safavian and Landgrebe, 1991). All other nodes (except the root) are called internal nodes.

We may consider the decision tree as a way to partition the feature space to arrive at the members of the class. To illustrate the basic concept, we shall consider four classes C_1, C_2, C_3

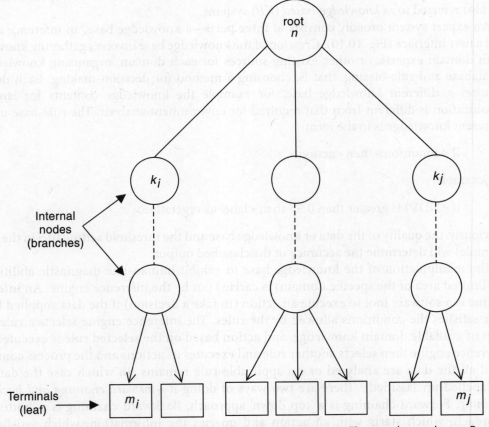

Fig. 10.11 Schematic showing the general structure of a decision tree. The root has n classes. Based on decision rules, these n classes are divided into j nodes, each containing k_i classes. The method is applied recursively at each node till terminals (leaf) are reached, that is, all classes are separated and labelled.

and C_4 in a feature space [Fig. 10.12(a)]. Here the decision boundaries a_1, a_2 and b are derived from training data statistics. Figure 10.12(b) shows the decision tree for classifying the features. The example shown is a *uni-variate decision tree*, since the decision at each node is evaluated based on a single feature. When a combination of more than one feature is required to define decision boundaries, then the tree is called a *multi-variate decision tree* (Pal and Mather, 2003).

A number of studies have been carried out to evaluate the use of decision tree classifiers (DTCs) for the classification of remotely sensed data. For high-resolution data (a resolution of a few metres) within the class variability increases and the spectral distributions do not have a normal distribution. It could be even multi-model in urban areas. Under such circumstances, the DTC performs better than statistical classifiers like MXL (Pavaluri, 2003; Sugumaran et. al., 2003). A number of studies on classifying remote sensing data using DTC can be found in literature (Lees and Ritman, 1991; Byungyong and Landgrebe, 1991; Friedl and Bradley, 1997; Friedl et. al., 1999).

Artificial neural network

Artificial Neural Networks (ANN) are computers whose architecture is modelled after the human brain. ANN consist of a number of interconnected nodes, similar to biological neurons. An artificial neuron, like its biological counterpart performs four basic functions: (i) receives inputs from other sources, (ii) combines them in someway, (iii) performs an operation (generally non-linear) on the result and (iv) outputs the results. This is schematically shown in Fig. 10.13. Here, x_0, x_1, x_2,....x_n represent various inputs to the network which, for

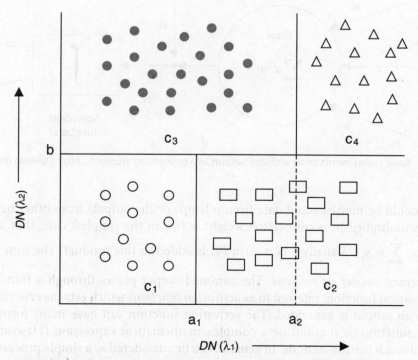

Fig. 10.12(a) A feature space with decision boundaries parallel to the axis.

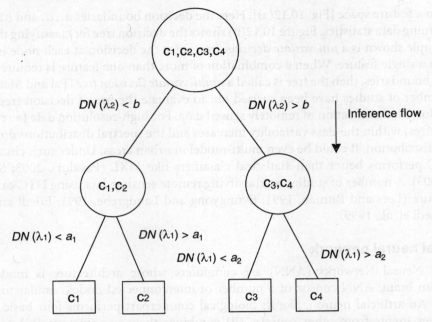

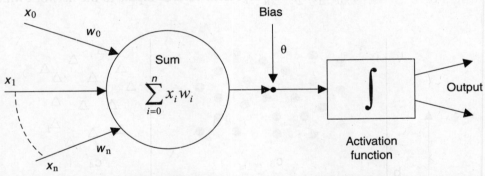

Fig. 10.12(b) Schematic showing a uni-variate decision tree classifier for four features.

Fig. 10.13 Basic components of an artificial neuron as a processing element. (After Dawson and Fung, 1993)

example, could be multispectral data from n bands or the outputs from other neurons. Each of these is multiplied by a connection weight $w(n)$. In the simplest case, they are summed up (that is, $\sum_{i=0}^{n} w_i x_i$). Usually a bias term (θ) is added to this product. The sum $\Sigma x_i w_i + \theta$ is usually termed as '*net*' of neurons. The summed output passes through a transfer function (a mathematical function, referred to as *activation function*) which sets the criteria, depending on which an output is generated. The activation function can have many forms—a simple threshold function or it could be a complex mathematical expression (Dawson and Fung, 1993). Thus each neuron or node, in general, can be considered as a simple processing element which responds to the weighted input it receives from other nodes and produces an output when the sum exceeds a threshold value. A single neuron processing element, which receives weighted inputs and thresholds the results according to a rule is called a *perceptron*.

In a practical ANN, the neurons are grouped into layers. The input layer receives inputs from the external environment—feature vector, for example the LISS-III bands or the texture or any other feature related parameter. The output layer communicates the output of the system to the user—for example, the classified output as classes (water, forest). The number of nodes in the output layer should be at least equal to the number of classes. There may be a few layers in between these two layers. Since they have no contact with the outside world, they are called hidden layers. The number of hidden layers is a part of the optimisation of the ANN design. A neural network with at least one hidden layer is called a *multi-layer perceptron (MLP)*. Figure 10.14 gives the schematics of an MLP network. A neuron receives input from many neurons of the previous layer, but produces a single output, which is forwarded to other neurons of the next layer. That is, when neurons of the input layer receives the input, its output becomes the input to the first hidden layer and so on. Thus the input presented at the input layer passes to the nodes in the next layer in a *feed-forward* manner (Fig. 10.14), and as the signal passes from node to node it is modified, each time by the weights associated with the connections. When the signal reaches the output layer, it forms the network output, activating a particular node depending on the class.

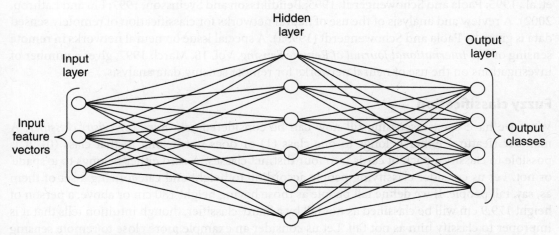

Fig. 10.14   Multi-layer perceptron of three layers, with three input, six hidden and four output neurons.

How do we decide the weights? For this purpose, the network needs to be 'trained'. As in digital classification, there are two approaches to train the network: supervised and unsupervised. Since supervised training is maximally used, we shall discuss the basic concepts, without getting into the details of the algorithm used. In the supervised training stage, the network is provided with training sets—the input (for example, DN value from the various bands) and the desired output (expected classes for the given input). Initially random values are assigned to the connection weights. Learning is done by updating the connection weights in an iterative manner, based on certain algorithms (learning laws). One of the most widely used algorithms is the *back-propagation* algorithm. Here the network output is compared with the desired output (based on the training set) and the error calculated. For each class the error is found and with a suitable algorithm the error derivative of the combined error is propagated back and the weights changed such that the overall error decreases. This process is repeated and with each iteration the network output comes closer to the desired value. Once the system has been correctly trained, that is, the error is below a user defined level, the weights can be 'frozen'. Obviously the training must be carried out for all the expected classes.

In the above scheme if the iterative process does not converge (cannot recognise the class), the designer has to consider the adequacy of the number of layers, the number of nodes per layer and so on (the topology). The major challenge to the designer of an ANN is to keep the training time as low as possible, yet maintain the desired accuracy and ensure the network's capability for generalisation, that is, the ability to handle new sample data not included in the training data set. Finally, to evaluate the accuracy of classification, it is a good practice to set aside some training samples from each class, which are not used for training. After the network has been trained, these data can be applied to the network in order to assess how accurately the classification is performed.

Classification using neural networks has been used in remote sensing for various applications, in particular land cover classification (Ritter and Hepner, 1990; Hepner et. al., 1990; Hermann and Khazenie, 1992; Bischof et. al., 1992; Civico, 1993; Yoshida and Omatu, 1994; Chen et. al., 1995; Paola and Schowengerdt, 1995; Bendiktsson and Sveinsson, 1997; Liu and Lathrop, 2002). A review and analysis of the use of neural networks for classification of remotely sensed data is given by Paola and Schowengerdt (1995a). A special issue on neural networks in remote sensing of *The International Journal of Remote Sensing*, Vol. 18, March 1997, gives a number of investigations on the use of neural networks for remote sensing data analysis.

Fuzzy classification

What we have been discussing till now can be considered as a *hard (or crisp) classifier*. A member (feature) either belongs to one class (1) or does not belong to that class (0). It is possible to classify a pack of cards into four distinct classes. A card either belongs to a 'spade' or not. Let us consider classifying people according to height and categorising a set of them as, say, tall people. If we define tall people as those having height 180 cm or above, a person of height 179.9 cm will be classified as not tall by a 'hard' classifier, though intuition tells that it is improper to classify him as not tall. Let us consider an example more close to remote sensing applications. A terrain slope(s) can be classified into the following three classes:

Gentle	$0\% \leq s \leq 20\%$
Moderate	$20\% < s \leq 40\%$
Steep	$s > 40\%$

To which class does a terrain with slope of 20.5% belong? A 'hard' classifier will label it as moderate. However, our intuition shows that to make any deduction using the slope parameter, it is not out of place even if it is termed as gentle. Thus, many parameters take continuous values, which experts express in terms of linguistic variables like, gentle, tall, moderate, steep, and so on. Forcing these variables into three or four distinct classes according to its measured value, is too gross and ignores the fact that the transition from one class to another is rather gradual and the boundary not sharp; in other words the *class boundaries are fuzzy*.

Let us consider another problem in remote sensing. We have seen in Chapter 5 (Fig. 5.8), that when measurements are made with a remote sensor, there are pure pixels and boundary pixels. The boundary pixels are 'mixed' pixels, representing an area occupied by more than one ground cover. If the mixed pixel is assigned to one class only, the area calculated by simple pixel counting will be erroneous, since the pixel does not really belong to that class only, but a mixture of two (or more) classes. That is, class boundaries represented by pixels, are not sharp but fuzzy. *Fuzzy classification deals with situations, when we have one 'item' which partly belongs to one class and partly to another*. In fuzzy logic, the truth of any statement becomes a matter of degree. In hard classification, true value is assigned 1 and 0 for false. However, fuzzy logic also permits in-between values. That is, according to fuzzy logic, there are various degrees of 'belongings' to a class based on measurement values. Let us say, 60% of a land is flat and 40% is gently sloped. In the fuzzy logic jargon, we may say that the field belongs to a class 'flat' with *membership function* 0.6 and to class 'gentle' with *membership function* 0.4. In the framework of fuzzy logic when a measurement input is given to the membership function it gives an output, which can be considered as the probability with which the variable (that is, the input) can be assigned to a class. In other words, the membership function essentially gives a number that expresses how much something belongs to a class. We have to define a membership function for each class, based on some measurements or other a *priori* knowledge. The primary task of any fuzzy logic is to specify the membership function. Commonly used fuzzy based classifiers include fuzzy c-means, fuzzy MLC and fuzzy rule base. It is beyond the scope of this book to give details of these classifiers. Readers interested in getting more information can refer to the book *Fuzzy Classifier Design* by Ludmila I Kuncheva. There are a number of studies applying fuzzy classifiers for remotely sensed data (Fisher and Pathirana, 1990; Wang, 1992; Warner and Shank, 1997; Zhang and Foody, 1998; Bardossy and Samaniego, 2002; Melgani et. al., 2000; Shackelford and Davis, 2003, 2003a).

10.2.3.4 Object Based Classification

The classification techniques discussed above are based on the classification of individual pixels utilising the concept of a multi-dimensional feature space and the procedure mainly depends upon the spectral signature (DN values from different spectral bands) for differentiating land cover features. With the availability of high spatial resolution (metre and sub-metre class) images, the pixel-based classification technique becomes less efficient due to a significant increase of the *within-class* spectral variability (scene noise—see Section 5.3) and therefore, decreases the accuracy of a purely pixel-based classification. Per pixel classification of high resolution image produces 'salt and pepper' noise (due to heterogeneous variation in the class values of neighbourhood pixels) in the classified image which also contributes to the inaccuracy of the classification (Gao and Mas, 2008). Let us go to the basics of how we recognise objects in nature. In an image, human eyes catch patches/objects rather than pixels. Identification of objects by human vision is based on a combination of factors such as shape, size, pattern, tone, texture, shadows and association (Olson, 1960). Hence, instead of a single pixel we need to consider group of pixels in a neighbourhood and a classification approach utilising such neighbouhood information is called *contextual* classification. However in, the contextual approach, classification occurs at pixel level only. With the advancements in computer processing, memory handling and algorithms, contextual information could be estimated and integrated at a multiple scale which in turn contributes to the development of *object based classification technique.*

Object based classification technique (OBCT) tries to mimic a human interpreter for detecting objects by creating vector polygons (called segments) over a homogenous region based on several criteria including colour, shape and texture characteristics together with the association of the neighbourhood information in an image (Abkar et. al., 2000). Segmentation is the key process in the object based image analysis approach. Segmentation is a process in which the input image will be divided into homogeneous and separated regions. Its main goal is to divide an image into meaningful parts that have a strong correlation with objects or areas of the real world contained in the image. In segmentation, pixels are grouped into polygons of homogeneous image 'objects' using spectral and spatial criteria. The image object is a group of connected pixels in a scene. Thus, a digital image is no longer considered as a grid of pixels but as a group of homogeneous regions of image objects. In the next step, the delineated segments are classified into real world objects based on spectral, textural, neighbourhood and object specific shape, hierarchy parameters. We shall elaborate on these points below.

There are many segmentation methods for different applications (Pal and Pal, 1993).One of the commonly used techniques for segmentation is *Multi-Resolution Segmentation* (MRS). MRS is a bottom up method, where starting with one pixel as seed, the algorithm tests if the neighbouring pixels can be merged with the starting pixel, by checking with the user established homogeneity criteria. The neighbouring pixels are thus joined to these initial 'regions' and the process is continued until a certain threshold is reached, thus producing one segment. This threshold is normally a homogeneity criterion or a combination of size and homogeneity (Blaschke et. al., 2004). A region grows until no more pixels can be attributed to the segment and new seeds are placed and the process is repeated. This continues until the whole image is partitioned into regions that are similar according to a set of predefined criteria.

The homogeneity criterion includes colour (spectral values) and texture. The shape parameter helps to differentiate linear, circular and square features as well as other types. It uses *compactness* information to quantify the relative closeness of pixels detected under a segment with reference to a circle, and *smoothness* information to quantify the similarity between the cluster circumferences with reference to that of a square (E-Cognition, 2001). The *size* or *scale* parameter helps to detect clusters of varying size based on spectral variance threshold. At a smaller scale, heterogeneity (DN variance) would be less important and hence bigger clusters/segments can be created, and higher scale would result in many smaller size clusters. Texture information quantifies frequency of change in DN values, and it helps to increase the accuracy by 10% to 15% (Franklin et. al., 2000). Colour parameter uses spectral information (DN values). It is important to understand here that there are no pre-defined reference values for each of these parameters because different study areas will have different land cover features with different shapes and sizes. So, the user needs to experiment with these parameters (by applying suitable weights) till an acceptable segmented image truthfully representing the ground features is obtained. The segments have additional information compared to the single pixels (such as mean value per band, and also median values, minimum and maximum values, mean ratios, variance), and importantly their spatial relationship (topology) such as connectivity, area and distances with the neighbourhoods provide much more valuable information during the final class allocation (Blaschke, 2010).

The segmented image does not have any association to land cover, and it only shows clusters which are homogeneous with reference to spatial and spectral characteristics (with respect to chosen threshold of shape, scale and colour) (Ryherd and Woodcock, 1996). So, the next step is creating land cover association, and we need to define land cover (LC) classes. Then, we need to provide training sites for each of the LC classes. Finally, based on training sites, classification is carried out to assign segments to representative a LC class based on spectral, spatial and/or geometry based membership functions (degree of belonging of a segment towards a land cover class—see fuzzy classifiers for details). Figure 10.15 gives the schematics of implementation flow of OBCT.

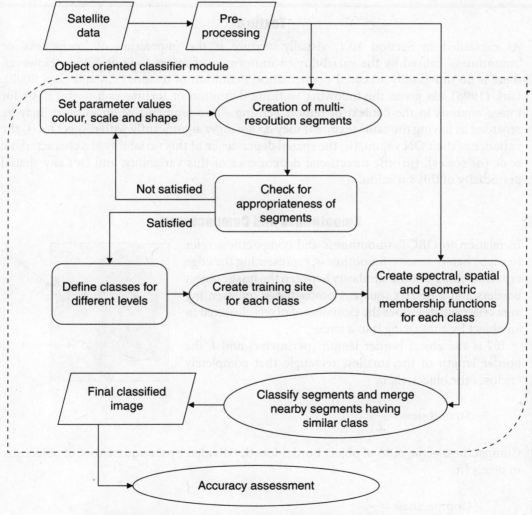

Fig. 10.15   Flow chart explaining object based classification process.

In the case of *per-field classification*, the segmentation process is not required and the polygon file (field) need to be provided by the user and algorithm tries to allot each polygon to a land cover category utilising a similar approach as in contextual or in OBCT.

Object based image analysis has shown improved classification accuracy compared to per-pixel classifier in diverse areas such as urban land cover/land use information, change detection, vegetation studies, forest boundary mapping and so on (Blaschke, 2010). Jeganathan et. al. (2002) compared the performance of OBCT and maximum likelihood classifier (MXL) for clustering aerial image, and found that OBCT performed better, and the accuracy from OBCT and MXL for aerial image was 89.6% and 68.8% respectively.

Lu and Weng, 2007, provide a survey of image classification methods and techniques for improving classification performance.

Texture

As explained in Section 10.1, visually, texture is the impression of 'coarseness' or 'smoothness' caused by the variability or uniformity of image tone or colour. However, there is no universally accepted mathematical definition of texture (Yin and Guo, 2007). Lark (1996) has given the following working definition of texture as a useful basis for image analysis in the context of remote sensing. 'Two segments of an imagery may be regarded as having the same texture if they *do not differ* significantly with respect to: (i) the variance of their DN values, (ii) the spatial dependence of this variability at a characteristic scale (or scales), (iii) the directional dependence of this variability, and (iv) any spatial periodicity of this variation.'

Smoothness and Compactness

In relation to OBCT, smoothness and compactness refer to shape heterogeneity. Smoothness, representing the edge criterion, describes the similarity between the image object borders and a perfect square. Compactness, representing area criterion, describes the closeness of pixels clustered in an object by comparing it to a circle.

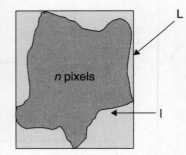

If l is the object border length (perimeter) and L the border length of the smallest rectangle that completely encloses the object, then,

$$\text{Smoothness} = \frac{l}{L}$$

Compactness is the ratio of object border length l divided by the square root of object size in pixels (n)

$$\text{Compactness} = \frac{l}{\sqrt{n}}$$

10.2.4 OUTPUT STAGE

The classified information has to be presented suitably for further utilisation of the information. A thematic image can be generated after classification. Here each theme may be assigned a colour or shade or symbols as in the case of visual interpretation. This gives a good pictorial display of the spatial extent of each theme. In general, such images will have 'speckle' like noise (salt and pepper noise) due to misclassification, or scattered isolated classes among dominant classes. When one looks for dominant classes (for planning purposes), a 'smoother' image is desirable. This is generally achieved by some special smoothing techniques.

Many times it is desirable to have the information as tables, for example, the area under each category. In still other cases, graphic representation is needed. With the varied output devices available with the computers, these output information can be generated in varying media such as paper prints, photographs, CDs, and so on.

10.3 CLASSIFICATION ACCURACY

A major advantage of remote sensing technology is its ability to quantitatively assess the spatial extent of the ground features. To use this methodology, it is necessary to quantitatively assess the accuracy of classification. For example, in a land use map generated from remote sensing data, the area delineated and classified as a particular category may not be correct at all locations due to various reasons.

Although the analyst has used the field data in the construction of an interpretation key, the classified map has to be checked by comparing the classified data with actual ground information by visiting the sites or comparing with standard maps. Obviously one cannot check each point on the ground. Therefore, some sampling technique has to be adopted. A simple method in a visually interpreted map is to lay a grid over the map and choose random samples for each category to check on ground. That is, first to identify n samples at random within a class on a classified image and to check the identity of these sample areas in the field. One usual question is what is the minimum sample size (n) required? Suppose $n = 10$, and after field check it has been observed that 9 out of 10 have been correctly classified, can we say that the classification accuracy is 90%? Since the sampling is done on a random basis, it may be possible that all the 9 points may be by 'chance' chosen at locations which are correctly classified. Any accuracy estimate based on sampling lies within a confidence interval dependent on the number of samples (Hord and Brooner, 1976). The upper and lower confidence limit narrows as the number of samples increase. For example, with 50 samples and for a 95% confidence level, if 90% of the samples are found correct then the actual accuracy lies between 79% and 96%. If 400 samples are used, the limits lie between 87% and 93%. In non-specialist language, we may say that one has more confidence of the results obtained from a 400 sample data than for a 50 sample data. The upper and lower limits widen as the confidence level tends to 100%. Table 10.5 gives the upper and lower accuracy limits for 95% confidence level for various sample sizes and observed accuracy based on the procedure given by Richards and Jia (2006) (Eq. 11.2).

The equation is reproduced below

$$\frac{X + 1.921 \pm 1.960 \left[\dfrac{X(N - X)}{N} + 0.960 \right]^{1/2}}{N + 3.842}$$

Table 10.5 Upper ($p+$) and lower ($p-$) accuracy limit for observing a correct class of size X, from a sample size of N, at 95% confidence level

N	X	p+	p−	N	X	p+	p−	N	X	p+	p−
60	30	0.623	0.377	50	25	0.634	0.366	40	20	0.648	0.352
	31	0.638	0.393		26	0.652	0.385		21	0.671	0.375
	32	0.654	0.409		27	0.670	0.404		22	0.693	0.398
	33	0.669	0.425		28	0.688	0.423		23	0.715	0.422
	34	0.684	0.441		29	0.706	0.442		24	0.736	0.446
	35	0.699	0.457		30	0.724	0.462		25	0.758	0.470
	36	0.714	0.474		31	0.741	0.482		26	0.779	0.495
	37	0.729	0.490		32	0.759	0.501		27	0.799	0.520
	38	0.744	0.507		33	0.776	0.522		28	0.819	0.546
	39	0.758	0.524		34	0.792	0.542		29	0.839	0.572
	40	0.773	0.541		35	0.809	0.563		30	0.858	0.598
	41	0.787	0.558		36	0.825	0.583		31	0.877	0.625
	42	0.801	0.575		37	0.841	0.604		32	0.895	0.652
	43	0.815	0.592		38	0.857	0.626		33	0.913	0.681
	44	0.829	0.610		39	0.872	0.648		34	0.929	0.709
	45	0.842	0.628		40	0.888	0.690		35	0.945	0.739
	46	0.856	0.646		41	0.902	0.692		36	0.960	0.770
	47	0.869	0.664		42	0.917	0.715		37	0.974	0.801
	48	0.882	0.682		43	0.930	0.738		38	0.986	0.835
	49	0.894	0.701		44	0.944	0.762		39	0.996	0.871
	50	0.907	0.720		45	0.957	0.786		40	1.000	0.912
	51	0.919	0.739		46	0.968	0.812				
	52	0.931	0.758		47	0.979	0.838				
	53	0.942	0.778		48	0.989	0.865				
	54	0.953	0.799		49	0.996	0.895				
	55	0.964	0.819		50	1.000	0.929				
	56	0.974	0.841								
	57	0.983	0.863								
	58	0.991	0.886								
	59	0.997	0.911								
	60	1.000	0.940								
30	15	0.668	0.332	20	10	0.701	0.299				
	16	0.698	0.361		11	0.742	0.342				
	17	0.726	0.392		12	0.781	0.387				
	18	0.754	0.423		13	0.819	0.433				
	19	0.781	0.455		14	0.855	0.481				
	20	0.808	0.488		15	0.888	0.531				
	21	0.833	0.521		16	0.919	0.584				
	22	0.858	0.556		17	0.948	0.640				
	23	0.882	0.591		18	0.972	0.699				
	24	0.905	0.627		19	0.991	0.764				
	25	0.927	0.664		20	1.000	0.839				
	26	0.947	0.703								
	27	0.965	0.744								
	28	0.982	0.787								
	29	0.994	0.833								
	30	1.000	0.887								

where X is the number of correctly labelled pixels in a sample of N. The equation is based on binomial statistics.

Van Genderen and Lock (1977) has suggested at least a sample size of 30 for each category for an accuracy estimate of 90%.

The result of the accuracy check is usually tabulated in the form of an $m \times m$ matrix, where m is the number of classes under investigation. This matrix is referred to as the *confusion matrix* (or error matrix or contingency table). How the ground truth class and interpreted class are represented in the row and column varies in literature. Here we shall follow the convention given by Jensen (1986). The thematic map classes derived by remote sensing is given as columns and the rows represent the ground truth (true) classes.

(i) Omission error—the class A for which accuracy is estimated is classified as another class, that is, the sample is 'omitted' from the true class or there is omission from correct category;

(ii) Commission error—samples from other classes are misclassified and added to the class A. That is, samples are added (committed) to the wrong class, there is commission into another category.

The confusion matrix enables one to understand omission and commission errors and will help to identify classes which are difficult to separate. The diagonal elements give the correctly identified samples to that class. In an ideal case, all non-diagonal elements will be zero, indicating no misclassification. Values off the diagonal below a column heading indicate errors of commission (erroneously including a pixel from other classes), whereas values off the diagonal along a row heading indicate errors of omission (erroneously excluding a pixel from a class).

Table 10.6 shows a simulated confusion matrix for 5 classes. For each class, 50 samples are chosen, which is given by the total of each column. In the case of forests, only 41 samples belong to the forest class. Of the rest 9 samples, which were interpreted as forest, 2 samples belong to water, 5 to pasture and 2 to soil (commission errors). On the other hand, two samples from water and five samples from the pasture have been classified as forest (commission error). In other words, during the field survey, 48 samples of forest were

Table 10.6 Illustration of confusion matrix

Actual land use class	Interpreted land use							
	Forest	Pasture	Soil	Urban	Water	Total	C	O
Forest	41	5	0	0	2	48	9	7
Pasture	5	40	2	0	0	47	10	7
Soil	2	5	42	6	0	55	8	13
Urban	0	0	6	44	0	50	6	6
Water	2	0	0	0	48	50	2	2
	50	50	50	50	50	250		

O – Omission error, C – Commission error
The values given are only illustrative.

Table 10.7 Type of accuracies based on the confusion matrix of Table 10.5

	Producer's accuracy	Mapping accuracy	User's accuracy
Forest	41/48	41/41 + 9 + 7	41/50
Pasture	40/47	40/40 + 10 + 7	40/50
Soil	42/55	42/42 + 8 + 3	42/50
Urban	44/50	44/44 + 6 + 6	44/50
Water	48/50	48/48 + 6 + 6	48/50

found against 50 classified. Of these 48, only 41 were correctly classified as forest. On the other hand, five forest samples were interpreted as 'pasture' and two forest samples were interpreted as 'water' (omission error). Thus the proportion of forest classified correctly is 41/50 which according to Table 10.7 gives a classification accuracy between 69% and 90% at 95% confidence level. Thus the accuracy for each class can be estimated. The overall apparent accuracy is the sum of the diagonal elements divided by the total samples for all classes (215/250 = 86%).

Story and Congalton (1986) have coined two accuracy terms—producer's accuracy and user's accuracy. According to this, the number of correctly classified samples of category x, divided by the total number of that category observed on ground is called 'producer's accuracy'. The producer of the classified map is interested in how well a specific area on earth can be mapped.

When the number of correctly classified samples of category x are divided by the total number of samples that were classified as category x, it is called 'user's accuracy', because a map user is interested in the reliability of the map, or how well the map represents what is really on the ground.

Let us consider a case where the commission and omission errors are exactly equal. Here the area depicted under each class in the classified map will be close to the true area on the ground, but they will be mapped at wrong positions, that is, the mapping accuracy is poor even though there is no error in the proportion of class represented in the map.

The mapping accuracy is given by

$$\frac{\text{pixel correctly classified (diagonal pixel} = a)}{a + \text{omission pixels} + \text{commission pixels}}$$

I may add one more type of accuracy 'category accuracy' or category error. If we are not interested in the actual location of a category and interested only in the area covered under that category, then we may find out the error in the area estimate of each category irrespective of its location. Such situations do happen, for example, when we are interested only in the statistics of the type of agricultural cover in a district or state. In some other cases, at policy level, the interest may be the total forest cover in an area and not the distribution of trees. The category can be overestimated or underestimated.

$$\text{Category error} = \frac{\text{Commission error in category } i - \text{Omission error in category } i}{\text{Ground truth number for category } i}$$

When omission error is more than the commission error, the category is underestimated, while when the commission error is more than the omission error, the category is overestimated. Table 10.6 shows category error in the forest is (2/48)%, that is, the forest category is overestimated by 4.2%, while soil is underestimated by 9%. Of course, actual upper and lower bounds for a certain confidence limit has to be evaluated as mentioned earlier. For urban areas, the category error is zero, since omission error and commission error are the same.

When carrying out computer classification, the training sites data (which are not used for determining the classification decision boundary) can be used to generate the confusion matrix to estimate classification accuracy. The data from these sites are classified using the algorithms already developed. In this case, since pixels from homogeneous data are used, the classification accuracy in general will show a higher value than what is representative of the whole image.

When the aim is to produce tabular data from remote sensing, instead of maps, as in the case of estimation of crop acreage or crop production in a district or state, the accuracy is given based on sampling error and relative bias error (with respect to a standard, say, actual field survey or government report). A criteria used during the LACIE experiment is 90/90—meaning the error is within 10% of the true value at a confidence level of 90% (NASA 1987c). Similar criteria are now used as standard criteria for crop production estimation in India (Sridhar et. al., 1994).

FOR FURTHER READING

1. *Manual of Remote Sensing,* Vol. 1, Colwel R N, Ed., ASPRS, Chapter 24.
2. *Theory and Application of Optical Remote Sensing,* Asrar G, Ed., John Wiley and Sons, Chapter 14.
3. *Introductory Digital Image Processing: A Remote Sensing Perspective,* Jensen J R , Prentice-Hall, N, Chapter 8.
4. *Remote Sensing Digital Image Analysis: An Introduction,* Richards J A and Jea Xiuping, Springer, Chapters 3, 8, 9, 11.
5. *Remote Sensing: The Quantitative Approach,* Swain P H and Davis S M , Eds, McGraw-Hill Book Col, NY.
6. *Remote Sensing and Image Interpretation,* Lillesand T M and Kiefer R W, John Wiley and Sons.
7. *Remote Sensing Models and Methods for Image Processing,* Schowengerdt R A, Academic Press (1997), Chapter 9.
8. *Classification Methods for Remotely Sensed Data,* Brandt T S O and Paul M Mather, Taylor & Francis (2001).
9. *Fuzzy Classifier Design,* Ludmile I Kuncheva, Springer-Verlag (2000).
10. *Pattern Classification: Neuro-Fuzzy Methods and their Comparison,* Shigco Abe, Praxis Publishing (2001).
11. *Introduction to Expert Systems* (3rd Ed.), Peter Jackson, Addison Wesley Longman.
12. *http://booksite.elsevier.com/9780750676052/content/Resources/Chapter6.htm*
13. *http://homepages.inf.ed.ac.uk/rbf/HIPR2/glossary.htm*

14. *www.austinlinks.com/Fuzzy*
15. *https://crisp/nus.edu.sg/~acrs2001/pdf/046PAL.PDF*
16. *http://nature.berkeley.edu/~gong/textbook/chapter7/html/home7.htm*
17. *www.doc.ic.ac.uk/~nd/surprise_96/journal/vol4/cs11/report.html*
18. *http://rfhs8012.fh-regensburg.de/~saj39122/jfroehl/diplom/e-1-text.html*
19. *http://www.jars1974.net/pdf/11_Chapter10.pdf*
20. *http://www.jars1974.net/pdf/12_Chapter11.pdf*

11 Applications of Remote Sensing for Earth Resources Management

Remote sensing data (the images) have been used to derive thematic information on various natural resources and the environment. The type and level of information extracted depends on the expertise of the analyst and what he is looking for in the data. For example, the remote sensing image of land can be used to derive information on vegetative cover, water bodies, land use pattern, geological features, soil, and so on. Remote sensing in the OIR region provides data based on the surface 'expression' and even for microwave regions, though sub-surface data can be obtained at times depending on the situation. The received data is influenced to a large extent by surface or near surface features. The utilisation of remote sensing data can be broadly classified into three categories.

(i) To identify the category to which the earth surface expression (manifested as data) belongs, based on signature differences. For example, the area under a particular crop, the extent of surface water body, flood affected area, and so on. For specific themes, one may have to optimise the spectral bands or combination of bands, the scale (resolution) of the image, the season of acquisition, and others. Since remote sensing data is the direct result of the surface expression, such inferences are fairly accurate to meet most user needs.

(ii) To infer a particular parameter or phenomenon (which is only partly represented in the data) using suitable modelling. For example, yield of a crop, volume of timber from forest and ocean currents. Since the extraction of these 'secondary' information cannot be solely dependant on the information available from remote sensing, models have to be developed which integrate remote sensing data with other data. The accuracy therefore also depends on how good the model is, apart from the quality of the data from remote sensing.

(iii) In the third category, surfacial expressions are indicators of certain resources, which are not directly observable by remote sensing. For example, lineament and paleochannels are good indicators for possible ground water resources.

The details of how remote sensing is utilised for various disciplines is beyond the scope of this book. Instead, we will present typical application potential (not necessarily exhaustive) in some disciplines.

11.1 AGRICULTURE

The economy of most developing countries is mainly governed by agriculture. In India, the agriculture sector sustains the livelihood of around 70% of the population and contributes to about 35% of the net national product. The major concern is to increase food grain production. Many players have to contribute to achieve this. We require judicious and optimal management of both land and water resources along with the use of high yielding variety seeds, optimal fertiliser input, pest management, and so on. Remote sensing can provide valuable information for land and water management. Other important areas of application of remote sensing in agriculture include monitoring crop production estimation well before harvesting, optimal use of farm inputs, drought monitoring and others. In this section we shall discuss the operational use of remote sensing for some of these applications.

11.1.1 CROP PRODUCTION FORECASTING

Knowledge of food grain production well in advance of harvest enables the country to adopt suitable measures to meet shortages, if any, and assist in making policy decisions like the level of buffer stock, imports and fixing of support prices. In fact, one would like to have a global scenario of food production to outline the necessary strategy for one's country. No wonder the first global experiment using satellite remote sensing was to demonstrate the operational capability of remote sensing for crop inventory and forecasting, called Large Area Crop Inventory Experiment (LACIE) (Macdonald, 1984). The goal of LACIE was to develop, test and evaluate a system for predicting wheat production through the use of LANDSAT data for area estimation and weather based empirical regression yield models to predict yield. Since then, a large number of methodology development cum demonstration studies for crop monitoring have been carried out in various countries. One of the major efforts in this direction has been taken up by the European Union (EU) under the Monitoring Agriculture through Remote Sensing (MARS) project for making Europe-wide crop production estimates (Sharman, 1993; Gallego, 1999). The CropWatch programme of China is a global crop-monitoring system, which uses remote sensing data combined with selected field data to determine key crop production indicators: crop acreage, yield and production, crop condition, cropping intensity, crop-planting proportion, total food availability, and the status and severity of droughts (Wu et. al., 2014). In India, the project 'Crop Acreage and Production Estimation (CAPE)' funded by the Ministry of Agriculture was taken up in 1983 (and is still running), in order to provide pre-harvest production estimation of major crops such as rice, wheat, sorghum, groundnut, rapeseed/mustard, cotton, and so on. While earlier estimates were carried out using OIR sensors (LANDSAT MSS/TM, IRS, LISS-I, II, III, WiFS), of late, microwave SAR data have been successfully used to provide avreage estimation of rice, which is mainly a Kharif crop.

Crop production estimation has two components—estimation of area under the crop and forecasting yield (production per unit area). In India, conventional methodology for crop production estimation involves complete enumeration/ sample survey for crop acreage estimation and yield estimation based on crop cutting experiments conducted on sample plots identified on the basis of complex sampling design that is based on a stratified multistage random sampling (Singh et. al., 2002). These conventional techniques are labour intensive, time consuming, especially to get information at smaller units (tehsil/block) for state/country level. In addition, the production estimation is available only after harvest, since one has to depend on crop cutting experiment for yield. We shall discuss in the following sections the methodology developed under the CAPE project to estimate crop acreage based on remote sensing data and yield estimation with inputs from remote sensing.

11.1.1.1 Crop Acreage Estimation

Identification and discrimination of various crops is based on the subtle spectral signature differences between the crops and the use of digital image processing techniques. Vegetative cover, other than the crop under investigation, makes crop identification a challenging task. Many factors such spatial resolution, spectral band, time of observation in the crop growth cycle, and so on, make crop identification and mensuration a demanding task. We shall discuss later in the section how some of these parameters affect the accuracy of crop acreage estimation using remote sensing. The stages involved in the crop acreage estimation using remote sensing data are: (a) study area extraction, (b) crop discrimination/ identification from satellite data, (c) estimation of area under a crop in the study area, and (d) assessment of accuracy of crop identification and area estimates (Dadhwal et. al., 2002).

The study area of interest, say a district, may not fall in a single image frame. Therefore, it is required to mosaic different frames containing the study area. The district boundaries are transferred to the image and all the pixels inside the boundary are analysed. With current computer systems, it is possible to analyse the complete data at district level. Estimation of crop acreage for large areas, like states, requires handling of large volumes of data. In such cases, suitable sampling techniques need to be adopted. Under the CAPE project, various sampling plans were experimented with. In the initial stages, systematic sampling or simple random sampling was used. Later on, in order to improve the accuracy, a stratified random sampling technique was used (Sharma and Parihar, 2009). Here, study area is stratified into homogeneous regions based on crop area proportion within a segment (say, 5×5 km) as inferred from satellite images of previous years. Then, random sample segments from each homogenous stratum is analysed for crop classification and acreage estimation. Using suitable statistical techniques (Cochran, 1977), the results are aggregated to the district/state level. Figure 11.1a gives a simplified flow chart showing the steps involved in generation of crop production using the sampling approach. However, with the availability of high speed computers with large storage space and because of the requirement of the crop maps for various other purposes (such as yield modelling), currently complete enumeration approach is followed—the whole image within the administrative (district/state) boundary is classified.

Crop discrimination is based on the spectral response variation of the land cover in a multi-dimensional feature space produced by different spectral bands. Generally, per pixel classification is used based on the training samples obtained from 'ground truth'. Though multiple observation in a growth cycle is desirable for crop separation, when such data is not available due to poor temporal resolution of the imaging system, single date data corresponding to near maximum vegetative growth stage of crop is used. Non-agricultural area is removed in the beginning, using Land Use Land Classification (LULC) maps, or can be derived from the data itself based on the NDVI profile. Usually a supervised classification procedure is

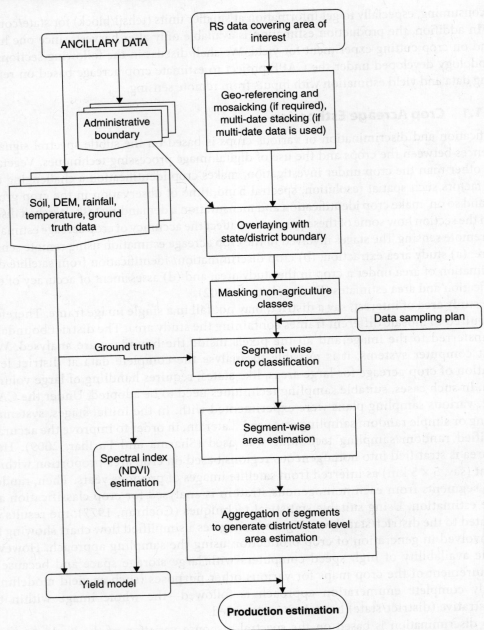

Fig. 11.1(a)   Simplified flow chart showing steps involved in the generation of crop production using sampling approach.

applied (Chapter 10), when comparatively higher resolution Resourcesat LISS III (23 m, 24 day repetivity) or other satellite data of comparable resolution (for example, Landsat 8 OLI, Sentinel 2 MXI) is used for district level crop classification. For state level area estimation, multi-date Resourcesat AWiFS data (56 m resolution and 5 day revisit) is used.

Ground truth (GT) data is a critical component for crop classification. The classification accuracy and confidence level improves with the availability of better quality and higher number of GT sites. Typical ground truth information includes latitude and longitude, location (village, block, district), land cover, crop type, stage and condition, and other competing crops, along with one or two photographs of the fields. As discussed in Chapter 10, currently GT is collected using smartphone-based Android Application. The photographs, location and the ground truth data are collected through the App and real-time uploaded to the Bhuvan geo-platform of ISRO.

The next step after classification is the area estimation. The simplest method is to assign the proportion of classified pixel over the total pixel in the study area as the acreage of the crop under study. If A is the area of the study region the cropped area A_C is given by

$$A_C = A \times \left(\frac{N_C}{N_T} \right)$$

where, N_C and N_T are the number of pixels identified as crop and total number of pixels in the study area respectively. However, depending upon the classification accuracy the estimate could be biased. There are statistical techniques to include the information on the classification accuracy for obtaining improved crop area estimates (Dadhwal et. al., 2002).

Accuracy assessment or validation is an important step in remote sensing analysis which determines the value of resulting data to a particular use. Statistical accuracy used in crop area estimation consists of two components—precision and bias. Precision refers to the reliability (repetivity) with which a certain estimate is made. Bias refers to the deviation of the estimate from the 'true' value or value assumed to be 'true'. To achieve high accuracy, it is necessary for an estimate to have a good reliability (high precision) and small deviation from true value (low bias). Bias is measured in terms of relative deviation (RD) and precision of estimate is measured in terms of coefficient of variation (CV) of the remote sensing based estimation.

$$RD = \frac{RS - RT}{RS} \times 100$$

where RS is remote sensing based estimate, RT is the 'true value' from external standard (for example, Department of Economics and Statistics data) or internal standard (estimate from wall to wall GT or high resolution aerial photography, Dutta et. al., 1994; Singh et. al., 2005). When a supervised classification is used to estimate the area covered by a land cover type, this estimation can have bias depending up on misclassification and the relative proportion of commission and omission error. Confusion matrices (Section 10.3) computed on training sites that have not been used as training for the image classification can be used for estimating accuracy of area estimation (Gonzalez-Alonso and Cuevas, 1993). Craig and Atkinson, 2013, gives a literature review of crop area estimation.

A number of investigations have been carried out to identify factors which affect the crop identification accuracy. This is summarised by Dadhwal, 1999, and is given below.

The spectral, spatial and radiometric characteristics of the sensor affects crop identification. Data collected by sensors with higher spectral and radiometric resolution, in general, lead to higher classification accuracy (Dadhwal and Parihar, 1988, 1990). The use of higher spatial resolution can sometimes lead to lower classification accuracy (when one uses only spectral information) than moderate resolution, especially when training sites and locations are kept constant, due to increased variance of training sites (Medhavy et. al., 1993). Markham and Townshend (1981) have shown that two counteracting factors affect classification accuracy as a function of spatial resolution. With higher spatial resolution, spectral heterogeneity (scene noise) increases leading to higher overlap between classes and decreased classification accuracy. But, the proportion of boundary pixels reduces, which leads to reduced misclassification. The final accuracy obtained is dependent on the relative importance of these two factors but cannot be predicted since it is also 'dependent in a complex way on relative location of categories within the feature space' (Markham and Townshend, 1981). Inclusion of new spectral regions can bring more information that can be used in crop discrimination. Thus, classification using SWIR as one of the bands shows improved crop separability in wheat, gram and mustard growing regions (Dadhwal et. al., 1989). Similar results have been obtained for groundnut – other crop separation (Sharma et. al., 1995) and rice – other vegetation separation (Panigrahy et. al., 1992). Even in SWIR regions, better crop discriminability using TM band 5 (1.55–1.75μm) in comparison to TM band 7 (2.08–2.35μm) has been observed, which could be related to the higher within-crop variability in TM band 7 (Dadhwal et. al., 1996).

The important scene characteristics influencing classification accuracy are time of acquisition and atmospheric conditions during satellite pass. For wheat acreage estimation, usage of data acquired early in comparison to peak vegetative growth stage leads to under estimation of acreage. The field size was shown to have a strong effect on classification accuracy, small fields tending to have low accuracies even when the effect of mixed pixels was eliminated due to adjacency effect (see Section A1.2) (Dadhwal et. al., 1991).

Timeliness of the availability of acquired data is important to generate timely prediction. Thus the 'turn around time' (TAT—the time between the acquisition of the data and its availability to the end user) of the data product should be kept as minimum as possible. Non-availability of data at the right season due to cloud cover is the major constraint for use of OIR data. This necessitates the use of microwave data, which has all-weather capability.

Study of C band SAR data from ERS and RADARSAT has established the feasibility of using SAR for discrimination of rice crop (Panigrahy et. al., 1999; Panigrahy et. al., 1997). Radar backscatter increases with time from planting to the reproductive phase of the growth cycle (Fig. 4.49). It is found that multi-temporal backscattering observation is essential to improve classification accuracy. SAR multi-temporal data is not suitable for maximum likelihood (MXL) classification. Therefore, Chakraborty et. al., 1997, 2005, developed a specialised classification technique for rice area estimation which has an accuracy of more than 90% for rice acreage estimation at an all India level. Haldar et. al. (2014) developed the procedure to discriminate jute crop using three date SAR data. Subsequent to availability of SAR data from India SAR satellite RISAT 1, these procedures are used for district and state level rice (Kharif and Rabi) and jute area estimation under FASAL project (Ray and Neetu, 2017).

11.1.1.2 Yield Forecasting

The conventional procedure for crop yield estimation by the Bureau of Economics and Statistics (BES) in India involves crop cutting experiments (CCE) conducted during harvesting in the plots selected based on a pre-designed sampling scheme using available ground data (Dadhwal and Ray, 2000). This has the major drawback that the stratification based on the past crop pattern may not be applicable for the current season. Stratification for CCE can be improved by using NDVI data derived from images (Murthy et. al., 1994; Murthy et. al., 1996; Singh et. al., 1992). However, CCE based information is available only at post harvest and hence is not a forecast. Therefore, this information is not very useful for planning of procurement/ pricing strategy.

Crop yield forecasting using remote sensing is more complex than cropped area estimation, because of the high variability involved. Crop yield is a function of various parameters such as soil, weather, cultivation practice, fertiliser used, irrigation, date of sowing, genotype, pests and diseases. Spectral data of a crop is a manifestation of the overall effect of all these factors on its growth. There can be two broad approaches for the use of remote sensing data in yield forecasting. Remote sensing observed data in the form of some kind of vegetation index can be correlated with crop yield, based on the actual field data. Thus, an empirical relationship can be established. In the second case, some biophysical parameter which is derived based on remote sensing observation (say leaf area index) can be one of the input parameters in yield prediction models (for example, crop simulation model).

Empirical regression model

Here the basic assumption is that certain plant parameters such as, leaf area index (LAI), biomass, and so on, at the critical stage of plant growth are related to yield. Field experiments have shown that these plant parameters can be related to one of the vegetation indices (VI) derived from remote sensing data. Many investigators have used single date data near heading/ anthesis and found a good correlation between yield and average VI. Usually, a linear regression equation as given below is used,

$$Y = A + B \times VI \qquad (11.1)$$

where, Y is yield, usually expressed as quintal/hectare, and A and B are constants. The constants can be derived using the yield and VI from past data. Though this approach is simple, the accuracy achieved is not good, as only 65% to 80% of yield variability is explained by the variation of VI. It was also found that the coefficients of the regression equation (that is, A and B) are not constant, but changes with cultivars, environments and agronomic practices. In tropical countries like India, it is at times difficult to get even a single day cloud free image during the appropriate bio-window. It has been observed that a shift in the data acquisition of one week from peak vegetative stage introduces an error of 0.6% in yield prediction. A solution to the problem is to use remote sensing data for the entire growth cycle of a crop. Various growth parameters of the spectral growth curve seen in Section 4.1.1 can also be used in the empirical model (Dubey et. al., 1991; Potdar, 1993; Kalubarme et. al., 1997; Ray et. al., 1999; Manjunath and Potdar, 2004). SAR backscatter from the crop has also been used for crop parameter estimation. Chakraborty et. al. (2005) could estimate rice crop parameters (phenology and plant height) using multi-temporal, multi-incidence angle Radarsat SAR data. This study was extended to estimate rice canopy biomass from SAR data by Choudhury et. al. (2007). Once biomass is estimated with high confidence, it can be multiplied with Harvest Index (available from literature or through field experiments) to get the final yield. Harvest Index is the ratio of crop yield and the above ground biomass.

Remote sensing with other parameters

When only remote sensing derived parameter does not explain the variability in the district level yield, attempts have been made to include other yield controlling parameters such as agro-meteorological variables and time trend variables (which show the combined effect of technological improvements on yield, expressed as a function of chronological year) (Dadhwal and Ray, 2000). Kalubarme et. al. (1995) developed agromet-spectral-yield models for two zones in Punjab using district level area weighted NDVI, trend predicted yields and meteorological indices like growing degree days (GDD) and temperature difference (TD) accumulated over critical growth phases of wheat.

$$Y(q/ha) = A + B.X_1 + C.X_2 + D.X_3 + E.X_4 \tag{11.2}$$

where, X_1 = NDVI, X_2 = temperature range at the reproductive phase = $T_{max} - T_{min}$, T_{max} and T_{min} are maximum and minimum temperatures, X_3 = growing degree day (GDD) = $\frac{1}{2}(T_{max} + T_{min}) - T_b$ where, T_b is the base temperature below which, physiological activity of the crop ceases, X_4 = trend predicted yield and A, B, C, D, E are coefficients of the equation.

There are various other methods for yield prediction. Interested readers may refer to Bouman (1995), Nieuwenhuis and Mucher (1998), Doraiswamy et. al. (2003), Dorigo et. al. (2007) and FAO (2016).

11.1.2 MULTIPLE IN-SEASON CROP PRODUCTION FORECAST

The CAPE project was based on the use of multispectral data acquired at the peak of the concerned crop cycle using Maximum Likelihood Classification (MXL) technique of stratified sample segments. It established the methodology of state level forecasting of major crops like wheat and rice. While the results of the CAPE project were used and performance was evaluated, the need for national scale, multiple, in-season forecasts was expressed by the Ministry of Agriculture, Govt of India. Realising that remote sensing data alone cannot provide multiple and reliable forecasts, and examining the relative strength and weakness of each system of information gathering on crops, led to the formulation of an integrated approach called 'Forecasting Agricultural output using Space, Agro-meteorology and Land-based observations (FASAL)' (Parihar and Oza, 2006). As remote sensing, weather and field observations provide complementary and supplementary information for making crop forecasts, FASAL used an approach which integrated inputs from the three types of observations to make forecasts of desired coverage, accuracy and timeliness. The concept of FASAL thus strengthens the capabilities of early season crop estimation from econometric and weather-based techniques followed by the use of remote sensing data at an appropriate stage.

Under the FASAL approach, the first (before sowing) crop forecasts are given using econometric models, which is revised using early season weather data. During the mid-season, moderate resolution remote sensing data is used for crop area estimation, which is combined with ground truth data and agro-meteorological yield models. Pre-harvest production forecasts are given using high resolution remote sensing data and remote sensing based yield models. These forecasts are revised, if there is any crop damage due to some disaster. For crops like rice and wheat, selected crop cutting experiments (around 100–200 in each state) are carried out using the sampling plan based on remote sensing data. These data are also used

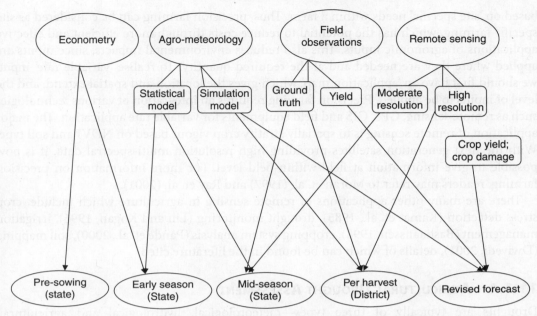

Fig. 11.1(b)   Conceptual framework for multiple crop production forecasting under FASAL.
(*Source:* Ray and Neetu, 2017)

for improving crop forecasts. Figure 11.1b gives the conceptual framework for multiple crop production forecasting under FASAL.

The FASAL project was approved the Ministry of Agriculture in 2007. Under the FASAL project, approaches were developed for multiple pre-harvest crop production forecasting at District–State–National levels for seven major crops—rice (kharif and rabi), wheat, rapeseed and mustard, cotton, sugarcane, sorghum (rabi) and jute. After maturity of the technology, it was transferred to the newly established centre (Mahalanobis National Crop Forecast Centre, MNCFC) under the Ministry of Agriculture and Farmers' Welfare. MNCFC operationally prepares the crop production forecasts, in collaboration with State Agriculture Departments, State Remote Sensing Centres, Space Applications Centre, India Meteorological Department and State Agricultural Universities. Currently, under the FASAL project, national and state level multiple forecasts are being issued for 5 crops—rice (kharif and rabi), jute, rapeseed and mustard, winter potato and wheat. From 2013–2014 onwards, state and district level forecasts are generated for cotton, sugarcane and rabi (winter season) sorghum (Ray et. al., 2015).

11.1.3   PRECISION FARMING

In conventional cropping practice, a similar dose of fertiliser, water and other inputs are applied to the whole farm. However, the input requirement may not be the same in the entire area. If we can find out various 'homogenous management zones' within a farm, based on the information of soil fertility, crop vigour and soil moisture, the inputs could be tailored for each specific site. The goal of precision farming is to gather and analyse information about the spatial variability of soil and crop conditions in order to optimise the efficiency of crop inputs based on 'site specific' needs within a farm. Thus, precision farming can be considered as site specific farming, which has the potential to reduce costs through more efficient and effective applications of agronomic inputs. This also reduces environmental impacts, since inputs are applied where they are needed and at the required quantity. To realise 'variable rate' input, we should first have an 'application map', which gives the location and spatial extend, and the level of inputs to be applied. Precision farming requires an integration of various technologies such as remote sensing, GPS, GIS and field equipments for variable rate application. The major application of remote sensing is to spatially stratify crop vigour based on NDVI and soil type. With the next generation satellites providing high resolution multi-spectral data, it is now possible to give information at field/within-field level. For more information on precision farming, readers may refer to Moran et. al. (1997) and Ray et. al. (2001).

There are many other applications of remote sensing in agriculture which include, crop stress detection (Kamat et. al., 1985), drought monitoring (Liu and Kogan, 1996), irrigation management (Bastiaanssen, 1998), cropping system analysis (Pande et. al., 2000), soil mapping (Dwivedi, 2001), details of which can be found in the literature cited.

11.1.4   AGRICULTURAL DROUGHT ASSESSMENT

Droughts are typically of three types—meteorological, hydrological and agricultural. Meteorological drought occurs when the actual rainfall in an area is significantly less than the climatological mean of that area or the distribution is very poor. Hydrological drought takes place when there is a marked depletion of surface water causing very low stream flow and drying of lakes, rivers and reservoirs. Agricultural drought happens when crops get affected due to inadequate soil moisture resulting in acute crop stress and fall in agricultural productivity. Timely information about the onset, magnitude and duration of drought during a crop cycle is crucial to establish local/national agricultural drought strategies. The conventional method for monitoring drought is most often based on point or sample observations which are averaged over an area and hence do not provide the actual impact of drought situation of the region under study. Usually drought impact is seen over large areas and hence it is laborious to monitor them at district/state level using conventional systems. As vegetation abundance and condition (vigour) are strongly related to the overall effect of rainfall, soil moisture, weather and agricultural practices, space-based remote sensing is the best tool to make observations on vegetative cover at regional and global level to provide a basis for agricultural drought monitoring. A number of indices have been derived from remote sensing data to assess vegetation status. One of the most extensively used indices is the normalised difference vegetation index (NDVI) (Section 4.1.1). The NDVI is a measure of greenness or vigour of vegetation. It varies from +1 to −1. NDVI values of 0.1 and below corresponds to barren areas of rock and sand while high values of (0.6–0.8) indicate temperate and tropical rainforests. NDVI derived from AVHRR and MODIS has been extensively used for drought assessment.

Owing to the strong absorption of vegetation water content in the Short Wave Infra Red (SWIR) region, a remote sensing index incorporating SWIR can provide an integrated measure of the amount of water contained in the foliage canopy and hence could be a good indicator for drought. The index – Normalised Difference Water Index (NDWI) – is derived using radiation detected in NIR and SWIR and is given by

$$NDWI = \frac{NIR - SWIR}{NIR + SWIR}$$

There are many other vegetation indices derived from remote sensing data for drought assessment (Wu et. al., 2014).

The vegetation indices itself do not reflect drought or non-drought conditions. When considering NDVI the intensity of vegetative drought can be inferred from the deviation of the current NDVI (that is, measured during the period of interest) from its long-term average of the same period (Rulinda et. al., 2012). An index, which has been developed to account for long term data in NDVI, is called Vegetation Condition Index (VCI) (Kogan, 1995), which when expressed in percentage is given by,

$$VCI = \frac{(NDVI_{cur} - NDVI_{min})}{(NDVI_{max} - NDVI_{min})} \times 100$$

where $NDVI_{cur}$, is the current NDVI for the location under consideration and $NDVI_{max}$ and $NDVI_{min}$ are the maximum and minimum values of NDVI for that location taken from a long-term dataset (at least ten years) for the same period of the year. VCI can be expressed in terms of NDWI also in the same way explained earlier but NDVI replaced by NDWI. Thus, VCI compares the current NDVI/NDWI to the range of values of same period in earlier years. VCI is expressed in percentage. The VCI gives an idea where the current value is placed within the extreme values (minimum and maximum) in the historical datasets normalised to a scale of 0%–100%. Lower and higher values indicate bad and good vegetation status conditions, respectively. VCI is a promising index in that it has the advantage of being comparable over space and time on account of the normalisation of differences in cropping patterns, crop calendars, atmospheric parameters. The limitation arises from the requirement of long term time series data for NDVI/NDWI (at least 10 years) and the risk of VCI values getting affected by the differences in cropping patterns, crop calendars and atmospheric parameters (DAC&FW, 2016).

The commonly used NDVI from remote sensing, often falls short in real-time drought monitoring due to a lagged vegetation response to drought. Therefore the use of combination of surface temperature and NDVI which provides vegetation and moisture conditions simultaneously has been used for monitoring drought (Patel et. al., 2012). Remote sensing derived indices are used along with meteorological, hydrological and agricultural parameters for agricultural drought assessment (Liu and Kogan, 1996).

In India, the National Agricultural Drought Assessment and Monitoring System (NADAMS), developed by the Indian Space Research Organisation, uses satellite, ground and meteorological data for periodic assessment of agricultural drought. The NADAMS programme, which is now being implemented by Mahalanobis National Crop Forecast Centre, provides district/sub-district level drought assessment for 14 major drought-prone agricultural states of India (Ray et. al., 2014). The agriculture drought assessment and monitoring, under NADAMS project, is carried out using multiple satellite data, rainfall, soil moisture index, potential sowing area, irrigation percentage and ground observations. A logical modelling approach is followed to classify the districts into *Alert, Watch and Normal* during June, July and August and *Severe, Moderate and Mild* drought conditions during September and October. The monthly Drought Assessment Reports are communicated to all concerned state and national level agencies and also published on the MNCFC website (www.ncfc.gov.in). Recently, the Government of India, brought out the Drought Manual (DAC&FW, 2016), which identifies remote sensing based indices (NDVI/NDVI deviation or VCI) as one of the four categories of impact indicators to be used for drought declaration.

11.2 FORESTRY APPLICATION

Forests are one of the most valuable ecological resources of global interest. They are the source for many of our essential requirements such as fuelwood, timber and raw material for paper. In addition, forests play an important role in balancing the earth's CO_2 supply and exchange. Forests also provide the habitat for numerous animal species. People generally consider the product of forests rather than the forests themselves as useful. This leads to biotic interference of the forests. Thus our forests are continuously disappearing at an alarming rate. A study by FAO shows that the overall forest area is decreasing at the rate of 11.25 million ha/year for the period 1990–1995 (Russian federation excluded), which is about 0.33% of the global forest cover. It is now well established that the decrease of forest cover will create a number of serious environmental problems such as soil erosion, flood, increase in CO_2 affecting climate, and will seriously affect the bio-diversity. Unfortunately, in the past, the degrading trend of the forest has not been taken up very seriously. With the Rio Conference in 1992, eco-consciousness has found a place in national and global policies. Thus, sustainable development of our renewable resources has been taken up seriously. Sustainable forest management requires reliable information on the type, density and extent of forest cover, wood volume and biomass, forest fire, pest and disease induced losses and encroachment to name a few vital areas. Hence, there is a need for timely, reliable information and integration of this information in management decision-making. More emphasis is laid on estimation of changes, which requires periodic inventory of forest resources. Remote sensing provides potential to improve upon the conventional in situ monitoring.

Early methods used to compile information about forests is from interpreting aerial photographs. panchromatic, B and W IR and CIR photographs were extensively used to find out species and density (here density refers to crown cover). The photographic characteristics of tone, texture, shape and pattern, as mentioned in Chapter 10 are used in interpreting the data. With the advent of space-based remote sensing, traditional aerial photographs are being replaced by satellite imagery. Both visual and digital interpretation have been used. The broad areas in forestry for which remote sensing techniques can be used are

- mapping/statistics generation of forest cover,
- change detection, and
- modelling for resource management.

This is shown schematically in Fig. 11.2. The first two activities are essentially carried out either by visual interpretation or by digital classification. The third uses remote sensing derived information as one (some) of the inputs along with other databases in a GIS environment and a model to generate the final derived product.

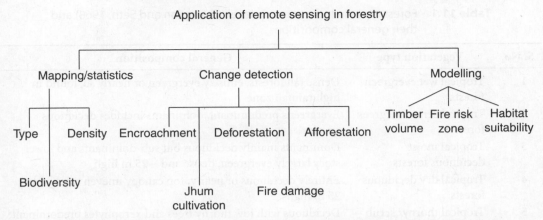

Fig. 11.2   Possible application of remote sensing in forestry. The list is not exhaustive, but only indicative.

All this information in a GIS environment can generate various scenarios for forest management plans at local, national or global scales, depending on the level of details available. We shall now discuss the details of some of these possibilities, with special reference to India.

11.2.1   TYPE AND DENSITY MAPPING

Forest type is defined as a unit of vegetation, which possesses (broad) characteristics in physiognomy (external appearance) and structure, sufficiently pronounced to permit its differentiation from other such units (Champion and Seth, 1968); that is, association of different species forming a community. They are evolved and distributed as per the bio-climate, physiography, altitude zones, soil types and human interaction. Champion and Seth documented the forest types of India for the first time based on systematic inventories. They attempted forest type classification of India based on broad climatic, physiographic, soil and local conditions, with five major types, 16 type groups, 46 sub-types and 221 ecologically stable formations in different geographic zones. Reddy et. al. (2015), give an account of nationwide classification of forest types of India using remote sensing and GIS based on multi-season IRS Resourcesat-2 Advanced Wide Field Sensor (AWiFS) data. Tropical dry deciduous and tropical moist deciduous forests account for more than 60% of the forest cover of India. Table 11.1 gives first level 16 groups.

Forest Canopy Density (FCD) is a major factor in evaluating forest status and is an important indicator for possible management action plan. Forest canopy cover or crown cover, is defined as the proportion of the forest floor covered by the vertical projection of the tree crowns (Jennings et. al., 1999). FCD refers to the proportion of an area in the field/ground that is covered by the crown of trees and is expressed in percentage of the total area. Various density classifications as per the Forest Survey of India (FSI) are as follows.

- *Very dense forest* All lands with tree canopy density of 70% and more.
- *Moderately dense forest* All lands with tree canopy density of 40% and more but less than 70%.
- *Open forest* All lands with canopy density of 10% and more but less than 40%.
- *Scrub* Degraded forest lands with canopy density less than 10%.

Table 11.1 Forest types in India at group level (Champion and Seth, 1968) and their general composition

S. No.	Vegetation type	General composition
1	Tropical wet evergreen forests	Dense tall forests, entirely evergreen or nearly so, found in high rainfall zone
2	Tropical semi-evergreen forests	Evergreens predominant, dominants includes deciduous species
3	Tropical moist deciduous forests	Dominants mainly deciduous but sub-dominants and lower story largely evergreen, dense and ~ 25 m high
4	Tropical dry deciduous forests	Entirely deciduous or nearly; top canopy uneven rarely over 25 m high
5	Tropical thorny/ scrub forests	Deciduous with low thorny trees and xerophytes predominant, top canopy more or less broken, less than 10 m high
6	Tropical dry evergreen forests	Hard leaved evergreen trees predominate with some deciduous emergent often dense but usually under 20 m high
7	Littoral and swampy forests	Mainly evergreens of varying density and height but always associated predominantly with wetness
8	Subtropical broad-leaved hill forests	Broad-leaved largely evergreen high forests
9	Subtropical pine forests	Pine associated predominates
10	Subtropical dry evergreen forests	Low xerophytic forest and scrubs
11	Montane wet temperate forests	Evergreen without coniferous species
12	Himalayan wet/ moist temperate forests	Evergreen forests mainly scleriphyllous oak and coniferous species
13	Himalayan dry temperate forests	Coniferous forests with sparse xerophytic undergrowth
14	Sub-alpine forests	Stunted deciduous or evergreen forests, usually close formation with or without confers
15	Moist alpine	Low but often dense scrub of evergreen species
16	Dry alpine	Xerophytic scrub in open formation mostly of deciduous in nature

As mentioned earlier, forest maps can be prepared from satellite/aerial imagery using either visual interpretation or digital classification. Forest maps are prepared on various scales from small (1:1 million) to large (>1:12,500) depending upon the need. The scale of a map is related to the information content of the map and thus, holds high importance. Nationwide forest mapping in India was done initially on a 1:1 million scale. Such maps, which depict broad forest types or densities, were used in national level planning. Maps on a 1:250,000 scale depict larger number of forest type/densities and enable mapping of the relatively smaller forest patches. In forestry, such maps have found their use at the Forest Circle level for large area development. Forest management maps made on a 1:50,000 scale allows their use at Forest Division level. Micro-level planning in forestry requires larger scale maps on a 1:25,000 scale keeping in view the average size of the Forest Subdivision, Range and Beat. Such maps show details of different forest patches, block plantations, forest blanks, degradation and thus prove to be helpful in field level working. IRS LISS-I (70 m) and LISS-II (36 m) could be used for mapping at a 1:250,000 and 1:50,000 scale respectively. IRS LISS-III (23 m) and PAN (5 m) data together support preparation of 1:25,000 scale maps. Experience has shown that merging of LISS-III and PAN data is advantageous compared to one of them alone. IRS PAN data has also been used for the preparation of maps on larger than a 1:25,000 scale and have been found useful in delineation of smaller forest patches, strip plantations and so on. Mapping on a 1:25,000 scale can be taken as optimal, for planning at forest sub-subdivision, considering various aspects of forest resources survey and mapping tasks. IKONOS/IRS-CARTOSAT data (about 2.5 m ground resolution and better) could be used to prepare maps of scale larger than 1:12,500. Such maps will be highly useful for growing stock estimation (using stratified random sampling) and revision/updation of detailed stock maps. However, the effort needed is tremendous due to large data volume.

The choice of spectral bands and the season during which the image is acquired are very important to reduce classification error. The study of Roy et. al. (1991) shows that visual interpretation of vegetation types can be improved by using various enhancement techniques compared to using standard False Colour Composite of G, R and NIR bands. Roy et. al. (1993) studied various band combination of LANDSAT TM data with a view to optimise the combination of spectral bands which provides highest accuracy to discriminate forest types using supervised classification. The study area was Baratong forest division of Andaman Island. The study shows the band combination 2, 3, 4 and 5 (G, R, NIR, SWIR) for LANDSAT TM gave the best results. Addition of band 2 only marginally improved the accuracy compared to 3, 4 and 5. Hence, the authors have suggested that a colour composite of 3, 4 and 5 bands should be good for visual interpretation.

The repetitive coverage provided by the satellite helps in selecting the optimum season/period data for forest studies. Proper seasons for studying natural forest cover in different bioclimatic regions and vegetation zones are given in Table 11.2.

Table 11.2   Proper season for studying natural forest cover in different bio-climatic regions and vegetation zones

	Region/Vegetation Zone/Geographical Set-up	Proper season
1	Humid and moist evergreen and semi-evergreen vegetation in the Western and Eastern Ghats	January–February
2	Humid and moist evergreen and semi-evergreen vegetation of the North-Eastern region and Andaman and Nicobar Islands	February–March
3	Tropical moist deciduous vegetation of Northern and Central India	December–January
4	Temperate evergreen vegetation of Western Himalayas	March–May
5	Temperate, sub-alpine, alpine, evergreen and deciduous vegetation of Jammu and Kashmir	September–October
6	Arid and semi-arid dry deciduous and scrub vegetation	October–December
7	Tropical coastal mangrove vegetation	February–March

Source: Ranganath et. al., 2000

11.2.2 FOREST COVER CHANGE

Multi-date assessment of the forests in terms of either density or type provides the opportunity to monitor the changes in the forest area over a period of time by studying multi-temporal images. Various methods of change detection have been used by various workers. They range from direct visual comparison to image differencing using automatic techniques. Such change detection methods facilitate assessment of fire damage, encroachment, afforestation, and so on. Kimothi and Jadhav (1998) have used multi-temporal IRS LISS-1 data to assess the extent and spatial distribution of forest fire. Another practical example is the encroachment studies carried out in the Sanjay Gandhi National Park, Borivali, Maharashtra and in a few other places (Jadhav, 1995). Judicial courts have found remote sensing and GIS-based techniques reliable and three cases have been disposed off based on these findings. Change detection techniques also help in the assessment of forest degradation, deforestation, afforestation/reforestation and joint forest management (JFM) related forest cover change monitoring.

11.2.3 FOREST STATUS IN INDIA

India with only 2.5% of the world's geographic area, is at present supporting 17.5% of the world's population and 11.6% of the cattle population (2011 census). India is rich in biodiversity (biodiversity is defined as the variability among living organisms from all sources, including terrestrial, marine and other aquatic ecosystems and ecological complexes of which they are a part; this includes diversity within species, between species and ecosystems). India is one of the 17 mega diversity countries of the world. 11.4% of the world's recorded flora and about 7.43% of the world's recorded faunal species are in the Indian subcontinent (Singh and Dash, 2014). Hence, protection of forests which are the major contributors to the flora and fauna is not only of national importance but of global interest to preserve the biodiversity of the planet.

Therefore it is important to periodically monitor to assess the status of the forest. The forest cover map of India using satellite data was first carried out by the National Remote Sensing Agency (NRSA). The data from Landsat MSS was used to generate the forest cover map of India on a 1:1 M scale. NRSA interpreted MSS data during the period 1972–1975 and 1980–1982 to determine the change in the forest cover during the 7 year period. Thereafter, Forest Survey of India generates the State of Forest Report (FSR) every two years with satellite data as one of the inputs.

The total geographic area (TGA) of India is 328.7 million ha and forest cover is supposed to be 23.4% of the TGA. However, as per the latest Forest Survey of India (FSI) report (FSI, 2015), the actual forest cover is only 70.17 million ha which is 21.34% of the TGA. Of this, only about 50% has crown density >40% (the FSI estimate does not include about 16 million ha of tree cover on non-forest land). Due to large human and cattle population and widespread rural poverty, the forest of the country is subject to enormous pressure resulting in deforestation and degradation. The major factors contributing to this phenomenon are overgrazing, over-exploitation for fuelwood, forest fires, shifting cultivation and diversion of forest land by encroachment. Realising the seriousness of depletion and degradation of forests, the Government of India has evolved a forest policy and enacted a number of laws to ensure protection of the existing forest land and to have a massive afforestation drive with the participation of the people. In the context of the National Forest Policy of 1988, the Joint Forest Management (JFM) program has been initiated wherein state forest departments support local forest dwelling and forest fringe communities to protect and manage forests and share the costs and benefits from the forests with them, thereby protecting and sustainable exploitation of the forest as a peoples' movement.

11.3   LAND COVER/LAND USE MAPPING

In order to use land optimally, it is necessary to have information on existing land cover/land use, and the capability to monitor the dynamics of land use resulting out of newer demands of increasing population and changed lifestyles. Some of the areas in which land cover/land use maps are important include preparation of development plans both in rural and urban sectors, environmental impact assessment, environmental hazard zonation, utility and infrastructure planning, and so on. The properties derived from remote sensing techniques relate to land cover, from which to infer land use, one may require ancillary data or a priori knowledge. Both visual and digital analysis techniques are employed for the preparation of land cover/land use maps using satellite data. Use of three season data (*Kharif*–rainy season, *Rabi*–winter season and summer) improves the accuracy and are hence recommended for preparation of the land cover/land use maps. The classification systems adopted for land cover/land use mapping at different levels of classification are hierarchical in nature. Land cover/land use mapping at National level on a 1:250,000 scale has been carried out for the entire country using satellite data (Rao et. al., 1996).

Spatial information on land cover/land use is required at different scales depending upon its use. We have seen in Chapter 5 that the scale of a map refers to the ratio of a distance on a map to the corresponding distance on ground. When digital data is converted to a map, the spatial resolution plays a role on the scale of mapping. The information content that can be extracted depends on the map scale. Thus digital data with a particular spatial resolution can generate map only up to a certain scale and in a map higher than this scale, no additional details can be seen. For example, an image with 100 metre spatial resolution can be represented at a scale of 1:250,000, which can give Level-I information (Chapter 10). Thus we can identify say, urban area in the image. However, if the same data is represented at 1:50,000 by zooming (enlarging), the details available are still the same (we cannot see Level-II information such as built up area, parks, and others, which is normally possible at 1:50,000 scale.) Hence the scale of mapping of digital data has to take into consideration the spatial resolution of the basic data. Based on the number of studies, Ajai (2002) has given an indicative guideline for resolution, scale of mapping and its usage (Table 11.3).

Table 11.3   Spatial resolution, scale and area coverage for thematic mapping

Spatial resolution	Scale	Area coverage
200 m–1 km	1 : 1–5 million	Regional
70–100 m	1 : 250,000	National/state
20–40 m	1 : 50,000	District
10–15 m	1 : 25,000	Tehsil/block
1–5 m	1 : 4000–10,000	Village/implementation level

Source: Ajay, 2002

11.3.1 WASTELANDS

Improper land management, excessive irrigation without proper drainage and uncontrolled use of chemicals has resulted in vast stretches of wasteland which are salt affected, water-logged or gullied.

Mapping of wastelands and their type is required to chalk out programs of reclamation for productive use such as afforestation, establishing industry, infrastructure and other development activities. National Remote Sensing Centre (NRSC, formerly NRSA) at the instance of National Wasteland Development Board—NWDB (currently Department of Land Resources—DoLR) initiated mapping of wastelands at a 1:50000 scale in 1986 and completed the mapping task for the entire country in 14 years in a phased manner using satellite data and identified 13 categories. These maps were of immense help in identifying different types of wastelands, their spatial distribution and extent for undertaking appropriate reclamation measures. Afterward wastelands maps were generated using multi-season satellite data of 2005–06 and adopted a classification system with 23 categories of wastelands. At the request of DoLR, NRSC took up mapping of wastelands in the 2008–2009 time frame (Fig. 11.3) and studied the changes in spatial distribution of wastelands between 2005–06 and 2008–09.

These studies have been carried out using 3-season Resourcesat-1 LISS-III data on a 1:50000 scale. The 3-season (belonging to *kharif*, *rabi* and *zaid* seasons of 2008–09) satellite data was geo-rectified with that of 2005–06. Survey of India topo maps on a 1:50000 scale were used as reference. The wasteland vector layer of 2005–06 was overlaid with the geo-rectified satellite data of 2008–09, and changed areas/categories/polygons were updated. These changes were later confirmed using limited ground checks and the wasteland change vector layer of 2008–09 was generated. The main goal of the study is to bring out the spatial changes of various wasteland categories during 2005–06 and 2008–09 for the whole country on a 1:50,000 scale. The comparative study shows that compared to 2005–06, during 2008–09 about 32,000 sq. km of wasteland has undergone a positive change in the entire country by getting converted into non-wasteland.

11.3.2 URBAN SPRAWL

Urban sprawl refers to the process, whereby urban developments spread out and interfere with the ecosystems that are vital to the health and survival of the earth. Continuous migration of rural population to urban centres/settlements, results in overcrowding and puts pressure on infrastructure facilities.

Haphazard urban sprawl also decreases productive agricultural land and open space. To address these issues effectively, planners require up-to-date information on urban land use. Visual/digital/hybrid methodology is used to prepare the urban land use maps employing multi-date satellite data. The optimum periods for satellite data acquisitions for urban mapping is October–February for urban land use such as residential, industrial, transportation and recreational, and April–May and August–September for delineating flood hazard areas. Urban sprawl is one of the important inputs for the preparation of urban development plans. Satellite images pertaining to winter season, at the interval of every 3–5 years, are required for studying urban sprawl. The urban sprawl map of Ahmedabad city is given in Fig. 11.4.

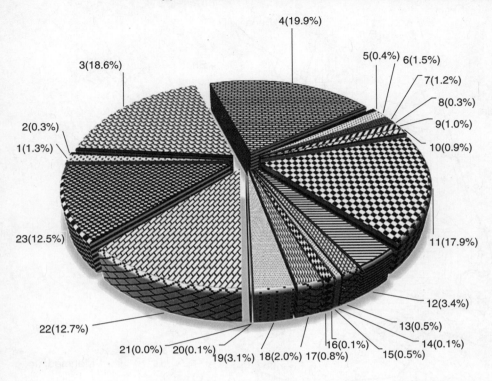

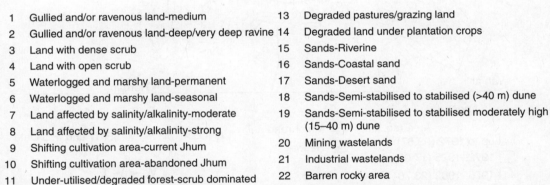

Fig. 11.3   Category-wise wasteland of India and its relative contribution.

1	Gullied and/or ravenous land-medium
2	Gullied and/or ravenous land-deep/very deep ravine
3	Land with dense scrub
4	Land with open scrub
5	Waterlogged and marshy land-permanent
6	Waterlogged and marshy land-seasonal
7	Land affected by salinity/alkalinity-moderate
8	Land affected by salinity/alkalinity-strong
9	Shifting cultivation area-current Jhum
10	Shifting cultivation area-abandoned Jhum
11	Under-utilised/degraded forest-scrub dominated
12	Agricultural land inside notified forest land
13	Degraded pastures/grazing land
14	Degraded land under plantation crops
15	Sands-Riverine
16	Sands-Coastal sand
17	Sands-Desert sand
18	Sands-Semi-stabilised to stabilised (>40 m) dune
19	Sands-Semi-stabilised to stabilised moderately high (15–40 m) dune
20	Mining wastelands
21	Industrial wastelands
22	Barren rocky area
23	Snow cover and/or glacial area

Site suitability analysis for selection of best possible sites for urban and infrastructure development is carried out using multi-thematic layers in GIS environment (Pathan et. al., 1991, 1993). These include, land use, physiography, slope, soils, hydrogeomorphology/ground water prospects, surface water bodies, natural hazards (earthquake, flood and erosion), heritage sites and land values. Many of the thematic maps required are prepared by interpretation of multi-date satellite data. Urban land use suitability analysis can be carried out using multivariate index analysis. This is further elaborated in Section 11.6.4.

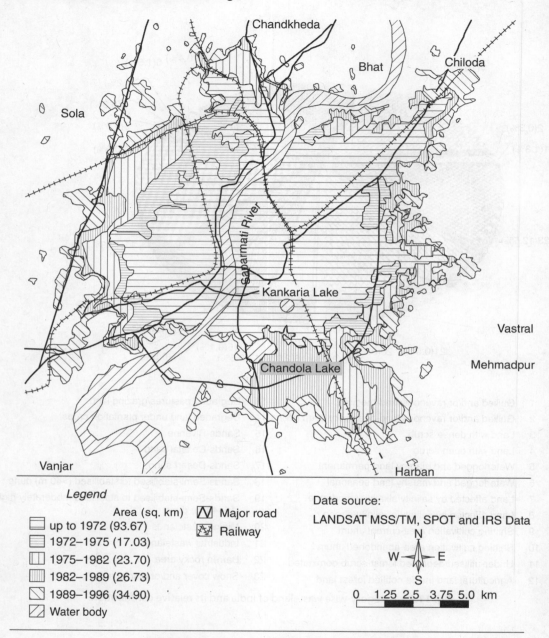

Fig. 11.4 Urban sprawl map of Ahmedabad city.

11.4 WATER RESOURCES

The synoptic and repetitive information provided by orbital sensors is integrated with in situ data for development and management of water resources. Remote sensing data has been used in many applications related to water resources such as surface water body mapping, ground water targeting, wetland inventory, flood monitoring, reservoir sedimentation, water quality monitoring, run-off modelling, snow cover monitoring, glacier inventory, glacial mass balance studies, irrigation water management, and many more. One of the most simple applications is inventorying surface water bodies. In FCC water bodies appear in different hues depending on their physical characteristics such as depth of water (bottom reflection) and turbidity (Plate 11.1). Water absorbs all infrared radiations and thus appears dark. Hence the distinct contrast between water and land in near-infrared band helps in easy distinction. This property is also used for identification of flood inundated areas and wetlands. The periodic inventory of water bodies for its physical and biological parameters is very significant in water management. Some of the parameters amenable to remote sensing are the extent of water spread and its seasonal fluctuation, volume of water, turbidity, emergent and floating vegetation, and so on. The capacity of surface water bodies like ponds and dams are reduced due to silting because of soil erosion. Remote sensing can be used to find out the extent of soil erosion and the consequent sediment load on to the tanks/dams. One can prioritise areas which are more prone to soil erosion so that immediate attention for preventive action by soil conservation techniques can be taken up.

Ground water is one of the most important sources of water. Almost 85% of the rural water supply in India is dependent on ground water (Ministry of Rural Development, Govt of India). Remote sensing plays a vital role in delineating potential areas of ground water occurrence for detailed exploration, thus reducing the cost and time involved in ground water exploration. Ground water occurs in porous and permeable rock formations called aquifers, which facilitate storage and movement of water beneath the earth's surface. Potential ground water areas cannot be seen on satellite images directly. The clue to ground water search is the fact that sub-surface geological elements forming aquifers have almost invariable surface expressions, which can be detected by remote sensing techniques. Satellite data provide information about geomorphic features, structures, land uses and rock types (in a few cases) indicating the presence of ground water. Some selected landforms and structural features that are indicators for potential ground water zones – valley fills, palaeochannels, alluvial fans, dykes, interdunal depression – are described below. Plate 11.2 gives some examples how these appear in satellite imagery.

Valley fills are narrow valleys formed in the hills and over a period of time which are filled with loose, unsorted, coarse sediments. Those with sufficient thickness of loose material form very good aquifers. Alluvial fans are fan-like deposits of loose sediments at the base of the hill slopes facilitating storage and recharge of ground water. Palaeochannels are the ancient streams or riverbeds cut into the surrounding soil or rock, which have been reburied by other sediments after the stream changed its course or dried up. As these comprise loose, unconsolidated and unsorted alluvial material, they form very good ground water aquifers. Dykes are naturally occurring linear or curvilinear bodies (lineaments) of consolidated magma which act as carriers or barriers to water flow. A massive and compact dyke can stop ground water flow thus restricting all the water to the uphill side of the dyke. Sometimes when the dyke is less resistant as compared to the host rocks it breaks up and acts as a carrier of water all along it. In arid and semi arid regions, highly interconnected inter-dunal depressions occur among the dunes and are suitable for storage of water. They usually form shallow aquifers.

Maps showing such information are called hydro-geomorphological maps. Hydro-geomorphological maps showing ground water potential area have been prepared on a 1:250,000 scale for the entire country to provide inputs to scientific source finding for the

National Drinking Water Mission. A typical map is shown in Plate 11.3. These maps are used for identifying potential areas of ground water where detailed geophysical surveys are carried to confirm availability of water. This helps in concentrating the field efforts in areas where greater potential exists and eliminating other zones, thus reducing the cost and time involved in field exploration. Based on the feedback received for more than 1,70,000 bore wells dug based on locations identified using satellite-derived information, it has been observed that the success rate has gone well above 90% compared to the 45% achieved using purely conventional methods alone (Sahai et. al., 1991).

The indiscriminate withdrawal of water from ground water aquifers of limited potential to meet the growing demand has put acute pressure on the ground water aquifers. Erratic and poor rainfall coupled with negligible attempts to recharge or replenish the groundwater aquifer has created an alarming situation. In many aquifers, either the water level has gone down or the aquifers have completely dried up. In coastal aquifers excessive withdrawal has led to salinity ingress.

Optimal water management through harvesting the available rainfall and recharging the underground aquifer appear to be the only solution to the above problems. During water harvesting, water can be stored in surface reservoirs or in underground aquifers. Location of potential sites and zones for this purpose is of utmost significance. Sometimes indicators for suitable sites for water harvesting can be identified directly on the satellite data. For example, if a check dam is constructed at the crossing zone of stream and dyke (that is, vertically extending the dyke on the surface), the dyke itself acts as a barrier and will prevent all surface as well as underground water flow on the uphill side to form a very good surface storage reservoir. Similarly, to facilitate recharge if a check dam is constructed across a stream following or intersected by a fracture, the fracture will allow sufficient water to percolate to cause effective recharge to the ground water aquifer.

In the Himalayas, the glaciers cover about 33,000 sq. km and melt-water forms an important source of run-off for the North Indian rivers during critical summer months. Run-off is one of the most important hydrologic variables used in water resources management. Aerial extent of snow can be mapped repeatedly and the quantity of snowmelt run-off can also be predicted. This information is vital for downhill reservoirs to program the conservation of water resources.

Glacier maps show the extent and location of glaciers and also give certain other glacier features such as ablation area, accumulation area, snow line, and so on. Glacier inventory mapping on a 1:250,000 scale for the entire Himalayan region including Beas, Sutlej and Spiti basins has been done and an atlas prepared. Such maps on a 1:50,000 scale have also been prepared for the Sutlej river basin to map seasonal snow cover areas and specific models developed to estimate snowmelt run-off during summer seasons. These estimates are provided 3–4 months in advance of actual run-off period (Ramamoorthi, 1986). More information on the use of remote sensing for snow and glacier studies is given in Section 11.5.

11.5 SNOW AND GLACIERS

11.5.1 SNOW STUDIES

Snow cover is an important natural resource in the Himalayas. The area under snow can change significantly during winter and spring. Increase in atmospheric temperature can influence snowmelt and stream runoff pattern (Kulkarni et. al., 2002a) which in turn affects stream flow during spring and summer for rivers originating in the Higher Himalayas (Chenab, Beas, Sutlej, Bhagirathi). In addition, snow pack ablation (melting) is highly sensitive to climatic variation. Therefore, mapping of aerial extent and reflectance of snow is an important parameter for avalanche and hydrological applications. Since the accessibility to the Himalayan snow covered region is very difficult, one has to depend on remote sensing for snow cover studies. Therefore, remote sensing techniques have been extensively used for snow cover monitoring in the Himalayan region with the help of numerous satellite sensors such as LISS-I, WiFS, LISS-III, AVHRR, MODIS and AWiFS (Kulkarni and Rathore, 2003). Various analysis techniques such as visual, hybrid (visual and supervised classification), supervised and normalised difference snow index (NDSI) methods have been used to estimate aerial extent of snow cover. Choices of satellite data and interpretation techniques depend upon the purpose of investigation, scale of mapping, frequency of observation required and availability of satellite data.

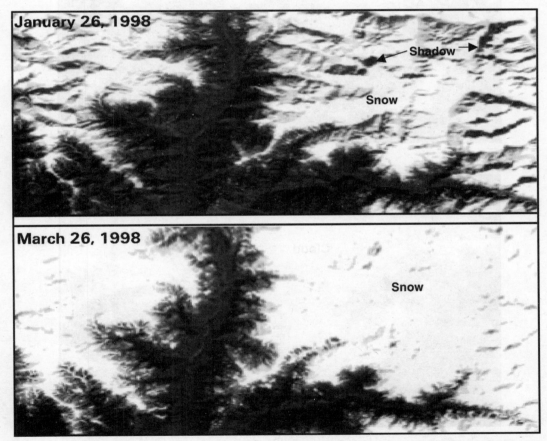

Fig. 11.5   0.62–0.68 μm band imagery of WiFS sensor of IRS. The satellite imagery of 28 January 1998 shows long mountain shadows. Mountain shadows are negligible on 26 March 1998. The amount of cliff shadow depends upon solar elevation and azimuth. In addition, cliff direction is also important, maximum shadow being observed when the cliff is perpendicular to the azimuth of the sun.

Major difficulties in snow cover monitoring using automated techniques in the Himalayan region are mountain shadow and confusing signatures of snow and cloud in the visible and near infrared region. Mountain shadows in the months from November to February normally make it difficult to use digital technique only (Fig. 11.5). From the month of March, mountain shadows are negligible and snow extent can be estimated using the supervised classification technique.

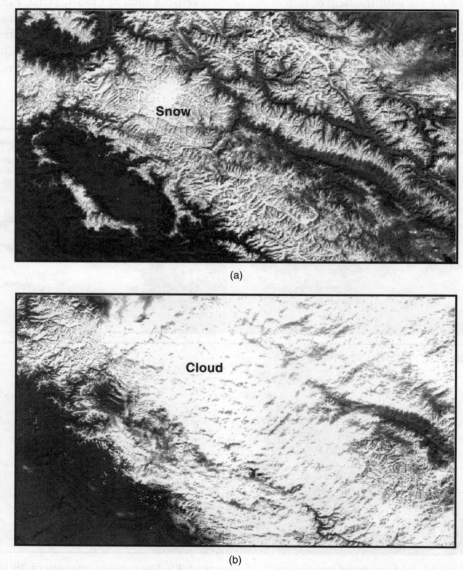

(a)

(b)

Fig. 11.6   Band1 (0.62–0.68 μm) imagery of WiFS of IRS dated 11 January 2001 and 18 December 2000. Note the change in texture, as in imagery (a) valleys and mountains are clearly visible and free of clouds. In imagery (b) texture is smooth and characteristic with the mountain pattern not being visible. This is due to clouds. (*Source:* Kulkarni et. al., 2004)

Another major difficulty in operational snow cover mapping is cloud cover and associated shadow. It is further compounded due to the similar reflectance characteristics of snow and cloud. The discrimination between snow and cloud can be done by using various techniques such as textural analysis, association with shadow and by using multi-temporal analysis. In the Himalayas, snow/ cloud discrimination can be done by using texture analysis, where snow shows a characteristic *drainage pattern* which cannot be seen when the area is covered by clouds (Fig. 11.6).

Because of the above-mentioned reasons, visual interpretation technique is mostly used to monitor snow cover and to a lesser extend digital classification. This makes snow cover mapping cumbersome and time-consuming. Spectral reflectance of snow has been discussed in Section 4.1.4. In the optical region, snow reflectance is higher as compared to other land features such as vegetation, rock and water. However, in the SWIR region, snow reflectance is lower than rock and vegetation. Therefore, snow on satellite images appears white in the visible region and black in the SWIR region (Fig. 11.7). This characteristic can be effectively used to develop a normalised difference snow index (NDSI) for snow cover mapping. NDSI is expressed as:

$$NDSI = \frac{(\text{Green reflectance} - \text{SWIR reflectance})}{(\text{Green reflectance} + \text{SWIR reflectance})} \tag{11.3}$$

Band2 (0.52–0.59μm) and 5 (1.55–1.70 μm) of AWiFS can be used for generating an NDSI. Initially, digital numbers are converted into reflectance. The various parameters needed for estimating spectral reflectance include sensor transfer characteristics (DN value to radiance), mean solar exo-atmospheric spectral irradiances in the satellite sensor bands, satellite data acquisition time, solar declination, solar zenith and solar azimuth angles and the mean Earth–Sun distance (Srinivasulu and Kulkarni, 2004). For each pixel, NDSI values are obtained using Eq. 11.3. The pixel is classified as snow, if the NDSI value is grater than 0.4. NDSI values for various features is given in Table 11.4 (Kulkarni et. al., 2002b). This technique classifies water pixels also as snow depending on the quality of water. Therefore, to remove water pixels, a mask of water body is used. This is a useful technique in the Himalayan region, as it can be applied under mountain shadow condition. This is an possibly due to reflectance from diffuse radiation in shadow areas. This technique has been used to monitor snow cover in the Himalayas using AWiFS data of RESOURCESAT (Plate 11.4).

11.5.2 GLACIAL INVESTIGATIONS

Glaciers are normally described as masses of ice slowly moving down a slope. A glacier consists of ice crystals, water and rock debris. Out of these, ice is the major part of the glacier. In the Himalayas, the glaciers cover approximately 33,000 sq. km. This is one of the largest concentrations of glacier-stored water outside the polar regions. Since the Himalayas have a very rugged terrain, conventional in situ observational methods are difficult. Remote sensing is useful to collect information on various aspects of glacial studies such as glacier inventory, glacial mass balance, advance and retreat of glaciers, mapping and modelling of crevasses, moraine-dammed glacier lakes and snow-glacier runoff modelling.

Standard false colour composites (FCC) prepared from B2 (0.52–0.59 m), B3 (0.62–0.68 m) and B4 (0.77–0.86 m) of LISS-III sensor of IRS were found useful for mapping of various glacial features such as ablation area, accumulation area, glacier boundary, equilibrium line and moraine-dammed lakes (Kulkarni et. al., 1999). These features are explained below.

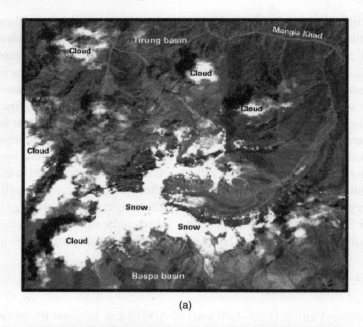

(a)

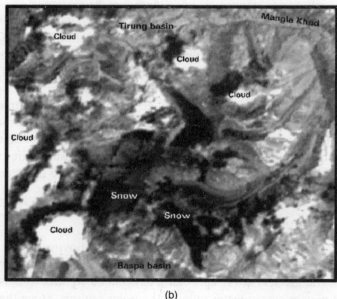

(b)

Fig. 11.7 IRS LISS-3 image over part of Himalayas. (a) is in Band2 (Green) and (b) in Band5 (SWIR). Both cloud and snow have higher reflectance in the visible region and hence cannot be discriminated (except from shadow). In the SWIR region, low reflectance of snow can discriminate snow from cloud.

Glacier boundary Differentiation between a glacial and non-glacier area is easily possible on the FCC, except where glaciers are covered by debris. Sometime during the August–September season, grass appears on the lateral and terminal moraine. This gives a red tone on the FCC around the glacier snout and makes it easy to delineate the lower boundary of the glacier. In

Table 11.4 Radiance, reflectance and NDSI values for various land features near Manali, from field measurements using a spectral radiometer. Please note that the amount of radiance is substantially low under mountain shadow, however the NDSI values are comparable with the non-shadow condition. (Kulkarni et. al., 2002b)

Target	Radiance (mW cm^{-2} sr^{-1} μm^{-1})		Reflectance (%)		NDSI
	Green	SWIR	Green	SWIR	
Fresh and clean snow	11.88	0.011	88.6	3.9	0.90
Clay contamination snow	23.05	0.054	65.4	1.4	0.96
Wet and patchy snow	12.30	0.005	74.5	1.4	0.96
Clean snow under shadow	0.83	0.009	83.8	4.0	0.91
Dense ice clouds	–	–	78.0	75.8	0.01
Middle layer clouds	–	–	72.0	45.1	0.23
Dry soil	6.64	1.019	23.8	33.0	−0.16
Dry soil under shadow	0.58	0.020	29.5	35.5	−0.09
Moist soil	3.81	0.713	14.8	25.4	−0.26
Moist soil under shadow	0.41	0.020	21.8	33.0	−0.21
Vegetation	1.63	0.586	4.9	15.4	−0.52
Water	1.53	0.005	5.2	0.1	0.96

the upper part of the ablation area, glacier edges are characterised by dirty snow, which gets accumulated due to avalanches from adjoining cliffs. This gives a distinctly higher reflectance along the edges. In the accumulation area, the glacier boundary is normally associated with mountain cliffs and hence can be easily delineated using cliff shadow.

Accumulation area In this region, snow accumulation in winter is more than summer melting; therefore, it is characterised by snow and gives higher reflectance. Spectral reflectance is higher in all three bands. Hence, it appears white on the FCC and can be easily demarcated.

Ablation area In the ablation area, summer melting is more than winter snow accumulation. Therefore, glacier ice along with debris gets exposed on the surface. Glacier ice has substantially lower reflectance than snow, but higher than rocks and soil of the surrounding area. Therefore, it gives a green-white tone on FCC and can easily be differentiated from the accumulation area and surrounding rock and soil.

Transient snow line/equilibrium line Equilibrium line is the snow line at the end of the snow ablation season. This separates yearly accumulation from ablation, and the mass balance along the equilibrium line is zero. Therefore, equilibrium line is an important indicator of mass balance. The line can be easily marked on FCC, by systematic temporal analysis of satellite images.

Moraine-dammed glacier lake Formation of lakes due to obstruction of water flow by moraine (rock transported by glacier) is a common phenomenon in the glaciated terrain.

Sometimes rupture of moraine-dammed lakes can cause floods in the valley. Rupture can be triggered either due to excess melting or by an ice avalanche. These lakes can be identified by their dark-blue and black colour and characteristic shape.

Permanent snowfields   A snowfield which exists for two or more consecutive years is classified as a permanent snowfield. These areas are characterised by a white tone due to high reflectance in all three bands of FCC.

Satellite imagery of the Parbati glacier showing various glacial features is given in Plate 11.5.

Glacial Mass Balance

Mass balance of a glacier is usually considered as the total loss or gains in glacier mass at the end of a hydrological year. Mass balance is one of the important parameters used to assess the health of glaciers. It is estimated by measuring total accumulation of seasonal snow and the ablation of snow and ice. This can be measured by various ways. In direct measurement, net balance is measured at representative points on a glacier. In the photogrammetric method, contour maps are prepared at the interval of a few years. Two maps can be compared to determine change in glacier volume. In the hydrological method, net balance can be determined for the whole basin, by measuring precipitation, runoff and evaporation. These methods need extensive field investigations and due to the rugged terrain of the Himalayas, the mass balance of only few glaciers can be obtained. In order to obtain the mass balance of a large number of glaciers, the accumulation area ratio (AAR) method can be used (Kulkarni, 1992). AAR is a ratio between accumulation area and total glacier area. Accumulation area is an area of the glacier above the equilibrium line. In temperate glaciers, the extent of superimposed ice zone

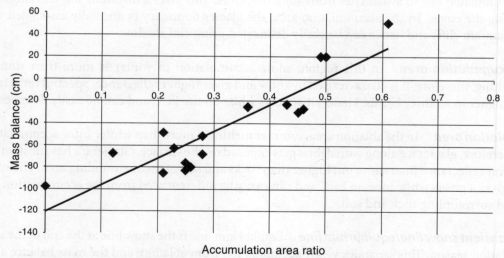

Fig. 11.8   A regression relationship between accumulation area ratio and mass balance. This relationship was developed using field measurements of AAR and mass balance for the Shaune Garang and Gor Garang glaciers in the Baspa river basin in Himachal Pradesh. This relationship was used to estimate mass balance for other glaciers in the Baspa basin, where field data were not available. AAR values were obtained using weekly analysis of WiFS data of Indian Remote Sensing Satellites. (Kulkarni et. al., 2004)

is insignificant and therefore, the equilibrium line coincides with the snow line at the end of the ablation season (Paterson, 1998). In the Himalayas, field investigations have shown a good regression relationship between AAR and mass balance with r^2 as 0.80 (Fig. 11.8). The snow line at the end of ablation season and AAR can be estimated using satellite data (Kulkarni et. al., 2004). Weekly WiFS and AWiFS data are used to monitor the snow line on the glaciers and to estimate mass balance.

Glacial Retreat

Glacier retreat is normally considered as an important indicator of climate change. The Himalayan glacier retreat is generally difficult to study due to the rugged, mountainous terrain, but remote sensing offers a useful tool that can be used to assess retreat. The retreat can be estimated using high resolution (5.8 m) stereo data from the Indian Remote Sensing Satellite-1C. From a stereo image, an ortho map-aligned satellite image can be obtained, which

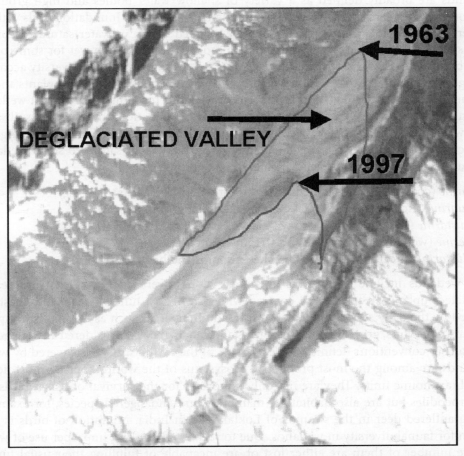

Fig. 11.9 Ortho map-aligned PAN imagery on 20 July 1997 showing retreat of the Janapa glacier from 1962. The snout position at 1963 was taken from the topographic map of the Survey of India. The ortho image was generated using stereo images of PAN sensor. Since the snout is often an abrupt ice wall, its correct identification is possible when viewed in a satellite stereo pair. (Kulkarni and Bahuguna, 2002)

is corrected for height distortion (Fig. 11.9). The raw images contain geometric distortions due to satellite orbit, altitude variations, sensor geometry, tilt angle and terrain relief, but are corrected for these distortions using ground control points (GCP). GCP are stable ground features, which can be easily identified on topographic maps and satellite images. Digital photogrammetric techniques were used to generate a digital elevation model and ortho-images from raw images. Monitoring of glacier advance and retreat requires correct identification of the glacier snout. The snout is often an abrupt ice wall that can be easily identified when the glacier is viewed in a satellite stereo pair. Once identified, its location can be transferred to a topographic map by relating the snout position to nearby streams, lakes or other features (Kulkarni and Bahuguna, 2002). By comparing the snout position at different years, the extent of glacier retreat can be estimated.

11.6   WETLAND MANAGEMENT

Wetlands are broadly defined as a variety of shallow water bodies and high groundwater environments that are characterised by permanent or temporary inundation, soils with hydric properties, and plants and animals that have adapted to life in water-saturated conditions (Lewis et. al., 1995). That is, the wetlands are those areas which are wet for some period of time, but not necessarily permanently wet. Wetlands exhibit enormous diversity according to their genesis, geographical location, water regime and chemistry, dominant plants and soil or sediment characteristics. Existing definitions of wetlands recognise the fact that wetlands are driven by wetland hydrology (permanent or periodic inundation), hydric soils (soil saturated with water for so long that it becomes anaerobic, that is, has no molecular oxygen) and characteristic hydrophytes (plants adapted to grow in water or saturated soil). Wetlands are generally associated with the following major systems:

- *marine* (coastal wetlands including rock shores and coral reefs),
- *estuarine* (including deltas, tidal marshes, and mangrove swamps),
- *lacustarine* (wetlands associated with lakes),
- *riverine* (wetlands along rivers and streams), and
- *palustarine* (meaning 'marshy'–marshes, swamps and bogs)

Thus wetlands include floodplains and areas along rivers and lakes that are seasonally inundated, upland areas that are covered with peat lands, tundra areas, and coastal areas affected by the daily sea level fluctuations. In addition, areas such as fish and shrimp ponds, saltpans, reservoirs, gravel pits, sewage farms and canals are also considered as wetlands as per the Ramsar convention's definition. Nearly 10% of the earth's surface is covered by wetlands. Wetlands are among the most productive ecosystems of the world, housing most floral and faunal taxonomic units. They are not only important for the survival of fishes, birds, turtles and crocodiles but are also habitats of many rare and endangered species, for example, the brown antlered deer in the swamps of Loktak lake in India. Migration of birds is another reason for faunal diversity in wetlands. Due to reckless filling and improper use of wetlands, a large number of them are either lost or are incapable of fulfilling their usual functions/ uses. Wetlands are under constant threat resultant from encroachment, siltation, aquaculture development and pollution. Therefore, it is important to monitor the wetlands and take adequate steps to conserve them.

Wetland Definitions

Wetlands have been defined for specific purposes, such as research studies, general habitat classification, natural resource inventories and environmental regulations. Before the legislation of wetland protection laws in the 1960s, wetlands were defined as per the speciality of the scientist (USGS website). Thus, scientists working in their specialised fields such as botany or hydrology have defined wetlands according to their perception. A botanical definition focusses on the plants adapted to flooding and/or saturated soil conditions, while hydrologists emphasise the position of the water table relative to the ground surface over time. Two broad definitions of wetlands are given below.

Ramsar Convention 'Submerged or water saturated lands, both natural and man-made, permanent or temporary, with water that is static or flowing, fresh, brackish or salt, including areas of marine water the depth of which at low tide does not exceed 6 metres.'

US Fish and Wildlife Service 'Wetlands are lands transitional between terrestrial and aquatic systems where the water table is usually at or near the surface or the land is covered by shallow water level. For purposes of this classification, wetlands must have one or more of the following three attributes: (i) at least periodically, the land supports predominantly hydrophytes; (ii) the substrate is predominantly undrained hydric soil; and (iii) the substrate is nonsoil and is saturated with water or covered by shallow water level at some time during the growing season of each year.'

Ramsar Convention

The Convention on Wetlands, signed in Ramsar, Iran, in 1971, is an inter-governmental treaty which provides the framework for national action and international cooperation for the conservation and wise use of wetlands and their resources. The convention's mission is the conservation and wise use of all wetlands through local, regional and national action and international cooperation, as a contribution towards achieving sustainable development throughout the world. Upon joining the Ramsar Convention, each contracting party is obliged to designate at least one wetland site for inclusion in the list of wetlands of international importance. Sites are selected by the contracting parties, or member states, for designation under the convention by reference to the criteria set up for identifying wetlands of international importance. There are presently 138 contracting parties to the convention, with 1364 wetland sites (totalling 120.4 million hectares), designated for inclusion in the Ramsar List of Wetland of International Importance. India has identified 19 wetland sites to be part of the Ramsar list. For more than 30 years, the Ramsar Convention has been the principal instrument for international cooperation for the conservation and wise use of wetlands and their resources.

Source: ramsarconvention website

11.6.1 REMOTE SENSING OF WETLAND ECOSYSTEMS

Satellite remote sensing has proven to be a very useful technique for inventorying, mapping and monitoring of wetland ecosystems due to its synoptic coverage, multi-spectral character and repetitive nature. In fact, remote sensing alongwith GIS is the only cost-effective and reliable technology for effective monitoring and management of wetland resources. Studies have also been carried out using orbital remote sensing for monitoring water spread, turbidity/siltation, aquatic vegetation infestation, and the trophic status of various inland and coastal ecosystems.

On a false colour composite (FCC), the water part of wetland shows up in various hues of blue depending on the depth of the water column and suspended material (Plate 11.1). Vegetation if totally covering the water surface (as for example water hyacinth mats) appears pinkish red while emergent and submerged vegetation appear brownish-red in colour depending on the extent of background water exposure, condition and age. In addition to this, watermark impression can also be picked up easily on the satellite imagery which helps in setting the boundary of the wetlands.

The scale of mapping for inventory depends on the objectives and the level at which the information is desired—national, regional or local and the smallest area to be mapped. Scales of 1:250,000 may be adequate for national inventory of wetlands while for wetland specific investigations (depending on the wetland size) scales of 1:50,000 and 1:25,000 or larger are appropriate. For inventory, at least one satellite data set pertaining to post-monsoon and pre-monsoon seasons is desirable.

Mapping and monitoring of wetland ecosystems presupposes the usage of temporal satellite data. The main considerations in the selection of data are:

- Remote sensing data of a proper season should be selected to study the wetland parameters. For example, to find out the presence or absence of aquatic vegetation, pre-monsoon data is more appropriate. Similarly, for turbidity assessment post-monsoon and pre-monsoon sequential imagery may be required.
- For monitoring purposes, multi-temporal data should be of the same season and preferably of nearby dates.

The multi-date data should be accurately registered either with respect to each other or available topographical maps. For analysis of multi-temporal data, appropriate corrections should be applied for changes in sun angle, sensor parameters (gain, bias) and so on.

11.6.2 WETLAND INVENTORY OF INDIA

In India wetlands exist in all geographical regions, though no scientific estimate of their aerial extent and condition existed till recently. A scientific inventory of wetlands, based on the analysis of data from an Indian Remote Sensing satellite, has been carried out in India (Garg, 2002; Garg et. al., 1998). The first step towards this was to evolve a classification system. A national wetland classification system for carrying out national wetland inventory was evolved after considerable deliberations with experts and planners. The classification system besides including all wetlands, incorporates deep-water habitats and impoundments. The main criteria followed in this system are: (i) wetland hydrology, that is, manifestation of water on the satellite imagery; (ii) wetland vegetation, that is, mainly hydrophytes and other aquatic vegetation in a part or whole of the water body as observed on satellite data. As per these classification criteria, wetlands are categorised into 24 categories out of which 10 are inland and 14 are coastal (Table 11.5).

Table 11.5 Wetland classification system in India

Inland wetlands	1. Natural	1.1	Lakes/ponds
		1.2	Ox-bow lakes/cut-off meanders
		1.3	Waterlogged (seasonal)
		1.4	Playas
		1.5	Swamp/marsh
	2. Man-made	2.1	Reservoirs
		2.2	Tanks
		2.3	Waterlogged
		2.4	Abandoned quarries
		2.5	Ash pond/cooling pond
Coastal wetlands	3. Natural	3.1	Estuary
		3.2	Lagoon
		3.3	Creek
		3.4	Backwater (kayal)
		3.5	Bay
		3.6	Tidal flat/mud flat
		3.7	Sand/beach/spit/bar
		3.8	Coral reefs
		3.9	Rocky coast
		3.10	Mangroves
		3.11	Salt marsh/vegetation
		3.12	Other vegetation
	4. Man-made	4.1	Salt pans
		4.2	Aquaculture ponds

- *Rivers have not been included in the classification system, but are shown in the maps.*
- *The extent of vegetation, if present, in the inland wetlands is indicated on the maps.*
- *Qualitative turbidity ratings (low, moderate, high) are given for inland wetlands, wherever possible.*
- *Wetlands put to regular agriculture use have not been included.*

Source: Garg et. al., 1998

Pre-monsoon and post-monsoon seasons IRS-1A/1B LISS-I/II data pertaining to 1992/93 in the form of false colour composites (FCCs) were used for delineation of wetlands. Besides the satellite data, SOI topographical maps, ground truth information along with collateral data were also made use of in delineating the wetland categories. Current operational digital classification systems, such as maximum likelihood classifiers, depend solely on the spectral signature. However, other information such as texture, shape and association are very important in classifying wetlands. Therefore, visual analysis techniques (see Section 10.1) have been used for wetland inventory (Garg et. al., 1998). Base maps are prepared using Survey of India topographical maps of the same scale. Prominent land features such as railways, embankments, roads and other major settlements are marked onto the base maps as these serve as controls in the process of interpretation. Rivers have not been used as control points since their path/courses have shown marked changes with respect to SOI topographic sheets. Base maps can be prepared SOI topographical sheet-wise, basin-wise or district-wise. Subsequently, analysed/interpreted satellite data is transferred onto these maps. For better accuracy, ground truth data is collected and correlated with tonal variations as observed on the imagery. The schematics showing the procedure for generating wetland inventory maps is given in Fig. 11.10. Among all the wetland types in India, tidal/mud flats occupy maximum area (2362056 ha), while reservoirs, lakes/ponds and tanks occupy 1481987, 679530 and 558344 hectares respectively. In terms of numbers, tanks are maximum in number (5549) and backwater minimum (32). Relative area of wetland types in India is given in Fig. 11.11.

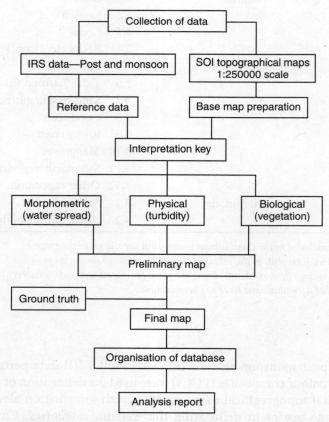

Fig. 11.10 Schematic of methodology for nationwide wetland mapping/inventory. (*Source:* Garg et. al., 1998)

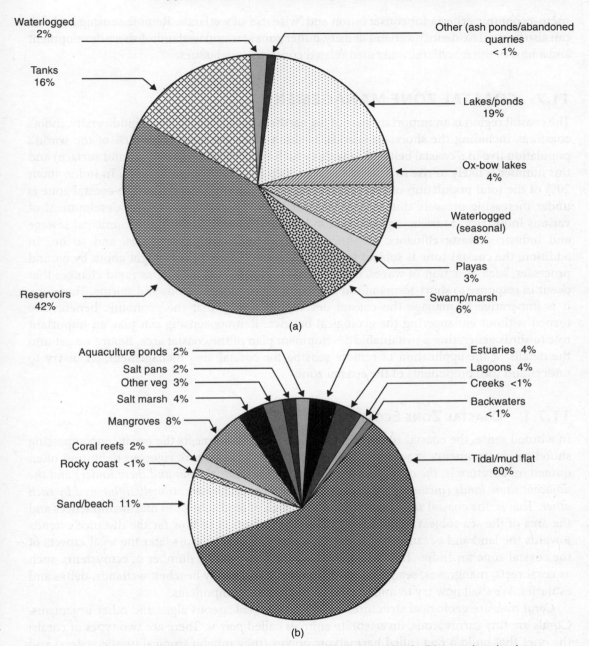

Fig. 11.11   Relative area of wetland types in India. (a) Inland wetlands; (b) coastal wetlands.
(*Source*: Garg, 2004)

Conservation and management of wetlands for their sustainable use requires voluminous data on physical, biological and socio-cultural aspects to understand the structure and functions of a wetland. Remote sensing and GIS can play a significant role in wetland conservation and management. It helps spatial modelling taking cognisance of physical, biological and socio-economic criteria for conservation and 'wise use' of wetlands. Remote sensing and GIS can also be used to identify wetland density, buffer zones around wetlands, fishery development and a host of other wetland watershed related conservational issues.

11.7   COASTAL ZONE MANAGEMENT

The coastal region is an important part of the earth's ecosystem with a rich biodiversity. India's coastline, including the shores of islands, is about 7500 km long. Over 60% of the world's population live in a coastal belt 60 km wide (which is only about 18% of the land surface) and this number is likely to rise to 75% by the year 2025 (UNESCO report, 1998). In India, about 20% of the total population of the country is concentrated on the coast. The coastal zone is under increasing pressure due to high rates of human population growth, development of various industries (tourism, aquaculture, mining, chemical), discharge of municipal sewage and industrial waste effluents, off-shore petroleum exploration activities, and so on. In addition, the coastal zone is subject to continuing gradual changes brought about by natural processes, such as action of waves, currents, tides, storm surfs, as well as rapid changes that occur in response to short-term natural events such as cyclones, floods and storms. Therefore, it is imperative to manage the coastal development such that the economic benefits are reaped without endangering the ecological balance. Remote sensing can play an important role towards generating a sustainable development plan of the coastal area. Before we get into the details of the application of remote sensing for coastal area management, let us try to understand the components of the coastal zone.

11.7.1   COASTAL ZONE ECOSYSTEM

In a broad sense, the coastal zone is the interface where land meets the ocean, encompassing shoreline environments as well as adjacent coastal waters. A more rigorous definition often quoted in literature is: *the coastal waters (including the lands therein and there under) and the adjacent shore lands (including waters therein and there under) are strongly influenced by each other*. That is, the coastal zone includes both the area of land subject to marine influences and the area of the sea subject to land influences. The definition of how far the distance extends towards the land and ocean varies in each country. We shall discuss later the legal aspects of the coastal zone for India. The Indian coastal zone consists of a number of ecosystems, such as coral reefs, mangroves, sea grass, mudflats, rocky and sandy beaches, wetlands, deltas and estuaries. We shall now try to understand some of these components.

Coral reefs are geological structures built by corals, calcareous algae and other organisms. Corals are tiny carnivorous, invertebrate animals called *polyps*. There are two types of corals; the ones that build a reef called hermatypic polyps (they inhabit tropical photic waters) and those that are not capable of building reefs, called ahermatypic polyps (found in temperate and deep water). The polyps that build reefs use calcium from seawater to create an external hard cup-like skeleton of calcium carbonate (limestone) around them. The polyps divide as they grow and form coral colonies. As coral colonies build on top of each other, coral reefs are produced. (Other types of animals or plants also contribute to the reef.) The size, shape and colour of the coral reefs depend on the species and their location. As mentioned earlier, coral reefs grow in warm water (mainly between 30°N and 30°S latitude) and in shallow water where sunlight is available. In short, coral reefs are shallow-water tropical marine ecosystems, which are formed by cementing together millions of coral skeletons over a period of time ranging from a few thousands to millions of years.

Coral reefs are the most diverse marine ecosystems in the world and a vast variety of marine life depends upon its health. In fact, coral reefs are equivalent to tropical rain forests in species richness. We may consider coral reefs as 'living laboratories' for ecological studies. The utility of coral reefs are many—shelter for fishes, removal and recycling of carbon dioxide thereby playing an important role in global biochemical processes and reproduction of marine food resources in the tropical regions. Coral reefs, in addition, act as a barrier against wave action along the coastal regions, thereby preventing coastal erosion. They are also of medicinal importance and attract tourists, thus providing economic benefits.

The world's coral reefs are threatened by human interference such as toxic waste disposed to sea, forest clearance, which in turn produces sedimentation from land, oil spills, destructive fishing practices, coral mining, and so on. It takes thousands of years to build reefs, which is all the more reason why we should preserve them.

Mangroves are tropical coastal vegetation which live under extreme environmental conditions, such as high salinity, periods of inundation and exposure and anaerobic conditions. (The word 'mangrove' has traditionally been used to describe either the total community or the individual tree/bushes.) They have unique characteristics and growth habits that allow them to survive in harsh conditions. For example they produce stilt roots which project above the mud and water in order to absorb oxygen. Mangrove vegetation shows distinct zonation characterised by factors such as salinity, soil characteristics, geomorphic settings and frequency of inundation. Mangroves have important ecological functions as well as economic uses. Since they are situated at the 'border' between the land and the open sea, they protect the coastline against wave action and sand erosion. Mangroves create friction and reduce intensity of storms and hurricanes, thereby protecting the coastal upland. Mangrove canopies and aerial roots offer a wealth of habital opportunities for many species of fish and other estuarine fauna.

India has about 7% of the world's mangroves. These are primarily located in the deltas of rivers such as the Ganga, Mahanadi, Godavari, Krishna and Cauvery as well as in the Andaman and Nicobar islands. Small patches of mangroves are found on the coasts of Andhra Pradesh, Goa, Gujarat, Karnataka, Kerala, Maharashtra, Orissa and Tamil Nadu (MOEF annual report, 1997–98). Because of the geomorphic setting, and since there are no major west-flowing rivers, mangrove wetlands of the west coast of India are small in size, and less in diversity compared to wetlands of east coast. The Sunderbans are the single largest mangrove wetland in the world. They cover about 1 million hectares (Selvam, 2003). According to the Forest Survey of India (FSI) about 57% of the mangrove wetlands of India are along the east coast and about 24% are present along the west coast and the remaining is found in the Andaman and Nicobar islands (FSI report, 1999).

Various landforms of the coastal zone include beach, mudflats, coastal dunes, spits and bars.

Mudflats are wide expanses of fine-grained soft mud along the shore. They generally consist of deposits of clay, silt and ooze. They are further classified into high tide or supratidal flats, intertidal slopes and subtidal zones (Davies, 1972). High tide flats are more or less flat and are near the high waterline. Deposition is provided by the highest tides. Intertidal slope is an area of instability and is affected by daily tides. The subtidal zone is normally exposed during very low tides.

Paleomudflats are defined as mudflats lying above the high tide flats and are formed by marine deposition of the past sea level (Nayak and Sahai, 1984; 1985). These mudflats are related to the phenomenon of regression of the sea. They represent the sites of older mudflats when the sea level was several metres higher than the present.

Beach is defined as a shore consisting at least partly of unconsolidated material. Most often that material is of sand grade (~ 2 mm to 1/16 mm size), hence sandy beach. But sand may be replaced by cobbles, shingles or mud (Fairbridge, 1968).

Spit is a small point or low narrow tongue of land commonly consisting of sand or gravel deposited by long shore drifting and having one end attached to the mainland and the other protruding into the open water, usually the sea, a finger-like extension of the beach (Campbell, 1972).

Bars are submerged ridges of detrital (depicted) sediments which are longer and less regularly shaped than ripple marks (Fairbridge, 1968). They are formed typically in shallow shelf waters by waves and currents. They are found singly or together and internally terminated.

Shoals are either submerged ridge, bank or bar producing shoal, consisting of or covered by sand, mud, gravel or other unconsolidated material (Campbell, 1972).

Coastal dunes cover small areas and are defined as topographical features of eolian origin composed of sand grains deposited downwind from a natural source of sand (Fairbridge, 1968). They develop in any environment in which loose rock particles of sand size are exposed to wind action and are free to migrate and accumulate as unconsolidated masses.

Some of these coastal features are shown in Plate 11.6.

11.7.2 COASTAL REGULATION ZONE

As mentioned earlier, human interference is the major cause for the damage of coastal areas. With the increase in population in the coastal areas, the developmental activities have also increased resulting in enormous stress on the coastal marine environment, thus affecting the ecological balance of the coastal zone. Therefore, the coastal zones need to be protected from unplanned development that lead to ecological disasters. Planned development necessarily involves some restrictions to current activities and hence requires some legislative framework to impose such restrictions. The Government of India realising the importance of protecting the coastal zone, issued a major notification in 1991, framing rules for the regulation of various coastal zone activities. These rules are called Coastal Regulation Zone (CRZ). Under these rules, the entire coastal stretch from the lowest low tide, to the highest high tide line and the coastal land within 500 m from the high tide line on the landward side is termed as the coastal regulation zone. For regulating development activities, the CRZ is classified into four categories as under.

CRZ I covers areas that are ecologically sensitive and important as well as being the zone between low and high tides.

CRZ II covers areas that have already been well-developed with all infrastructures like roads, sewerage lines and water supply pipes laid out within urban and municipal limits. No new construction on the seaward side of the road can come up here and reconstruction of existing structures will be restricted.

CRZ III covers areas that are relatively undisturbed and not falling under the above two zones. Any further activity is considered on a case-by-case basis.

CRZ IV covers areas in islands except those designated as CRZ I, II and III.

Plate 11.7 shows the CRZ categories for the Okha region of Gujarat.

Thus the CRZ policy restricts unplanned development in the Coastal Zone. Any further activity needs approval. Generally, socially-oriented activities will get priority over profit-oriented activities. It accepts the past developments and attempts to minimise further damage in zones that already had urban growth.

Any restriction has its own impact on development and makes way for litigations, between the Government and developmental agencies. Apart from the legal aspects, CRZ does not address activities below low tide line (towards sea) an area which is ecologically very important.

11.7.3   USE OF SATELLITE DATA FOR COASTAL MANAGEMENT

One of the major requirements for the coastal zone management is the availability of up-to-date and accurate information on coastal habitats, shore processes, water quality, and so on. Such information will be required periodically to study the impact of developmental activities and the implementation of laws governing the coastal zone. Remote sensing technology is the only timely and cost-effective means to monitor and map the coastal area at the local, regional and global scale. Thus coastal resource inventory information through remote sensing forms a basis for a comprehensive coastal zone management plan.

In India coastal wetlands, land use and landform, and shore-line change maps have been produced on a 1:250,000, 1:50,000 and 1:25,000 scale for the whole country using primarily LISS-I, II and III data. The first step towards generating the map is to evolve a classification system. Space Applications Centre, Ahmedabad has evolved a classification system for coastal land use mapping (Table 11.6). Information at levels I and II are of interest to most users who desire data at the state/national level. Maps are produced based on the visual interpretation technique (Chapter 10). Mapping up to level II can be carried out using LISS-II /III false colour composites (FCC) generated using green, red and near IR bands. Level III mapping can be made using LISS-III merged with PAN. However, LISS-IV 5 m multispectral data is better suited for level III information delimitation.

Selection of data at the proper time is essential. Data during low tide should be selected for coastal land use mapping so that the total area under wetland can be studied. The period can be selected based on the tide table available from the Maritime Board. The reproductive cycle of vegetation present in the wetland areas should be taken into account for selection of data. Mangroves are evergreen (perennial) plants, but algal growth on rocks and reefs is seasonal (occurs from October to February under favourable conditions, and senescence takes place in April). Due to this, images of the period December–February should be selected. For coastal zone regulation mapping, the satellite data of 1990–91 just before CRZ notification was selected to serve as baseline information.

Mangroves are located in difficult terrain and in many places they are almost inaccessible. Therefore, remote sensing provides a reliable tool for providing information on mangroves. Mangroves have been mapped for their extent and density at 1:250,000, 1:50,000 and 1:25,000 scales using Landsat TM, IRS LISS-II and III, and SPOT data. Density-wise classification gives an idea about the condition of the mangrove habitat. Mangroves having >40% crown density are termed as dense (closed forest), those having 10%–40% crown density are termed as sparse (open forest) and degraded mangroves have <10% crown density. The status of the Indian mangroves from 1991 to 1999 is shown in Table 11.7. Satellite data has been used recently

Table 11.6 Classification system for coastal land use mapping (SAC report, 1991)

Level I	Level II	Level III
Agricultural land		
Forest	Natural	
	Man-made	
Wetland	Estuary	
	Lagoon	
	Creek	
	Bay	
	Tidal flat / mudflat	
	Sand/beach/spit/bar	
	Coral reef	
	Rocky coast	
	Mangroves	Dense
		Sparse
	Salt marsh/ marsh vegetation	
	Other vegetation	
Barren land	Sandy area/dunes	
	Mining area/dumps	
	Others	
Built-up land	Habitation	
	Habitation with vegetation	
	Open/vacant land	
	Transportation	Roads
		Railways
		Harbour/jetty
		Airport
		Waterways
Other features	Reclaimed area	
	Salt pans	
	Aquaculture ponds	
	Ponds/lakes	
	Rivers/streams	
	Drains /outfalls /effluents	
	Sea wall/embankments	
High tide line		
Low tide line		
District/state boundary		
CRZ boundary		

Table 11.7   State-wise mangrove cover (area in sq. km)

Sl. No.	State/Union territory	1991	1993	1995	1997	1999
1	Andaman and Nicobar	971	966	966	966	966
2	Andhra Pradesh	399	378	383	383	397
3	Goa	3	3	3	6	5
4	Gujarat	397	419	689	991	1031
5	Karnataka	–	–	2	5	3
6	Maharashtra	113	155	155	124	108
7	Orissa	195	195	195	211	215
8	Tamil Nadu	47	21	21	21	21
9	West Bengal	2119	2119	2119	2123	2125
	Total	4244	4256	4533	4830	4871

Source: FSI Report, 2001

to zone the major pure and mixed communities of mangroves based on their ability to grow under varying tidal conditions, substrate and salinity (Nayak et. al., 2003). Plate 11.8 shows how different mangrove communities appear in a satellite FCC image.

Coral reef features (fringing, atoll, platform, patch, coral heads, sand cays), reef-flat, reef vegetation, degraded reef, lagoons, live corals and coral line shelf have been mapped using IRS LISS-II and III data on a 1:50,000 scale for Indian reefs (Bahuguna and Nayak, 1998). These maps can be used as a basic input for identifying the boundaries of protected areas and biosphere reserves. It was also possible to map uncharted extensive coral line shelves, atolls and coral heads, and live coral platforms in the Lakshadweep Islands, coral pinnacles in the Gulf of Kachchh and new coral growth in a few places in the Wandoor National Park, and the Andaman and Nicobar Islands. Coral reefs exhibit distinctive patterns of morphological and ecological zonations. These zonations help in planning proper conservation of the reef. IRS-1C LISS-III and PAN merged data have been found to be extremely useful for coral reef zonation study (Nayak et. al., 2003). With the availability of 5 m multispectral data from LISS-IV, the accuracy of mapping can further increase. Plate 11.9 shows how different types of coral reefs appear in a satellite FCC image.

Indian coral reefs are mainly distributed on the coasts of Lakshwadweep Islands, Andaman and Nicobar Islands, Gulf of Kutch, Gulf of Mannar, Palk Bay and the Ratnagiri Coast of Maharashtra. The Indian coast has about 2300 sq. km of coral reefs. The reef area in four major coral reef regions is shown in Fig. 11.12.

The High Tide Line (HTL) and Low Tide Line (LTL) have been delineated based on tonal discontinuity observed on the satellite image as water leaves its mark on whatever it travels. Apart from the presence of mangroves, certain landforms should be taken into account while arriving at HTL. The Government of India has issued a notification to use satellite data for the preparation of 1:25,000 scale maps for regional planning. Maps showing wetland features between HTL and LTL and coastal land use features up to 500 m from the HTL on 1:25,000 scales for the entire Indian coast, using IRS LISS-II and SPOT and recently with IRS LISSIII and PAN merged data, were prepared. The accurate demarcation of HTL and LTL is

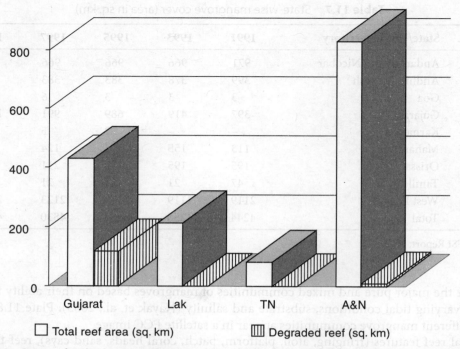

□ Total reef area (sq. km)   ▥ Degraded reef (sq. km)

Fig. 11.12 Status of Indian coral reefs in the four major coral reef regions—Gulf of Kachchh (Gujarat), Lakshadweep Islands, Gulf of Mannar and Palk Bay (Tamil Nadu) and the Andaman and Nicobar Islands. The data is generated using IRS LISS-II, Landsat TM and SPOT data of the year 1990. (Bahuguna and Nayak, 2004)

important as they control boundaries of regulation zones. CRZ maps are being used by the State Governments to prepare coastal zone management plans. Efforts are on to use remote sensing data on cadastral level.

Shoreline is a rapidly changing landform. The accurate demarcation and monitoring of shoreline (long-term, seasonal and short-term changes) are necessary for the understanding of coastal processes. The rate of shoreline change varies depending up on the intensity of causative forces, warming of oceanic waters, melting of continental ice, and so on. Shoreline-change mapping (1967–68, 1985–89, 1990–92 periods) for the entire Indian coast has been carried out using LANDSAT MSS/TM and IRS LISS-II data on a 1:250,000 and 1:50,000 scale (Chauhan and Nayak, 1996). Information about areas under erosion, deposition, shifting of river mouths, shoals, growth of spit has been provided for the entire country (Nayak et. al., 1992; 1997). These maps have been found to be useful by the Beach Erosion Directorate, Ministry of Water Resources, Government of India and has been used for planning protective structures.

Classification accuracy is tested on a sample basis. The locations on ground were identified with the help of SOI topographical maps and GPS (Nayak et. al., 1991). Observations are noted in the specified proforma. A confusion matrix is then drawn and the accuracy is estimated (see Section 10.3 for details).

11.7.4 INTEGRATED COASTAL ZONE MANAGEMENT

The coastal area has been put to use for many things – for pure economic consideration to societal needs – all of which could impact the ecological health of the land unless an optimal development plan is adopted. We must balance economic, social, cultural and recreational objectives in order to minimise environmental impacts. To ensure such a sustainable development, all stakeholders should understand the strengths and limitations of a given coastal area and work together to achieve the developmental goals of that coastal area. That is, we need to combine the management of the coastal zone in a coordinated way so that the interest of all stakeholders can be taken care of. A variety of terms have been used internationally for just such an integrated development – Integrated Coastal Zone Management (ICZM), Integrated Coastal Area Management (ICAM), or simply Integrated Coastal Management (ICM) – but all refer to the same concept. Here the term integration is used in the larger context of integrating relevant policies, sectors and various levels of administration, apart from the natural resources of the area and its dynamics. ICZM covers a host of things such as information collection, planning, decision-making, management and monitoring of the implementation. An important part of resource management is carrying out an inventory of coastal zone habitats and other resources, the land forms, existing land use, and so on. These inputs about the coastal area are best derived using remote sensing technology. Ultimately the development plan should take into account the local requirements and existing government policies. The use of GIS to integrate all these data provides the resource manager with valuable tools to enable decision-making.

Integrated Coastal Zone Management is a more advantageous approach over the traditional sectoral (single use) approach, as it provides a framework for broader participation and resolution of conflicts between a variety of economic and resource conservation needs. The overall objective of the ICZM is to provide for sustainable use of natural resources, for the maintenance of high levels of biodiversity and conservation of critical habitats. It provides an opportunity for policy orientation and development of management strategies to address the issue of resource use conflicts and to control the impact of human intervention on the environment.

Unless the local communities are aware of the importance of protecting the coastal zone, the developmental programme will never be a success. The participation of local people in decision-making will go a long way to having a sustainable development of the region. Therefore, public outreach should be an integral part of the ICZM programme.

11.8 MARINE FISHERIES

11.8.1 INTRODUCTION

Fishery resources from the Indian Exclusive Economic Zone (EEZ) have been estimated as 3.9 million tonnes per year (Sudarsan et. al., 1990). Recent estimates by the Fishery Survey of India for the year 2002 also indicate a figure close to this. India contributes to about 40% of the fish landing of the Indian Ocean. However, when viewed against the world production of 90 million tonnes, India's contribution is about 2% which works out to be less than 2 million tonnes. Remote sensing data provides knowledge of the distribution of high productivity sites where the probability that fish would accumulate for feeding is more. Fishermen can exploit this knowledge by directing fishing efforts only to probable fishing grounds. Thus satellite inputs reduce search time for locating fishing sites, thereby also saving fuel required for fishing vessels.

Oceanic conditions such as sea surface temperature (SST), upwelling, salinity, ocean currents, wind-speed and the primary and secondary productivity – all aspects of physical, biological and chemical process of marine environment – affect the spawning, distribution and abundance of fish population. However, it is not possible to get all these parameters from satellites at the spatial and temporal resolution required for predicting the location of a school of fish. The two parameters obtained from remote sensing which are generally used for operational fisheries forecast are SST and amount of chlorophyll.

It is realised that thermal or colour gradients formed due to circulation of water mass indicate sites of high biological productivity. Thermocline acts as a barrier for transport of nutrients from the bottom to the euphotic zone. It causes stratification in the water mass and as a result, active photosynthesis does not occur. However, if some physical force breaks this stable stratification, upwelling of nutrients cross thermocline and enter the euphotic zone. As a result, productivity of the waters increases by a large factor. Thus upwelling regions represent feeding grounds for fish and hence are potential sites for fish occurrence.

At the site of upwelling, there are water masses of dissimilar properties which manifest as colour/thermal gradients. In remote sensing images these manifest as colour/thermal fronts. Methods for locating potential fishing zones (PFZ) from satellite data were initially developed through the detection of SST gradients revealed by oceanic features such as fronts and eddies (Lasker et. al., 1981; Laurs et. al., 1984; Maul et. al., 1984; Xingwei, 1988; Narain et. al., 1990). However, all the fronts are not conducive to fish aggregation. Therefore, exploitation of these fronts to find locations of fish aggregation requires selective filtering. Some criteria for the selection of front are:

(i) *Areal extent* The front should be of meso scale. Small fronts are transient and dissipate faster.

(ii) *Persistent front* A front stable in time is a promising feature because the fish shoal would have more time to encounter this ground.

(iii) *Magnitude of gradient* A front with a large gradient is a desirable feature because time spent by the fish shoal in locating the front (or feeding ground) is inversely proportional to the gradient.

(iv) *Shape of the front* A curved non-linear front is preferred over a linear open front since the phytoplankton remains confined to the enclosed pocket.

Amongst the various countries, the fisheries forecasting system is most well-organised in Japan. Yamanaka (1988) has discussed the utilisation of satellite imagery in Japanese fisheries services. Studies on the Gulf Stream rings indicate that the number, sizes and persistence of the warm core Gulf Stream rings can alter the condition of the fishing grounds. Maul et. al. (1984) observed using NOAA AVHRR thermal infrared data, that a high Catch Per Unit Effort (CPUE) was correlated with the proximity to the surface thermal front. The distribution of albacore tuna off the west coast of US is reported to be associated with oceanic fronts seen on NOAA AVHRR and Nimbus-7 CZCS.

In India, the methodology for predicting the potential zone for fishing (PZF) was evolved at the Space Applications Centre, Ahmedabad. The work started in 1989 by studying the SST from NOAA AVHRR data. Channel 4 (10.3–11.3 μm) and Channel 5 (11.5–12.5 μm), data were used to derive the SST, using multi-channel SST (MCSST) algorithm (see Section A1.5.2). To improve the geometric location accuracy all the images were registered with respect to a

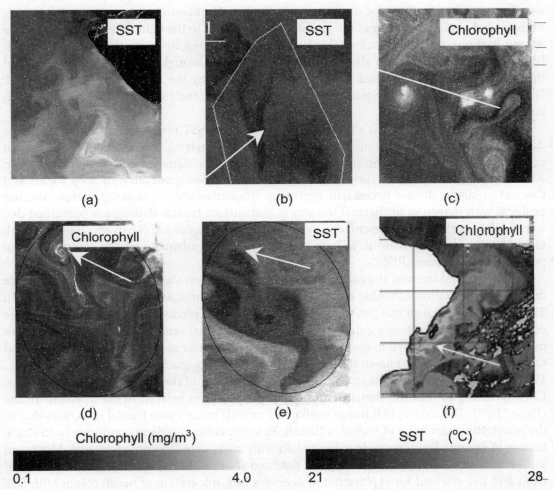

Fig. 11.13 Oceanic features relevant for Potential Fishing Zone, detected from SST/Chlorophyll images of the Arabian Sea. (a) Linear front: detected as an SST/colour gradient, it is associated with transport of nutrients from bottom to euphotic zone that eventually results in increased productivity; (b) Diverging front: when formed, chlorophyll concentration increases at the point of divergence; (c) Meander: retains chlorophyll within enclosure formed by U-shaped front; (d) Cyclonic eddy in chlorophyll image: distinct signature of streamer and spiral is seen. Increased phytoplankton occurs at the centre; (e) Cyclonic eddy in SST image: corresponding to (d), only a dark patch of cool water can be seen without the details as seen in chlorophyll image; (f) Upwelling: caused due to Ekman transport of water mass, pattern of increased chlorophyll concentration can be seen. All these features represent productive sites and hence, probability of fish occurrence there is relatively higher. (*Source:* Dwivedi, 2005)

master image from an overhead pass which was projected to a mercator grid. The next step was to look for oceanic features which could be correlated with fish aggregation. Certain features like warm core ring, upwelling and meanders were monitored and selected as prospective sites in fishery forecast (Fig. 11.13). The features thus selected were compared with the previous date images to ascertain its persistence. The technique was first tested along the Gujarat coast. Due to lack of navigational aids available to fishermen, the information on potential grounds were generated in the form of direction and distance of potential grounds from the fishing harbour and compass bearing of the ground with reference to the light house of the respective fishing harbour. This approach enabled the local fisherman to reach the fishing grounds. Information in this form was also easier to communicate through facsimile. At the users end this information was published in the local newspapers by the officials located at Veraval, Gujarat. The details were also put up on the notice board of the auction halls located near fish landing sites.

However, this approach has a basic limitation since the SST image generated from satellite data represents skin temperature (from upper ten micrometres). Therefore, the information on productivity caused by the sub-surface front cannot be detected with a thermal sensor. Also the so-called biological–physical coupling breaks down quite often in deep waters and thermal gradients do not necessarily represent productive sites in oceanic waters. Another problem with detection of thermal features is that surface frontal structure is perturbed due to prevailing surface winds or current, even of moderate magnitude (Dwivedi, 2000; Dwivedi et. al., 2005). For these reasons, SST images are not always adequate for the identification of potential fishing zones (PFZ).

Unlike thermal sensors, the ocean colour sensor can detect signals from below the surface due to the penetration of visible radiation down to one attenuation depth (see Section 4.1.3). The ocean colour sensor can give chlorophyll as an index of phytoplankton distribution in the ocean. Just as thermal fronts can be observed using thermal sensors, chlorophyll fronts can be observed in chlorophyll maps produced from ocean colour sensors such as SEAWiFS and OCM. These features are known to be reliable indicators of potential fishing zone (Laurs et. al., 1984). Cool water observed in an SST image is an indicator of the presence of high nutrients. Corresponding to this, the signature of high chlorophyll can be seen in ocean colour image (Plate 11.10). The chlorophyll image unlike SST reveals many more frontal structures due to the penetration capability of visible radiation. To select colour gradient conducive to PFZ, the history of oceanic features needs to be studied with multi-date chlorophyll images. Moreover, unlike SST, since the ocean colour front detected from a chlorophyll image is a biological front it is also relevant for exploration of deep-sea fish. Integration of ocean colour with SST has enhanced the ability to detect oceanic features in tropical waters, which can be correlated with fish shoals. Feedback received from users against such forecasts reflects improvements in terms of reliability of the forecasts (Solanki et. al., 2003). Also, it has become possible to identify new fishing grounds, which was not possible from SST images alone.

One of the lessons learnt from the Fishery Forecast Validation Experiment is that spatial shift in oceanic features by the time fishing operation is attempted in the forecasted areas results in poor catch. There is a need to predict spatial shift over a short time-scale. This requires data on wind vector synchronous to SST and ocean colour. Besides, there are other parameters known to be related with fishery abundance and distribution. These include current, mixed layer depth, sea surface height, water quality and bottom topography, and also conventional fish catch details. Focussed research is underway at the Space Applications Centre and Fishery Survey of India to provide species-wise forecast and also to enrich the forecast using additional parameters (wind, tides, current) using data from Oceansat series of satellites and a chain of in situ ocean observing systems (Dwivedi, 2005).

The methodology for locating PFZ from satellite data has been transferred to the Indian National Centre for Ocean Information Services (INCOIS) of the Department of Ocean Development. INCOIS has operationalised the PFZ advisory services to many end users. The information derived from the satellites is translated as advisories in terms of latitude, longitude and depth of the shelf at such locations as well as the direction and distance from the landing centres/light houses. These forecasts are now disseminated during the fishing season for all cloud-free areas in local languages to the entire coastline thrice a week (Tuesday, Thursday and Saturday). Fax, telephone, newspaper, electronic display boards and information kiosks, multilingual websites and audio broadcast are used for timely delivery of the advisories (Radhakrishnan, 2004). Frequent and intense interactions at the fishing harbours between scientists and the fishing community ensure improved awareness and effective use of these advisories. Concurrent validation and feedback are integral to this mission. A study from the Kerala coast during 2001–03 suggests that these advisories have helped in reducing search time by 30% to 70%, depending upon the time lag between the satellite data acquisition and the fishing activity, the fishing gear used and the species targetted (Radhakrishnan, 2004). Consequent reduction in fuel consumption and also valuable human effort as well as improvement in Catch Per Unit Effort (CPUE) has also been reported.

11.9   DESERTIFICATION

The term desertification is defined in different ways by researchers. We shall follow the definition as given by UNEP (United Nations Environmental Program) in 1992 and adopted by the United Nations Convention to Combat Desertification (UNCCD). '*Land degradation in arid, semiarid and dry sub humid areas resulting from various factors, including climatic variations and human activities.*' In other words, land degradation occuring in drylands is termed as desertification. Land degradation is defined as '*the long-term loss of ecosystem function and productivity caused by disturbances from which the land cannot recover unaided*'. Thus, land degradation is a process which may finally turn a 'productive land' into 'waste land'. Arid, semiarid and dry sub-humid lands put together are called *drylands*. Drylands can be categorised by an aridity index (AI), which is a numerical indicator of the degree of dryness of the climate at a given location. AI as defined by the UNEP is,

$$AI = \frac{P}{PET}$$

where, P is the average annual precipitation (precipitation is any product of the condensation of atmospheric water vapour that falls under gravity such as rain, drizzle, snow, hail), and PET is the potential evapotranspiration (a measure of the ability of the atmosphere to remove water from the surface through the processes of evaporation and transpiration from the land surface assuming no limitation on water supply and canopy cover). Lower the precipitation (supply of water) and higher the PET (higher loss of water), the more dry the land becomes. Thus, lower the AI value, more arid is the land. Areas for which the aridity index falls within the range 0.05–0.65 are considered as drylands. The term *desert* and *desertification* is often treated as having the same meaning. However, the term desert is used to describe a particular state of the land and its environment, whereas desertification is a process which may finally turn a productive land into a desert.

The processes leading to desertification are a combination of natural factors such as extreme climatic fluctuation and human (anthropogenic) activities. Climate has a major influence through rainfall, solar radiation, temperature and wind which all affect physical and mechanical erosion phenomena and chemical and biological degradation of the land. Human activities which accelerate the desertification process include unsustainable land use, cultivation on sloppy and marginal lands, over grazing, shifting cultivation, deforestation (for fuel wood), use of wrong agricultural practices such as over irrigation and inappropriate use of chemical fertilisers. Socio-economic issues such as increased population, poverty, lack of awareness of the consequences of unsustainable practices, and so on, further aggravate the desertification processes. The consequence of desertification reduces the ability of the land to support life and decreases biodiversity and has significant impacts on society and human well-being.

About 33% of the earth's surface exhibits desert-like conditions to some degree. Additional desert-like conditions are added at the rate of 60,000 sq. km per year (Kemp, 1998). In Asia, about 35% of the productive land seriously faces desertification hazards (Arya et. al., 2011). India has a total geographical area of about 328.73 million hectares (Mha) of which about 69% of the geographical area (about 228 Mha) fall within the dryland category. Thus land degradation/desertification is a major economic, social and environmental problem of concern to many countries in all regions of the world.

Desertification manifests as degradation of the soil and vegetative cover. The process of land degradation includes vegetal degradation, wind/water erosion, salinisation/ alkalisation, acidification, water logging and frost shattering. Vegetal degradation manifests as reduction in cover and quality of vegetation growth. Vegetal degradation is observed mainly as deforestation/ forest-blanks/shifting cultivation and degradation in grazing/grassland as well as in scrubland. Agriculture within forest lands is also considered as vegetal degradation within the forest area. The land degradation we discussed earlier leads to depletion of soil fertility, resulting in poor yield and reduced biological diversity. These changes of land surface conditions can be inferred/monitored through changes in the spectral emission/reflection characteristics of the surface which can be monitored by satellite sensors to discriminate different types of land cover (Plate 11.11). Vegetal status can be inferred from image-based indices, such as NDVI, SAVI and others (Section 4.1.1). Other key information derived from remote sensing data such as land surface temperature, soil moisture and so on, will also be useful as input for models to assess desertification related aspects. Therefore remote sensing can be used to detect, monitor and map several key indicators leading to desertification. Li et. al. (2009), gives a detailed account of remote-sensing-based assessment of biophysical indicators pertaining to land degradation and desertification. Chabrillat (2006) gives a review of possible land surface variables that can be derived from remote sensing data which can be directly linked to the land degradation status. Thus, earth observation satellites provide significant contributions to desertification assessment and monitoring. However desertification is a complex problem dependent on many socio-economic problems and policy issues. Therefore remote sensing data *has to be integrated* with other field data; GIS provides an ideal tool for combining spatial and non-spatial data to model various scenarios leading to desertification. Broadly, remote sensing is useful in the following areas,

- desertification status mapping,
- change in the extent of desertification over a period of time,
- as input to models to asses likelihood of land susceptible to desertification, and
- as input to action plan aims at reversing desertification in areas wherever it is possible.

We shall briefly discuss in the following sections how information from remote sensing is used in some of these areas.

11.9.1 DESERTIFICATION STATUS MAPPING

Preparation of desertification status map requires understanding of desertification/land degradation processes, knowledge of land-use-land-cover and interpretation of multi-season satellite data. Ancillary data and field verification also plays an important role for preparing these maps. Understanding of seasonal behaviour/variation of land cover classes is essential for proper identification of areas affected by land degradation. Satellite images of the study area pertaining to three season, namely, *kharif* (September–November), *rabi* (December–March) and *zaid* (summer: April–June) are used to prepare land degradation and desertification maps. Use of three season data helps in better discrimination of the classes which are otherwise difficult to distinguish (Plate 11.12). We shall now discuss the process of generating Desertification Status Map (DSM) based on the methodology developed at the Space Applications Centre (SAC) of ISRO.

Desertification Status Map of India using satellite data on a 1:500,000 scale was first developed by Ajai et. al., (2007 and 2009) using Resourcesat-1 AWiFS geo-coded False Colour Composite (FCC) imagery. The classification system and the broad methodology for the desertification/land degradation mapping have been standardised during these studies and other projects.

Table 11.8 National classification system in India for desertification status mapping

Level-I: Land use		Level-II: Process of desertification		Level-III: Severity	
Agriculture irrigated	I	Vegetation degradation	v	Low	1
Agriculture unirrigated	D	Water erosion	w	High	2
Forest / plantation	F/P	Wind erosion	e		
Grassland / grazing land	G	Salinity / alkalinity	s/a		
Land with scrub	S	Water logging	I		
Barren	B	Mass movement	g		
Rocky area	R	Frost heaving	h		
Dune / sandy area	E	Frost shattering	f		
Glacial	G	Man-made	m		
Periglacial	L				
Others	T				

(*Source:* Ajai et. al., 2007)

Three-level hierarchical classification system has been used in mapping of desertification and land degradation status. Level-I in the classification system comprises broad classes of 'land use/land cover (LULC)', level-II considers the 'processes of desertification' and level-III provides the 'severity of degradation' (Table 11.8). For small scale maps (1:500,000), two levels of severity are demarcated while the severity can be categorised to three levels for large scale maps (greater than1:50,000 scale).

Preparation of DSM is an ordered process of steps carried by visual interpretation of satellite data along with information available from ancillary and field datasets. The stepwise methodology used for preparation of DSM is as follows:

(i) Selection of suitable satellite data (IRS AWiFS, IRS LISS3), multispectral (false colour composite) and multi-temporal (three season—*kharif, rabi* and *zaid*).
(ii) Geo-referencing of satellite data and standardisation of datum and projection.
(iii) Identification of major processes of desertification and land degradation using satellite data, available ancillary information and literature survey.
(iv) Collection of supportive data (administrative boundaries, forest cover, LULC reference data and so on).
(v) Defining interpretation key for identifying desertification and land degradation features.
(vi) Visual interpretation/on-screen digitisation of satellite data and to identify areas affected by desertification and land degradation and digitisation of the same in GIS environment.
(vii) Preparation of preliminary land degradation map.

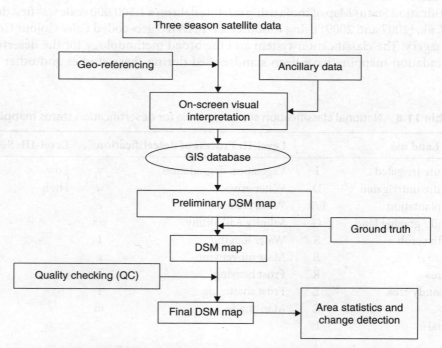

Fig. 11.14   Methodology for desertification mapping using satellite data. (SAC, 2016)

(viii) Field visits for verification of desertification indicators identified on satellite images.

(ix) Incorporation of interim corrections observed during field verification and preparation of pre-final map.

(x) Quality checking and finalisation of land degradation map.

Figure 11.14 shows the schematic representation of the methodology described above.

11.9.2 MONITORING CHANGE IN DESERTIFICATION OVER A PERIOD OF TIME

Multi-date remote sensing data can be used to monitor how desertification has changed over a definite time period. This is important in order to assess key desertification indicators (such as vegetative cover, NDVI, bare soil cover) undergoing change over time and to evolve remedial measures and also assess the effect of any corrective measures implemented. This involves comparing multi-temporal datasets to quantitatively analyse the temporal effects of the various indicators—it is a process of detecting temporal change. The change detection for monitoring desertification should provide the nature of change, its aereal extent, and spatial pattern (Macleod and Congalton, 1998).

There are a number of satellites providing uninterrupted data with similar characteristics for more than 25 years. These include Landsat, NOAA–AVHRR, SPOT and IRS, to name a few systems. Choice of data set and appropriate pre-processing before applying change detection algorithm is very important. The data set to be compared should be of proper season. The images should be acquired on the same anniversary or near anniversary date (close to same month and date) in order to minimise external effects such as sun elevation angle. Precise geometric registration (Section 10.2.2) in the order of sub-pixel size is essential to get high accuracy. If the comparison is made after classification, then radiometric normalisation can be avoided. However, if direct comparison of images has to be carried out, it is necessary to carryout relative radiometric normalisation (Schroeder et. al., 2006), so that the DN values are normalised to a reference image. This can be carried out by identifying temporally invariant objects in the images. Absolute radiometric correction is not desirable since it can have poor radiometric consistency between images due to lack of in situ atmospheric data such as aerosol optical depth which can produce low accuracy in change detection studies (O'Connella, 2013). Many change detection techniques are available in the literature. Lu et. al. (2004) have summarised and reviewed all these techniques exhaustively.

For Ministry of Environment, Forest and Climate Change (MoEF&CC), Government of India, SAC studied the change in desertification /land degradation for 2003–05 and 2011–13 time frames. Based on this investigation, an atlas has been prepared on a 1:50,000 scale depicting desertification /land degradation status and changes over the periods 2003–05 and 2011–13 in India. SAC study shows that area under desertification (arid, semi-arid and dry sub-humid regions) in India during 2003–05 was 81.48 Mha which increased to 82.64 Mha during the period 2011–13 .The most significant process of desertification/land degradation in the country is water erosion (10.83% in 2003–05 and 10.98% in 2011–13). The second most significant process is vegetal degradation (8.60% in 2003–05 and 8.91% in 2011–13) which is followed by wind erosion (5.58% in 2003–05 and 5.55% in 2011–13)—the percentage is with reference to the total geographic area of India.

11.9.3 SUSCEPTIBILITY TO DESERTIFICATION

It is useful to identify potential areas sensitive to desertification so that corrective measures can be implemented to reverse the trend or reduce the progression of desertification. A number of studies have been carried out to generate an index of Environmentally Sensitive Areas (ESA). This is carried out by modelling various degradation processes based on the assessment of both environmental quality indicators (vegetation, soil, climate) and anthropogenic factors (land management, socio-economic aspects). Three general types of Environmentally Sensitive Areas (ESAs) to desertification can be distinguished based on the stage of land degradation (Kosmas et. al., 1999):

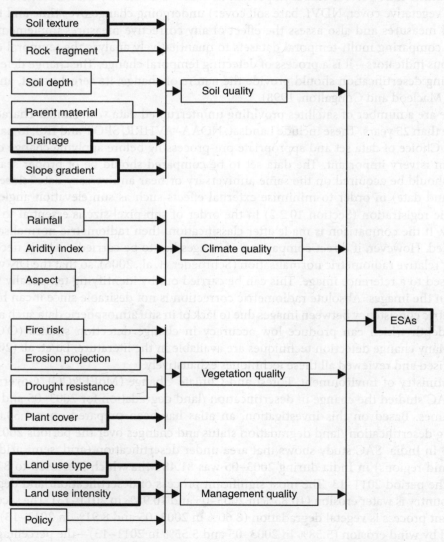

Fig. 11.15 Parameters used for the definition and mapping of the ESAs to desertification (after Kosmas et. al., 1999). The information required in boxes with thick outline are directly amenable to remote sensing.

(i)   areas already highly degraded through past misuse (Type A),

(ii) areas in which any change in the delicate balance of natural and human activity is likely to bring about desertification (Type B), and

(iii) areas threatened by desertification (Type C). This is a less severe form of Type B, for which nevertheless planning is necessary.

These are potential ESAs. We shall now describe the model developed in the framework of European project MEDALUS (MEditerranean Desertification And Land USe), which generates the ESA index to classify desertification of different severity (Kosmas et. al., 1999). In this model, parameters which have an effect on desertification such as landforms, soil, geology, vegetation, climate and human action are analysed. Each of these parameters is grouped into various uniform classes with respect to its behaviour on desertification and weighting factors are assigned in each class. The geographical information system (GIS) is a valuable tool to store, retrieve and manipulate the huge amount of data needed to compute and map different quality indices. The following four qualities are evaluated (i) soil quality, (ii) climate quality, (iii) vegetation quality, and (iv) management quality (Fig. 11.15). In the figure, information which can be derived using remote sensing are shown in boxes with thick outlines. All the data defining the four qualities are combined in a GIS with proper weight as per the developed algorithm to generate the ESA index.

11.9.4   Desertification Mitigation

All the information we have gathered from the above investigations are useful only if we can take some proactive steps to reduce further progress of desertification and reverse the trend. Most desertification research focusses on degradation assessments without putting sufficient emphasis on prevention and mitigation strategies (Schwilch et. al., 2009). Mitigation can be effective only by participatory management of all stake holders. Remote sensing can give scientific input to prioritise soil and water conservation strategies. For example, multispectral and multi-temporal remote sensing data when integrated with land use, geological, geomorphologic and hydrogeological information have the potential for identification of suitable areas for the construction of check dams. Interception of surface runoff by check dams across drainage at appropriate locations is one method for artificial recharge of groundwater aquifers to increase ground water potential (Mukherjee, 2008; Krishnamurthy et. al., 2000). To manage within the resources available, one needs to find out where immediate action for soil conservation has to be carried out. Intensity of soil erosion can be evaluated from slope, soil and vegetal cover (all accessible from remote sensing) and priority areas for soil conservation and land reclamation.

11.10   ARCHAEOLOGY

Archaeology is the study of the human past through systematic recovery and analysis of material remains or objects (referred to as artifacts) which are the evidence of past cultures. Archaeology allows us to delve far back into the time before written languages existed and enable us to have a glimpse of the lives and changes that have occurred in human cultures. Archaeology which had its origin in treasure hunting and grave robbing (Fagan and

Durrani, 2014) has evolved into a highly precise science to understand the past of the human civilisations. Major progress in archaeology is due to the multidisciplinary nature of modern archaeological research. Among the new technologies, remote sensing plays an important role especially for landscape archaeology which studies landscapes as a whole. According to the types of remote sensing platforms used for investigation, archaeological remote sensing can be broadly divided into ground-based and aerial/satellite based (Deng et. al., 2010). Ground-based archaeological remote sensing mainly refers to electromagnetic (for example GPR-refer Section 7.6) magnetic and gravitational field exploration which are important investigation means used in many archaeological applications. Air-borne or space-borne archaeological remote sensing refers to the full range of sensors operated from aircraft and spacecraft, both imaging (like cameras) and non-imaging (LIDAR) instruments. However, for the present discussion we shall restrict ourselves to aerial and satellite based remote sensing which are maximally used for archaeological investigations.

11.10.1 ARCHAEOLOGICAL SIGNATURES

A common concern of people who are new to remote sensing is, how an optical-IR (OIR) imagery that detects surface features can find out objects underneath. We have seen in Section 11.4 that though an OIR camera cannot 'see' ground water directly, if there are surface features which can be identified on the images that along with other collateral information, can be used to asses ground water prospects. The same principle is used in extracting archaeological information from remote sensing imagery. One of the premises of archaeological signature is that buried structures and discontinuities of the first subsoil produce inhomogeneous distribution of humidity, creating preferential lines along which water accumulates, producing lineation phenomena and thermal anomalies. This anomalous distribution affects some parameters, such as the colour of naked soil, the density and physical state of vegetation, thermal and electric properties such as conductivity (Orlando and Villa, 2011). The resultant structural and layout features invisible when observed from ground become conspicuous when viewed from above. Some of the major indicators of archaeological interest which are discernible from remote sensing are the following.

- *Crop marks*: These are subtle differences in the growth of vegetation caused by buried archaeological remains. Archaeological remnants such as moats, canals, tanks and pits collect silt over the years obscuring their surface forms. When this area is covered by vegetation, the growth is more luxuriant compared with adjoining regions since the vegetation benefits from extra moisture and nutrients held by the loose deposition of silt in the subsurface cavity. In contrast, when archaeological structures such as brick or stone walls and foundations, streets and solid floors are buried beneath soil, then vegetation over such locations show relatively poor growth compared to the surroundings. Such subtle variations in growth are nearly not discernable during field survey. In aerial/satellite imagery, especially combining with the near-IR bands, one can readily differentiate vegetation growth patterns over the ground following the lines of the buried features, revealing their plan and layout. The use of near-IR is helpful since reflection of vegetation in near-IR depends on the cell structure which is sensitive to external growth stress. Application of vegetative indices like NDVI (Section 4.4) may further enhance the difference. Although one is able to see more variation in the reflectance of vegetation in infrared, patterns indicating subsurface archaeological remains may be visible only under certain weather/ moisture conditions. Therefore, the vegetation cover should be analysed across seasons in order to isolate all potential archaeological features, which should then be analysed in the context of the layout of known archaeological remnants (Rajani, 2007; Rajani, 2016). The principle on which crop-marks are formed following buried archaeological features, formed the basis of several discoveries in Britain using aerial photos and is also applicable to marks formed by tree growth.

- *Earth works*: These are subtle surface undulations caused by structures buried immediately below. They are conspicuous by their shadows in photographs taken in the early morning or late evening.
- *Soil marks*: These are visible differences in the colour of soil caused by sub-surface archaeological objects.
- *Thermal anomaly*: The first subsoil water, accumulated in preferential lines produced by buried structures, rises to the surface due to capillarity action and it subtracts heat form the soil, leaving as a trace a drop in soil temperature producing some thermal anomaly (Orlando and Villa, 2011).
- *Fields or parcel boundaries*: These collectively form a pattern along the lines of buried layout. These features, represented in the image as regular shapes, correlate to potential buried structures.

Remote sensing provides much more information about the landscape compared to field survey because of its synoptic view covering a large area in one image frame. For example, certain features like long lineament are difficult to identify by field survey. The ability to observe in the spectral range beyond human vision can distinguish features based on their spectral signature. The penetrating capability of microwave sensors such as SAR and GPR can provide information below the surface.

Another important parameter in locating archaeological sites is topography, that is, height information to generate digital elevation model (DEM). Traditionally, elevation contour has been carried out using ground-based survey instruments such as engineer's levels. These instruments provide accurate data but are slow to operate and ground coverage takes considerable time. Later topographic surveys have been carried out using survey grade global navigational systems (like GPS) which have increased area that can be surveyed in a day compared to conventional techniques. From aerial/satellite photography height information to generate digital elevation model (DEM) is carried out with overlapping aerial photographs— stereo pairs and photogrammetric techniques (Section 6.9). Now there are other methods which can generate much faster and better accuracy. These include LIDAR and interferometric SAR–InSAR (Section 7.4.2).

11.10.2   DATA COLLECTION AND PROCESSING

Early remote sensing applications in archaeology started in the 1920s, immediately after the First World War, using aerial photography for the detection of archeological sites. The imageries were collected using both aircraft and hot air balloons. Introduction of colour-IR film in the 1940s enhanced the interpretability of aerial photographs.

The US spy satellite CORONA images collected from 1960 to 1972 were declassified at the end of cold war and these were the first satellite images used in archaeology. Studies using these images revealed a number of archaeological sites not known earlier. Starting with the launch of Landsat in 1972, now there are a number of earth observation satellites covering different parts of the electromagnetic spectrum with resolutions of a few hundreds of metres to sub-metre levels, and providing multispectral to hyperspectral information. Since the data is available in the digital format, they can be subjected to various image processing techniques such as filtering and contrast stretching to bring out certain features more clearly. These space systems enhanced the discriminability of archaeological targets. For example, crop marks (discussed above) may be hard to identify in visible-wavelength imagery. Addition of infrared bands, however, can readily discern vegetation growth patterns over the ground following the lines of the buried features, revealing their plan and layout (Rajani and Kasturirangan, 2014; Rajani 2007). Teams of researchers at University of Alabama, Birmingham, Alabama, discovered several Egyptian tombs, settlements and pyramids using satellite imagery covering bands in infrared. Studies at National Institute of Advanced Studies (NIAS), Bangalore, have found moats surrounding settlements belonging to the Hoysala period using infrared images and palaeochannels of past river systems using microwave imagery (Rajani and Kasturirangan, 2014; Rajani et. al., 2011; Rajani and Rajawat, 2011).

Surface undulations can give useful information in archaeological investigations since subtle 'bumps and humps' on the ground surface can be due to buried archaeological features. Thus, generating elevation maps which can produce 3D models of the landscape is an important part of archaeological investigation. Virtual 3D models/flythrough can complement archaeological studies as they help in planning fieldwork (Rajani et. al., 2009) since such models help in studying sites holistically and can be used for preservation, conservation and management of the site. DEM of Mahabalipuram was used to simulate the old coastline similar to the one depicted in a Portolan chart (Maritime map) dated 17th century, to analyse the erstwhile sea level and its effects on monuments thereof (Rajani and Kasturirangan, 2012). Three dimensional perspective views of the hill fort of Chitradurga were simulated using digital elevation model, they were compared with old paintings to analyse changes in land use and modern development in the vicinity (Nalini and Ranjani, 2012; Menze et. al., 2006) detected ancient settlement mounds in northern Mesopotamia using DEM, from SRTM (the NASA Shuttle Radar Topographic Mission) data.

Data Integration

For proper understanding of the site under consideration in relation to archaeology, it is necessary to study them with reference to data available from various sources such as derived information from remote sensing images (lineaments, vegetation distribution, soil type distribution, topography), field data (distribution of cultural sites, location of artefacts collected), additional facts about the site drawn from sources such as literature, epigraphy, travellers' accounts/records and prior archaeological reports. GIS is an ideal tool to store, manipulate and combine multiple data sets. Nalini and Rajani, 2012, discuss the methods of integrating the information from different sources using the GIS platform, thereby studying the change in the landscapeover a period of time of the city of Chitradurga (Karnataka state), known for its seven-tiered stone fort. GIS can also accept aspatial tabular information. The satellite data is usually geo-referenced (Section 9.3.2) and hence the derived information from these images are tagged to geographic coordinates. For other data, the first step to port into a GIS data base is attaching geographical references to every 'layer' of data, that is, attaching geographical references to every known archaeological object. Thus GIS database establishes a 'geospatial context' for the site which allows one to analyse individual archaeological objects in relation to adjacent objects (at various scales) (Rajani et. al., 2012), and ask questions such as:

- Why is this object located here?
- What is up/down hill from it?
- How far is it from objects that are known to be related to it?

Answers to these basic questions, in turn, can be used to pose and answer novel research questions, which can shed new light on our understanding of the site (Iyer et. al., 2012). This exercise can be fruitfully used for determining the most productive areas for detailed exploration on ground. Figure 11.16 gives a flowchart illustrating the integration and analysis of the data.

11.10.3   EXAMPLES OF RS IN ARCHAEOLOGY

Several archaeological studies have been conducted using RS-based techniques. These studies have either provided new evidence at known archaeological sites, or have led to the discovery of new archaeological sites/features and their connection with the environment. These techniques have made a significant impact on our understanding of archaeology.

Case study 1:   A multidisciplinary team from the University of Central Florida has studied the jungle-covered archaeological remains at Caracol (western Belize) for more than 25 years. Caracol was inhabited from 600 BC to AD 900, and had a peak population of about 115,000. The team initially used traditional on-the-ground techniques to survey buildings, pyramids and stone buildings around a central plaza, establishing Caracol as the largest known archaeological site in the southern Maya lowlands. Nevertheless, a lingering doubt remained among experts that the city was even larger than this. In order to better estimate the size, and also to study the density of the terrace systems that the ancient Maya constructed for agriculture, the team used LiDAR to 'see through' the dense forest covering. (In such thick canopy cover, optical images from space can only show features that extend above the canopy, or ones that lie in areas devoid of vegetation.) The study resulted in a detailed topographical map of 80 square miles of the site, only 1% of which had previously been mapped. New structures, causeways and agricultural terraces were identified (Chase et. al., 2010). Another example involves the area surrounding the famous Angkor Wat temple in Cambodia. RS analysis of the landscape has identified unknown sites buried under the thick cover of forest (Evans et. al., 2007).

Case study 2:   Tipu Sultan's Lalbagh palace at Srirangapatna was described as '...the handsomest building...' of the time by Francis Buchanan (Buchanan, 1988). It was destroyed by the British after Tipu Sultan's death, but scholars have nevertheless tried to identify at least the foundational remains of this beautiful palace (Swamy, 2010), whose location is marked on an old 19th century map. An analysis of multispectral satellite imagery of this location clearly marks a shape that correlates well with Lalbagh palace's layout as depicted on the map

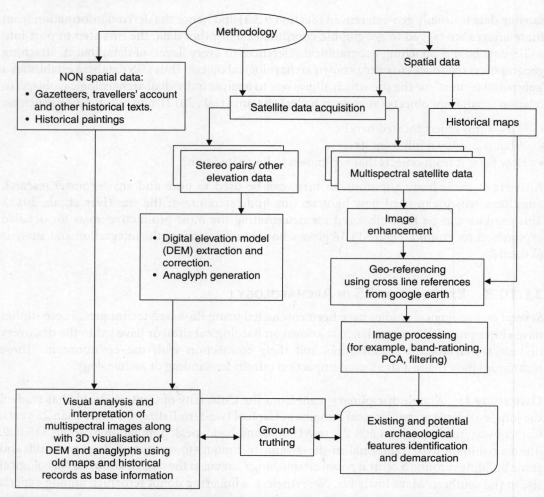

Fig. 11.16   Flow chart to find out potential archaeological site using RS image and other supporting information. (Rajani, 2017)

(Plate 11.13). It has a central structure, with axial paths dividing the surrounding large square garden into four parts, resembling the typical Persian *Charbagh* (four gardens) architecture. The synoptic satellite view also shows a pattern in the agricultural field boundaries—the land within and outside this square layout has been divided into smaller parcels without disturbing the overall boundary, so the layout's original shape is preserved. A ground survey of the location using GPS identified the basement of the palace, which was completely covered with vegetation, as well as two Kabutar khanas (dovecotes or pigeon-houses), marking the entrance to the palace. Three concentric tiers of forts and alternating moats (Plate 11.14) were also identified (Gupta et. al., 2017).

Case study 3:   Nalanda Mahavihara is believed to have been the world's oldest residential monastic university, active from the 5th to the 12th centuries AD. At its peak, it is believed to have accommodated thousands of scholars. A cluster of man-made water bodies (including former water bodies) are found near the site. One theory suggests that these were dug for the sole purpose of extracting earth for bricks, but synoptic view clearly shows that these water bodies are distinctly geometrical (squares or rectangles), with sides roughly parallel to cardinal directions. Clearly, such precision would be unnecessary merely for excavation, and hence these are more likely to be tanks marking the extent of the site. The layout of the largest tank, Dighi Pokhar, is markedly different from the others (Fig. 11.17). This anomaly is explained by the identification of a paleochannel (using CARTOSAT1 Aft image) that drew water from river Panchana toward Nalanda (Rajani, 2016).

Fig. 11.17   A regional view of the archaeological site of Nalanda together with surrounding pattern of square/rectangular water bodies indicating extent of old site and the palaeochannel that drew water from the river Panchana towards the site. (*Image:* Cartosat1 Aft 29 Feb 2008)

To summarise, the application of remote sensing along with GIS provides a new perspective for archaeological landscape. This helps archaeologists to map, analyse and interpret large areas faster and at a much lower cost in comparison to field survey. However, it does not mean field investigations – such, as collecting and analysing cultural relics – can be avoided, but archeological remote sensing helps to narrow down areas for detailed investigation and if necessary, excavation.

11.11   REMOTE SENSING FOR EARTH SYSTEM SCIENCE STUDIES

Though our main emphasis in the present chapter is the application of remote sensing for earth resources management, a satellite-based earth observation system enhances our understanding of the entire earth as an integrated system. Scientific studies show that the earth has changed over time and continues to change due to natural and human induced interventions. To understand these changes – its cause and effect – it is necessary to systematically and periodically monitor the earth and its environment. Satellite-based earth observation, along with ground and aircraft-based measurements provide the scientific basis for understanding the earth system and its variation. A total study of Earth System Science, would call for an understanding of the natural interaction among its different components and the potential role of human activities in influencing the earth on a global scale. This requires a multi-pronged approach: a paleoclimatic component to unravel past (mainly natural) global changes and cycles, a study of micro-level interactions of relevance (such as the emission rate of methane from different ecosystems, CO_2 fixation efficiency of terrestrial and marine vegetation, laboratory investigations of ozone chemistry) and finally a global scale observational and modelling programme to monitor and understand the changes taking place and to make intelligent predictions of future scenarios under different strategies. These studies should help us to understand 'how the earth is changing and what the consequences for life on earth are' (*http://www.earth.nasa.gov/*).

Of the three broad programmes of Earth System Science mentioned above, the third, namely, global scale observations of relevant parameters, processes and components, is the most amenable to satellite remote sensing—indeed, satellite data are nearly indispensable in many cases. The unique vantage point of space provides information about the earth's air, land, water and life, as well as interactions among them, which is not available using any other means. The Earth Science Enterprise Programme is NASA's contribution to developing a vastly improved understanding of the earth. One of the major international initiatives to study the earth system is the International Geosphere Biosphere Programme (IGBP). These programmes lay the foundation for long-term environmental and climate monitoring and prediction.

Various earth observation satellites are launched/being planned to make a variety of observation of the land, ocean and atmosphere, which will provide inputs to various studies of Earth Sciences. NASA's Earth Observing System (EOS) is the major initiative to have a long-term database of many aspects of the earth's atmosphere, land and ocean characteristics. A series of satellite missions carrying advanced instruments are currently operating (being planned) under the EOS programme, which will enhance our understanding of the entire earth system on a global scale. A broad classification of sensors for various components of the Earth System Science Studies can be thought of as follows.

For terrestrial mapping, low or medium-resolution 'optical' sensors, operating in the visible and near-infrared are generally used (SPOT VEGETATION, TERRA MODIS, IRS WIFS). Different surfaces have different spectral reflectivity signatures, facilitating classification of land cover. Microwave sensors are also used, especially during cloud covered seasons. Elevation is obtained by steoroscopic (optical) and interferometric (microwave) techniques.

For marine mapping, as far as biological parameters are concerned, optical narrow band sensors are used (OCM, MERIS, SEAWiFS). However, for temperature, thermal infrared sensors (based on emitted long wave radiation) are called for (NOAA AVHRR). For sea-state, sea-ice, and so on, microwave sensors are found useful.

Atmospheric sounding is done mainly using the absorption/emission of infrared/microwave radiation by the target gases in question. Viewing geometry is earth-oriented for tropospheric gases and limb-oriented (tangent view above cloud tops) for stratospheric gases. For aerosols, their scattering property is used, mainly in near-infrared or the visible region of the spectrum (Appendix 2).

What we have presented above, is only a few typical examples of the vast possibilities of using remote sensing for various disciplines. An exhaustive account of them is beyond the scope of this book.

The resource manager or decision-maker is more interested in getting a solution to the problem he is facing than just getting information about a resource. For example, one would like to know how best a parcel of land can be utilised, considering the soil, terrain and socio-economic conditions of the inhabitants/people around it and not just the land use pattern. Similarly, one is interested in forest management plans, taking into account all relevant factors, than just a forest map. The final solution to a problem requires integration of many spatial and aspatial information. That is, we have to relate information from different sources. Integration of data from different sources can help to resolve 'conflicts' of interest on a scientific basis providing different trade-offs that exists for planning its pros and cons including the costs involved. Currently, this is very conveniently carried out by using Geographic Information System (GIS).

FOR FURTHER READING

1. Remote Sensing Applications in Agriculture, in *Manual of Remote Sensing* (Colwell R N, Ed.), Myers V I (1983), American Society of Photogrammetry, pp. 2111–2228.
2. *Introduction to Remote Sensing*, Campbell J B (1996), Taylor & Francis Ltd., London. 622 p.
3. *Remote Sensing of Environment: An Earth Resource Perspective*, Jensen J R (2000), Prentice Hall, New Jersey, 544 p.
4. *Remote Sensing for the Earth Sciences – Manual of Remote Sensing*, Renz A N, Ed., (1999), Vol. 3, ASPRS and John Wiley & Sons Inc. USA, 707 p.
5. *http://www.indiawaterportal.org/sites/indiawaterportal.org/files/Remote%20Sensing%20 Applications_NRSC_2010.pdf*
6. *http://www.marinespatialecologylab.org/wp-content/uploads/2010/11/Green-et-al-1996-Coastal-Management.pdf*
7. *http://gis.geog.queensu.ca/publicationpdfs/2004rsinplanning.pdf*
8. *http://water.usgs.gov/nwsum/WSP2425/definitions.html*
9. *http://www.wmo.int/pages/prog/hwrp/chy/chy14/documents/ms/remote_sensing_snow_cover_methods_mapping_snow.pdf*
10. *http://www.mdpi.com/127316*
11. *www.fao.org/docrep/W8440e/W8440e02.htm*
12. *www.cep.unep.org/issues/czm.html*
13. *http://link.springer.com/article/10.1007/s12518-010-0024-y/fulltext.html*
14. *http://people.ucalgary.ca/~aaosicki/RS_Arky.pdf*
15. *http://www.fao.org/fileadmin/templates/ess/documents/meetings_and_workshops/GS_SAC_2013/Improving_methods_for_crops_estimates/Crop_Area_Estimation_Lit_review.pdf*
16. *http://www.iasri.res.in/ebook/GIS_TA/index.htm*
17. *http://www.fao.org/docrep/003/t0355e/T0355E00.HTM#toc*
18. *http://www.ndma.gov.in/images/guidelines/droughtguidelines.pdf*

12 Geographical Information System (GIS)

One of the common forms of representing remote sensing data as information is in the form of thematic maps [examples: soil, geology, land use/land cover (LULC), vegetation-type], by means of visual or computer classification. For many applications such maps may be adequate. However, thematic maps are not an end in itself. It is only the starting point for a variety of applications to which remote sensing data can be potentially used. For this, in general, integration of remote sensing data with both spatial and non-spatial data derived from various other sources and suitable modelling of their interrelationship will be required to arrive at certain possible decision scenarios or other action. Generally, *spatial data* refers to maps, and specifically any data containing location information. For example, point or line or polygon maps and aerial/satellite images can be called spatial data because they inherit *x,y* coordinates for every element in the map and can be tagged to location on the earth-**latitude and longitude, or height and depth**. Non-spatial data refers to tabular data or any textual information describing some geographic entity without revealing their spatial locations. Attribute information like area or perimeter or population or names of places or identification number are examples of non-spatial data.

All planners and managers do such integration in one way or another. For example, to decide upon the treatment for avoiding soil erosion, one tries to find out the slope, type of soil and land cover, and mentally integrates them based on one's experience. This process of using brain as a 'synthesiser' can be done for a specific site, but will be cumbersome, if not impossible to extend to large areas with varying characteristics.

Information merging was historically performed by map overlay method (Lillesand and Kiefer, 1979). Here each theme is prepared on a transparent map sheet in varying grey tone according to the severity of the condition. For example, a slope may be represented with increasing darker shade as the slope increases. These maps for each derived data, when overlayed, depending on the dark tone, can be used to draw inferences. These manual methods are not only cumbersome and time consuming, especially when large volume of data has to be handled, but also do not provide the flexibility of modelling the inter-relationship between various layers to arrive at different possible scenarios for decision making. The impasse can be overcome if the data, both spatial and non-spatial, can be organised in a computer in a suitable format, such that it is possible to retrieve, manipulate, analyse with an user defined specification and display the information generated in the desired medium. Organising the remote sensing data in the environment of a Geographical Information System (GIS) makes data integration and manipulation very convenient. *GIS can be thought of as a system of hardware and software wherein geographically referenced data (spatial data) and associated attributes (non-spatial data) can be captured for manipulation, analysis and modelling to assist and speed up decision making and management tasks.* The components of a GIS is schematically shown in Fig. 12.1.

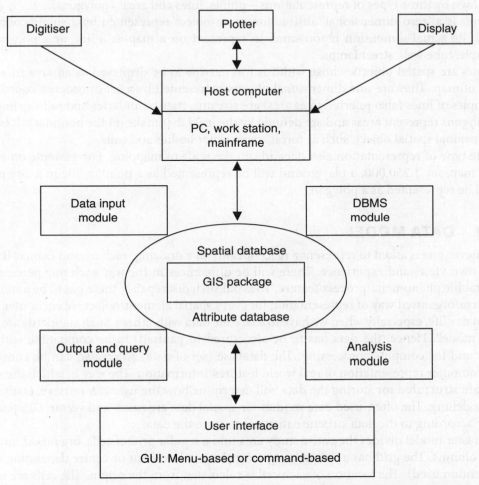

Fig. 12.1 Components of a GIS. (Adapted from UN-ESCAP document ST/ESCAP/1615, 1996)

Geographical features can be described by two types of data—*spatial data* which describes location and *attribute data* which specifies the characteristics at that location. Hence GIS primarily deals with spatial data and attribute data in an organised manner, using computer hardware and associated software. Spatial data essentially tells, '*where is it?*', that is, specifies location; while attribute data tells '*what (how much) is it?*', that is, characteristics at that location, natural or human created. Spatial data has to be suitably referenced, generally in terms of longitude and latitude, or could be with respect to a regular grid, whose origin is known. Attribute data are descriptions, measurements, and/or classification of geographic features. The attributes can be both qualitative (crop type) and quantitative (yield per hectre, elevation, temperature). Attribute data stored in the database can be related to the spatial data.

The location of the Central School at Gandhinagar is spatial data. It can have attributes, such as number of students, number of teachers, number of classrooms, percentage pass in the last 10 years, and so on. The attributes can be both numeric and textual. Spatial locational data can be shown by three types of representations—points, lines and areas (polygons).

Point is a 'zero-dimensional' abstraction of an object represented by a single coordinate (*x, y*). Its actual dimension is too small to represent on a map as a line or a polygon, for example, tube well, street lamps.

Lines are spatial objects whose width is too narrow to be displayed as an area in a given scale of map. They are one dimensional objects represented by a set of ordered coordinates. Examples of lines (also referred to as arcs) are streams, state boundaries and railway lines.

Polygons represent areas and are defined by the lines that make up the boundary. It is a two dimensional spatial object, such as forest cover, water bodies and soils.

The type of representation also depends on the scale of mapping. For example on a small scale map, say 1:250,000, a playground will be represented as a point, while in a city map, it could be represented as a polygon.

12.1   DATA MODEL

Whenever one is asked to represent a place/locality in a drawing, each person depicts it as per their own views and experience. There will be differences in the way each one perceives the geographic phenomena/process/feature. To avoid such discrepancy there has to be a standard/uniform/organised way of representation for every spatial element/object we encounter in our day to day life, especially when we have to share the data with others. Such standards are called 'data model'. Hence, the data has to be structured (organised) to be compatible with each other and for computer processing. The database (set of data) so created can be considered as a computer representation of real world features/information. The way in which the spatial data are structured for storing the data will determine how the user can retrieve, analyse and do modelling. The often-used data models for spatial data are *raster* and *vector*. GIS packages differ according to the data structure they use to store the data.

A raster model divides the entire study area into a regular grid of cells, organised into rows and columns. The grid has a defined origin (upper left, lower left or centre depending on the convention used). The location of each cell is calculated from the origin. The cells are usually square, however their shape can vary—triangle, hexagonal. These cells (or called pixels in images) are the basic units for which information is explicitly recorded in a raster model. Each cell is assigned a single attribute value; for example, soil type, land use, temperature. Rules need to be applied to assign a value to a cell if the object does not cover the entire cell (majority of area, value at the centre).

In the raster model, a point is represented by a single cell. A line is represented by multiple cells usually with only 1 or 2 neighbours. A polygon is represented by a group of contiguous cells joined at the edges or corners (Fig. 12.2). In a raster based system, our ability to specify a location in space is limited by the cell size, since we are not able to know about the different locations within a raster cell. The angle between the true north and the direction defined by the column is taken as the orientation.

Since the cells are of a fixed size and location, the raster produces a blocky appearance. This effect can be reduced if the cell size is decreased. However, this increases the data volume.

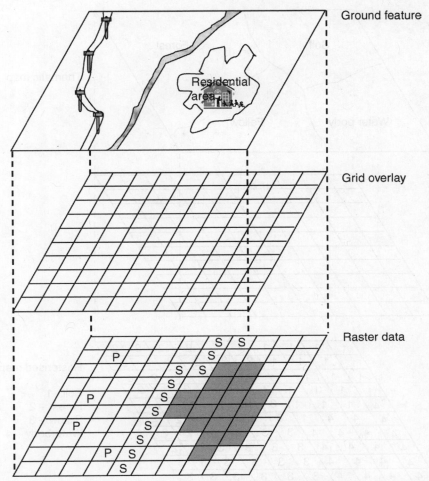

Fig. 12.2 Schematics showing raster representation of point (electric pole-P), line (stream-S) and polygon (residential area-shaded).

There are various compression techniques used to reduce the data volume, that is, ways to store the same amount of information in a smaller space in the computer. All compression methods take advantage of the fact that the contents of a cell tend to be similar to the contents of neighbouring cells—spatial dependence. Thus only changes from the adjacent cells are stored. If multi-date imagery is being used, temporal correlation can be made use of, that is, only changes from one date to the next date data are stored.

Remote sensing data, except from the photographic camera, are generally in the raster form. For example, a single band data of the LISS camera represents the radiance variation in a raster form. The data is represented as numbers, which can vary from 0 to the saturation level, say 255. If we have a map, say a land use map, then it can be digitised to the raster format using techniques such as scanning. Here each category can be assigned a 'number' or 'alphabet' to indicate the difference (Fig. 12.3).

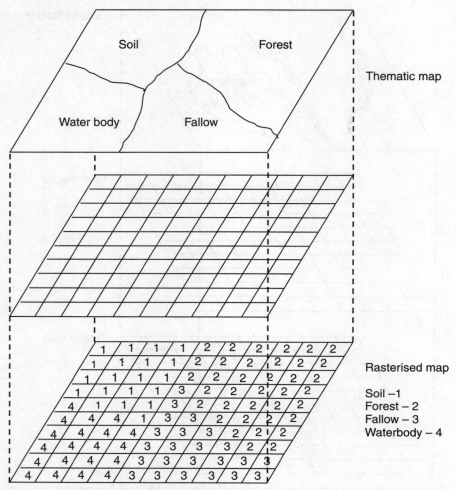

Fig. 12.3 Schematics showing rasterising of a thematic map.

The fundamental theory of a *vector model* is that all geographic features in a real world (or on a map) can be represented as, points, lines (arcs) or areas (polygons). In this model, the spatial location of features are defined on the basis of coordinate pairs. A point (node) is represented by a single (x, y) coordinate pair [Fig. 12.4(a)]. A point has no dimension. Besides the (x, y) coordinates, other data must be stored to indicate what kind of point it is and other information if any associated with it.

Lines can be built up of a number of points. It requires a minimum of two (x, y) coordinates (straight line) to define a line [Fig. 12.4(b)). To describe a continuous complex line, a larger number of (x, y) coordinates are required—it is represented by a sequence of points [Fig. 12.4(c)]. Each pair of coordinates defines a straight line segment. Smaller the line segment, closer will be the data model to the real world feature.

Polygons are represented by listing coordinates of points in order as you 'walk around' the outside boundary of the polygon. The coordinate pairs at the beginning and end are the same thus making it a closed area [Fig. 12.4(d)].

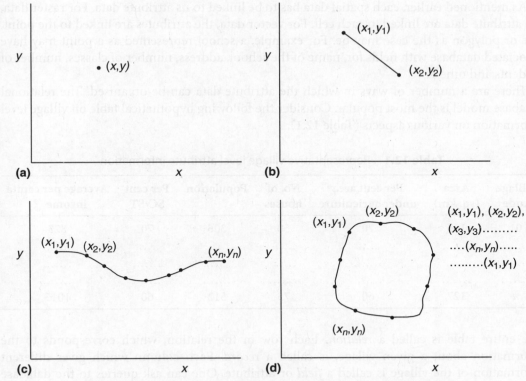

Fig. 12.4 Schematics showing vector representation of a point, line and polygon.

The spatial data constructed in this manner is essentially a collection of coordinate strings, with no inherent structure and is referred to as a *spaghetti model*. Here although all spatial features are recorded, the spatial relationship between these features are not encoded. To show explicit relationships between the spatial objects, *topological models* are used (topology is the mathematical method used to define spatial relationships, such as the information about which area bound a line segment, which polygons share a boundary, which points fall along the edge of a particular polygon and so forth). Here we will not get into details of such models.

The attribute data pertaining to the individual spatial feature is stored as a table and maintained in an internal or external database engine. An internal database engine refers to the in-built storage mechanism within the GIS software and external database engine refers to third-party storage mechanism. A vector model represents more accurately, the real-life features without any 'blocky' appearance (as in a raster model) and allows complex data to be stored in a minimum space. The raster data though voluminous is more amenable for spatial analysis. Currently GIS software can handle both models. Thus data can be stored in vector models using minimum storage space and can be converted to raster models for spatial analysis and analytical modelling.

Compared with the raster GIS, some of the vector GIS operations are more accurate. For example, estimates of area based on polygons are more accurate than counts of raster cells, because boundary raster cells are not 'pure' and contain part of an adjacent feature.

As mentioned earlier, each spatial data has to be linked to its attribute data. For raster data, the attribute data are linked to each cell. For vector data, the attributes are linked to the point, line or polygon as the case may be. For example, a school represented as a point may have associated database with fields for, name of the school, address, number of classes, number of students and others.

There are a number of ways in which the attribute data can be organised. The relational database model is the most popular. Consider the following hypothetical table on village level information on various aspects (Table 12.1).

Table 12.1   Representative village level attribute information

Village code	Area (sq. km)	Per cent area under agriculture	No. of houses	Population	Per cent SC/ST	Average per capita income (₹)
01	106	70	50	306	70	825
....	....	....	....	......	......	....
....	....	....	....	....	....	....
....	....	....	....	....	....	....
n	127	60	75	512	60	1015

The entire table is called a *relation*. Each row in the relation, which corresponds to the information about a given village, is called a *record*. Each column which gives different information of the village is called a *field* or attribute. One can ask queries to the database using suitable software. Queries could be, for example, print out all villages with area greater than 70 km^2 and agriculture area less than 50%. In GIS, the advantage is that these queries can be linked to spatial data. For example, show the location of these villages on the base map.

Comprehensive spatial data bases contain physical features such as roads, drainage, soil types and vegetation, as well as layers of defined features, such as district boundaries, postal zones, and so on, which cannot be observed on the ground. A topographic map contains all the spatial features including height information. However, in GIS the database is organised in *layers*. Groups of similar features are combined in one layer. One item (theme) of data is available for each location within a single layer and multiple items of information require multiple layers. The layers can be overlayed and registered such that they are spatially aligned one over the other. Such layered data is more amenable for further spatial analysis.

12.2   DATA ENTRY

Data collection, and digitisation/editing (to be compatible for computer storage) are the most time-consuming activity. Features which are dynamic (like vegetative cover) require periodic updating of data. For creating a multi-layer GIS database, features may be extracted from a range of topographic maps, field observations and reports. Generally, remote sensing digital data is available directly as raster structure. However, it needs to be converted into thematic layers through a digital classification procedure (see Chapter 10). Visually interpreted thematic maps and topographical maps need to be digitised. We shall briefly state some of the generally used techniques.

Video frame grabbing is one of the simplest techniques used to convert paper maps to raster data structures. The system essentially consists of a video camera connected to a PC with a special interface card. The camera output is digitised and stored as a raster file. Unfortunately all the information on the map whether required or not is collected and needs editing to remove unwanted data.

A *scanner* also performs the same way as a video grabber, but is a dedicated device for this purpose. Drum and flat bed scanners are available. The output is a raster image of the map.

Conversion to vector structure is undertaken using a *table digitiser*, linked to a computer. The table digitiser is a large board, the surface of which is underlayed with a very fine mesh of wires. Attached to the board is a mouse with a magnetic coil inside and can be moved freely on the board. The mouse has a cross-wire, which the user aligns with the feature to be digitised and a button is pressed to send the coordinates to the computer. Thus moving the cross-wire along the feature, the data will be captured in the vector format.

The attribute data available as reports and tables are entered through the keyboard, *key coding*. Table 12.2 gives possible encoding methods for different data sources. The data is drawn from different sources and hence could have different scales, projections, referencing system, and so on. Therefore there is a need to standardise the database to a common coordinate system. GIS software enables this operation to be done. In addition, all the layers need to be registered. This is achieved by Ground Control Points (GCPs) through a process known as geocoding in which each point on the map is fixed at the right ground coordinate system through coordinate transformation technique (refer Section 9.3.2).

Table 12.2 Possible encoding methods for different data sources

Data source	Analogue or digital source	Possible encoding methods	Examples
Tabular data	Analogue	Key board entry Text scanning	Address lists of hotel guests Tables of regional tourism statistics from official publications
Map data	Analogue	Manual digitising Automatic digitising Scanning	Historical maps of settlement and agriculture Infrastructure and administrative maps
Aerial photographs	Analogue	Manual digitising Automatic digitising Scanning	Extent of flood inundation
Tabular data	Digital	Digital file transfer (with reformatting, if necessary)	National population census data Data from meteorological station recording equipment
Map data	Digital	Digital file transfer (with reformatting)	Digital data from national mapping agency Digital height (DTM) data
Satellite imagery	Digital	Digital file transfer Image processing and reformatting	Land use data Forest condition data

After Heywood et. al., (1998)

As mentioned earlier, data collection and its management to create a reliable spatial database is the major time-consuming and costly part of any GIS. For a dynamic situation like agriculture, the data need to be periodically updated, which adds to the effort and cost. It is obvious that the quality of the GIS output is critically dependent on the accuracy of the database which in turn depends upon the accuracy of GCPs, the projection system and digitisation/editing methods.

12.3   DATA ANALYSIS AND MODELLING

GIS is not just a 'single window' data source. What makes GIS attractive is its ability to carry out integrated analysis in order to spatially combine multiple features to generate a composite theme. The attributes of the composite theme can be analysed to obtain the combined characteristics of a polygon. Thus GIS is able to come out with answers for simple queries to complex mathematical modelling, which makes it a powerful tool for decision making. The capabilities of the GIS package include a wide range of functions such as queries, proximity analysis, overlay operations, network analysis, various optimisation techniques—to name a few. How these are used to give a solution to an user's problem depends on his experience and expertise. Elaboration of various aspects of using GIS data analysis package is beyond the scope of this book. We shall instead give some of the possibilities of data analysis without getting into the details.

Performing queries is one of the often used functions. Since GIS stores both spatial and non-spatial data, which are linked, it can answer questions linking the two like non-spatial queries and questions about the attribute features. For example, how many villages are there whose area is greater than 70 km^2. This could be performed on the attribute database itself. Whereas 'display all the villages whose area is greater than 70 km^2 and connected by national highway' needs linking both attribute and spatial databases. We could click on a map display and ask *what is at* that location. We can ask the query *where does it* exist; for example, display all the tube wells in a particular village. Another possibility is trend analysis—how things have changed with time. For example, the change in forest cover between 1980 and 2000 (assuming you have the required data of both the years in your database)

Buffering – identifying a zone of interest around, a point, line or polygon – is another often used capability of GIS (Fig. 12.5). Buffering is useful in a variety of applications such as forestry, environment, transportation, and so on. For example, 1 km around a hospital may be protected for noise pollution (no horn zone—buffering around a point). 500 m from the high tide line on the coast can be buffered as a no industry zone (line buffering). A specified distance around a lake may be protected (buffering around a polygon).

Network analysis is another important application area of GIS. For example, to determine the optimal bus routing. The network analysis is carried out based on a connected linear feature (network) that form a framework through which resources flow. In the example cited, the linear features are roads. To optimise, we should know various attributes necessary to do the analysis. For the example considered, these include, connectivity of roads, resistance due to traffic, turns, and so on.

The ability to integrate data from two or more map layers is one of the useful functions of GIS. The overlay function allows the user to 'stack' map layers one over the other. As mentioned earlier each layer usually contains a single theme, as vegetation, soil type, road to minimization, could be increased by another 'x' metres or what will be the city growth after 10 years given the current details about population and other parameters in a city. It is amenable to various mathematical modelling studies. It is possible to change the model parameters, decision rules and find out the impact, which provides the decision maker a wide range of choices.

Predictive models of a real world process could tell how the world might react under certain situations, for example, impact on rainfall on a landscape with due consideration, predicting spread in forest fires, in various conditions, and so on.

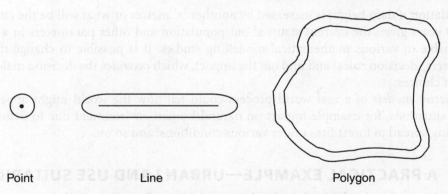

Point   Line   Polygon

Fig. 12.5 Schematics showing the concept of buffering.

network, drainage, and so on (Fig. 12.6). Overlay functions create a new layer of spatial data by merging the data from different existing layers by using simple Boolean operators (that is, Union/merging of two layers using OR, Intersection/common area from two layers using AND, Non-intersecting area in two layers using NAND and so on). For example, a map of all vegetated area having a certain soil type and slope less than a specified value but a certain distance away from the highway. Overlays in vector data structure are more complex and hence it is convenient to convert them to the raster structure and do the overlay. Arithmetic operations are not possible between two vector layers. Hence, raster data structure is generally preferred for modelling purposes.

The spatial multi-criteria modelling capability of the GIS is one of the most powerful tools for decision-makers. It is usually referred to as 'what if' analysis. For example, what happens

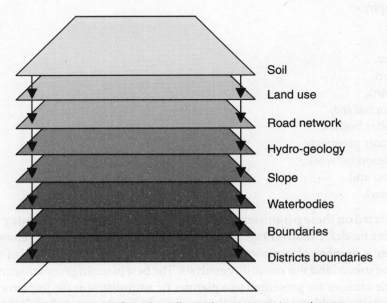

Soil

Land use

Road network

Hydro-geology

Slope

Waterbodies

Boundaries

Districts boundaries

Fig. 12.6 Schematics of the concept of overlay. All map layers are registered to a common base map. The different layers can be integrated depending on some rules to produce a new map.

to inundation if dam height is increased by another '*x*' metres or what will be the city growth after 10 years given the current status about population and other parameters in a city. GIS is amenable to various mathematical modelling studies. It is possible to change the model parameters (decision rules) and find out the impact, which provides the decision maker a wide range of choices.

Predictive models of a real world process could tell how the world might appear under certain situations, for example impact on natural/human environment due to deforestation, predicting spread of forest fires under various conditions, and so on.

12.4   A PRACTICAL EXAMPLE—URBAN LAND USE SUITABILITY

The suitability of the land for urban development is dependent on a set of physical parameters and also on economic factors. The cumulative effect of these factors determines the degree of suitability and also helps in further categorising of the land into different orders of development. The assessment of the physical parameters of the land is possible by analysing the land use, soil, slope, geology, flood hazard, physiography and distance from the road network and railway station. which are very much amenable to GIS analysis. The assessment of physical parameters gives an identification of the limitations of the land for development. For example, if the slope is high, the limitation it offers is more than for a land which has gentle slopes or a flat terrain. Practically, this would mean that the development of the high slope land would require considerable inputs (finance, manpower, materials, time) and thus may be less suitable as against flat land where the inputs required are considerably less. Similar consideration is possible for other parameters also. Various parameters generally considered for urban land use suitability analysis, are:

- urban land use,
- physiography,
- slope,
- soil depth,
- soil texture,
- soil erosion,
- flood hazard,
- earthquake hazard,
- surface water bodies,
- ground water prospects,
- transportation network,
- land values, and
- urban sprawl.

The data collected on these parameters are analysed in a GIS environment using a multi-variate weighted index model. The advantage of multi-variate index analysis in GIS environment is that one can create a number of planning scenarios by changing the weightage of the parameters considered for urban land use suitability analysis. The best planning scenario can be considered when multiple choices are presented to a planner or administrator for implementation.

One of the classic problems in decision theory or multi-parameter analysis is the determination of the relative importance (weights) of each parameter with respect to the other. As all parameters of the land cannot be weighted equally for the suitability assessment, it is essential that a weighted method needs to be employed where the relative importance of the parameters defines the weightage. This requires human judgement supplemented by mathematical tools. A number of methods are available to deal with such problems (Saaty, 1980).

After determining the weightages for the parameters, a rating (or score) for each category within the parameter is assigned. The ratings to the individual categories are assigned in

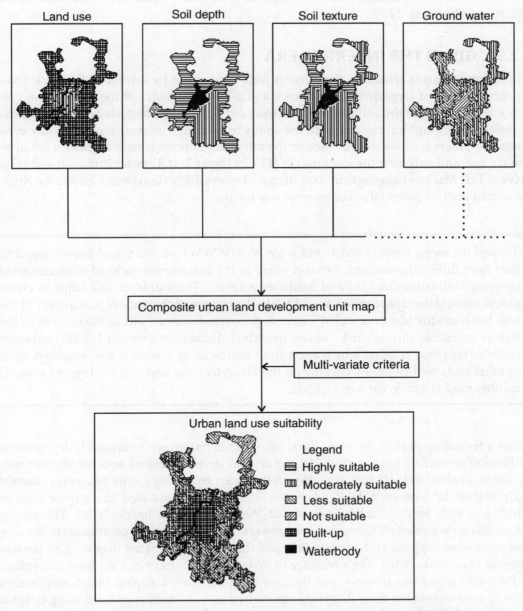

Fig. 12.7 Schematics showing integration of various thematic maps for urban use suitability mapping.

such a way that higher the rating, higher the suitability and lesser the limitations; lower the rating, lower the priority for urbanisation and higher the limitations for development. So, the categories of parameters considered for suitability are studied carefully and arranged in four (or more) ranges for the assignment of ratings.

Integration analysis is then carried out in a GIS environment and a composite urban land development unit map is generated. Composite suitability indices are obtained by multiplying weightages with rank numbers of each category and by summing up the values of all categories. The entire area is then divided into four categories of suitability based upon mean and standard deviation values (Fig. 12.7).

12.5   GIS IN THE INTERNET ERA

Initial developments related to the internet were carried out by Advanced Research Project Agency (ARPA) of Department of Defence and a few universities of the USA in the 1960s. The main aim behind this initiative was to create a group of interconnected computers located at different geographical regions, with the ability to exchange information seamlessly even if some computers were destroyed. Though the initial developments were successful it had very limited use, and only after the invention of HTTP (Hyper Text Transfer Protocol) and HTML (Hyper Text Markup Language) by Tim Berners-Lee of CERN (European Council for Nuclear Research) the real potential of the internet was realised.

Though the terms *Internet* and *World Wide Web* (WWW) are often used interchangeably, they have different meanings. Internet refers to the massive networks of interconnected computer infrastructure (physical hardware entities). This infrastructure helps to create global information space called World Wide Web where each member (computer) of the web has a unique identifier called Uniform Resource Locator (URL). The content in the web is accessible through inter-linked hypertext documents through HTTP (software/codes). Hypertext is a text which apart from representing a word it also possesses links to other texts/web pages. By clicking on the Hypertext, the user can be directed towards another page at a different web location.

From a few computers in the early days, the internet has grown enormously to encompass millions of computers today. In this 21st century, any development without the internet would be unimaginable, and GIS has also adopted this latest technology to its advantage (since the early 90s) in the form of WebGIS where the GIS software is installed in a remote computer which has Web Serving Capabilities (called Web Server) (Alesheikh, 2002). The user can access this server-side GIS through a web browser. The browser sends commands to the server and processing happens at the server-side, and the resultant maps are displayed on the user's browser (Karnatak, 2016). The advantage of WebGIS is that user need not have GIS software at their end (this saves money), and the user need not learn complex analytical/processing steps (this saves time) as these things are customised as ready-made functions using Graphical User Interface (GUI) under a web page where focussed functionalities and solutions can be made available for different customers. Big organisations can place WebGIS at one place, and many of their sister-organisations and clients can access the maps remotely. The advantages of webGIS are:

- it provides enhanced outreach (global access),
- reduces redundancy (copy at multiple places) of data,
- facilitates single end data updation (helps to avoid wrong data if we have multiple copies), and
- improves the inter-operability (cross platform connectivity, that is, accessibility of content through computers/devices using different operating systems).

One of the important contribution of WebGIS is its ability to seamlessly interconnect and serve diverse databases created by different government organisations (such as Survey of India, Geological Survey of India, Forest Survey of India, Botanical Survey of India, Zoological Survey of India, National Bureau of Soil Survey and Land Use Planning, and so on). In this mode, the individual organisation's database will be located in their own server with security credentials in order to maintain copyright. Free access for reading can be provided which will facilitate display and query using the concept of web map service (for only displaying maps/images) or web feature service (for query and updation) or Geo mashup (helps to attach geographic location to any posting on web).

Bhuvan (http://bhuvan.nrsc.gov.in) is one such WebGIS platform developed by the Indian Space Research Organisation (NRSC, ISRO, Hyderabad) where different applications (theme-wise) are customised and the user can see and query many different spatial databases available in India. There are numerous commercial webGIS softwares and freewares available. Some of the freewares are MapServer, Geoserver, MapGuide, QGIS, GRASS, GeoTools, and so on. WebGIS is also known as InternetGIS or Distributed GIS. Today one can access GIS using mobile phones through an internet connection, and GIS on the mobile is called MobileGIS which is highly useful at the time of disasters and data collection in the field. The user can access the maps and can embed their ground photos directly to maps using MobileGIS.

12.6   SPATIAL DATA INFRASTRUCTURE

In the emerging information era, geographic and geo-spatial information occupies a pre-eminent position. The use of reliable geo-spatial information is critical to virtually every sphere of socio-economic activity—disaster management, natural resources management, environmental restoration to name just a few examples. Until recently, maps (usually in paper form) have been the mainstay for a wide variety of applications and decision making. The advent of remote sensing, GIS and GPS allow us to capture, store and process an unprecedented amount of geographical and spatial information about a wide variety of themes, such as land use, land form, soil and environmental changes. Current and accurate spatial data must be readily available to decision makers to carry out development at local, state and national level in order to contribute to economic growth, environmental quality and stability. However, much of the geo-spatial data is generally scattered across a large number of organisations, following different standards and is not sufficiently integrated and networked to make it readily available to a large community of users. Therefore, to optimally and efficiently use the spatial and other data sets by various government and private agencies, there is a need to integrate these data to be easily accessible to the user community, into what is called *Spatial Data Infrastructure*. The creation of such an infrastructure will be of enormous significance for a knowledge-enabled society.

Department of Space (DOS) and Department of Science and Technology (DST), Government of India, have taken the initiative to create a National Spatial Data Infrastructure (NSDI) by integrating and networking the data sets available with various agencies such as Survey of India (SOI), Geological Survey of India (GSI), National Remote Sensing Centre (NRSC) and other large number of organisations engaged in collection and collation of a variety of spatial and aspatial data. The NSDI will be a set of GIS database servers – one NSDI node for each participating agency – suitably networked so that users can access the data of their interest from a single 'window'. Thus NSDI ensures the availability of standardised and organised spatial (and non-spatial) data and multi-level information networking to contribute to local and national needs for sustained economic growth, environmental quality and stability and social progress.

FOR FURTHER READING

1. Burrough P A and McDonnell R, (1998), *Principles of Geographical Information Systems*, Oxford University Press, Oxford; New York.
2. Database Issues in GIS, Reeve D, (1999), Taylor & Francis, London.
3. *http://server.arcgis.com/en/portal/10.4/administer/windows/tutorial-creating-your-first-web-gis-configuration.htm*
4. *www.utdallas.edu/~briggs/poec5319/anal.ppt*
5. *http://researchguides.library.wisc.edu/GIS*
6. *https://www.geospatialworld.net/articles/case-studies/*
7. *www.geog.ubc.ca/courses/klink/gis.notes/ncgia/u01.html*
8. *http://esripress.esri.com/storage/esripress/images/188/115391_webgis_chapter01.pdf*
9. *http://www.esri.com/news/arcuser/1009/geoweb20.html*
10. *http://www.geotec.uji.es/pubs/2008-BookChapter_submitted.pdf*

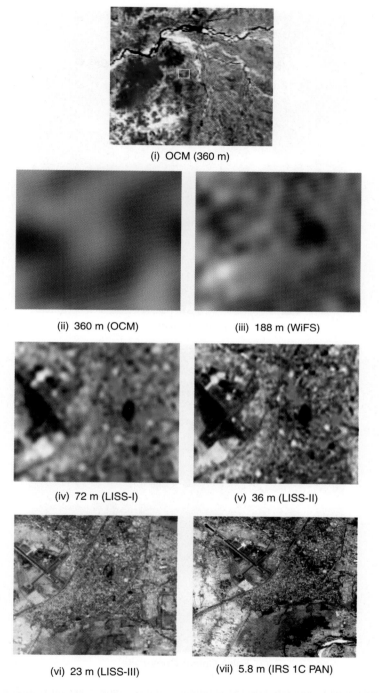

(i) OCM (360 m)

(ii) 360 m (OCM)

(iii) 188 m (WiFS)

(iv) 72 m (LISS-I)

(v) 36 m (LISS-II)

(vi) 23 m (LISS-III)

(vii) 5.8 m (IRS 1C PAN)

Plate 1.1 Information content Vs resolution. (i) is from a scene from IRS Ocean Colour Monitor (OCM). The area in the small square marked (≈ 4 km × 4 km) is shown in various resolutions from (ii) to (vii). The feature showing airport runway is not at all discernable at 360 and 188 metre resolution; can be barely identified at 72 metres and the details one can discern increases as the resolution improves. At 5.8 m even the markings on the runway can be identified.

Natural Colour

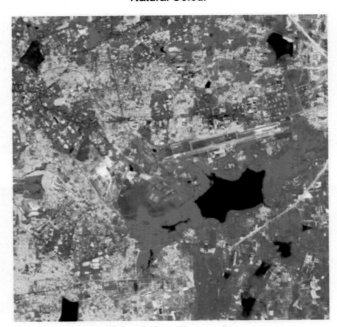

False Colour Composite

Plate 1.2 Natural colour is generated using the primary colours—blue, green and red. The green vegetation appears green. The false colour composite image uses green, red and near infrared bands as blue, green and red colour respectively. Here vegetation appears in different hues of red.

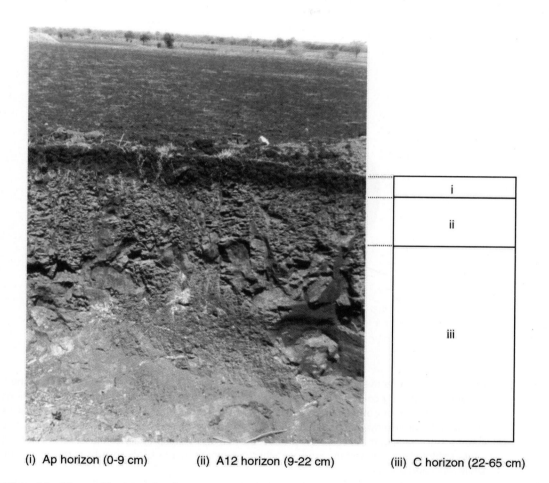

(i) Ap horizon (0-9 cm)   (ii) A12 horizon (9-22 cm)   (iii) C horizon (22-65 cm)

Plate 4.1   The profile represents how soil formation has taken place. The example shows the ALI series in the soil order Entisol, found in the village Talanpur, MP. Ap is the ploughed horizon, A12 is the leached horizon while C horizon represents the parent material.

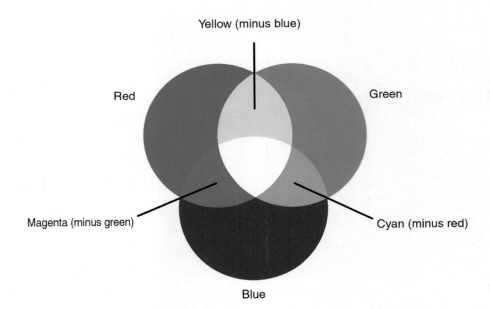

Plate 6.1 Additive and subtractive colours. Blue, green and red are the primary colours. When combined, the additive primary colours produce the appearance of white. By adding different proportions of these three colours, other colours can be generated. Television screens and computer monitors are examples of systems that use additive colours. Yellow, cyan and magenta are called subtractive colours, since each of these colours is produced when one of the primary colours is removed from white light. Subtractive colours are seen when a pigment in an object absorbs certain a colour, while reflecting the rest.

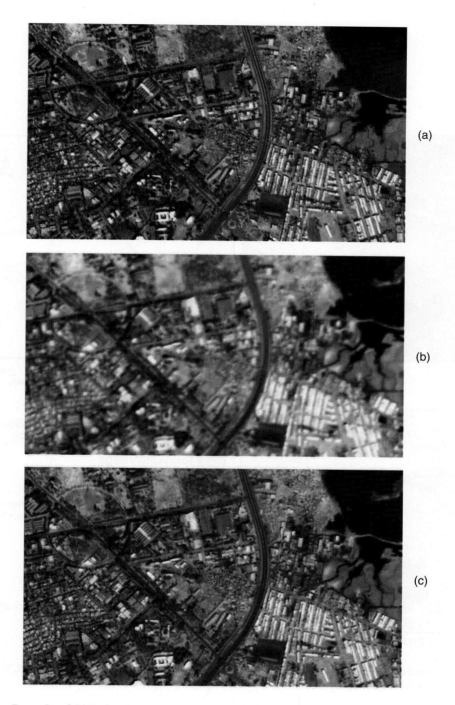

(a)

(b)

(c)

Plate 9.1 Example of PAN sharpening (a) CARTO-1 PAN 2.5 m (b) LISS-4 multispectral—5.6 m (c) PAN sharpened image.

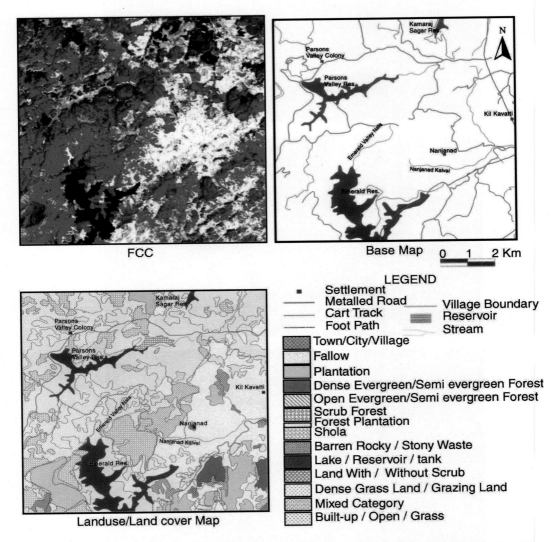

FCC

Base Map

0 1 2 Km

LEGEND

- ▪ Settlement
- Metalled Road
- Cart Track
- Foot Path
- Village Boundary
- Reservoir
- Stream

- Town/City/Village
- Fallow
- Plantation
- Dense Evergreen/Semi evergreen Forest
- Open Evergreen/Semi evergreen Forest
- Scrub Forest
- Forest Plantation
- Shola
- Barren Rocky / Stony Waste
- Lake / Reservoir / tank
- Land With / Without Scrub
- Dense Grass Land / Grazing Land
- Mixed Category
- Built-up / Open / Grass

Landuse/Land cover Map

Plate 10.1   Land cover/land use map generated from LISS-III FCC covering part of Nilgiris District, Tamil Nadu. The base map is prepared from the SOI topographic map.

IRS LISS III NIR Image   FCC Image

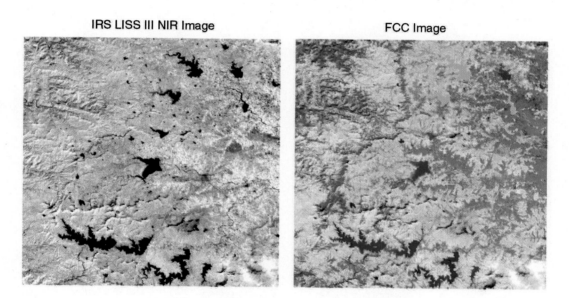

Plate 11.1   In the NIR image all water bodies are seen in dark black tones irrespective of the turbidity levels of the water. There is a very sharp separation between land and water. The FCC image shows water bodies in different shades ranging from dark black to different hues of blue which represent various levels of turbidity, bottom reflection and depth of the water body.

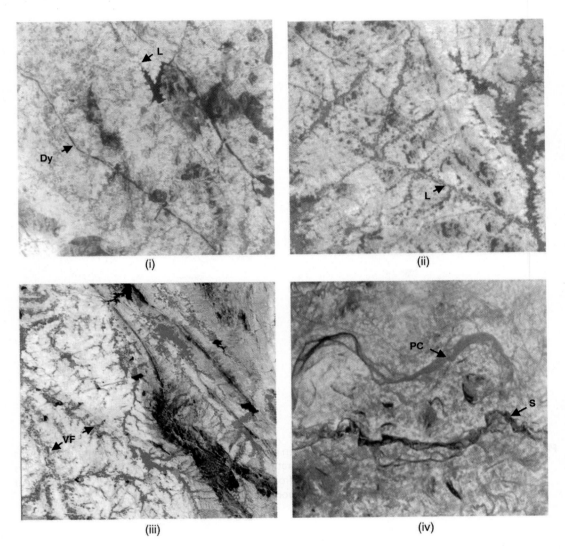

Plate 11.2 Ground water prospect indicators: (i) Dykes (Dy) and lineaments (L). The reservoir at the junction of two fractures will recharge the groundwater aquifer. (ii) Vegetation along the lineaments (L) indicates the presence of groundwater. (iii) Valley fills (VF) in the gneisses shows the presence of groundwater. (iv) Paleochannels. Paleochannel (PC) with vegetation is seen in red; current stream (S) with water is in black. Note that the PC has a stream-like pattern and is associated with the current stream.

IRS LISS III AND PAN MERGED SATELLITE DATA

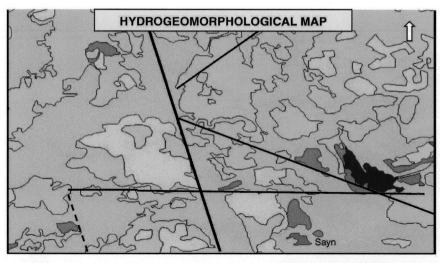

HYDROGEOMORPHOLOGICAL MAP

Sayn

MAP SYMBOL	HYDROGEOMORPHOLOGICAL UNIT	GROUND WATER PROSPECTS
— / – –	LINEAMENT MAJOR / MINOR	GOOD ALONG LINEAMENT
——	FAULT	GOOD
	PEDIPLAIN MODERATE (SHALE)	MOD. TO GOOD
	PEDIPLAIN SHALLOW (SHALE)	MODERATE
	PEDIMENT	MODERATE
	STRUCTURAL HILLS	POOR
	RESIDUAL HILLS	POOR
/	WATER BODY / SETTLEMENT	

Plate 11.3 An IRS (LISS III and PAN Merged) satellite image with the corresponding hydrogeomorphological map and legend (part of the Kachchh district, Gujarat). Hills form areas of high runoff and hence are poor groundwater prospects. The lineaments (fractures, faults, and others) are mainly plains of weakness on earth, through which water can percolate and hence form a good groundwater prospect zone.

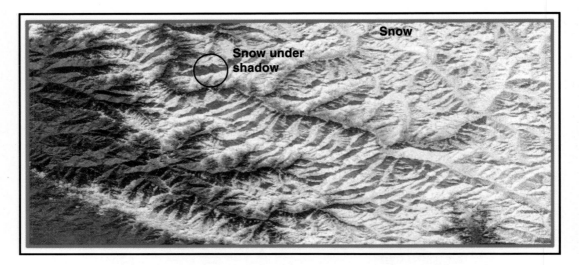

(a)

(b)

Plate 11.4 (a) Standard false colour composite of AWiFS sensor of IRS (RESOURCESAT) dated 17 December 2003. The imagery shows various features such as snow, shadow, vegetation and rock. (b) NDSI image of the same area. The white region gives the aerial extent of snow. Please note that the snow extent can also be estimated in the mountain shadow region. (*Source:* Kulkarni, 2004)

Plate 11.5 A merged imagery of LISS-III and PAN sensor of an IRS dated 5 September 1998 showing the Parbati glacier. Various glacial features as accumulation area (A), ablation area (B), snow line (C), moraines (D), moraine-damned lakes (E), snout (F), permanent snow field (G) and glacier boundary (H) can be seen on the imagery. (*Source:* Kulkarni, 2004)

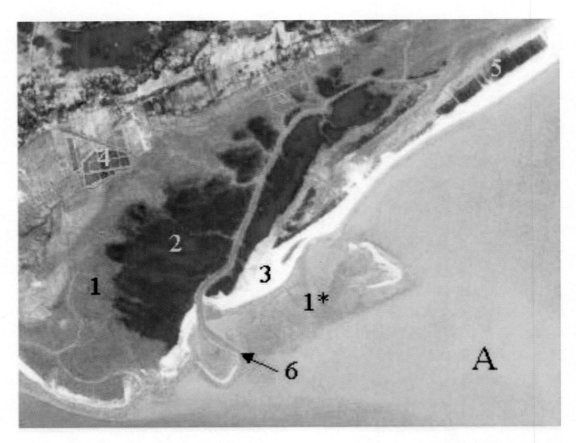

Plate 11.6   A: IRS-1D LISS III and PAN merged data of Subarnarekha estuarine region in Orissa. The mudflats (1) appear greyish blue on the image. The intertidal mudflats (1) are located in the intertidal region, that is, in between the high tide line and the low tide line. The sub-tidal mudflats (1*) are found in the sub-tidal region, that is, the region that lies below the normal low tide and gets exposed only during very low tides. Mangroves appearing in red tone (2), sandy beach in white tone and linear and narrow in shape (3), aquaculture ponds (4), dune plantation (5) and creeks (6) are also seen in the image.

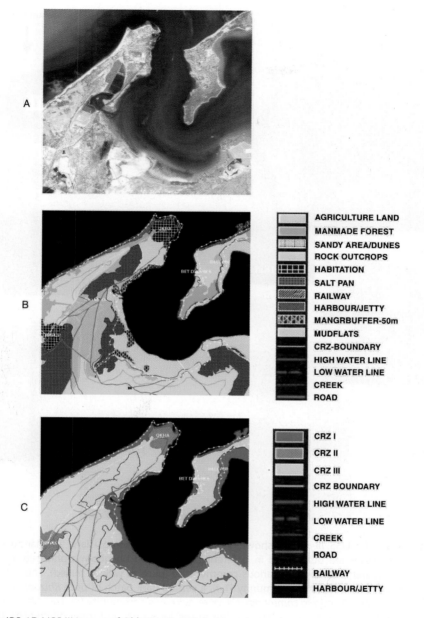

Plate 11.7   A: IRS-1D LISS III image of Okha region, Gujarat.
B: The coastal wetland/landuse map covering LTL to HTL and 500 m above HTL.
C: Based on the criteria of the CRZ notification, a model was generated that helped in classifying the coast into different categories.
(*Source:* Bahuguna, 2004)

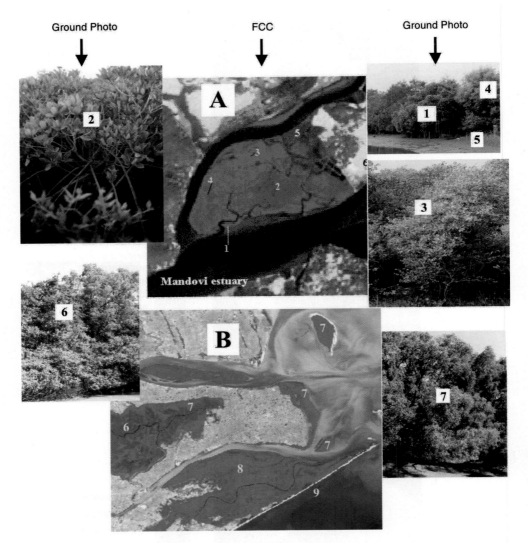

Plate 11.8 A: IRS-1D LISS III image showing mangroves (on Chorao island in Mandovi estuary, Goa). Mangroves are distributed in different zones (based on geo-morphic setting, tidal influence and salinity) comprising various communities (pure as well as mixed). This island has fringing *Rhizophora-Avicennia* community (1,4), a central dark patch of pure *Rhizophora* community (2), *Sonneratia-Avicennia* community (3), pure *Avicennia* community (4). The differentiation between various communities is primarily due to the locational and tonal differences. In between the mangrove trees usually mud flats (blanks) are found (5).

B: The deltaic mangroves of the Bhitarkanika forest in Orissa is viewed by IRS-D LISS III data. This forest is a sanctuary harbouring endangered salt water crocodiles. The forest is dominated by *Heritiera* community (6) in the central portion wherein the influence of tide is less. The regions where tides play a major role have *Avicennia* community (7). The forest region (8) has mixed mangrove communities. (9) shows the site where the famous Olive Ridley turtles, now on the endangered list, come for mass nesting.

FCC   Ground Photo

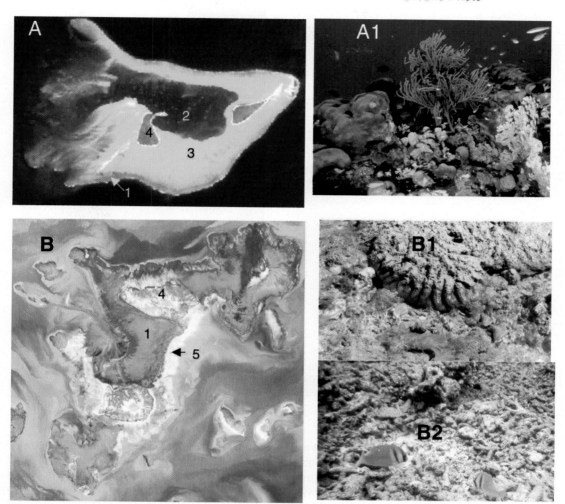

Plate 11.9   A: IRS 1D LISS III image showing coral reefs (Bangaram, Lakshadweep) in good condition. It is an atoll type of reef having reef area (1) with a central deep lagoon (2), shallow lagoon (3) and islands (4). The reef area (1) looks like (A1) on ground with a column of water over it.

B: A Platform type of reef (Bural Chank, Gulf of Kachchh) with an almost exposed platform type reef area (1). There is no lagoon on a platform reef. The islands are seen (4). This is a degrading reef having mud deposition in the east (5). The mud blocks the coral polyps and stops them from breathing thereby destroying the corals (B1) and the reefs (B2). The cause of mud deposition is excessive sedimentation as a result of deforestation and industrial/anthropogenic activities.

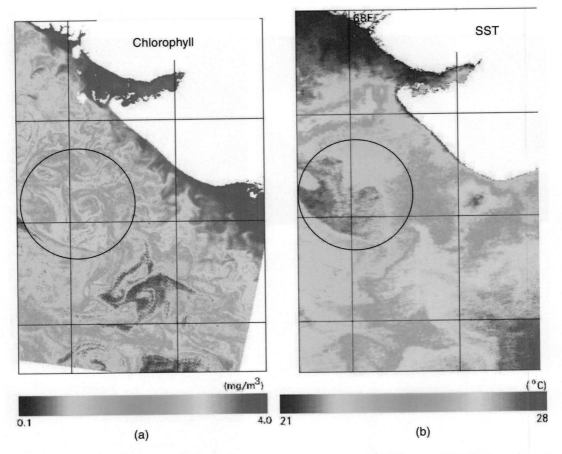

Plate 11.10 (a) Chlorophyll (Oceansat-I/OCM) and (b) SST (NOAA/AVHRR) image of 29 February 2000 over the North-West Coast of India. High productivity patch (bright area within circle) in chlorophyll image has a corresponding pattern of cool water patch (dark area in SST). More distinct fronts can be seen in the chlorophyll image compared to the SST image since visible radiation penetrates water surface up to one attenuation depth, while SST represents features of only the 10 micron top layer. (*Source:* Dwivedi, 2004)

(a)

(b)

Plate 11.11 Land degradation as seen on satellite FCC imagery and the corresponding ground photograph on the right side. (a) Sand dunes. In satellite imagery it produces striations and characteristic colour. (b) Salinity in agricultural field. In satellite FCC imagery salinity appears as bluish-white or white in colour.

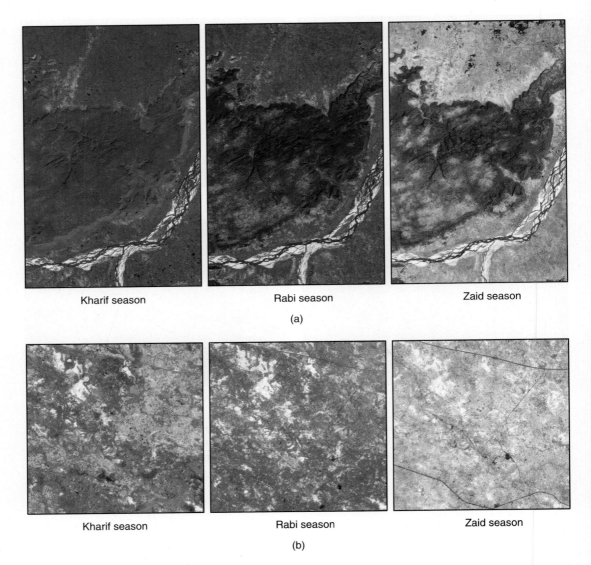

Kharif season | Rabi season | Zaid season

(a)

Kharif season | Rabi season | Zaid season

(b)

Plate 11.12 Seasonal variation of land cover as seen in satellite imagery (FCC). (a) Forested area. The degraded area is not discernable in the kharif season, but well prominent in the imagery of zaid season. (b) Seasonal variation of agricultural area affected with salinity appears prominently in zaid season.

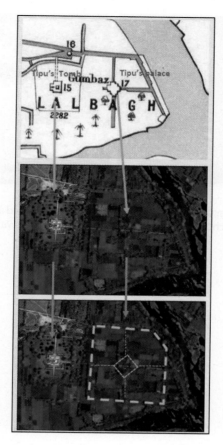

Plate 11.13 Patterns in field boundary indicate location of buried central structure of Tipu Sultan's Lalbagh palace along with axial paths forming the persian *Charbagh* (four gardens) architecture. (*top*: old map of 19th century; *middle*: FCC image, World View 2, March 2014; *bottom*: FCC image with annotations)

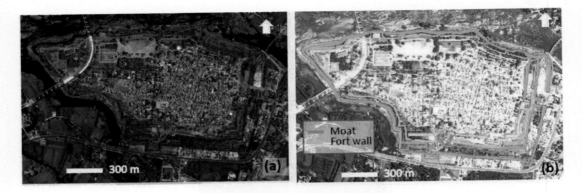

Plate 11.14 The fort of Srirangapatna which has three concentric walls and alternating moats; (a) FCC image, World View 2, March 2014 showing the fort; (b) same image with annotations.

A1 Influence of Atmosphere on Remote Sensing

Earth's atmosphere, which is an essential component of our very existence, is a nuisance for remote sensing of the earth's surface. The radiation (solar radiation or electromagnetic radiation from an active sensor) falling on earth and the reflected/emitted radiation from the earth's surface reaching the sensors are modified spectrally and spatially by the intervening atmosphere. However, the very interaction of the EM radiation with the atmosphere can be advantageously used to infer aspects related to the composition and physical state of the atmosphere. We shall discuss this in detail in Appendix 2. Here we address how the constituents of the atmosphere affect or modify the incident radiation as well as the reflected or emitted radiation from the earth's surface reaching the sensors and its impact on remote sensing data and its interpretation. We shall also briefly touch upon how to remove the atmospheric effect from the observed data. The principal constituents of the atmosphere are nitrogen (~78%), oxygen (~21%), argon (~0.93%), carbon dioxide (~0.03%) and other minor constituents such as neon, helium, krypton, methane, ozone and others. In addition, there is also water vapour, whose concentration is highly variable and greatest in the lower atmospheric layers. In addition to the molecules mentioned above, the atmosphere also contains liquid and solid matter suspended in air generally referred to as 'aerosols', which vary in size and shape depending on their origin. Aerosols consist of natural (such as very finely divided soils carried aloft by strong surface mixing, sea salts deposited by sea spray) and man-made products (combustion smoke), whose radii usually lie in the 0.1 to 10 μm range. The concentration and the size distribution vary widely both geographically and temporally. Depending on the season and geographic location, the atmosphere also contains clouds of liquid and solid water – rain, mist, snow and hail which are the end products of the precipitation process and range in size from 1 μm to a few millimetres – called hydrometeors (hydrometeor is a general term for atmospheric water in any of its forms—clouds, fog, hail, ice crystals, rain). In summary, to assess the effect of the atmosphere on remote sensing, we have to consider the interaction of electromagnetic radiation with molecules and atoms at one end, to macroscopic particles of a few millimetres at the other extreme.

When the EM radiation passes through the atmosphere two basic processes take place—(i) absorption, and (ii) scattering.

In either case, the energy is lost from the initial direction and the combined effect is called attenuation or extinction.

The effectiveness of the species (encountered by the EM radiation) for absorption or scattering is specified in terms of absorption (σ_a) or scattering (σ_s) cross-section, which has the units of area. It is essentially the product of the ratio of the total scattered (or absorbed) power to the incident intensity and the geometric cross-section of a particle normal to the incident beam. If a flux density F (Wm^{-2}) is incident on a single particle, the scattered power is $F\sigma_s$ watts. The sum of the scattering and absorption cross-section is called extinction cross-section σ_e.

$$\sigma_e = \sigma_s + \sigma_a$$

If we have N scatterers in unit volume, then the scattering coefficient $k_s = N\sigma_s$. The k_s has units of inverse metre [$N(m^{-3}) \times \sigma_s(m^2)$] and represents the loss of radiation intensity due to scattering by particles, while propagating a distance of one metre. In general, we can have attenuation (extinction) coefficient k_e which describes the fraction of the radiation taken out from the direct beam while travelling a distance of 1 m through the medium.

Absorption in the atmosphere mostly occurs when the EM radiation interacts with the atmospheric atom or molecule in order to excite the molecule to a higher energy level. In this process, the incident radiation transfers all or part of its energy to the molecule. Ozone, water vapour and carbon dioxide are the predominant absorbing molecules in the OIR region, while O_2 and H_2O molecules contribute towards the absorption in the microwave region. The internal energy of a single molecule is made up of:

(i) electronic energy due to the electronic motion in specified orbits around the atomic nuclei,
(ii) vibrational energy due to the vibration of atoms in a molecule, and
(iii) rotational energy due to rotation of the whole molecule about any axis.

Since these energy states are 'quantised', they can assume only discrete values specified by one or more quantum numbers.

An incident energy can be absorbed when transition takes place from a lower to a higher energy level. Considering the atmospheric composition, electronic transitions give absorption lines in the ultraviolet and visible region, while vibrational and rotational transitions give absorption lines in the IR and microwave region respectively. The transition, mentioned above, taking place between sharply defined energy levels (quantised levels) is possible only for an isolated stationary molecule. In practice, there are a number of molecules in motion and many factors like doppler shifts and pressure broaden the absorption line giving a maxima and slowly decaying wings (Fig. A1.1). Since the wings can extend far away from the centre of the line, there can be continuous absorption even outside the absorption bands, but its magnitude will be less. This is referred to as non-resonant absorption. Table A1.1 gives the central wavelength of major absorption lines in the atmosphere.

As mentioned earlier, this very phenomenon of molecular absorption is advantageously used for atmospheric sounding, since gases may be regarded as blackbodies at wavelengths for which they are highly absorbing (at line centres). Thus, the gaseous atoms or molecules absorb and re-emit at the wavelength characteristics of the species. This characteristic radiation can be used to sound the atmosphere to get the vertical distribution of temperature and concentration of the species. This aspect will be dealt with in Appendix 2.

Apart from molecular absorption which mainly results in absorption lines and associated wings, absorptions can also take place in particles. The major parameter which decides particle absorption is the imaginary part of its refractive index. The absorption by hydrometeors is particularly important in the microwave region.

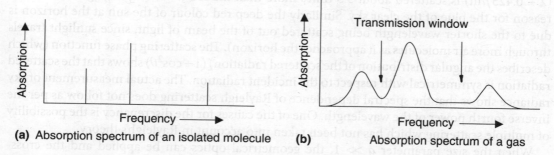

Fig. A1.1 Absorption spectrum of (a) a single isolated molecule and (b) a gas containing many molecules. (Reprinted with permission from *Microwave Remote Sensing – Active and Passive*, Ulaby, Moore and Fung, Artech House Inc., Norwood, USA, www. artechhouse.com)

Table A1.1 Major molecular absorption lines in the atmosphere

Molecules	OIR (μm)	TIR (μm)	Microwave (GHz)
H_2O	0.9, 1.1, 1.4, 1.9, 2.7	–	22.235
	~ 6		183.3
O_2	0.8		~60, 118.75
CO_2	2.7, 4.3	14	–
N_2O	4.6, 7.7	–	–
O_3	–	9.5	–

We shall now consider the scattering process. Unlike absorption, in which energy is directly removed from the beam by raising the internal energy of the atoms or molecules, in scattering, spatial redistribution of energy takes place without a change in photon energy. Scattering processes dominate the atmospheric effects on remote sensing in the UV and visible wavelength region and to a lesser extent in the IR region. In the microwave region, scattering occurs mostly with hydrometeors. The scattering cross-section and the angular scattering pattern are important factors influencing remote sensing observation.

The nature of scattering depends on the relative size of the scatterer with respect to the wavelength. To categorise the type of scattering, a scattering element with size parameters $q = 2\pi r/\lambda$ is used, where r is the radius of the scattering element (q essentially represents the normalised circumference of the scatterer). There are three possibilities—when $q \ll 1$, the scattering process is Rayleigh type. Here it can be shown that the scattered intensity I_θ in a direction θ (that is, the angle between the incident and scattered flux) is proportional to

$$\frac{(n-1)^2 (1 + \cos^2\theta)}{N\lambda^4}$$

where n is the refractive index of the scatterer and N is the number of molecules per unit volume. The important consequence of this type of scattering is its wavelength dependence which shows that the lower wavelength is scattered preferentially. For example, the blue light

($\lambda \sim 0.425\,\mu$m) is scattered about 5.5 times more than the red ($\lambda \sim 0.65\,\mu$m) light (this is the reason for the blue of the clear sky. Similarly the deep red colour of the sun at the horizon is due to the shorter wavelength being scattered out of the beam of light, since sunlight travels through more air molecules as it approaches the horizon). The scattering phase function (which describes the angular distribution of the scattered radiation) $(1 + \cos^2\theta)$ shows that the scattered radiation is symmetrical with respect to the incident radiation. The actual measurement of sky radiance shows that the spectral dependence of Rayleigh scattering does not follow as per the inverse fourth power of the wavelength. One of the causes for the discrepancy is the possibility of multiple scattering which has not been taken into account in Rayleigh's theory.

When the size parameter $q \gg 1$, the geometrical optics can be applied and the cross-section can be approximated to physical size. The scattering intensity is hence independent of wavelength (sometimes referred to as non-selective scattering). In the intermediate case when $q \simeq 1$, the scattering is a complex function of λ and this regime is called *Mie scattering*. It has been observed that even in a clear atmosphere, the wavelength dependence of scattering is between $\lambda^{-0.7}$ and $\lambda^{-2.0}$. Figure A1.2 gives relative scatter as a function of wavelength of various magnitudes of atmospheric haze.

In summary, the variability in optical characteristics of the atmosphere results primarily from the variability in the gaseous absorption due to the variation in the concentration of the major absorbing gases (H_2O, CO_2, O_3) and from the variability of the aerosol characteristics and its loading. The important properties of aerosols in deciding the scattering characteristics are size distribution, refractive index and the density variation.

What we presented earlier, in general, applies to microwave radiation also. However, due to its longer wavelength ($\simeq$ mm), the major source affecting the propagation of microwave

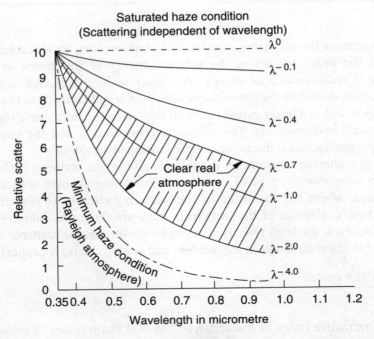

Fig. A1.2 Relative scattering as a function of wavelength for various magnitudes of atmospheric haze. (Adapted from Slater, 1980 with permission)

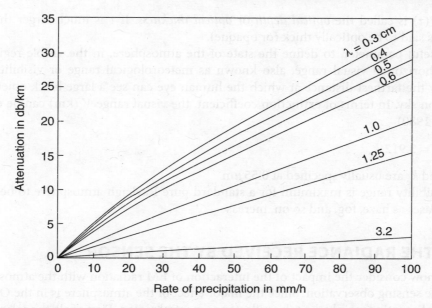

Fig. A1.3 Attenuation by rain as a function of the precipitation rate for different wavelengths in the microwave region. (Adapted from Farrow, 1975)

radiation through the atmosphere is hydrometeors. The absorption of solids and liquids is quite different from the resonance molecular absorption. Here absorption depends on the imaginary part of the dielectric constant and hence is very different for water droplets and ice pellets in the atmosphere and also depends on temperature. The following general conclusions can be drawn regarding the attenuation of microwave radiation in the atmosphere (Farrow, 1975).

(i)   Attenuation decreases with increasing wavelength. This is true for both water clouds and ice clouds.

(ii) Attenuation is found to depend on the total water content per unit volume, independent of particle size distribution.

(iii) Major attenuation in the microwave region is due to rain, hail and snow. At frequencies below 3 GHz, rain attenuation is negligible. Between 3 and 30 GHz frequency, it roughly increases in proportion to the precipitation rate (Fig. A1.3).

A1.1   OPTICAL DEPTH AND VISUAL RANGE

Let us consider a thin slab of thickness d and a monochromatic radiation passing through it. EM radiation will be attenuated (absorption and scattering) by the medium. If I_o is the input intensity, I_d the intensity after travelling through the thickness d and k_e is the total volume extinction coefficient, then

$$I_d = I_o e^{-(k_e)d} = I_o e^{-\tau}$$

$$\tau = (k_e)d$$

The term (τ) is called the *optical depth* or *optical thickness*. If τ is much larger than 1, the medium is said to be optically thick (or opaque).

One useful parameter, to define the state of the atmosphere, in the visible region is the sea level horizontal visual range, also known as meteorological range or visibility. This is essentially the farthest distance at which the human eye can see a large black object against the horizon sky. In terms of extinction coefficient, the visual range V (km) can be expressed as (Slater, 1980)

$$V = 3.912/k_e$$

Both V and k_e are usually specified at $0.55\,\mu$m.

The visibility range is maximum for a standard pure Rayleigh atmosphere to be ~336 km and decreases as haze, fog, and so on, increase.

A1.2   THE RADIANCE RECEIVED BY THE SENSOR

We shall now consider the impact of the interaction of EM radiation with the atmosphere, on the remote sensing observation. Since the major effect of the atmosphere is in the OIR region we will be discussing mainly the solar reflectance spectral region. First of all, the solar radiation incident on the earth's surface is modified such that:

- the solar radiation is absorbed to a large extent in certain wavelength regions so that the remote sensing observation of earth from space is possible only in certain window regions,
- even within the window region there are specific absorption lines, whose strength varies according to the change in the concentration of the absorbing species. Therefore, it is desirable to avoid these absorption lines in the observation bandwidth, and
- the scattering in the sky produces a diffuse radiation which also illuminates the target in addition to the direct solar radiation.

Let us consider a sensor placed on a space platform. The sensor sees the energy reflected from the target and the scattered radiation entering its field of view. This is schematically shown in Fig. A1.4.

The radiance L_t measured at the top of the atmosphere consists of

$$L_t = L_a + L_b + L_c + TL_s \tag{A1.1}$$

where L_a is the contribution by single/multiple scattering of the atmospheric constituents and reaching the field of view (FOV) of the sensor, L_b is the contribution from the direct and downward diffused component reflected by an adjacent target and further scattered by the atmosphere to get into the FOV (adjacency effect), L_c is the contribution from the diffused (produced by scattering) downward radiation reflected by the target of interest, L_s is the reflectance of the target by the direct solar radiation. The information from the target surface L_s is attenuated by the atmosphere while reaching the sensor to TL_s, where T is the diffuse transmittance of the atmosphere at the wavelength of observation.

All the quantities are wavelength dependant. $L_a + L_b + L_c$ is usually called the *path radiance* (some authors do not consider L_c as path radiance. However, since diffuse radiation varies with the atmospheric state we consider only L_t as the real signal for earth surface observation).

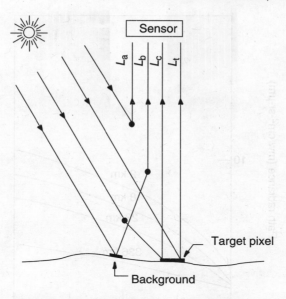

Fig. A1.4 Schematics showing atmospheric effect.

From the remote sensing application point of view we have to retrieve L_s (the reflectance from the surface of interest) from the total radiation received by the sensor. This requires knowledge of the aerosol size distribution, density distribution and related optical parameters and the concentration and distribution of absorbing molecules. Even if all these aspects are known it is an involved task. The atmospheric effect is generally derived using radiative transfer equations. We will not consider the details of such calculations, instead the result relevant for remote sensing will be discussed.

We have to consider two competing atmospheric effects. The atmospheric attenuation of radiation emanating from the surface tends to reduce the magnitude of the radiation received by the sensor, whereas scattering (or emission) from the atmosphere, that is, path radiance produces additional radiation to the sensed data. The relative contribution between the two depends on the reflectivity of the target, background reflectance and the optical depth. The most simple case to consider is a uniform Lambertian surface. Some general inferences are given below.

- Transmittance is least for shorter wavelength.
- Transmittance decreases with optical depth (or lower visual range).
- Path radiance increases with optical depth and target reflectance (Fig. A1.5).

One of the components of path radiance is the contribution from adjacent pixels referred to as the adjacency effect. The reflectance from a neighbouring target (which is not in the IFOV of the sensor), can get scattered upward and reach the sensor. Thus the radiance received by the satellite sensor not only depends on the atmospheric optical property and surface reflectance but is also greatly influenced by the contrast between adjacent fields.

We shall now consider how the total radiance L is influenced by the adjacency effect with varying optical thickness. The qualitative explanation given by Kaufman and Fraser (1983) is given below. Figure A1.6 gives three types of background surrounding a target which is much smaller than the

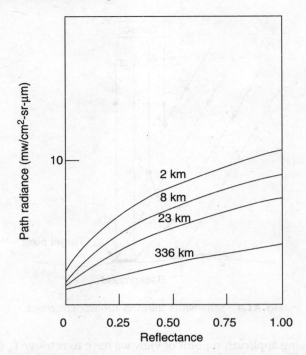

Fig. A1.5   Dependence of path radiance on diffuse surface reflectance (albedo) for different atmospheric visibility. Wavelength = 0.55 μm; solar zenith angle = 55°; nadir scan angle = 0°; altitude = 50 km. (Adapted from Turner et. al., 1974)

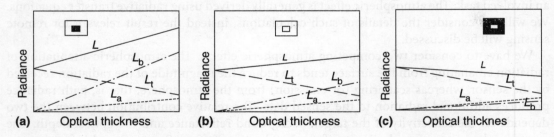

Fig. A1.6   Schematic of the atmospheric effect on the upward radiance. Both the radiance and the optical thickness are given in arbitrary units and increasing from origin L total radiance, L_t attenuated target radiance, L_a is scattered radiation from atmosphere, L_b due to adjacency effect. (Reprinted from Advances in Space Research, Vol. 2, McCormick M P and Lovill J E, 'Space observations of Aerosols and Ozone', No. 5, 1982, with permission from Elsevier Science)

background. The figure (a) corresponds to a brighter background while in (c) the background is much darker than the target and in (b) the reflectance is same for the target and the background. You will see that in all the three cases, the target radiance L_t decreases with optical thickness while the diffuse radiance L_a increases in an identical manner. However, the contribution from the background L_b is highest for (a) and lowest for (c). Thus, with respect to optical thickness there is a strong increase in the total radiance of the target, when the background is bright, marginal increase for a uniform surface, while a dark background causes a decrease in the total radiance. From this we infer that for the same target reflectance and atmospheric characteristics, the radiance received by the sensor is dependent on the neighbouring target characteristics. Since the reflectivity of the surrounding fields may vary from place to place, the radiance L_b will also vary, thereby producing fluctuating components in the received signal due to this adjacency effect. This effect can be considered as atmospheric noise which increases the $NE\Delta\rho$. Thus for the same surface with different types of adjacent features, the sensor will record different radiance values (in addition to the MTF effect, Fig. 5.11), thereby leading to misinterpretation or misclassification.

The path radiance, apart from producing the radiometric error discussed above, also reduces the contrast, thereby affecting the 'effective resolving capability' of the sensor. The atmospheric effect we discussed can be modelled as an atmospheric MTF. The advantage of modelling atmosphere in terms of MTF is that it can be combined with the sensor MTF to evaluate total sensor-atmosphere effect on the image quality.

To illustrate the atmospheric MTF, let us consider a series of black and white bars, with L_{max} and L_{min} as the radiance of white and black bars respectively (Fig. A1.7), with a contrast modulation such that,

$$CM = \frac{L_{max} - L_{min}}{L_{max} + L_{min}}$$

At a distance d, the radiance is attenuated depending on the extinction coefficient k_e and the path radiance added; giving a contrast modulation

$$CM_d = \frac{(L_{max} - L_{min})e^{-k_e d}}{(L_{max} + L_{min})e^{-k_e d} + L_p} \tag{A1.2}$$

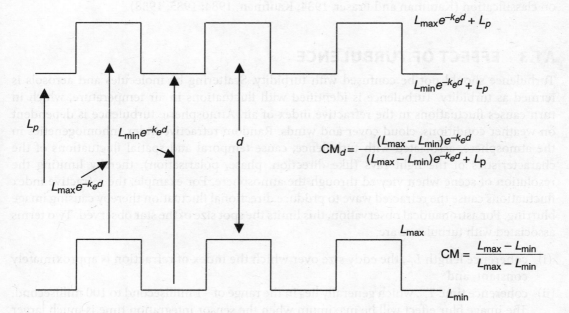

Fig. A1.7 Schematic showing the effect of path radiance on contrast reduction.

Table A1.2 Degradation of spatial resolution due to atmospheric effect (Kaufman, 1984) (value in metres)

	MSS Resolution for MTF of		TM Resolution for MTF of	
	0.35	**0.5**	**0.35**	**0.5**
Sensor alone	70	90	30	40
Sensor and atmosphere	170	790	100	830
Sensor and correction for uniform surface	95	140	50	85

The MTF due to the atmosphere of thickness d is then given by,

$$\text{MTF}_{\text{atmosphere}} = \frac{CM_d}{CM}$$

It can be seen that if the path radiance L_p is zero, the modulation transfer function of the atmosphere is unity. Thus the atmosphere reduces the overall MTF of the imagery in addition to that produced by the sensor.

Table A1.2 gives the spatial resolution of MSS and TM at the MTF values of 0.35 (laboratory measured value at the specified resolution) and 0.50 (EIFOV). It is interesting to note that EIFOV for TM is poorer compared to MSS if atmospheric correction is not taken into account. This may be due to the nature of how sensor MTF falls with spatial frequency.

The above discussion shows that the path radiance reduces the resolving capability of imaging sensors. In addition it can reduce the separability between field classes, producing classification error (Fraser et. al., 1977). There are a number of studies on atmospheric effect on classification (Kaufman and Fraser, 1984; Kaufman, 1984; 1985; 1988).

A1.3 EFFECT OF TURBULENCE

Turbulence should not be confused with turbidity. Scattering by molecules and aerosols is termed as turbidity. Turbulence is identified with fluctuations in air temperature, which in turn causes fluctuations in the refractive index of air. Atmospheric turbulence is dependent on weather conditions, cloud cover and winds. Random refractive index inhomogeneties in the atmosphere, associated with turbulence, cause temporal and spatial fluctuations of the characteristics of the light rays (like direction, phase, polarisation), thereby limiting the resolution of scene when viewed through the atmosphere. For example, the refractive index fluctuations cause the refracted wave to produce directional fluctuation thereby causing image blurring. For astronautical observation, this limits the spot size of the star observed. Two terms associated with turbulence are:

(i) coherence length L_C, the eddy size over which the index of refraction is approximately constant, and

(ii) coherence time T_C, which generally lies in the range of ~1 millisecond to 100 millisecond. The image blur effect will be maximum when the sensor integration time is much larger than T_C.

The magnitude of image degradation depends on how far the observer is from turbulences; closer to the turbulence, larger will be the degradation. Thus the atmosphere affects observation of a star in space from the ground and observation of the ground from space differently, the effect being less serious for the latter. As one observes the ground from the sky, the size of the smallest detail resolvable increases with increasing altitude until about 10 km, beyond which the value reaches an asymptotic limit (Fried, 1966). Using large enough optics, this asymptotic value has been shown to be ~5 cm. That is, the impact of turbulence will be felt only when one goes to a resolution of the order of a few cm. Hence this is of not much concern for the present day remote sensing for resources application.

A1.4   PARTIAL CLOUD COVER

If a pixel is totally covered by cloud then it can be easily eliminated because of its high reflectance value, or very low temperature during sea surface temperature measurement. However, if a pixel is partly covered with cloud, it is difficult to identify this effect. Therefore, especially for those observations with coarse spatial resolution, the partial cloud cover of the pixel is a cause of concern.

A1.5   ATMOSPHERIC CORRECTION

To carry out atmospheric correction, first we should have a complete knowledge of atmospheric 'optical' properties. We have seen that the factors which produces an atmospheric effect on the remote sensing data are mainly aerosols in the OIR region (if molecular absorption bands are avoided), while it is mainly water vapour in the TIR region. Aerosol scattering is the major variable component of the atmospheric effect for dark surfaces (reflectance less than 1%), whereas a combination of absorption and backscattering is important for bright surfaces (Fraser and Kaufman, 1985). Therefore, one should have to first estimate the aerosol optical thickness, its size distribution, single scattering albedo, concentration and the distribution of gaseous absorbing molecules. Once these properties are known, then one can use suitable radiative transfer models to apply the correction. But the primary task is how to get the atmospheric parameters mentioned above. This information can be obtained from one of the following three sources:

  (i)   an average value from climatology based on documented observations,
 (ii)   from ground measurements, and
(iii)   derived from satellite data.

Climatological data will only give a broad indication and can never be accurate enough of a specific scene of interest. The ground measurement cannot be used on an operational basis due to the amount of effort involved. At the most it can be used for a few specific sites for scientific studies.

Various techniques have been developed to derive information about the optical characteristics of the atmosphere from the imagery itself. These include off-nadir observation (Martonchik, 1997), step function response from land and sea (Kaufman and Joseph, 1982), 'dark' object deletion (Kaufman and Sendra, 1988). Kaufman et. al. (1997) have reviewed various aspects related to atmospheric correction over land. Inspite of a number of studies, atmospheric correction has not been used on an operational scale, routinely for land surface studies. However, in ocean observation for chlorophyll estimation, atmospheric correction is applied. As seen in Section 4.1.3, more than 85% radiation seen by the sensor over the ocean is due to atmospheric effect and hence without correcting for the atmosphere, no worthwhile result can be obtained. Another area, where atmospheric corrections are being performed on an operational basis is for sea surface temperature retrieval using thermal imaging. We shall describe these briefly in the subsequent sections.

A1.5.1   ATMOSPHERIC CORRECTION OVER THE OCEAN IN THE OIR REGION

The total radiance measured by a sensor viewing the ocean at a given wavelength can be expressed as

$$L_t(\lambda) = L_p(\lambda) + L_w(\lambda)\, T(\lambda) \tag{A1.3}$$

where, L_w = water leaving radiance which is of our interest to measure, T = the diffuse transmittance of the radiation to the top of the atmosphere and L_p = path radiance.

The wavelength λ indicates that the values are specific to wavelength. Here it is assumed that the sensor receives negligible sun glint radiation.

The path radiance consists of two components; one due to molecular scattering (Rayleigh scattering) and the other due to aerosol scattering. Since the molecular composition is fairly well known, the Rayleigh path radiance can be calculated using basic Rayleigh scattering theory. But the aerosol path radiance depends on the concentration and optical properties of the aerosol. The diffuse transmittance $T(\lambda)$ depends mainly on Rayleigh scattering and gaseous absorption, which can be modelled well, and the viewing zenith angle. It is only a secondary function of aerosol attenuation (Gordon et. al., 1983).

Let us consider a wavelength λ_o at which $L_w(\lambda_o) = 0$. Such a situation is possible for Case 1 waters, at wavelengths greater than about 0.7 μm. Therefore, the radiance received at the sensor, when measurements are made at wavelengths beyond 0.7 μm, essentially gives the path radiance. The path radiance consists of the Rayleigh component (L_R) and the aerosol component (L_a), that is

$$L_t(\lambda > 0.7) = L_R(\lambda > 0.7) + L_a(\lambda > 0.7) \tag{A1.4}$$

The Rayleigh component can be calculated from scattering theory and radiative transfer equations. Thus the L_a due to aerosol is known. From the aerosol path radiance for the wavelength above 0.7 μm, and using a model for its variation with respect to the wavelength, the aerosol path radiance in the visible spectrum ($\lambda < 0.70$ μm) is computed through extrapolation.

One of the models for extrapolation is based on the extensive observations on different types of aerosols which indicate that the wavelength dependence of the aerosol optical depth τ_a can be modelled by a power law (to a good degree of approximation) by

$$\tau_a\, \alpha\, (\lambda)^{-\alpha} \tag{A1.5}$$

This is called the Angstrom relation where α is known as the Angstrom exponent. For a first approximation in the wavelength region considered for ocean colour monitoring, the path radiance L_a can be expressed as

$$\frac{L_a(\lambda)}{F_0(\lambda)} = A'\tau_a = A\lambda^{-\alpha} \tag{A1.6}$$

where A and A' are constants and $F_0(\lambda)$ is the solar flux at the top of the atmosphere at the wavelength λ, which is known. If the measurements are made at two wavelengths – λ_1 and λ_2 – beyond $0.7\,\mu m$ (where $L_w = 0$), the above equation can be solved to find out the unknowns A and α. Using this, $L_a(\lambda)$ at lower wavelengths can be estimated. In the case of OCM, $\lambda_1 = 0.765\,\mu m$ and $\lambda_2 = 0.865\,\mu m$. The water leaving radiance L_w is then given by,

$$L_w = T^{-1}[L_t - (L_R + L_a)] \tag{A1.7}$$

In another approach, Gordon (1997), has suggested that the aerosol optical depth has an exponential relationship to the wavelength, instead of the power law assumed earlier. That is

$$\frac{L_a(\lambda)}{F_o(\lambda)} = \text{constant exp.} \ (-c.\lambda) \tag{A1.8}$$

$L_a \ (\lambda < 0.7)$ can be deduced from the measurement at two wavelengths above $0.7\,\mu m$ and L_w can be computed. From the water leaving radiance, the ocean water constituents are generated using suitable empirical biogeophysical algorithms (O'Reilly et. al., 1998; Chauhan et. al., 2002).

The interested reader may refer to Gordon (1978), Deschamps et. al. (1983), Gordon and Clarke (1981), Kaufman (1993), Fukushima et. al. (2000), Gordon and Wang (1994) for more information on atmospheric correction algorithms.

A1.5.2 ATMOSPHERIC CORRECTION FOR EXTRACTION OF SEA SURFACE TEMPERATURE

Even in a cloud free, clear atmosphere, the radiation emitted by the sea surface is attenuated by water vapour and the emission from the atmosphere itself is added to the sea surface radiation. In the infrared region, the effect of the atmosphere is greatest at $6.30\,\mu m$, $9.6\,\mu m$ and $15\,\mu m$, corresponding to the molecular absorption band of water vapour, ozone and CO_2 respectively. Therefore, the SST is measured in the window region, usually in the 10.5–$12.5\,\mu m$ band. Even in this window region, the atmospheric transmission can range from ~90% for a dry atmosphere (~1 cm precipitable water) to only 30% for a humid atmosphere (~5.5 cm precipitable water). The transmittance depends on the vertical distribution of water vapour, as well as total water vapour content.

The instrument (like the Advanced Very High Resolution Radiometer, AVHRR) measures the radiance emitted by the sea surface within the observation band. The radiance is transformed to units of temperature through the use of the Planck function. Observations when carried out in a single channel at the 10–$12\,\mu m$ band, can be corrected with a radiative transfer model in which the atmospheric states (pressure, temperature, humidity profiles) are used. The atmospheric parameters are obtained from a companion sensor like the Vertical

Temperature Profile Radiometer (VTPR) or from climatological data. However, the accuracy of correction of this procedure is limited, since coarse resolution of VTPR is used to estimate the correction required for the higher resolution sensors, used for temperature measurements. The generalisation of the atmospheric parameters from a climatological model also has limited accuracy since the model cannot exactly describe the state of the atmosphere at the time of observation.

A method of avoiding this problem by splitting the window channel was first proposed by Anding and Kauth (1970). Here, atleast two wavelength regions are identified such that the absorption is different in both channels. Instead of two different wavelength bands, two different observation angles, (absorption is different in the observation directions) can also be used. The essence of these methods is that the radiance attenuation from atmosphere absorption is proportional to the radiance difference of two simultaneous measurements with distinct conditions (McMillin, 1975). This is possible since emissivity does not vary over the wavelengths under consideration. Based on radiative transfer equations and a number of reasonable simplifications, simple relationships have been evolved relating corrected brightness temperature to measured brightness temperature [McMillin and Crosby (1984), Njoku et. al. (1985), McClain et. al. (1985)]. These assume that there are no clouds in the field of view. The most widely used method for SST measurement is based on the following regression equation, usually referred to as Multichannel SST (MCSST) algorithm.

$$T_s = AT_1 + B(T_1 - T_2) + C \tag{A1.9}$$

where, T_s is the true brightness temperature, and T_1 and T_2 are the measured brightness temperature in the two bands. A, B and C are constants of the equation. This is based on the assumption that the temperature difference in one channel ($T_s - T_1$), is a linear function of the brightness temperature difference of the two different window channels.

When you have measurements in a number of spectral bands, the SST can be represented, in general, as a linear combination of measured brightness temperature at the different wavelengths (Coll et. al., 1994), such that

$$T_s = a_0 + \sum_{i=1}^{n} a_i T_i \tag{A1.10}$$

where T_i is the brightness temperature of the ith channel and n is the number of channels. AVHRR on board NOAA, has three channels. Two in the split window, that is, 10.5–11.5 μm and 11.5–12.5 μm and the third band around 3.7 μm. However, the 3.7 μm channel is not desirable during day, due to solar contribution.

With concurrent sea truth during the NOAA pass, the constants can be evaluated by regression. The constants are dependent on atmospheric conditions and the estimation of constants has to be done over a wide range of atmospheric conditions. As a consequence, the constants have regional dependence, that prevents the use of a single algorithm globally (Coll et. al., 1994). Since the introduction of MCSST, a number of improvements in the atmospheric correction have been carried out to get more accurate SST (Walton et. al., 1998; Barton, 1995). These techniques are operationally used for deriving SST with an accuracy better than 1 K.

Though the radiance measurements in the thermal IR wavelength band (10.5–12.5 μm) are successfully used for sea surface temperature retrieval, land surface temperature measurement is a difficult task. The sea surface can be approximated to a black body and hence the emissivity can be taken as unity. However, the land surface emissivity varies from target to target (Schmugge et. al., 1991), which should be known to convert the radiance from the surface to kinetic temperature. The radiation from the land surface consists of its characteristic emission (which depends on emissivity and temperature) and also the reflection of the downwelling radiation from the atmosphere (in the case of SST, the latter is absent, since the emissivity = 1 and hence absorbs all radiation falling on the sea; Chapter 2). Therefore, the land surface has to take into account both atmospheric and land emissivity effects. Several studies have addressed these issues, to derive land surface temperature (Becker and Li, 1990; Sobrino et. al., 1991; Coll et. al., 1994).

FOR FURTHER READING

1. *Theory and Applications of Optical Remote Sensing*, Asrar G, Ed., Wiley, NY, 1989, Chapter 9 (The atmospheric effect on remote sensing and its corrections, Kaufman).
2. *Optical and Photographic Reconnaissance Systems*, Niels Jenser, Wiley, NY, 1968, Chapter 5.
3. *Remote Sensing: Optics and Optical Systems*, Slater P N, 1980, Addison-Wesley Publishing Co., Chapter 8.
4. http://www.microimages.com/documentation/Tutorials/introrse.pdf
5. http://web.pdx.edu/~nauna/week4_atmosphericeffects.pdf
6. http://www.ssec.wisc.edu/library/coursefiles/07_sst.pdf
7. http://www.mrao.cam.ac.uk/~kjbg1/lectures/lect_2.pdf

Atmospheric Sounding

Till now we have been considering remote sensing of the earth's surface. The atmosphere which forms an integral part of our planet and is important for the very existence of life on earth has not been considered (with the exception of monitoring clouds), instead we have only found fault with its presence for interfering with the remote sensing observation of the earth's surface. Remote sounding of the atmosphere from space is usually not covered in books dealing with remote sensing, since they are usually dealt with as a part of meteorological studies. However, for completeness, the principle and techniques involved in remote sounding of atmosphere are covered briefly in this appendix.

Let us revisit the atmospheric composition dealt with in Appendix 1. The atmosphere consists of 78% of N_2 and 21% O_2 and the rest, generally referred to as minor constituents, consists of H_2O, CO_2, O_3, CH_4, CFCs, N_2O, and others. All these constituents influence various phenomena taking place on the earth. They absorb significant amounts of both solar and terrestrial radiation, thus considerably modifying the radiation field and temperature structure within the atmosphere and the earth. The average earth temperature would have been $-18°C$ (instead of the present $15°C$) if there were no water vapour and CO_2 in the atmosphere, which provide the *greenhouse effect*. Greenhouse gases (GHG) absorb a part of the IR radiation emitted from the earth's surface and re-emit it, thus retaining a part of the IR radiation and thereby warming the surface of the earth and the lower atmosphere. The dominant GHG in the earth's atmosphere is water vapour, followed by CO_2, added to the atmosphere naturally (volcanoes) and anthropogenically (fossil burning, decrease in forest cover). Industrial and agricultural activities have increased the GHGs and added new ones. The increased GHG leads to an increase in the global average temperature which can lead to sea level rise, weather extremes (floods, droughts) and their consequence on agriculture and water supply. These changes would happen over much shorter periods as compared to the adaptability of the existing ecosystems, thereby leading to the disappearance of many species.

Photochemical reactions in the atmosphere is another area of interest. Ozone (O_3) plays an important role in the energy balance of the middle atmosphere and also affects the ultraviolet dose on the earth. The species which are involved in the reaction affecting the changes in O_3 include the nitrogen family (N_2O, NO, NO_2, HNO_3, and others), the chlorofluro carbons (CFC) and so on. Information on the variability of O_3 and the predator species with the latitude, longitude, time and season is of importance to understand various photochemical processes and their coupling with the radiation balance in the atmosphere.

One of the most important parameters required for numerical weather forecasting is the global monitoring of the vertical temperature profile. Measure of the temperature also yields pressure via the hydrostatic equation

$$p(z) = p_0 \exp(-z/H)$$

where $p(z)$ is the pressure at height z, p_0 is the surface pressure, and H is the scale height.

That is, $H = \dfrac{KT(z)}{Mg}$, where M is the mean molecular mass.

In practice, due to gradual change of T with z, an 'effective' H has to be used. Therefore, knowledge of $T(z)$ and p_0 gives information on $p(z)$ also. Before the satellite era, temperature data was obtained by the in situ measurements carried out mainly by radiosonde balloons.

Thus understanding of the many processes – radiative, chemical and dynamical – that take place in the atmosphere requires global observation of temperature and composition of the atmosphere and their variability. The following section gives the principle behind making such observations by remote sensing and the techniques involved.

A2.1   PRINCIPLE OF ATMOSPHERIC SOUNDING

The basic principle behind the sounding of the atmosphere depends on the fact that the radiance leaving the top of the atmosphere will be a function of the emitting gas and the distribution of temperature throughout the atmosphere (Houghton et. al., 1984). It was first shown by Kaplan (1959), that the vertical temperature distribution in the atmosphere can be inferred from the measurements of upwelling emission around the absorption band of a relatively abundant gas in the atmosphere, which has a uniform distribution and does not vary with place and time. Conversely, the composition of a varying atmospheric constituent can be estimated if the temperature profile is known. To understand vertical sounding, consider an arbitrary spectral line shown in Fig. A2.1, which gives transmittance (1 – absorption) versus wavelength. At λ_3, where transmission is very low, most of the radiance received should be from the top layer of the atmosphere, since radiation originating from the lower atmosphere will get absorbed. For observation at λ_1, which is close to the transparent region, most of the radiation can come from close to earth surface, while a measurement in λ_2 should have most of the radiation from an intermediate height. In other words, by making observation from the top of the atmosphere in a highly absorptive region, the instrument (radiometer) will 'see' only a limited distance into the atmosphere, while when observations are made at wavelengths close to the transparent edge of the absorption line, the radiometer gets a deeper 'look' into the atmosphere. For observations in wavelengths between the above two, the sensor can see regions in between the top and bottom of the atmosphere. Thus, if measurements are carried out at a number of wavelengths from λ_1 to λ_3, the relative contributions from the different heights (more correctly, pressure) will vary. Or the radiation received has contribution from throughout the atmosphere but with different 'weights'. The weighting function is essentially the derivative of the atmospheric transmittance (τ) at a wavelength, to pressure (to be more precise $\partial\tau/\partial\log p$). The altitude of the peak of the weighting function depends on the absorption coefficient at the particular wavelength. The weighting function when multiplied by the Planck function gives the upwelling radiance from a given layer of the atmosphere at that pressure. The weighting function is represented as a function of p (in practice as $\log p$) for various wavelengths. Figure A2.2 gives the weighting function of a typical space-borne sounder. Since the weighting function is a convolution of falling density and rising transmittance, it is bell-shaped.

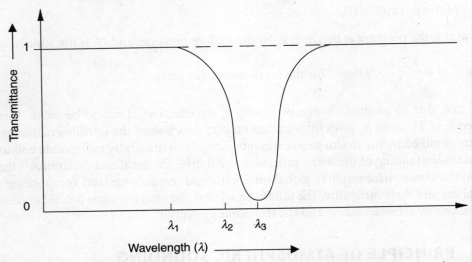

Fig. A2.1 Arbitrary absorption spectra of an atmospheric constituent transmittance is (1 – absorption).

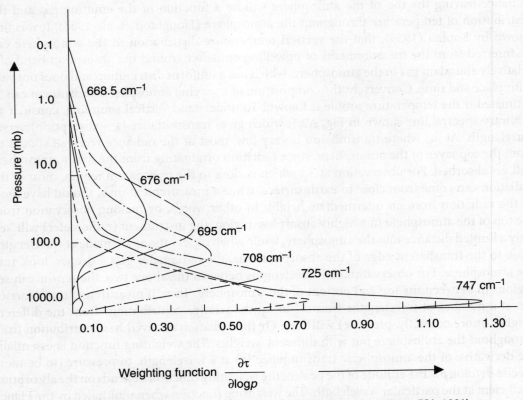

Fig. A2.2 Weighting function of a filter wheel vertical sounder. (From ESA, 1991)

The absorption band used should have the following characteristics to ensure that sounding gives reliable results.

(i) The absorption band selected should not overlap with bands of other atmospheric constituents.

(ii) Local thermodynamic equilibrium (LTE) should apply, in which case the emission from the band will be proportional to the Planck function. For this purpose, the probability of excitation by collision should be much larger than the probability of de-excitation by radiation process. As altitude increases, the collision frequency falls and LTE does not hold good.

(iii) The wavelength should be long enough so that the scattered solar radiation is insignificant compared to thermal emission.

In addition, for temperature sounding, the emitting constituent should be substantially uniformly mixed in the atmosphere so that the emitted radiation can be considered as a function of temperature distribution only.

For temperature sounding of the atmosphere both O_2 and CO_2 satisfy these conditions. CO_2 has two absorption bands at 15 μm and 4.3 μm, which can be used up to ~ 80 km for the 15 μm band and 35 km for the 4.3 μm band (Houghton, 1969). O_2 absorption band is in the microwave region (5 mm) which can be used up to 100 km.

The radiation received by an instrument viewing from the top of the atmosphere consists of

(i) upwelling radiance from the surface,

(ii) direct atmospheric emission, and

(iii) that part of the atmospheric emission, which is reflected back by the earth's surface in the same frequency.

In the infrared region, surface emissivity is close to unity and hence there is very low reflection. Therefore (iii) above can be neglected.

From the radiative transfer theory, it is possible to have an equation which essentially relates the vertical temperature distribution in the atmosphere to the intensity of outgoing radiation. For temperature sounding, we have to 'invert' this equation of radiative transfer in order to get temperature as a function of pressure. The inversion could be done mathematically if the transmitting function of the atmosphere is explicitly known with some mathematical approximation. The second approach is to have a regression between the satellite measured radiance and radiosonde measured temperature and the coefficients thus obtained are used for future temperature profile extraction. The details of the technique of inversion are quite involved and beyond the scope of this book. Interested readers may refer to Rodgers (1976), Susskind et. al. (1983), Liou (1980), Hayden et. al. (1979), Isaacs (1987).

The 15 μm band channels provide better sensitivity to the temperature of relatively cold regions of the atmosphere, while the 4.3 μm band channels provide better sensitivity at the warmer region of the atmosphere (Smith et. al., 1979). From a temperature sounding instrument, one would like to get the best temperature resolution, vertical resolution and horizontal resolution. Since these are interrelated with various instrument parameters of the sounder, one has to have trade-offs between the various resolutions that can be achieved from a sensor system. For example, to have good temperature resolution, the instrument should be able to measure small differences in radiance. 1 K temperature difference corresponds to a change in radiance of 1% at 15 μm and 4% at 4 μm. To discriminate such small changes in radiance, the actual radiance collected has to be adequate. The radiance collected increases with spectral bandwidth and FOV, which reduces the vertical and horizontal resolutions respectively. Conversely better vertical resolution requires a narrower weighting function (smaller half width), which is possible only with narrow spectral bandwidth, which reduces the radiance collected thereby giving poor temperature resolution. Nadir viewing sounders like HIRS flown in the NOAA series have typically a temperature resolution of $\sim$ 2 K, $\sim$ 2 km vertical resolution and about 50 km horizontal resolution.

A2.2   LIMB SOUNDING

The geometry we have considered for the above discussion is a nadir (or near-nadir) view, wherein radiation is observed leaving the atmosphere along the local vertical. An alternate technique to nadir sounding is to view the radiation leaving the atmosphere nearly tangentially, called limb sounding. The radiance received by the sensor is estimated by integrating along the line of sight. The geometry of limb viewing is shown in Fig. A2.3. The major advantages of limb viewing are the following:

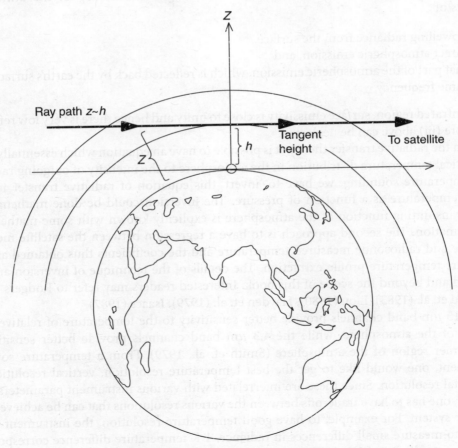

Fig. A2.3   The geometry of limb viewing.

(i) *High vertical resolution* This is the most important advantage of limb sounding compared to vertical sounding. Since atmospheric density and pressure fall off exponentially with height, a large fraction of radiance received by the sensor when viewing along the tangent height is from a few kilometers above the tangent point, provided the instrument has an infinitely small field of view. The instrument design for limb sounding takes into account the requirement of narrow field of view. However, since height resolution is obtained by scanning the limb, instead of spectroscopically, fairly wide spectral bandwidth can be used, enabling the collection of more energy, which partially offsets the very narrow field of view. Figure A2.4 presented by Gille and House, 1971 shows the weighting function of a wide spectral interval (585–705 cm^{21}) covering most of the CO_2 15 μm absorption band, for an instrument with infinitesimal field of view.

(ii) *'Black' background* Since the observation is made with cold space as background, the surface contribution (as in the case of vertical sounding) is not present and hence

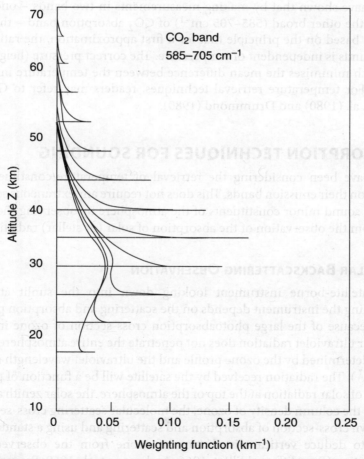

Fig. A2.4 Limb viewing weighting function $W(h; z)$ for the ideal case of an instrument with an infinitesimal field of view. These are computed for the spectral band 585–705 cm^{21}, covering most of the 15 μm band of CO_2. (From Gille and House, 1971)

temperature retrieval does not require the removal of this background signal which is not constant.

(iii) *Large opacity* There is 60 times more emitting material along a horizontal path grazing the surface than there is in the vertical path to the tangent point. This factor increases as the tangent height increases, thus enabling measurement of the received radiance with better accuracy even at higher altitudes. Thus for stratospheric sounding, limb observation gives better temperature accuracy.

(iv) *Large area coverage* Since the field of view of the radiometer can be oriented in any azimuth direction relative to satellite motion, it can cover a wide area.

The major disadvantage of limb sounding is poor horizontal resolution (~ 500 km). Any cloud in the path makes the data unusable and since in the earth's atmosphere clouds are usually in the troposphere, reliable observation using limb sounding is limited to the upper troposphere and above. The alignment uncertainty of the instrument to the satellite axis and the satellite attitude error affects the accuracy with which the absolute height can be deduced. Gille and House (1971) have shown that by making measurements in two bands – one narrow (630–685 cm^{-1}) and the other broad (585–705 cm^{-1}) of CO_2 absorption band – the height can be derived. This is based on the principle that for a first approximation, the ratio of the signals from the two bands is independent of temperature. The correct pressure (height) is estimated iteratively, which minimises the mean difference between the temperature inferred from the two channels. For temperature retrieval techniques, readers may refer to Gille and House (1971), Gille et. al. (1980) and Drummond (1980).

A2.3   ABSORPTION TECHNIQUES FOR SOUNDING

Till now we have been considering the retrieval of temperature/constituents by making measurements on their emission bands. This does not require any extraneous source. However, it is possible to sound minor constituents of the atmosphere by observing the scattered solar radiation or from the observation of the absorption of solar (or stellar) radiation.

A2.3.1   SOLAR BACKSCATTERING OBSERVATION

Consider a satellite-borne instrument looking down into the sunlit atmosphere. The radiation reaching the instrument depends on the scattering and absorption properties of the atmosphere. Because of the large photoabsorption cross-section of ozone in the ultraviolet region, the solar ultraviolet radiation does not penetrate the entire atmosphere, but is cut off at some altitude determined by the ozone profile and the ultraviolet wavelength region (~ 35 km height at 2840 Å). The radiation received by the satellite will be a function of parameters such as the intensity of solar radiation at the top of the atmosphere, the solar zenith angle at the time of observation, the column density of ozone, the molecular scattering cross-section and so on. Using the known cross-section of absorption and scattering and using a standard atmosphere, it is possible to deduce vertical distribution of ozone from the observed backscattered ultraviolet radiation (Rawcliffe and Elliot, 1966; Anderson et. al., 1969; Frederick et. al., 1977). This principle is used in the solar backscatter ultraviolet (SBUV) and total ozone mapping spectrometer (TOMS) instruments flown on board Nimbus satellites (Heath et. al., 1975).

A2.3.2 OCCULTATION METHODS

In the occultation technique, classical absorption spectroscopy techniques are used to determine the number density profile of the absorbing species. The sun or star is used as the source of light, the satellite instruments as detectors and the intervening atmosphere as the absorption cell. The Dobson spectrometer, which is extensively used for ozone measurement, essentially uses the principle of absorption by making observations of the solar UV spectrum from the earth. When satellite based observations are made, the sun as a source of radiation has the problem of its size (0.5°) to the earth, which extends over 30 km at the tangent point of normal satellite altitude (~ 1000 km), making it difficult to retrieve fine atmosphere structure. To take care of this, the observation of the sun is preferably carried out during sun rise and sun set, when only the edge of the sun is used as source. Since the satellite orbital period is roughly 90 m, for each instrument there are approximately 30 sampling opportunities per day (15 at sunrise and 15 at sunset). Since these events occur at different latitudes and longitudes, almost global coverage of the observation is possible. Stellar occultation measurement does not have the problem of finite size of the source and hence can give better resolution, though the source strength is lower. Measurement at successive satellite positions in the orbit corresponds to rays travelling the atmosphere at different heights, thereby providing a vertical profile of the absorber (Fig. A2.5). One of the advantages of the occultation technique is that only relative change in intensity is required, that is, only the ratio between unattenuated and attenuated spectral flux. This can be achieved by directly looking at the star before or after the observation cycle which provides self calibration. The wavelength region of observation depends on the absorption bands of the constituents to be measured.

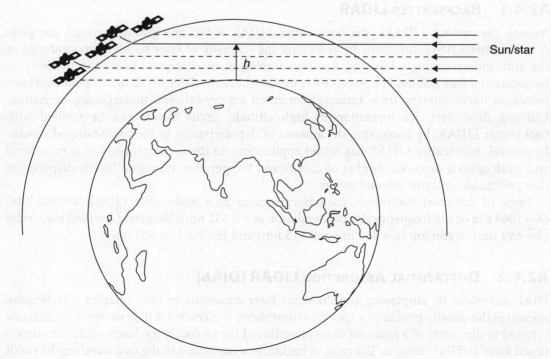

Fig. A2.5 Schematics showing the occultation technique.

The retrieval of the constituents should take into account various processes taking place in the atmosphere along the line of sight such as Rayleigh and Mie scattering, as well as refractive dispersion apart from the absorption due to the species. Relative contributions depend on the tangent height and spectral region. The best results are obtained when the absorption bands do not overlap and are well separated. For more details, readers may refer to Riegler et. al. (1976), Hays and Roble (1968) and Gunson et. al. (1990).

A2.4   ACTIVE SOUNDING OF ATMOSPHERE

Till now we have been discussing 'passive' sounding of atmosphere, since naturally occurring radiation (self-emission, sun, stars) was used for probing. Active remote sensing of the atmosphere using lasers has been used successfully for obtaining atmospheric parameters. LIDAR (acronym of LIght Detection And Ranging) is used to probe the atmosphere using laser pulses. The emitted laser pulse interacts with atmospheric constituents and a small fraction of the energy is scattered back to the LIDAR. Study of the intensity variation, changes in the polarisation or the frequency shift of the backscattered radiation can yield information on the physical state such as temperature, pressure, and wind profile, and the molecular composition of the atmosphere. The distance to the scattering medium can be deduced from the time delay of return signal, providing excellent vertical resolution. Some of the laser techniques which are of importance in atmospheric probing are given below. Only the basic principles will be given without getting into details of parameter retrieval or instruments.

A2.4.1   Backscatter LIDAR

Among the various LIDARs, the backscatter LIDAR is technologically the least complex. A backscatter LIDAR functions by recording the intensity of laser backscatter produced in the atmosphere through Mie and Rayleigh scattering mechanisms. From the intensity of backscattered data it should be possible to estimate the aerosol density. Linearly polarised laser pulses on backscattering from randomly oriented ice crystals will undergo depolarisation. Utilising this effect, ice formation in high altitude cirrus clouds can be studied with backscatter LIDAR, by measuring the amount of depolarisation in the backscattered signals. In general, backscatter LIDAR has found applications in the measurements of tropospheric and stratospheric aerosols, heights of clouds and temperature inversion layers, dispersal of dust pollutants, volcanic ash and others.

Some of the most commonly used laser sources in a backscatter LIDAR are Nd:YAG ($\lambda = 1064$ nm or the frequency doubled emission at $\lambda = 532$ nm), Nd:glass ($\lambda = 1060$ nm), ruby ($\lambda = 694$ nm), argon ion ($\lambda = 488$ nm and 515 nm) and He–Ne ($\lambda = 633$ nm).

A2.4.2   Differential Absorption LIDAR (DIAL)

DIAL technique by employing simultaneous laser emissions in two different wavelengths, measures the density profile of a specific atmospheric molecule. Of the two wavelengths, one is tuned to the centre of a resonant absorption line of the molecule (on line), while the other is tuned away (off line) from it. The ratio of backscatter intensities in the two wavelengths yields the molecule's concentration profile.

DIAL systems have been used to measure the vertical profiles of water vapour, temperature, pressure and concentrations of molecules like SO_2, NO, NO_2, O_3, CO, H_2O, NH_3 and CH_4.

The most commonly used lasers in DIAL systems are alexandrite ($\lambda = 750$ nm, tunable over 100 nm), Ti-sapphire ($\lambda = 800$ nm, tunable over 300 nm) and liquid dye lasers (tunable over the whole visible region of the spectrum).

A2.4.3 RAMAN BACKSCATTER LIDAR

This LIDAR makes use of Raman scattering mechanism to measure a number of atmospheric gaseous constituents as well as to detect the presence of new trace gas species. Raman scattering is an inelastic scattering process in which the incident radiation induces internal energy transitions in the scattering molecules (usually vibrational—rotational transitions) resulting in a small portion of the backscattered radiation undergoing wavelength shifts corresponding to these transitions. The respective frequency shifts are unique for each molecule and are independent of the wavelength of the laser radiation. Thus many gas molecules in the atmosphere can be identified and their density profiles determined by measuring the Raman shifted line intensities in the backscattered signals with a spectrum analyser. However, the Raman scattering cross-sections are about three orders of magnitude smaller than the Rayleigh scattering cross-sections and so, the best results with a Raman backscatter LIDAR are possible in night observations because of the masking effect of the bright solar radiation on the Raman lines during daytime. Raman LIDARs have demonstrated their capability for the measurements of water vapour, O_2, N_2, CO_2, CO, H_2S, CH_4, C_2H_4, and so on, and also the vertical temperature profiles utilising the temperature dependence of Raman scattering from N_2 molecules.

Some of the widely used lasers for Raman backscattering are Nd:YAG (λ frequency doubled at $\lambda = 532$nm), ruby ($\lambda = 694.3$nm) alexandrite ($\lambda = 750$ nm), argon ion ($\lambda = 488$ and 515 nm), N_2 ($\lambda = 337.1$nm) and the liquid dye.

Table A2.1 LIDAR systems used for atmospheric sounding

Scientific objective	Lidar system	Measurement accuracy	Height resolution
Tropospheric aerosols	Backscatter	10%	150 m
Cirrus ice/water discrimination	Backscatter polarisation	–	150 m
Cloud height	Backscatter	150 m	150 m
Stratospheric aerosol	Backscatter	20%	1 km
Water vapour profile	DIAL	10%	2 km
Ozone vertical distribution	DIAL	2%	1 km
Vertical pressure profile	DIAL	0.1%–0.5%	1 km
Temperature profile	DIAL	0.7–2 K	2 km
Total atmospheric content of species	DIAL (continuous wave)	2%	–
Atmospheric minor species	DIAL	10%–20%	1 km
Atmospheric minor species	Raman backscatter	1 ppb–100ppm	1 km

The application potentials and measurement accuracies of the above LIDARs are summarised in Table A2.1 (mostly from Lutz et. al., 1989). More details about the theory of retrieval of parameters and the instrumentation can be had from Hinkley (1976) and Lutz et. al. (1989).

A2.5   SENSORS FOR ATMOSPHERIC SOUNDING

The purpose of this section is to give a general outline of the techniques involved in realising an atmospheric sounding instrument without getting into the engineering details of the instruments. For sounding the atmosphere – either to measure temperature profile or the composition – we have to measure the emission/absorption spectra. For example, to measure the vertical temperature profile, measurements are to be made in a number of narrow spectral bands within the absorption band of CO_2. A generalised block diagram of an atmospheric sounder is given in Fig. A2.6. The instrument essentially consists of a collecting optics, which collects the energy in the wavelength region of interest and is followed by a system for spectral selection. The spectral selection could be achieved in the most simple case by a filter wheel or in more advanced systems, using an interferometric system. The spectrally selected radiation falls onto suitable detectors. The output of the detector is suitably amplified and further processed for recording or transmission. The major challenge is to realise an instrument with good resolution in the horizontal direction and vertical height with high radiometric sensitivity, to derive temperature/flux density of adequate accuracy. As mentioned earlier, high spectral resolution is required for better height resolution, while narrower the spectral band, lesser will be energy collected, resulting in poor temperature (flux density) accuracy. Different innovative techniques have been used to realise instruments to provide better performance. The basic difference in all these instruments is how the spectral selection is realised. However, in the occultation geometry, the measurement is carried out in the total absorption spectrum. Some of the commonly used spectral selection techniques and the instruments in which they

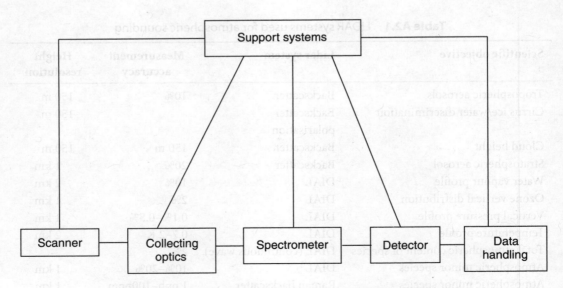

Fig. A2.6   Generalised configuration of a sounding instrument.

are used are given below. For their technical details, the reader may refer to the references provided.

A2.5.1 SPECTRAL SELECTION TECHNIQUES

(i) *Use of interference filter* Here the desired spectral region can be selected using a single detector and a filter wheel as in the High resolution IR sounder (HIRS) in TIROS-N and limb radiation infrared radiometer flown on Nimbus 6 (Gille et. al., 1980).

(ii) *Use of dispersive elements like prism or grating* For a given spectral resolution and size, a grating passes significantly more energy than a prism. A typical example is the satellite IR spectrometer (SIRS) developed for Nimbus programme to sense the vertical temperature and humidity profile (Wark et. al., 1970). The instrument uses diffraction grating and separate exit slits with associated 'order' filters for selection of the desired spectral interval.

Another example is SCIAMACHY (Scanning Imaging Absorption Spectrometer for Atmospheric Chartography) being developed for global measurement of trace gases. The instrument uses a combination of prism and grating to produce a spectral resolution of 0.1 to 0.2 nm covering a spectral range of 0.24 to 2.4 μm. SCIAMACHY is capable of making measurements in all the three modes—nadir scanning, limb scanning and solar/stellar occultation (Goede et. al., 1991).

(iii) *Use of interferometric techniques* The infrared interferometer spectrometer (IRIS) flown on Nimbus III, uses Michelson interferometric technique to get the infrared spectra in the 5 μm to 25 μm range (Hanel et. al., 1970). In a Michelson interferometer, a beam splitter divides the incoming radiation into two approximately equal parts to direct one on to a fixed mirror and the other onto a moving mirror. After reflection from the mirrors, the two beams interfere with each other depending on the phase difference and the recombined component is focussed onto a detector. The oscillation of the moving mirror produces different path difference and from the interferogram so generated, the spectral distribution can be inferred by inverse Fourier transformation. The interferometric measurement of greenhouse gases, (IMG) payload being designed for the Japanese earth observation satellite ADEOS works on the principle of the Michelson interferometer. The instrument covers a wave number region of 700–3000 cm^{-1} (3.3–14.3 μm) with a resolution of 0.1cm^{-1}. The measured spectra will retrieve altitude profiles of atmospheric temperature and GHG such as H_2O, CO_2, CH_4, N_2O, CO and O_3.

(iv) *Use of a gas cell in the optical path as a 'filter'* Here the basic principle is to use the absorption property of the gas (whose emission spectrum is being measured) as an optical filter. Thus for temperature measurements, a cell containing CO_2 is used as its own filter. There are various schemes in which an instrument using a gas cell can be realised for atmospheric sounding. Since the absorption band shape of the gas depends on the pressure and temperature, a suitable number of spectral channels can be obtained either using different gas cells with appropriate pressure and length (as in selective chopper radiometer SCR, Abel et. al., 1970) or by modulating the pressure of the same cell (as in pressure modulated radiometer PMR, Curtis, 1974; Drummond, 1980). The improved stratospheric and mesospheric sounder (ISAMS) instrument which is part of the Upper Atmospheric Research Satellite (UARS) is an improved version of PMR (Taylor, 1993).

Apart from the IR systems described above, microwave sensors are also extensively used to sound the atmosphere for temperature profiles and minor species concentration determination. For more details the interested readers may refer to Janssen (1993). Desai and Joseph (1994) gives a list of major instruments used for atmospheric sounding and their salient features.

A3 Decibels

Bel, named after Alexander Graham Bell who invented the telephone, is the natural logarithm (that is, logarithm to base 10) of the ratio of two powers

$$\text{Bel} = \log_{10} \frac{P_2}{P_1}$$

The decibel dB is given by,

$$\text{dB} = 10 \log \frac{P_2}{P_1}$$

P_1 is usually the reference power. If $P_2 > P_1$, the resultant decibel is positive and when $P_2 < P_1$, the dB is negative.

The decibel basically deals with power ratio, however it can be expressed in other units. In an electrical circuit

$$\text{Power} = \frac{V^2}{R}$$

where V is the voltage and R the resistance. Thus when input output impedances are equal,

$$\text{dB} = 10 \log \frac{P_2}{P_1} = 10 \log \frac{V_2^2}{V_1^2} = 20 \log \frac{V_2}{V_1}$$

In electrical engineering, the amplifier gain and antenna gains are expressed in decibel. Let us now take a practical example to appreciate the convenience of using dB. We know that when two amplifiers with gains A_1 and A_2 are cascaded, the total (combined) gain is $A_1 A_2$. Let us consider the voltage gain, $A_1 = 27.8$ and $A_2 = 36.3$. Then the total voltage gain is given by
$A_1 A_2 = 27.8 \times 36.3 = 1009.14$, which is not easy to do mentally.

But let us see what happens when we deal in dB.

$\text{dB}(A_1) = 20 \log 27.8 = 28.88$

$\text{dB}(A_2) = 20 \log 36.3 = 31.20$

Since $\log A \times B = \log A + \log B$

The combined gain in dB is dB (A_1) + dB $(A_2) = 60.08$

which is the same as 20 log 1009.4 = 60.08

Thus in a system when amplifiers are cascaded, the overall gain in dB, is the sum of the gains in dB of each amplifier.

Let us introduce the concept of the usually referred to 'magic' number 3 dB in communication engineering. The natural log of 2 is 0.301, so a power ratio of 2 is 3.01 (10 × 0.301), which is generally taken as 3 dB. Therefore, any two powers differing by a factor of two will be 3 dB apart. An increase in 6 dB, represents an increase of 4 times. That is, for every increase of 3 dB, the power doubles. −3 dB represents power reduced to half.

The decibel does not in itself indicate power, but rather is a ratio or comparison between two power values, a dimensionless quantity. In certain circumstances, it does not make much sense. For example, expressing the output power of a transmitter in dB is as meaningless as expressing the height of an object say 2000, without units (that is, metre, cm ... or what?). Therefore, there should be a 'defined reference' with respect to the ratio which can be stated, so that we know its absolute value. Thus when the reference is one milliwatt (1 mW), the unit will be dBm (The IEEE definition of dBm is 'a unit for expression of power level in decibels with reference to a power of 1 milliwatt'. Please note here that no reference is made to circuit impedance, though some authors specify 600 ohms). What does 23 dBm mean? If P is the power,

$$23 = 10\log\left(\frac{P}{1mW}\right)$$

$$P = \text{antilog (2.3) mW} = 200 \text{ mW}$$

Similarly, dBw is a power level relative to 1 W, that is, power rating in dBW is numerically equal to ten times the natural logarithm of the power output in watts. Thus power in absolute units can be expressed using 1 milliwatt (or 1 watt) as the reference power in the denominator of the equation of dB (generally the letters following B gives the reference).

What does dB mean in sound? Though we do not encounter this in remote sensing often except for testing satellites for acoustic levels; let us consider this for the sake of completeness. Because sound pressure squared is proportional to sound power, the sound power in dB is 20 times log of sound pressure ratio (as in the case when expressed in voltage). When you are measuring sound pressure levels, one uses a reference based on the threshold of hearing $(20 \times 10^{26} \text{ pascal} = 1 \text{ newton/m}^2)$

$$\text{dBspl} = 20\log\left(\frac{\text{pressure}}{20 \times 10^{-6}}\right), \text{ where pressure is measured in pascal.}$$

Physicists prefer using ratios, while engineers prefer dB!

A4 Map Projection

The earth is approximated in shape to a sphere (a better approximation is an ellipsoid with flatter poles). Any point on the earth is usually referred to in terms of latitude, longitude and height above mean sea level. The latitudes (also called parallels) are circles running around the globe. The plane of each latitude circle is at right angles to the axis of the earth. The equator is taken as the reference plane. The latitude of a point is the angle from the equatorial plane to the vertical direction of a line normal to the reference ellipsoid. In other words, the latitude of a point is the angular distance away from the centre of the globe measured towards north or south. Thus the latitude from the equator to the north pole (northern hemisphere) will be referred to as say *a* 'degree north' ($a°N$), similarly on the southern hemisphere as degree south. The latitude of equator is zero and poles 90°.

Longitude (or *meridian*) are semicircles, running north–south from one pole to the other. Two opposite meridians make one complete circle, whose plane contains the centre of the globe. Each meridian is of equal length, equal to the circumference of the globe. *Meridian of*

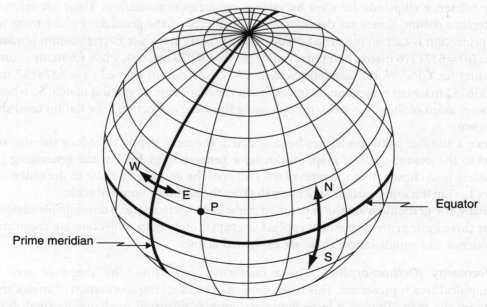

Fig. A4.1 Schematics showing longitudes and latitudes. Equator is the reference latitude (parallel). The reference of longitude (meridian) is the one going through Greenwich, England, called Prime Meridian. The point P is (10°N, 15°E).

Greenwich [called the prime (principal) meridian] is the reference meridian. The longitude of a point is the angle between the plane which contains the prime meridian and the particular meridian which contains the point in question, measured towards east (0 to +180°) or west (0 to −180°). Thus the longitude of a point to east of the prime meridian is referred to as, say, 23°E (Fig. A4.1).

Longitudes are all of equal length. They are widest apart at the equator, but converge towards the pole. On the other hand, latitudes are not all of equal length, but they range from a point at each of the poles to the circumference of the globe at the equator. Every longitude intersects every parallel at right angles. The network of longitudes and latitudes is known as *graticules*.

Thus the location of any point on the earth (ignoring relief for the present) can be specified in terms of longitude and latitude. How can we represent the earth, the shape of a sphere (three dimensional body) into a flat surface (two dimension)? Map projection is the representation of the longitude and latitude on a flat map. Let us perform a simple experiment of covering a spherical ball with a paper. You cannot do this over the entire surface without creasing. Or to cite another example, a hollow rubber ball cannot be cut open and placed flat on a table without stretching and distorting the surface. Thus we can easily appreciate the fact that when we draw the network of longitudes and latitudes on a flat surface, it is impossible to preserve all the properties of the globe surface on the projection. In an ideal case, while transferring the globe on a plane surface, one expects to preserve shape, area, scale and direction in a map compared to that on the globe. Distortion of one or more properties is inevitable while representing the globe on to a map. It may be possible to map a small area with great accuracy retaining all the above properties. However, as area increases some properties have to be sacrificed in favour of others.

The first thing to be considered is the characteristics of the curved surface of the globe. Many reference ellipsoids are used by various countries/organisation. These are referred to as reference datum. Reference datum can be considered as the generating globe from which map projection is carried out. The Survey of India (SOI) maps use Everest datum [equatorial radius (a) = 6377276 metres and polar radius (b) = 6356075 metres], while for many countries, including for GPS, World Geodetic System (WGS) 84 datum is used (a = 6378137 m and b = 6356752 m). Map projections using different datum obviously will not match. So when one compares maps of the same area, (though using the same projection), the datum used should be known.

Once a suitable solid model has been selected, the next step is to reduce the size of the model to the desired scale of map, producing a 'generating globe'. For the generating globe, the radius is so chosen, that the ratio of the radius of the generating globe to the radius of the sphere having the same surface area of earth gives the required nominal scale.

Finally, the graticule from the generating globe is projected on to a developable surface.

The three basic criteria generally applied to evaluation of map projection are conformality, equivalence and equidistance. These are explained below.

Conformality (Orthomorphic)   On a conformal projection, the shape of any small geographical area is preserved. This is accomplished by exact transformation of angles around points on the map. Though a large landmass appears distorted in shape, its small features are shaped correctly. Thus, a small circle on the globe will remain a circle on the projection, but scale or size may be different. On the conformal projection, the scale is constant in all directions about each point, but the scale varies from point to point on the map. The longitude and latitude intersect at right angles on this projection.

These projections are useful for large scale mapping, especially for military and other navigational uses where angular measurements are needed. Topographic maps and navigational charts use conformal projection.

Equivalence   Equal area or equivalent map maintains true relationships of area, at a given scale, for every part, as well as the whole. Map area is proportional to the corresponding area on the earth. However, shapes are distorted. Equivalent projections may be used for thematic maps that show distributions of agricultural land, forested area, and so on.

Equidistance   No map projections shows scale correctly throughout the map. In equidistant projections, the scale is preserved in the direction perpendicular to the line of zero distortion or radially outward from a point of zero distortion. Thus a planar equidistant projection centred around Hyderabad, would show the correct distance to any other location of the map only from Hyderabad. Azimuthal (zenithal) projections correctly represent selected angular relationship. Not all angular relationships can be represented correctly on a single map. But it is possible to correctly represent all angular relationships about a single point.

It is not possible for any one projection to retain more than one of the above characteristics over large areas of the earth.

A4.1   PROJECTION GEOMETRIES

Three types of surfaces are usually considered for projection. These are called developable surfaces. After projection, such surfaces can be cut open into a flat surface, producing map projection. Developable surfaces can be

 (i) a plane, which is generally tangential to the globe at some specified point,
 (ii) a cylinder, which either envelops or intersects the globe in some specified manner, and
(iii) a cone which either rests upon or intersects the globe in some specified manner (Fig. A4.2).

Although the cylinder and the cone are not flat surfaces, they can be flattened by cutting along the length and then unrolling the surface. Although distortion is introduced while projecting from the sphere to the developable surface, no further distortion occurs as a result of the unrolling process. The type of projection surface determines the basic pattern of the graticule and the distortion in the map. The above three projections are termed zenithal (azimuthal), cylindrical and conical.

There are two possibilities of how a developable surface meets the globe. In the simple case, the projection surface (plane, cylindrical or conic surface) touches the globe at one point or along one line (tangent case). In the other case, the projection surface cuts through the globe to touch the surface at two lines (secant case). In the case of a plane, the tangent case has a point contact on the globe, while for the secant case the plane intersects at one circle. The contact made by the developable surface with the globe gives the least distortion on the map projection. This line has true scale and is called the standard parallel or standard line. Since for a secant case there are two lines of contact, it gives a more even distribution of distortion over the entire area of the map.

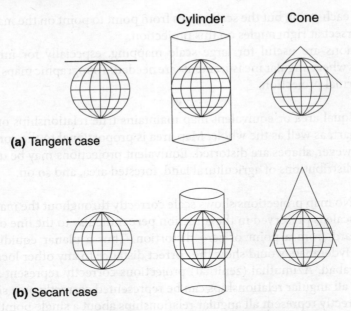

(a) Tangent case

(b) Secant case

Fig. A4.2 Schematics of developable surfaces.

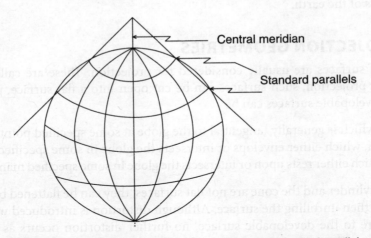

Fig. A4.3 Schematic showing central meridian and standard parallel.

When the developable surface cone or cylinder is cut along any meridian to produce the projection, the meridian opposite to the cut line is called the central meridian. Lines of constant direction are called *rhumb lines*. The longitudes touching the developable surface are called standard parallels (Fig. A4.3).

The orientation of the projection surface relative to the generating globe can have different possibilities referred to as aspects (Fig. A4.4).

(i) Normal aspect aligns the axis of rotation of the projection surface with the axis of rotation of the generating globe. For a cone, this implies that the apex of the cone lies on a line connecting the north and south poles and the cone is tangent to the globe

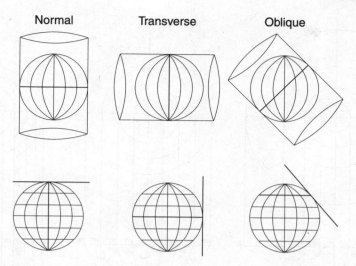

Fig. A4.4   Schematics showing normal, transverse and oblique orientation of a cylinder and plane as the developable surface.

along a parallel of latitude (tangent case) or intersects the globe along two parallels of latitude (secant case). In normal orientation in the case of a cylinder it is tangent along the equator or intersects the globe along two parallels (secant case) of latitude equidistant north and south of the equator. In normal orientation, a plane is kept tangent at the poles or intersects the generating globe along a latitude (secant case).

(ii) Transverse aspect rotates the projection surface 90 degrees relative to the generating globe. In this case, a plane is tangent at some point on the equator, a cylinder is tangent along an opposing pair of meridians of longitude, and a cone has axis of rotation in the plane of the equator. The transverse aspect is rarely used with conic projection but is relatively common in the case of azimuthal and cylindrical projections.

(iii) In the oblique aspect, the projection surface is placed on any position between (but not including) the equator and the poles. Oblique aspects are used for centering smaller regions on a map projection, thus reducing the map distortion. A land area such as India, for example would be distorted more when projected from either an equatorial or polar aspect than from an oblique aspect directly above the Indian sub-continent.

The point from which projection is carried out (viewpoint) can be chosen from three possibilities, that is, at the centre of the globe (gnomonic), on the diameter of the globe, opposite to the point of tangency (stereographic), or at infinity (orthographic). This is illustrated in Fig. A4.5 for azimuthal projection.

Thus there are a large number of projections possible. Here we shall give the basic principles in using the developable surface.

Cylindrical Projection

Cylindrical projections are formed by wrapping a large, flat plane around the globe to form a cylinder. If the graticules of latitude and longitude are projected on to this cylinder and

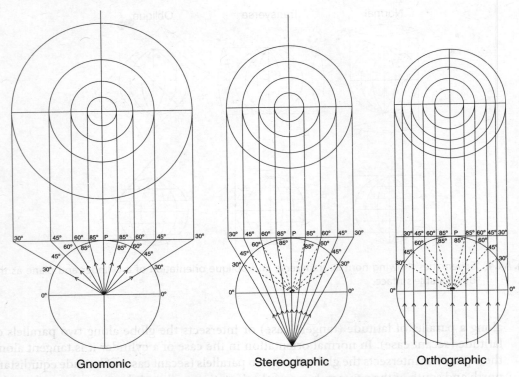

Gnomonic   Stereographic   Orthographic

Fig. A4.5 Schematics showing various viewpoints for a planar projection.

the cylinder unwrapped, then a grid-like pattern of straight lines of latitude and longitude intersecting at 90 degrees results, thus forming a rectangular map. The longitudes will be equally spaced, the latitudes also would remain parallel, but would not be equally spaced any more. The scale along the equator or standard parallel is true.

Mercator projection is one of the typical cylindrical projections. It is a conformal (preserving shape) projection. In this projection, the latitudes are drawn with increasing separation, as their distance from the equator increases in order to preserve shape (Fig. A4.6). This results in areas being exaggerated with increasing distance from the equator, thus giving an incorrect impression of the relative sizes of the countries of the world. Typical example is Greenland which appears larger than South America, although the area of Greenland is only 1/8th of the area of South America.

The Universal Transverse Mercator (UTM) is the most used cylindrical projection. In this case, the developing cylinder is tangential to a selected meridian. The world is divided into 60 north—south zones each covering 6 degrees width in longitude. Each zone has its own central meridian. The origin of each zone is the equator and its central meridian. The zones are numbered starting with the international date line 180 degree W and numbered from west to east (1st zone is 180 degree–174 degree W; 2nd zone 174 degree W–168 degree W). The coordinates within a UTM zone are expressed in metres with the central meridian equator as the reference axis. A number of countries use UTM projection for their large scale topographic maps.

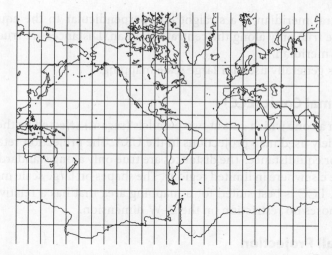

Fig. A4.6 The Mercator projection. All angles are shown correctly; therefore, small shapes are true, and it is called conformal. Since rhumb lines are shown straight on this projection, it is very useful in navigation. It is commonly used to show equatorial regions of the earth and other bodies.

Conic Projection

In a conic projection, the cone is placed on the globe, so that it is tangential to some latitude and the graticule is projected on to the cone. The cone is then cut along a convenient meridian and unfolded into a flat surface. In the normal aspect when projected from the centre of the globe, the latitudes are projected as concentric arcs of a circle, with the apex of the flattened cone as their common centre. The longitudes are projected as straight lines radiating at uniform angular intervals from the apex of the flattened cone (Fig. A4.7).

On the line of intersection of the cone with the globe (standard parallel), the map will be relatively error free and possess equidistance. The scale of the map rapidly becomes distorted as the distance from the standard parallel increases. Two variants of conic projection usually used are polyconic and Lambert Conformal Conic (LCC).

Polyconic Projection

Polyconic projection is mathematically based on an infinite number of cones tangent to an infinite number of parallels. These conic projections are placed in relation to a central

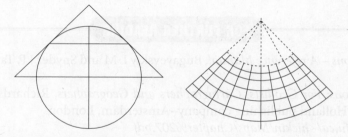

Fig. A4.7 Schematics showing the latitudes and longitudes in a conical projection. The latitudes are projected as concentrated circles with the apex of the flattened cone as the centre, while the longitudes are straight lines radiating at uniform angular intervals from the apex.

meridian. The central meridian is a straight line perpendicular to the equator. Directions, shapes and areas are true only along the central meridian. Distances are true only along each parallel and central meridian.

This projection is generally used for large scale mapping.

Lambart Conformal Conic (LCC)

LCC is projected on a cone which cuts at two parallels (secant) selected by the map maker. It is one of the most widely used map projections in the USA. The projection retains conformality but not equal area or equidistance. The distances are true only along standard parallels and are reasonably accurate elsewhere in limited regions. The shapes on large scale maps of small areas are essentially true. LCC is best suited for a mapping area that has a relatively narrow N—S dimension and imposes no restriction on the E–W dimension.

Plane (Azimuthal) Projection

Here a plane is placed tangent to a globe and the graticule is projected to the plane. The plane is normally placed over the north or south pole. Generally only one hemisphere, or a portion of it is represented in the planar projection (Fig. A4.5).

Space Oblique Mercator Projection

For projecting imageries taken by satellites like Landsat, IRS and so on, where the imageries are generally taken around the sub-satellite track, a few map projections have been conceived. One such scheme which is popular is Space Oblique Mercator (SOM) projection. This is a modified cylindrical projection, with the map surface defined by satellite orbits, designed especially for continuous mapping of the satellite imagery. This projection is conformal for a narrow band along the sub-satellite track. Practical limitation of using this projection for resource mapping application is that generally no base map is available in this projection.

Projections for IRS Data

IRS data products software has options to carry out various types of map projections. For the Indian region, since the Survey of India topographical maps for 1:25,000 and larger scales have polyconic projections, the data products of the Indian region are generally produced in polyconic projection for LISS I, II and III and PAN images. For WiFS, the projection used is Lambert Conformal Conic (LCC).

FOR FURTHER READING

1. *Map Projections – A reference Manual*, Bugayevskiy L M and Snyder J P, Taylor and Francis, 1995.
2. *Map Projections: For Geodists, Cartographers and Geographers*, Richards P and Adler R, 1972, North-Holland publishing company–Amsterdam, London.
3. *http://www.sfu.ca/~hickin/Maps/Chapter%207.pdf*
4. *http://www.auburn.edu/academic/classes/fory/7470/lab08/understanding%20map%20projections.pdf*
5. *http://ncert.nic.in/ncerts/l/kegy304.pdf*

A5 Visual Interpretation

Table A5.1   Land use/Land cover interpretation key using satellite remote sensing imagery

S. No.	Land use/Land cover category	Tone/Colour	Size	Shape	Texture	Pattern	Location	Association	Season	Remarks
1.	Built up land	Dark bluish green in the core and bluish on the periphery	Small to big	Irregular and discontinuous	Coarse and mottled	Clustered to scattered and non-contiguous	Plains, Plateaus, on hill slopes, deserts, water-front, road, rail, canal and so on	Surrounded by agricultural lands, forest cover, wastelands, network of river road and rail and so on.	October to March	Built up land can be big or small size. Settlements, industrial structures, buildings or any other artefact, physical spread or sprawl, along with density of transport network are useful surrogates to artifact it as urban or rural. Perceptible land transformation can noticed around built up land.
2.	Transportation	Very dark to dark bluish green, light yellow for minor roads, red if vegetation along the road	Small in width for roads and narrow for rail	Regular with straight/sharp and smooth curves	Smooth to fine	Linear to sinuous and contiguous	On all types of terrain, across water bodies, agricultural lands connecting settlements	Settlement nodes, amidst and around built up developed areas and so on	October to March	It be provides connectivity linkages between settlements and accelerates development. Road, rail and canal vary in dimension and importance. It can be mapped in detail using infrared bands and higher spatial resolution data. It forms part of non-agricultural area.
3.	Crop land	Bright red to red	Varying in size	Regular to irregular	Medium to smooth	Contiguous to non-contiguous	Plains, hill slopes, valleys, cultivable wastelands and so on	Amidst irrigated (canal, tank, well and so on) and un-irrigated (rainfed/ dry farming arable lands, proximity to rivers/streams and so on.	June to September and October to April	It consists of different crops grown in different seasons under different farming and land tenural systems. Mixed and multiple cropping patterns generate mixed spectral response on the images.
4.	Fallow land	Yellow to greenish blue (depending on soil type and mosture)	Small to large	Regular to irregular	Medium to smooth	Contiguous to non-contiguous	Plains, valleys uplands and so on	Amidst crop land as harvested agricultural fields and so on	January to December	It consists of different arable lands left un-cultivated as seasonal/temporary fallow for less than a year and as permanent fallow up to 5 years or more because of diverse reasons. Fallow lands devoid of vegetation, accelerates erosion.
5.	Plantation (agriculture)	Dark red to red	Small to medium	Regular with sharp edges	Coarse to medium	Dispersed, contiguous	Plains, foot hills and uplands	Dry lands or un-irrigated lands, uplands occasionally amidst cropland, proximity to rivers and on gentle hill slopes	January to December	Agricultural plantations consist of a variety of trees, orchards and groves. These occur throughout the year and are seen very prominently on the imagery. Those occurring in the forest areas (but outside the notified forest areas) are also treated as plantations like coffee, tea, arecanut and so on
6.	Evergreen/Semi-evergreen forest	Bright red to dark red	Varying in size	Irregular, discontinuous	Smooth to medium depending upon crown density	Contiguous to non-contiguous	High relief mountain/hill tops and slopes and within notified areas	High relief/slopes exposed to very heavy rainfall zones	January to December	These are closed (40% tree cover) or high density forest cover of conifers and other broad leaved forest. These coincide with the zones of high rainfall and relief. They provide shelter to wildlife and livestock. They influence the climate and water regime and protect the environment.

(Continued)

Standard False Colour Composite (FCC) generated with a combination of IRS (LISS-I) Bands 2, 3 and 4 on a scale of 1:250,000

Note: 1. This interpretation key provides a general overview for identification and mapping of the different land use/land cover classes. The key holds good for visual interpretation of IRS (LISS-I) imagery generated by the above spectral bands and of months June to September (*Kharif* season) and October to April (*Rabi* season)

2. This interpretation is subject to change, depending upon specific months of a season, scale, spatial resolution and spectral combination of IRS imagery selected.

3. Separate interpretation key is required to be developed for the area under study to supplement/complement the above key.

Source: NRSA, 1989, *Manual of Land use/Land cover Mapping*

No.	Class	Tone/Colour	Size	Shape	Texture	Pattern	Location	Associated features	Season	Remarks
7.	Deciduous forest	Dark red to red	Varying in size	Irregular, discontinuous	Smooth to medium depending upon crown density	Contiguous to non-contiguous	Medium relief mountains/hill slopes and within notified areas	Different forest types/sub-types of species which shed leaves	January to April	These are broad leaved tropical forests which seasonally shed their leaves annually. Dry forest trees are subject to wild forest fires particularly during summer/autumn. These occur on the lower elevations and slopes than the evergreen/semi-evergreen forests.
8.	Degraded or scrub land	Light red to dark brown (subject to canopy cover)	Varying in size	Irregular, discontinuous	Coarse to mottled	Contiguous to non-contiguous	Mountain slopes, isolated hills and foot slopes and within notified forest areas	Hill slopes having skeletal soil, different forest types/sub-types and where there is abiotic interference	January to April	It accounts for less than 20% of the tree cover and are also called open forests. The degradation is due to biotic and abiotic disturbances caused by dense forest cover. It contributes to land degradation found on uplands and on footslopes with this soil cover.
9.	Forest blank	Light yellow to light brown	Small	Regular to irregular	Coarse to mottled	Non-contiguous to non-contiguous	Hill slopes and hill tops	Amidst forest cover and slopes inhabited and accessible	January to April	Forest plantation consists of a variety of trees which occur both within and outside the notified forest areas. These result due to tree felling for timber, grazing, cultivation, habitation and so on. It contributes to deforestation and soil erosion.
10.	Forest plantation	Light red to red	Varying in size	Regular to irregular	Smooth to medium	Contiguous to non-contiguous	Uplands, foot slopes, coastal plains and within the notified area	Forest plantation of different types and sub-types, areas with thin soil cover and beach sands		It provides timbers, protects soil from erosion and provides greenery to the environment. Occuring amidst forest, it gives a mixed spectral response.
11.	Mangrove	Bright red to red	Small	Irregular, discontinuous	Smooth to medium	Linear to contiguous	Coastal estuaries, tidal creeks and lagoons near delta coasts	Coastal tidal waters and areas rich in coastal (saline) sediments	January to December	Mangroves like evergreen forests, are seen throughout the year. They provide a good source of timber, protection of wildlife and safeguard the coastal lands from massive erosion and tidal waves. These are the areas amenable for aquaculture, pisciculture and pearl culture. Their spatial distribution is limited to very small patches.
12.	Salt affected land	White to light blue (subject to moisture content)	Small to medium	Irregular, discontinuous	Smooth to mottled	Dispersed, non-contiguous	River plains, valleys coastal lowlands and desert plains and so on	Irrigated agricultural lands with excess salt and poor drainage amidst crop land and around tidal marshes lagoons, and inland/coastal salt/lakes	January to March	Salinity results due to capillary action in dry climate or due to excess use of fertilisers, intensive irrigation and impeded drainage or due to brackish water near coastal areas. They hamper the growth of vegetation.
13.	Waterlogged land	Light to dark blue (subject to water spread and organic matter)	Varying in size	Irregular, discontinuous	Smooth to mottled	Dispersed, non-contiguous	Flood plains/lowlands, coastal plains and along canals	Proximity to flood plains/lowlands, marshy/swampy grounds and near canal water [see Table A5.1 (19)]	December to March	It is associated with low lands having a high water table and surface impeded drainage due to flow of irrigation/flood/sea waters. It often has weeds/grasses occurring inland and marshes/swamps near coasts.
14.	Gullied/Ravinous land	Light yellow to bluish green (subject to surface moisture and depth of erosion)	Varying in sizes depth	Irregular, broken	Very coarse to coarse	Dendritic to sub-dendritic	Along river and stream courses and drainage on sloping grounds	Severely eroded areas in plains, along streams and on sloping grounds made of loose sediments, areas having entrenched drainage, good rainfall and surface runoff	January to March	Gullies and ravines contribute to soil erosion and land degradation. Gullies with deep and steep sides develop into ravines. These result due to excessive surface runoff on loose sediments.

(Continued)

No.	Feature	Tone/Colour	Size	Shape	Texture	Pattern	Terrain/Landform	Association	Time	Description
15.	Land with or without scrub	Light yellow to brown to greenish blue (subject to surface moisture and cover)	Varying in size	Irregular, discontinuous	Coarse to mottled (subject to vegetation cover)	Contiguous, dispersed in patches	Terrain with varying lithology and landforms	Gentle relief with moderate slope in plains and foot hills and surrounded by agricultural lands	October to March	Thin veneer of soil cover on the top supports, scrub and grass or devoid off vegetation where surface erosion is dominant. Such lands occur more in dry lands, foot hill areas, undulating uplands and also along fallows.
16.	Sandy area (coastal and desertic)	White to light yellow, blue subject to moisture content and red for vegetation	Varying in size	Regular to irregular	Smooth to mottled (subject to vegetation)	Contiguous to linear	Deserts, river beds and coastal onshore plains	River sand, shifting desert sands, sand-dunes, coastal beach/dune sands and river bed/natural levees	October to March	Areas which have an accumulation of sands which are in situ or transported. These occur as sandy (desert) plains, in the form of sand dunes, beach sands and dunes (with blown) sands and so on. They support vegetation wherever moisture is available.
17.	Barren rocky/ Stony waste/ Sheet-rock area	Greenish blue to yellow to brownish (subject to varying rock type)	Varying in size	Irregular and discontinuous	Very coarse to coarse and medium	Linear to contiguous and dispersed	Steep isolated hillocks, hill slopes/crest, plateau and eroded plains	Barren and exposed rock/stony wastes, lateritic out crops, mined areas and quarried sites, boulders	January to March	These are rock exposures of different rock types which occur as massive rocks, boulders, talus material, stony waste and so on, in hill forests, plateau, plains and so on. These are barren and are devoid of soil cover and vegetation.
18.	River/Stream	Light blue to dark blue	Long narrow to wide	Irregular, sinuous	Smooth to medium	Contiguous, non-linear to dendritic/subdendritic and so on	Natural rivers/streams, (perennial and non-perennial)	Drainage pattern on hill slopes, flood plains, uplands and so on also with vegetation along the banks and in river bed	January to December	These are water courses in the channels of different dimensions and lengths. It may be a perennial or non-perennial river or stream. These exhibit different drainage patterns depending on surface lithology, landform, climate and so on. Excess runoff of water results in overflow of river/stream banks causing floods.
19.	Lake/Reservoir/ Tank/Canal	Light blue to dark blue (subject to weeds/ vegetation)	Small/ medium to large	Regular to irregular	Smooth to mottled subject to vegetation	Non-contiguous dispersed, linear for canals	Tanks and lakes in lowlands/ plains, reservoirs surrounded by hills and across rivers, canals in plains	Amidst cultivated lands, low lands, reservoirs with hilly terrain and rivers, canals with irrigated arable lands	January to December	These are impounded water bodies in low lands, plains across river/streams, unirrigated lands and so on. Surface water spread of reservoir/tank/lake vary from season to season. These act as the source of irrigation, power generation and flood control.
20.	Shifting cultivation	Light yellow or greenish (subject to vegetation)	Small patches	Irregular	Coarse to mottled	Non-contiguous dispersed	On hill slopes/ hill tops	Mountains/hilly areas amidst forest cover and forest cover and forest cleared areas	January to April	These are more often known as Jhum lands. Jhuming is a cyclic process where forests are slashed and burnt to bring cleared land under cultivation. Jhum lands contribute to loss of forest wealth and erosion.
21.	Grassland/ Grazing land	Light red to light brown	Varying in size	Irregular	Coarse to mottled (subject to vegetation)	Contiguous to non-contiguous	Plains, uplands, hill slopes/foot slopes, close to river/ streams	Amidst agricultural lands, drylands and lands fenced from cultivation	December to March	It includes lands where grasses occur naturally, providing fodder to the cattle. It includes natural pasture and meadows. Excessive grazing contributes to loss of vegetative cover and accelerate erosion.
22.	Snow covered/ Glacial area	Bright to white (subject to moisture contents thickness)	Large and extensive	Irregular, continuous	Smooth	Contiguous	Mountain peaks and slopes	High relief and glaciers	December to March	It includes permanently snow(s) covered areas such as the Himalayas. A glacier is a mass of accumulated ice on permanently snow covered areas. Snow accumulates and melts resulting in surface runoff of water to form river/stream.

Table A5.2 Interpretation key for use with IRS merged (LISS-III + Pan) data

S. No.	Urban cover	Tone	Texture	Size	Shape	Shadow	Pattern	Association
I	BUILT UP LAND Residential	Dark cyan	Coarse	Variable	Variable	Shadows seen	Regular Roads/streets	Mixed with different rise buildings
	a) High rise	White	Coarse	Variable	Variable	Small shadows	Roads, (Regular) streets	A group of uniform houses
	b) Low rise	White	Medium	Variable	Variable	-	Roads, (Regular) streets	A group of uniform houses
	c) Detached	White	Coarse	Variable	Variable	-	Roads, (Regular) streets	A group of uniform houses
	d) Slums	Light cyan	Smooth	Variable	Variable	-	Unorganised	Surrounded by a marsh and along roads and railways
	e) Mixed	Mottled grey	Coarse	Variable	Variable	-	(Unorganised)	-
	Residential area without vegetation	White and cyan mixed with pinkish specks	Coarse	Variable	Variable	-	-	-
	Industrial	White	Medium	Variable	Rectangle	-	Regular	Interspersed with vegetation and open lands
	Recreational a) Gardens/Parks	Red	Medium	Variable	Variable	-	Dispersed	-
	b) Play grounds	Pinkish white	Medium	Variable	Variable	-	Dispersed	-
	c) Stadiums	Reddish	Medium	Variable	Definite	-	-	-
	Transportational a) Roads	Dark grey	Medium	Variable	Straight with blends	-	Linear	Interspersed by pink tone
	b) Railways	Light grey	Medium	Fixed	Straight	-	"	Interspersed by pink tone
	c) Plantations	Light blue	Smooth	Variable	Straight with streeps	-	-	-
II	AGRICULTURE a) Cropped land	Pinkish red	Fine	Variable	Variable	-	Scattered	-
	b) Fallow land	Whitish blue	Coarse	Variable	Variable	-	Scattered	-
	c) Plantations	Dark pink	Smooth	Variable	Variable	-	Scattered	-
III	FOREST LAND	Dark red	Medium	Variable	Variable	-	Scattered	-
IV	WASTE LAND Scrub land	Light pink to grey	Medium to coarse	Variable	Variable	-	Scattered	-
	Quarries	Whitish cyan	Coarse	Variable	Variable	-	Scattered	-
V	WATER BODIES a) Clear water	Dark blue	Smooth	Variable	Variable	-	Scattered	-
	b) Turbid water	Light blue	Medium	Variable	Variable	-	Scattered	-

Source: SAC Technical Report 1999: SAC/RESA/TR-03/July 1999

A6 | Hyper-spectral Image Analysis

The classification techniques used for multi-spectral data can in principle be used to analyse hyper-spectral data also, though the large volume of data generated makes the handling and computation complex. We may intuitively feel that as the number of bands have substantially increased in hyper-spectral data, the classification techniques discussed earlier should give more detailed classes and increased classification accuracy. However, this does not happen in practice. We shall try to analyse the reasons. Two dimensional data can be represented in a two dimensional space (feature space) as shown in Fig. 1.2. We say that the data has a dimensionality of 2. Data with n spectral bands has a dimensionality n. Let us consider a classifier such as the maximum likelihood classifier discussed in Section 10.2.3. In order to construct this classifier, we would have to estimate the classifier parameters (mean, standard deviation, covariance, and so on) from the training data. According to Schowengerdt (1983) for a maximum likelihood classifier, if n spectral bands are used, then the training set for each class must contain at least $n + 1$ pixels for classifying the classifier parameters. In practice, to obtain reliable class statistics, 10 to 100 training pixels per class per band are typically needed (Swain and Davis, 1978). Thus, as the dimensionality of the feature space increases, the number of training pixels also needs to be increased, so that the classifier parameters could be estimated with adequate accuracy. With a fixed number of training pixels, as the number of spectral bands is increased, the classifier performance increases up to a certain number of bands and then deteriorates. That is, at some point, adding more bands does not help to improve classifier performance unless more training pixels per class are added. This is referred to as the Hughes phenomenon (Hughes, 1968) (Fig. A6.1). With insufficient training data sets, the estimation of the statistical parameters of the classifier becomes inaccurate and unreliable. It has been shown that to retain the statistical accuracy of the estimated classifier parameters, as the dimensionality of the data increases, the training sample size also needs to be increased, linearly or to the square or exponentially, depending on the type of classifier (Jimenez and Landgrebe, 1999). This need for rapid increase in training sample size as the data dimension increases has been termed as the *curse of dimensionality* (Bellman, 1961). Since in practice the availability of training samples is limited, the 'curse of dimensionality' has severely restricted the practical applications of statistical pattern recognition procedures in high dimensional data. Thus, considering the limitation of generating large number of training samples, one may consider dimensionality reduction to improve classification accuracy. Two approaches are possible for dimensionality reduction. The first approach is to select a small subset of the band which is sufficient to separate the various classes with required accuracy and practical amount of computational resources. In hyper-spectral analysis, this dimensionality reduction

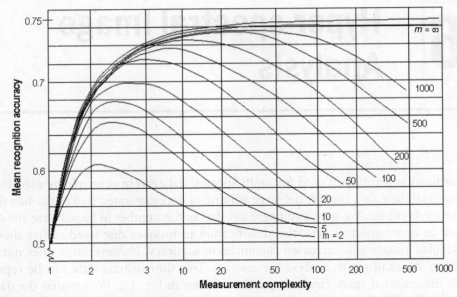

Fig. A6.1 Hughes phenomenon. Mean recognition accuracy on the *y*-axis is averaged over the ensemble of possible classifiers. Measurement complexity plotted on the *x*-axis is related to the number of spectral bands and quantisation. The result shown is for a two-class case and the two classes are assumed equally likely. *m* is the number of training samples available to define the class. Classification accuracy first increases as the number of bands are increased and then declines for the same number of training samples. From the graph, it can be seen that even for the same dimensionality (complexity), as the number of training sample is increased, the accuracy though it increases, does so only slowly (Landgrebe, 2002).

process is generally referred to as feature selection (we have been using the term 'feature' to denote a class of objects. But here, feature selection really means band selection). One of the approaches for band selection is to find out the correlation between the bands (Section 10.2.1) and select only uncorrelated bands. Bajesy and Groves (2004) have described a methodology for combining unsupervised and supervised methods under classification accuracy and computational requirement constraints to select the optimum bands.

The other approach is to use the data from all the spectral bands and map the useful information to a lower-dimensional subspace. Here, one determines a subspace of dimensionality *N* from the original space of dimensionality *M* ($N < M$) (spectral feature extraction) (Landgrebe, 2002; Jain, et. al., 2000). Principal component analysis (PCA) discussed in Section 9.7.4 is the commonly used method by the remote sensing community for reducing the dimensionality of the data. PCA projects the data from the original dimension to another orthogonal axis which has a lower dimension. The outcome is a number of principal components in a descending order of information content. Another dimensional reduction process is the minimum noise fraction (MNF) transformation, which is a modified form of PCA (Lee et. al., 1990; Chen, 2000). One can now use dimensionally reduced data for applying classification techniques.

The technique developed specifically for the analysis of hyper-spectral data essentially tries to match the spectral data obtained from the field (imaged spectral reflectance spectra) with known spectral data derived from laboratory measurements (reference data), in order to establish some kind of similarity measure between the unknown field-measured spectra and the reference spectra. The known spectral data used for comparison can also be obtained from the image pixels which contain only one specific target—spectrally pure pixels. The analysis is carried out on a pixel-by-pixel basis. The data collected by air-borne/space-borne sensors are modified by the intervening atmosphere (Appendix 1) and need to be corrected for atmospheric effect and solar spectral shape to convert the measured *radiance* to *reflectance*. The reflectance spectra usually contains a smoothly varying component, on which one can observe 'dips' due to absorption features (this is significantly prominent in minerals). Therefore, we can have two approaches to match the image spectra with reference spectra, that is, (1) to match only the absorption features or (2) match the full spectra. As mentioned earlier, the basic principle is to find out a match to the reflectance spectra of image pixels to a set of known reflectance spectrum. However, the observed data of a target will not exactly match with reference data of the same target in the library due to noise, and so on. The situation is further complicated by the fact that most hyper-spectral pixels contain spatial mixtures of different materials. In practice, the observed spectrum will match a number of reference spectra to varying degrees. Therefore, between the different matched spectra, a ranking can be made according to some statistical criteria for the goodness of fit. The reference spectrum with the best fit is assigned to the observed target. The matching could be to search whether a particular target is present in the image, by comparing the spectral data of that specific target available in the library against the image data (*detection*) or compare the image spectra against all data available in the library (*identification*). There are different techniques used for matching the measured spectrum with reference spectra depending on the criteria adopted for measuring the similarity (or closeness) between the two spectra. Broadly, these techniques are distance-based, angle-based and correlation-based measures (Homayouni and Roux, 2004). Some of the approaches followed are presented below.

Spectral Angle Mapper

A spectral angle mapper (SAM) is the most commonly used analytical technique in hyper-spectral remote sensing. The hyper-spectral data gives a set of reflectance values, one for each spectral band. To implement SAM, the data has to be reduced to *apparent reflectance* (true reflectance multiplied by a gain factor due to topography, shadow, etc (Leprieur et. al., 1995; Goetz and Boardman, 1997 and Granahan et. al., 2001). The dark noises including path radiance are removed so that zero reflectance value coincides with the origin. To understand the concept of SAM, let us consider the reflectance value for a pixel in two spectral bands λ_1 and λ_2—say, as 0.8 and 0.6 respectively. This can be plotted in a xy coordinate system as shown in Fig. A6.2(a). In two dimensional space, this is represented as a point A (0.8, 0.6). Mathematically, it can be treated as a vector with magnitude OA and an angle ϕ with respect to the λ_1 axis. If the illumination is halved, the reflectance value will be B (0.4, 0.3), giving half the vector length, although the *angle remains the same*. With three bands, the reflectance value can be represented as a vector in three dimensions. It is difficult to visualise more than three bands, but mathematically, a pixel whose reflectance is measured in n spectral bands can be represented as a vector in an n-dimensional space. Here, each band can be assigned to one axis of the space, wherein all axes are mutually orthogonal (since the reflectance value for the same material is not unique, but will have a mean and a distribution due to scene variability and

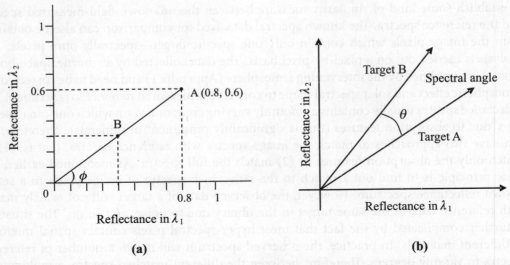

Fig. A6.2 (a) Representation of a pixel in two dimensional space. (b) Concept of spectral angle in a two dimensional feature space.

measurement noise (Fig. 4.1), a pixel will have a spread in n-dimensional spectral (feature) space, rather than a single location). The SAM analysis is based on this concept that a pixel of n-band image can be represented as a vector in an n-dimensional space, whose magnitude can be related to the illumination of the pixel and the angle to the spectral shape. Two different materials will have different angles. The angle between a pair of targets is called *spectral angle* [Fig. A6.2(b)]. The spectral angle is used as a measure of similarity between the targets.

In SAM, the angle between the unknown pixel (image pixel) and the library spectra is calculated for various reference spectra. Theoretically, when the laboratory target matches the image target, the angle should be zero. However, even for the same target, there will be a finite angle due to various types of noise. In practice, a smaller angle represents higher similarity between the image pixel and the library reference spectra. Pixels with angles less than a threshold value are assigned to the respective reference material.

Though SAM has been widely used as a spectral similarity measure, other techniques like spectral information measure (SIM) (Chang, 2000), spectral information divergence (SID) (Du et.al., 2003), and so on, are reported in literature.

Spectral Feature Fitting

The basic principle in the spectral feature fitting (SFF) technique for identification of the target is that the diagnostic absorption features are unique to a particular material (target) in terms of its shape (variation of absorption with wavelength) and its location in the spectral region. There could be one or more absorption bands depending on the material. SFF is an 'absorption feature' based method for matching the image spectra absorption curve to the reference spectra absorption feature. The absorption spectra are superimposed on a smoothly varying continuous curve (*continuum*), which may not contain much information specific to the target. The depth of an absorption band D, is usually defined relative to the continuum as:

$$D = \frac{R_c(\lambda_p) - R_b(\lambda_p)}{R_c(\lambda_p)} = 1 - \frac{R_b(\lambda_p)}{R_c(\lambda_p)}$$

where, $R_b(\lambda_p)$ is the reflectance at the absorption **band** minimum (λ_p) and $R_c(\lambda_p)$ is the reflectance at the **continuum** corresponding to **peak** wavelength λ_p (Clark and Roush, 1984) (Fig. A6.3). The band depth, shape and position are basically constant with viewing geometry. However, the depth of absorption is related to the abundance of the absorber.

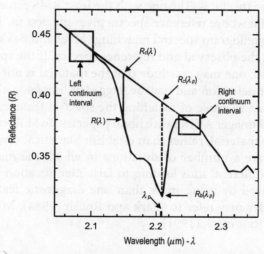

Fig. A6.3 Absorption band depth estimation. A continuum interval is chosen on each side of the absorption band to reduce noise. A continuum is fit between the end points. The reflectance at the band centre ($R_b \, \lambda_p$) and the corresponding continuum reflectance at the band centre wavelength ($\lambda_p R_c \lambda_p$) are found to compute the band depth. (Adapted from Clark et. al., 2003)

As we can easily infer from the above equation, the absorption band depth D is the 'dip' of the feature with respect to continuum and is normalised to the continuum value. To separate the diagnostic spectral feature for comparison, the continuum is removed from the reflectance spectra. Removal of the continuum makes the absorption spectra insensitive to other external effects like lighting geometry and grain size so that two spectra taken under different environmental conditions can be compared. In addition, if the continuum has a slope, it will result in an apparent shift of the reflectance minimum, thus misrepresenting the real position of the maximum depth of the absorption feature (Meer, 2000). The continuum is removed by division in the reflectance (emission) spectra. The method adopted for continuum removal in the Tetracorder software developed by the USGS for hyper-spectral analysis is as follows. Each spectral feature has its own continuum endpoints [Fig. 6.3]. Continuum is the straight-line fit between the endpoints. The continuum-removed spectra of the absorption band $R_a(\lambda)$ is given by

$$R_a(\lambda) = \frac{R(\lambda)}{R_c(\lambda)}$$

where $R(\lambda)$ is the reflectance spectra as a function of wavelength λ and $R_c(\lambda)$ is the reflectance of the continuum at λ (Fig. A6.3). The continuum is removed from both observed (unknown) spectra and the reference (library) spectra for comparison. Only the portions of the spectrum that are known to be diagnostic of the reference material need be used for comparison. The band depth (or band area) of the reference spectra is normalised with the unknown spectra; that is the continuum-removed reference reflectance spectra is scaled to match the continuum-removed observed spectra (Clark et. al., 1990). A least-square-fit is then calculated at each wavelength between the observed and reference spectra using standard statistical methods and the RMS error of the fit can be estimated for each of the reference spectra. The RMS error is a measure of how close the 'fit' is. The one with the least RMS error is the best fit. The target is assigned to the material whose reference spectra gives the best fit. There are other statistical techniques like cross correllogram spectral matching (Meer and Bakker, 1997) to calculate the goodness of fit between the observed and reference spectra. If the spectral match is too poor, that is, below a threshold, one may conclude that the material is not present or the signal-to-noise ratio is too low for detection and may be flagged as '*not known*'.

Figure A6.4b shows an example of matching the spectral features of data collected by the air-borne hyper-spectral imager AVIRS with library spectra. In SFF, we compare the underlying physical property of the material, rather than establish 'statistical similarity' between different pixels. However, there are a number of situations in which the materials can be spectrally similar but chemically different, thus leading to false identification (Clark et. al., 2003). The situation can be improved by using more than one diagnostic feature when available. For further details, the reader may refer to Clark and Roush (1984), Mazer et. al. (1988), Kruse and Lefkoff (1993) and Rast et. al. (1991).

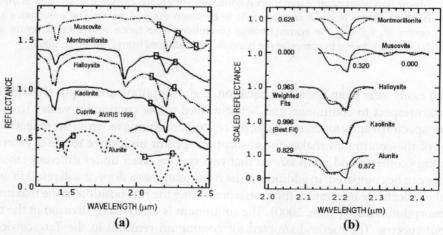

Fig. A6.4 (a) Air-borne hyper-spectral AVIRIS data along with USGS library spectra for five minerals which appear to have absorption features similar to AVIRIS data at around 2.15. The continuum endpoints are marked by boxes. The spectra are offset for clarity. (b) The continuous curve is the AVIRIS continuum-removed spectra. The curves are offset for clarity. The value 1.0 on the Y-axis is the normalised maximum value for each curve. The dotted curve shows the fit for library spectra for various elements shown in (a) using the Tetracorder software. The goodness of fit is also given on the left of each curve. The best fit is for kaolinite. (Adapted from Clark et. al., 2003)

Spectral Unmixing

An electro-optical sensor integrates the radiation received from a pixel. We have seen in Fig. 5.8 that a pixel may cover only one class (feature) which we referred to as *pure* pixel or may cover an area between the boundaries of two classes, which we referred to as *boundary pixel*. When the spatial resolution is coarse compared to the extent of the various classes of objects on the ground, a pixel can contain a number of different classes of objects each of which contributes to the pixel spectrum. Such a pixel is called a *mixed pixel*. In the case of a mixed pixel, the reflectance received by the sensor from the pixel is the sum of reflectances from each class within the pixel. In other words, the mixed pixel spectral data is formed by the integration of the unique spectrum from each distinct constituent of the pixel. The set of spectrally unique surface materials (pixels containing only one class) existing within a scene are often referred to as the spectral *end-members*, (or pure pixels) of that scene. In multi-spectral analysis, *generally*, such mixed pixels are either misclassified or labelled unclassified, though there are studies to decompose mixed pixels of the multi-spectral data to improve area estimation of agricultural fields and other land cover estimation (Lu et. al., 2003; Gong et. al., 1991). Analysis carried out to find the proportion of different classes within a pixel is referred to as *spectral unmixing,* or *spectral mixture analysis (SMA)*.

How the reflectance from each end-member in a pixel combines to give the spectral data of the pixel depends on how the end-members are mixed and the nature of the reflectance. When there are no multiple reflections within the target, then it is called *linear mixing*. However, when there is intimate mixing and the incident radiation makes multiple reflection, they mix in a non-linear way—*non-linear mixing*. This is the case for spatially fine-grained mixtures called intimate mixtures. In most cases, non-linear mixing is a second-order effect (ENVI Tutorial #6). We shall further discuss only linear mixing of two or more pure pixels. The problem is, can we estimate the extent of various classes present within a pixel? That is, can we find out the ground features at sub-pixel level? The linear mixing model (LMM) for a pixel containing four end-members is shown in Fig. A6.5. The reflectance measured by a pixel is the linear combination of the reflectance from each end-member weighted by their fractional abundance (Adams et. al., 1995). Consider a case of n spectral bands, and m end-members. If $R'(\lambda_1), R'(\lambda_2), \ldots\ldots R'(\lambda_n)$ are the measured reflectance for a pixel in $1 \ldots n$ spectral bands, then we have n linear equation such that:

$$R'(\lambda_1) = f_1 R_1(\lambda_1) + f_2 R_2(\lambda_1) + \cdots + f_m R_m(\lambda_1)$$

$$R'(\lambda_2) = f_1 R_1(\lambda_2) + f_2 R_2(\lambda_2) + \cdots + f_m R_m(\lambda_2)$$

$$\vdots$$

$$R'(\lambda_n) = f_1 R_1(\lambda_n) + f_2 R_2(\lambda_n) + \cdots + f_m R_m(\lambda_n) \tag{A6.1}$$

where, $R_1(\lambda_1), R_2(\lambda_1), \ldots\ldots, R_m(\lambda_n)$ are the reflectance of the end-members $1, \ldots\ldots, m$ at the spectral band λ_1 and so on and $f_1, f_2, \ldots\ldots, f_m$ are the corresponding fractional abundance of the end-members.

The fractional abundance is the fraction of the area of that end-member within the pixel. In addition, an error term 'e' is added to the above to account for noise. The linear mixture model can be expressed in a general way as:

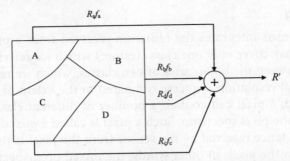

Fig. A6.5 Concept of linear mixing. Here, the pixel contains four end-members A, B, C and D (with spectra of R_a, R_b, R_c and R_d) and each occupies f_a, f_b, f_c, f_d fractions respectively within the pixel coverage. The radiance from the pixel is the sum of the radiance of each of the classes within the pixel. That is, $R' = R_a f_a + R_b f_b + R_c f_c + R_d f_d$ where $f_a + f_b + f_c + f_d = 1$.

$$R'(\lambda_i) = \sum_{k,i=1}^{m,n} f_k R_k(\lambda_i) + e_i \tag{A6.2}$$

where $k = 1,.....,m$ (number of end-members), $i = 1,.....,n$ (number of spectral bands), f_k is the proportion of the kth end-member and $R_k(\lambda_i)$ is the reflectance of the kth end-member in the ith spectral band. $R(\lambda_i)$ is the measured spectral reflectance of the pixel in the ith band. We have therefore n linear equations each corresponding to a band. To be physically meaningful, all abundance fractions (f_k) should be positive. Another constraint is that the sum of all the fractions should be 1, that is, all end-members should be accounted for.

Mathematically, the above constraints can be represented as:

$$f_k \geq 0 \tag{A6.3}$$

$$\sum_{k=1}^{m} f_i = 1$$

If we know all end-members, then $R_k(\lambda_i)$ is known. Then the above linear equations can be solved for f_k. Since there are $m + 1$ unknowns (m coefficients, that is, f_k and the error term, e), we require at least $m + 1$ equations to solve or the number of bands 'n' (each of which gives one equation) such that

$$n = m + 1; m = n - 1$$

That is the maximum number of end-members that can be derived from an image is one less than the number of bands (Gross and Schott, 1996).

The spectral un-mixing is a two step process:

(i) identification of end-members, and
(ii) use their spectra in Eq. A6.2 to estimate the proportion of the end-members.

The most difficult part in the spectral un-mixing is to find out the end-members. If there is an *a priori* knowledge of classes in the image, the end-member spectra can be taken from the spectral libraries (Adam et. al., 1986). This approach is suitable for mineral exploration (Smith et. al., 1985). However, for other land cover especially vegetation, the spectral libraries are not suitable, since a large number of processes and factors (for example, stage of crop growth) influence the observed spectra. In such cases, it is better to use the hyper-spectral image data itself to identify the end-members. This method has also the advantage that the end-member data is collected under identical conditions of the pixel to be un-mixed. Here one assumes that there are a few pixels which are 'pure' containing only one end-member. This is possible if, at some location in the image, the feature representing the end-member covers an area of a few times the pixel size. One way to approach the problem is to go to the field and find out the land cover classes and their location using GPS and identify them in the imagery (as one collects training samples for supervised classification). However, the approach is tedious and requires a lot of intervention by remote sensing experts. There are a number of algorithms for finding end-members straight from the image itself. We shall discuss the basic approach.

One of the approaches to derive the end-members from the hyper-spectral image data is based on the geometric property of the distribution of the reflectance values (Settle and Drake, 1993; Boardman, 1993; 1995). The pixels following a linear mixture model with the constraints as given in equation A6.3, are confined to a *simplex* in the feature space, that is, the scatter plot (according to 'convex geometry' in mathematics, a simplex is a Euclidean geometric spatial element having *minimum* number of boundary points, such as a line segment in one dimension, a triangle in two dimensional space, a tetrahedron in three dimensions and in n space, a geometric figure that has $n + 1$ vertices). Let us consider a scatter plot for two spectral bands. If all the mixtures are made up of two pure pixels, then the *mixed pixels* will be scattered around a line [Fig. A6.6(a)]. The pure pixels will fall at the two *ends* of this 'mixing line' (hence, the name end-members for pure pixels). If there are three pure pixels mixing, then all the pixels mixed will lie within a triangle with the pure pixels (A, B and C) at the vertices of the triangle encompassing the scatter points [Fig. A6.6(b)]. For four end-members, the mixing will be within a tetrahedron and so on. This geometric model can be extended to higher dimensions, where the number of mixing end-members is one more than the inherent dimensionality of the mixed data. In general, all mixed pixels, lie inside the smallest simplex formed with the end-members at the vertices. Based on this general principle, mathematical techniques are available to separate the end-members (Grana and Gallego, 2003). Once the pure pixels are identified, the spectra $R_k(\lambda_i)$ can be established from the data. However, it may be cautioned that the concept of pure pixels being at the vertices of a simplex is an ideal case.

Another technique is to have a pixel purity index (PPI) to find out the most pure pixels (Boardman et. al., 1995; Tompkins et. al., 1997). Plaza et. al. (2002), present an automated method that performs unsupervised pixel purity determination and end-member extraction.

In all these analyses, the data from the sensor is converted to apparent reflection, through proper sensor calibration, atmospheric correction, and so on. Many investigators first reduce the dimensionality using methods such as PCA, before automatic identification of the end-member.

Once the end-member spectra $R_k(\lambda)$ is known, the fractions of each end-member contributing to the pixel can be estimated by solving Eq. A6.2. To establish how good the fit is, the RMS of the residual error is calculated as

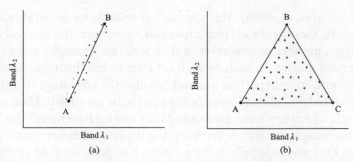

Fig. A6.6 Schematics showing geometric mixing model. (a) Case of only two end-members, (b) case of three end-members. All mixed pixels that are mixtures of A, B and C alone lie within the triangle—the 'mixing space'.

$$\text{RMS error} = \sqrt{\sum_{i=1}^{n} e_i^2 / n}$$

The RMS is calculated for all the pixels in the image which gives a measure of the accuracy of unmixing. A larger RMS error may indicate improper and/or insufficient selection of end-members.

In the SMA discussed, the end-members used are the same for each pixel and does not account for spectral variations present within an end-member, since it permits only one end-member spectrum for one class of ground cover. However, the reflectance values are not unique; it has a distribution around the mean. In order to accommodate end-member variability Bateson et. al. (2000) suggested a 'bundle' of points around the vertex representing end-members. Thus, we have *bundle mixing* which can give a maximum and minimum end-member fractions. To take into account this variability of spectral response within an end-member, multiple end-member spectral mixture analysis (MESMA) has been developed, wherein end-members are allowed to vary in number and type on a per pixel basis (Dennison and Roberts, 2003; Roberts et. al., 1998).

Readers interested in more details may refer to Adams et. al. (1986), David et. al. (2004), Asner and Lobell (2000), Marsh et. al. (1980), Tompkins et. al. (1997), Bateson and Curtiss, (1966).

In the conventional multi-spectral classification such as maximum likelihood, the classifier generates a thematic map giving the spatial distribution of each class. With spectral un-mixing, one can get a number of images for a scene, each giving quantitatively aerial proportion of each end-member. Spectral mixture analysis to get information at sub-pixel level has been used for a variety of applications. These include characterisation of planetary surface (Pinet et. al., 2000; Adam et. al., 1986), urban studies (Small, 2002), land degradation (Haboudane et. al., 2002), land cover change (Rogan et. al., 2002), vegetation studies (Riano et. al., 2002; Cross et. al., 1991).

There are commercial and R and D softwares available to analyse hyper-spectral data. These include ENVI (Research Systems Inc., USA), EASI-PACE (PCI Geomatics, Canada), IMAGINE (ERDAS, USA), SIPS (University of Colorado, USA), and so on, to name a few (Lucas et. al., 2004). The details provided here is to get an understanding of the basic principles behind the algorithms used in the softwares, which is very essential to intelligently interpret the output generated by these softwares.

FOR FURTHER READING

1. Techniques and Applications of Hyperspectral Image Analysis, Hans F Grahn, Paul Geladi, Eds, John Wiley & Sons Ltd.
2. *http://www.currentscience.ac.in/Volumes/108/05/0833.pdf*
3. *https://nrsc.gov.in/sites/all/pdf/SPIE%20APRS%20Tutorial_Hyperspectral%20RS_Vinay%20Kumar.pdf*
4. *https://arxiv.org/pdf/1202.6294.pdf*

A7 GNSS Remote Sensing

When GPS, the first constellation of the Global Navigational Satellite System (GNSS), was established by the USA its sole purpose was to precisely locate any point on the earth's surface by giving its longitude, latitude and height. Soon scientists realised that the microwave signal (L band- L1-1575.42 MHz and L2-1227.60 MHz) transmitted by the GPS satellites can be used to study many aspects related to the earth and its environs. A new discipline has emerged—*GNSS Remote Sensing*. Figure A7.1 shows different ways in which a low earth orbiting (LEO) satellite receives signal from a GNSS. The GNSS remote sensing can be broadly classified under two categories:

(i) When the GNSS signal propagates through the earth's atmosphere, it is delayed by the atmospheric refractive index, which results in lengthening of the geometric path of the ray.

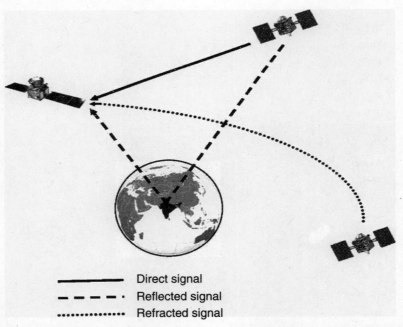

— Direct signal
- - - - Reflected signal
·········· Refracted signal

Fig. A7.1 Schematics showing different paths for the signal from GNSS to reach the LEO satellite. Direct signal used for positioning, reflected signal for reflectometry and refracted signal for radio occultation study.

The refraction and path delay of the signal is used to measure atmospheric variables such as tropospheric water vapour, temperature, pressure and tropospheric and ionospheric parameters. This is referred to as *GNSS meteorology*.

(ii) Based on the measurements of GNSS signals reflected from the earth's surface which could determine a number of surface parameters such as ocean surface height, ocean surface wind speed and wind direction, sea state in terms of sea surface roughness, soil moisture, ice, snow thickness—it is referred to as *GNSS reflectometry (GNSS-R)*.

In this Appendix, the basic principle involved to retrieve the geophysical parameters of interest using global navigation satellite system will be discussed. Readers interested in the details of the procedure and algorithms used for extraction of various parameters may refer to *GNSS Remote Sensing: Theory, Methods and Applications* (Shuanggen et. al, 2014) and the references therein.

A7.1   GNSS METEOROLOGY

GNSS meteorology has two components—space based observation, dependent on the refraction of the GNSS signal in the atmosphere, when the GNSS signal propagation path is close to the earth's limb—usually referred to as GNSS-RO. In the second category, a GNSS receiver is placed on the ground and from measuring the delay the signal has produced, one can extract the columnar water vapour (Fig. A7.2).

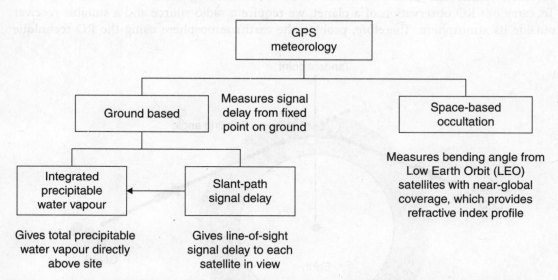

Fig. A7.2   Components of GNSS meteorology. Adapted from Businger Steven http://www.gps.gov/cgsic/states/2009/honolulu/businger.pdf

A7.1.1   GNSS RADIO OCCULTATION (GNSS RO)

GNSS RO is based on analysing the bending of the L-band radiation caused by the atmosphere along ray paths between a GNSS satellite and a receiver placed on a low-earth-orbiting (LEO)

satellite. For understanding the concept, let us consider GPS as a typical example of GNSS. We have seen in Chapter 8 that GPS orbits at a height of about 20200 km. The GPS signal, in order to reach a low earth orbiting (~800 km) satellite, has to first go through the ionosphere. Depending on the electron density, the ionosphere can be assigned a refractive index, which delays the propagation of the signal from GPS. Since the ionospheric delay is frequency dependent, it can be corrected by combining the data from the two frequencies L1 and L2. As the LEO moves behind the earth (Fig. A7.3) the rays from GPS enters the earth's atmosphere. Atmospheric mass decreases with increase of height from the surface of the earth, therefore the atmospheric refractive index also varies with height. As a result of the refractive index gradient of the atmosphere, the paths of EM waves propagating through the atmosphere are bent—this is referred to as *atmospheric refraction*. The deviation in the direction of propagationof the EM radiation, that is the bending angle, can be inverted to deduce the refractivity (refer Eq. A7.1) at the tangent height—the point of closest approach of the ray to the earth. The relative motion of the occulting GPS–LEO pair of satellites produces variation of ray-bending with tangent height which can be used to generate a vertical profile of the refractivity as a function of the distance from the centre of the planet. The refractivity profile in the neutral atmosphere (below 60 km from the surface of the earth) under certain assumptions, can be related to the vertical profile of the temperature and humidity. This is the basic principle of radio occultation.

The RO measurement technique began in the 1960s using the Mariner 3 and 4 satellites to probe the atmosphere of Mars. Till date, the atmosphere of several planets such as Venus, Mercury, Jupiter and Saturn rings have been probed using radio occultation technique. To carry out RO observation of a planet, we require a radio source and a suitable receiver outside its atmosphere. Therefore, probing the earth's atmosphere using the RO technique

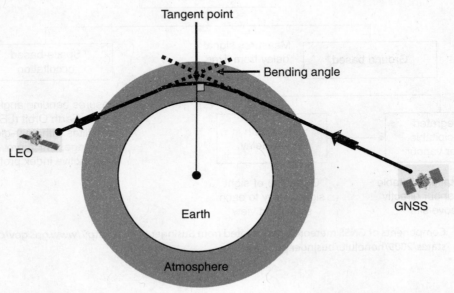

Fig. A7.3 Schematic diagram illustrating radio occultation of GPS signals. The radio signal emitted by the GNSS satellite is received by a receiver placed on the LEO. The path of the radio signal is bent as a result of refractive index gradients in the atmosphere. The motion of the LEO satellite enables the variation of ray bending with tangent height to be investigated.

had to wait till the GPS constellation was established. The launch of the proof-of-concept mission GPS/MET (Global Positioning System/Meteorology) in 1995 began a revolution in profiling the earth's atmosphere through radio occultation with several successful additional missions thereafter such as CHAMP, COSMIC, METOP-A, METOP-B (Bauer et. al., 2014) and including ISRO's Megha-Tropiques and Oceansat-2 missions. Megha-Tropiques is the first radio occultation mission dedicated to tropical atmosphere, while all other missions are in polar orbits with extensive geographical coverage (Desbois et. al., 2003). We shall briefly outline how the water vapour profile is derived from the bending angle without getting into the mathematical derivation.

Consider a setting occultation where the GNSS and the receiver satellite in LEO are moving away from each other (converse of this is called rising occultation). The radio signal at the receiver will be shifted to a lower frequency due to the Doppler effect (Section 7.4.2). The atmospheric bending increases the size of the shift to the lower frequency. The receivers on the LEO satellites measure the phase and amplitude of the signal. The bending introduced by the atmospheric refractive index gradients produces an additional phase delay from what would be expected if the ray followed a straight-line path between the satellites. The derivative of phase delay with respect to time gives the *Doppler shift*. After correcting for the ionospheric effect, the Doppler shift due to bending in the atmosphere can be calculated. Knowing the accurate position and velocity of the satellites, the additional Doppler shift can be inverted to derive bending angle and impact parameter. (The impact parameter is the distance of closest approach for the straight line path of the ray, which is close to the tangent height when bending angle is small. The bending angle is tagged to the tangent height to establish vertical profile.) The relative motion of the occulting pair of GPS–LEO satellites gives the variation of ray bending angle with tangent height thus providing vertical profile of the bending angle. (Given the distinct orbital plane of GPS and LEO satellite, there is an azimuth shift between each successive tangent point measurement. This implies that the vertical profile of atmospheric parameters does not correspond to a single point location on earth, rather, each tangent point measurement at distinct vertical level will have slightly different latitude and longitude coordinates when projected to the earth's surface.) Thus, RO observations are made in a limb scanning mode, where vertical scanning is provided by relative motion between the GPS and the LEO satellites. It can be shown that the vertical profile of bending angle can be inverted to give a vertical profile of refractive index under the spherical symmetry assumption on the shape of the atmosphere. The refractivity N, as defined below is generally used in place of refractive index n, for the processing of data.

$$N = (n - 1)10^6 \tag{A7.1}$$

The refractivity profiles can be used to derive profiles of electron density in the ionosphere, temperature in the stratosphere, and temperature and water vapour partial pressure in the troposphere. Additional information in the form of atmospheric pressure is used to derive geopotential height. (Geopotential height approximates the actual height of a pressure surface above mean sea-level.) GPS-RO is currently the only satellite-based technique providing a reliable estimate of the geopotential height of atmospheric pressure levels. The refractivity after correcting for ionospheric effect is related to the atmospheric pressure (P), temperature (T) and water vapour partial pressure (P_w) as:

$$N = \frac{c_1 P}{T} + \frac{c_2 P_w}{T^2} \qquad (A7.2)$$

C_1 and C_2 are empirical constants and have values 77.6 K/mbar, and 3.739×10^5 K²/mbar (Smith and Weintraub, 1953) (mbar = millibar, unit of pressure). The first term is called the *dry* (hydrostatic) *term*; the second term which is sensitive to water vapour is called the *wet term*. In the lower troposphere where water vapour has a dominant presence, due to the permanent dipole moment of water molecule, the contribution of each water molecule to refractivity is significantly higher than the contribution from the dry molecules (N_2 or O_2). Above the troposphere, the contribution of water vapour is negligible and the second term can be neglected. However, to compute the temperature we still need to know the pressure. The value of the pressure can be estimated using the hydrostatic equation assuming certain scale height for pressure. The temperature so derived is referred to as *dry temperature*. Since we have assumed that water vapour is not present, the retrieved temperature will be lower (cooler) than the real temperature of the atmosphere depending on the content of water vapour.

The moisture contribution to N is important in the middle and lower troposphere. To calculate the partial pressure of water vapour, the above equation is re-written as:

$$P_w = \left(N - \frac{c_1 P}{T} \right) \frac{T^2}{C_2} \qquad (A7.3)$$

To solve the above equation, we need independent knowledge of the temperature and pressure. The pressure is related to the temperature by the hydrostatic equation (Appendix 2). Usually, temperature is given by an external source (based on numerical weather model) and we solve for moisture iteratively. Recently, a one dimensional variational (1D-VAR) technique for retrieval of all the three geophysical parameters from radio occultation refractivity or bending angle has become state-of-the-art and has the advantage of deriving all the three geophysical parameters simultaneously (Healy and Eyre, 2000; Palmer and Barnett, 2001). GNSS-RO gives a vertical resolution of 0.1 km between 0 and 18 km and increasing to 1.5 km in the stratosphere and with a coarse horizontal resolution of 300 km (Kursinki et. al., 1997).

The humidity profile derived from GNSS-RO has many advantages compared to that derived from conventional sounding instruments. These instruments based on physical devices usually deteriorate with time and need to be calibrated in orbit periodically. Even in the laboratory, absolute calibration traceable to a standard is a complex problem with limited accuracy. The RO technique is based on measuring time delays, and hence no calibration is required due to the presence of precise atomic clocks on board the GPS as well as on the LEO receiver. Another issue with conventional sounders is the instrument to instrument bias. In RO measurement there is no instrument to instrument bias since it relies only on the time delay of electromagnetic radiation. With a number of GNSS in orbit, one can get a global coverage with high temporal resolution.

GPS RO observations from several missions are being assimilated at most operational Numerical Weather Prediction (NWP) centres. With the drift-free self-calibrating nature of GNSS-RO, this technique is well suited for establishing a stable, long-term record required for climate monitoring (Anthes et. al., 2008).

A7.1.2 GNSS METEOROLOGY—GROUND BASED

Ground based GNSS receivers were initially installed for geodetic studies by knowing the precise location of the site. The GNSS signals reaching the ground receiver are delayed and bent when propagating through the atmosphere because of the ionosphere and troposphere, compared to if it had travelled only through vacuum. This is because depending on its composition both the ionosphere and the troposphere can be assigned a refractive index. We have seen in Chapter 2 that the velocity of the EM radiation is slowed down in a medium compared to that in vacuum. In geodetic applications, these delays are removed by appropriate corrections applied to the GPS signals (Davis et. al., 1985). As discussed in the previous section, the delay due to the ionosphere can be estimated using the two L band signals. The atmospheric bending can be ignored, a reasonable assumption for satellites above 5° elevation angle (Sokolovskiy et. al., 2001).

The tropospheric delay is the integral of refractivity N along the path s taken by the GNSS signal through the atmosphere (Hofmann–Wellenhof et. al., 2001), which in turn depends on the constituent components of the troposphere. For a signal approaching the GNSS receiver from the local zenith direction, we can assign a Zenith Total Delay (ZTD). Since the measurement can be carried out using individual satellites visible from a ground receiver, apart from the zenith view we have also slant range view. As the elevation angle of a satellite decreases, the length of the path through the neutral atmosphere increases. Scaling the slant path delay to its equivalent delay if the satellite were at zenith is modelled by individual mapping functions with coefficients calculated using climatology, meteorological data or NWP output (Guerova et. al., 2016). As discussed in GNSS-RO, the refractivity is made up of a *hydrostatic* (dry) term and a wet term. Therefore, the zenith total delay (ZTD) is the sum of *Zenith Hydrostatic Delay* (ZHD) and the *Zenith Wet Delay* (ZWD). The wet delay, is approximately proportional to the quantity of water vapour integrated along the ray path. The ZHD component can be derived from a surface pressure modelling (Davis et. al., 1985), which when subtracted from ZTD, leaves the ZWD, which can be used to derive the integrated water vapour (Bevis et. al., 1992; 1994). To summarise, this technique measures the integrated amount of water vapour along the path between a transmitting GPS satellite and a receiving antenna. The measurement can be carried out using individual satellites visible from a ground receiver and therefore provides an improved sampling of the spatial distribution of atmospheric water vapour.

Integrated water vapour data from earth-based GNSS receivers and humidity profiles from space-based GNSS receivers represent an important new resource for operational numerical weather prediction.

A7.2 GNSS REFLECTOMETRY (GNSS-R)

Reflections from earth surfaces, which is referred to as *multi path radiation,* is a source of worry for geodetic applications of GNSS. However, the reflected GNSS signal contains a wealth of information on the characteristics of the reflecting surface which leads to a new discipline called *GNSS reflectometry.* The GNSS reflected signals from the ocean and land surface could determine the ocean surface height, ocean surface wind speed and wind direction (using multiple observations), sea state in terms of significant wave height, soil moisture, snow and ice coverage and thickness, and so on. Remote sensing using reflected signals from the navigation satellite is a relatively new remote sensing technique compared to the

GNSS-RO technique. The basic principle of application of GNSS reflectometry is similar to the conventional active microwave remote sensing discussed in Chapter 7. That is, the reflection of the microwave radiation from a surface depends on, among other things, the properties of the reflecting surface, primarily the surface roughness and dielectric constant. Therefore, by analysing the power received and the change in the phase of the reflected signal and proper modelling, one should be able to derive the properties of the reflecting surface. Conventional microwave remote sensing radar is a monostatic sensor wherein the transmitter and receiver are co-located to measure the backscatter, whereas, GPS reflectometry is a bi-static radar technology (Section 7.3). Transmitters are located on GNSS satellites and receivers mounted on a LEO satellite, an aircraft, or a structure on the ground and reflected radiation is measured in the forward specular direction. With L-band signals of the GPS having wavelengths of ~19 cm, the reflections are sensitive to ocean surface roughness at this scale and the signal is not affected by atmospheric effects caused by rain and cloud, thus precluding the need for their corrections. The available large number of GNSS signals can monitor the earth's surface as a continuous, all-weather and near-real-time remote sensing tool. We shall now discuss some of the applications of GPS reflectometry for land and ocean surface monitoring without getting into the data retrieval technique.

The GPS signal forward scattered from a land surface can be related to the near surface soil moisture, modified by surface roughness and possible vegetative cover. When the L-band GNSS signals impinge upon the ground surface, in addition to the energy reflected by the surface, a part also penetrates into soil and are reflected by deeper layers. The two parameters of significance in extracting information from the reflected signal are the power of the reflected signal and the excess phase of the reflected signal over the direct signal. Soil reflectivity estimates could be obtained from the ratio of the reflected and direct power. Details of how to obtain these values from GNSS signal can be found in the literature (Egido et. al., 2012; Katzberg et. al., 2006; Egido, 2013). Significant correlation has been found between reflected signal power and in situ soil moisture measurements for high levels of moisture when the top layer of soil of about 6 cm of thickness is moist enough (Zavorotny et. al., 2003).

Reflected GNSS signals from the sea carry significant information on the sea state and topography. GNSS reflectometry has been used as an altimeter for determination of sea surface height and as scatterometer for the retrieval of ocean surface wind speed, and later wind vector above rough seas using reflected signals from multiple GPS satellites (Komjathy et. al., 2004; Garrison et. al., 2002). GNSS-R sea state information (sea surface roughness) can be used for better retrieval of L-band radiometric measurements for sea surface salinity (Valencia et. al., 2011).

What is given here are only some typical examples of using GNSS-R for earth surface studies. For a detailed account, readers may refer to Shuanggen et. al. (2014).

We conclude by reiterating the broad objectives of GNSS-remote sensing. Traditionally active microwave remote sensing is carried out using radar techniques with dedicated transmitters and receivers at generally lower temporal resolution, whereas the GNSS remote sensing using the available transmitters from GNSS with only additional receivers, can measure the earth's surface/ environmental parameters as a new, highly precise, continuous, all-weather and near-real-time remote sensing tool.

FOR FURTHER READING

1. GNSS Remote Sensing, Theory, Methods and Applications, Jin Shuanggen et. al., Springer.
2. *https://www.springeropen.com/track/pdf/10.1186/1687-6180-2014-134?site=asp-eurasip-journals.springeropen.com*
3. *http://center.shao.ac.cn/geodesy/publications/Jin_2011ASR.pdf*
4. *http://clasp-research.engin.umich.edu/missions/cygnss/reference/gnss-overview/Gleason_Thesis_GNSS.pdf*

A8 Acronyms

AFS	–	Aerial Film Speed
AI	–	Aridity Index
AI	–	Artificial Intelligence
ALI	–	Advanced Land Imager
AMC	–	Angular Motion Compensation
AMI	–	Active Microwave Instrumentation
AMSR	–	Advanced Microwave Scanning Radiometer
AMSU	–	Advanced Microwave Sounding Unit
ANN	–	Artificial Neural Network
AOCS	–	Attitude and Orbit Control System
AOP	–	Apparent Optical Properties
APS	–	Active Pixel Sensor
ASAR	–	Advanced Synthetic Aperture Radar
ASCII	–	American Standard Code for Information Interchange
ASIC	–	Application Specific Integrated Circuit
ASTER	–	Advanced Space-borne Thermal Emission and Reflection Radiometer
ATS	–	Advanced Technology Satellite
AU	–	Astronomical Unit
AVHRR	–	Advanced Very High Resolution Radiometer
AVIRIS	–	Advanced Visible and Infrared Imaging Spectrometer
AWiFS	–	Advanced Wide Field Sensor
BIL	–	Band Interleaved by Line
BIP	–	Band Interleaved by Pixel
BRDF	–	Bidirectional Reflectance Distribution Function
BSQ	–	Band Sequential
BW	–	Black and White
C/A Code	–	Coarse Acquisition Code
Cal/Val	–	Calibration/Validation
CAPE	–	Crop Acreage and Production Estimation
CASI	–	Compact Airborne Spectral Imager
CCD	–	Charge Coupled Device
CCE	–	Crop Cutting Experiments
CCT	–	Computer Compatible magnetic Tape
CEOS	–	Committee on Earth Observation Satellites

CFC	–	Chloro Fluoro Carbon
CIR	–	Colour InfraRed
CMOS	–	Complementary Metal Oxide Semiconductor
CNES	–	Centre National d'Etudes spatiales (French Space Agency)
COIS	–	Coastal Ocean Imaging Spectrometer
CPU	–	Central Processing Unit
CPUE	–	Catch Per Unit Effort
CRZ	–	Coastal Regulation Zone
CTF	–	Contrast Transfer Function
CV	–	Coefficient of Variation
CZCS	–	Coastal Zone Colour Scanner
DACS	–	Data Acquisition and Control Subsystem
DAIS	–	Digital Airborne Imaging Spectrometer
DARPA	–	Defense Advanced Research Projects Agency
DEM	–	Digital Elevation Model
DGPS	–	Differential GPS
DIAL	–	Differential Absorption LIDAR
DLT	–	Digital Linear Tape
DN	–	Digital Number
DOS	–	Department of Space
DSM	–	Desertification Status Map/Digital Surface Model
DSP	–	Digital Signal Processor
DST	–	Department of Science and Technology
DTC	–	Decision Tree Classifier
DTM	–	Digital Terrain Model
EIFOV	–	Effective Instantaneous Field of View
EMR	–	Electromagnetic Radiation
ENVISAT	–	Environmental Satellite (ESA)
EOS	–	Earth Observation Satellite/Earth Observation System
ERS	–	European Remote-sensing Satellites
ERTS	–	Earth Resources Technology Satellite (later named as LANDSAT)
ESA	–	European Space Agency/Environmentally Sensitive Areas
ESMR	–	Electrically Scanning Microwave Radiometer
ETM	–	Enhanced Thematic Mapper
ETM+	–	Enhanced Thematic Mapper Plus
FASAL	–	Forecasting Agricultural output using Space, Agrometeorology and Land-based observation
FCC	–	False Colour Composite
FCD	–	Forest Canopy Density
FEFA	–	Front End Feed Assembly
FIR	–	Far InfraRed
FM	–	Figure of Merit/Flight Model
FMC	–	Forward Motion Compensation
FOG	–	Fiber Optic Gyros

FOV   –   Field-of-View
FPA   –   Focal Plane Assembly
FPAR   –   Fractional Photo-synthetically Active Radiation
FPN   –   Fixed Pattern Noise
FSI   –   Forest Survey of India
FTHSI   –   Fourier Transform Hyperspectral Imager
FTS   –   Fourier Transform Spectrometer
FWHM   –   Full Width at Half Maxima
GCP   –   Ground Control Point
GDD   –   Growing Degree Day
GHG   –   Greenhouse Gases
GIS   –   Geographic Information System
GLI   –   GLobal Imager
GNSS   –   Global Navigational Satellite System
GOME   –   Global Ozone Monitoring Experiment
GOMOS   –   Global Ozone Monitoring by Occultation of the Stars
GPR   –   Ground Penetrating Radar
GSD   –   Ground Sampling Distance
GT   –   Ground Truth
H/W   –   Hardware
HCMM   –   Heat Capacity Mapping Mission
HDDTR   –   High Density Digital Tape Recorder
HIRIS   –   High Resolution Imaging Spectrometer
HIRS   –   High resolution IR Sounder
HTL   –   High Tide Line
ICZM   –   Integrated Coastal Zone Management
I/O   –   Input/Output
IFOV   –   Instantaneous Field of View
IFTS   –   Imaging Fourier Transform Spectrometer
IGBP   –   International Geosphere Biosphere Programme
IGFOV   –   Instantaneous Geometric Field of View
HIS   –   Intensity Hue Saturation
IIMS   –   Integrated Information Management System
IMGEOS   –   Integrated Multi-mission Ground segment for Earth Observation Satellites
InGaAs   –   Indium Gallium Arsenide
InSAR   –   Interferometric SAR
INSAT   –   Indian National Satellite System
IOP   –   Inherent Optical Properties
IR   –   InfraRed
IRS   –   Indian Remote Sensing Satellite
ISRO   –   Indian Space Research Organisation
JERS   –   Japanese Earth Resources Satellite
LACIE   –   Large Area Crop Inventory Experiment

LAI	–	Leaf Area Index
LANDSAT	–	LAND observation SATellite
LCC	–	Lambert Conformal Conic
LED	–	Light Emitting Diode (Device)
LFC	–	Large Format Camera
LGSOWG	–	Landsat Ground Station Operators Working Group
LIDAR	–	Laser Image Detection and Ranging
LISS	–	Linear Imaging Self-scanning Sensor
LSB	–	Least Significant Bit
LTE	–	Local Thermodynamic Equilibrium
LTL	–	Low Tide Line
LULC	–	Land Use/Land Cover
LUT	–	Look Up Table
LWIR	–	Long Wave InfraRed
MARS	–	Monitoring Agriculture through Remote Sensing
MCSST	–	Multi-Channel SST
MCT	–	Mercury Cadmium Telluride
MEOSS	–	Monocular Electro-Optical Stereo Scanner
MERIS	–	Medium Resolution Imaging Spectrometer
MIPAS	–	Michelson Interferometer for Passive Atmospheric Soundings
MIR	–	Middle InfraRed
MISR	–	Multi-angle Imaging Spectro-Radiometer
MIVIS	–	Multispectral Infrared and Visible Imaging Spectrometer
MLI	–	Multi-Layer Insulation
MNCFC	–	Mahalanobis National Crop Forecast Centre
MODIS	–	MODerate resolution Imaging Spectroradiometer
MoEFCC	–	Ministry of Environment, Forest and Climate Change
MOPITT	–	Measurements of Pollution In The Troposphere
MOS	–	Modular Optoelectronic Scanner
MSB	–	Most Significant Bit
MSMR	–	Multi-frequency Scanning Microwave Radiometer
MSS	–	Multi-Spectral Scanner
MTF	–	Modulation Transfer Function
MWIR	–	Mid-Wave InfraRed
MXL	–	Maximum Likelihood Classifier
NASA	–	National Aeronautics and Space Administration (USA)
NDSI	–	Normalised Difference Snow Index
NDVI	–	Normalised Difference Vegetation Index
NDWI	–	Normalised Difference Wetness (water) Index
NEDL	–	Noise Equivalent Differential Radiance
NEDT	–	Noise Equivalent Differential Temperature
NEL	–	Noise Equivalent Radiance
NEP	–	Noise Equivalent Power
NESR	–	Noise Equivalent Spectral Radiance

NIMA	–	National Image and Mapping Agency
NIR	–	Near InfraRed
NNRMS	–	National Natural Resources Management System
NOAA	–	National Oceanic and Atmospheric Administration (USA)
NPOESS	–	National Polar-Orbiting Operational Environmental Satellite System
NRSA	–	National Remote Sensing Agency (now NRSC)
NRSC	–	National Remote Sensing Centre
NSDI	–	National Spatial Data Infrastructure
NUIS	–	National Urban Information System
OBCT	–	Object Based Classification Technique
OCI	–	Ocean Colour Imager
OCM	–	Ocean Colour Monitor
OCTS	–	Ocean Colour and Temperature Scanner
OIF	–	Optimum Index Factor
OIR	–	Optical Infrared
OS	–	Operating System
OTF	–	Optical Transfer Function
PAN	–	Panchromatic Camera
PCA	–	Principal Component Analysis
PET	–	Potential EvapoTranspiration
PFZ	–	Potential Fishing Zone
PMT	–	Photo-Multiplier Tube
POLDER	–	POLarisation and Directionality of the Earth's Reflectance
PRF	–	Pulse Repetition Frequency
PSF	–	Point Spread function
PSLV	–	Polar Satellite Launch Vehicle
PtSi	–	Platinum Silicide
PVI	–	Perpendicular Vegetation Index
QA/QC	–	Quality Assurance/Quality Control
QE	–	Quantum Efficiency
RAAN	–	Right Ascension of Ascending Node
RAIFOV	–	Radiometrically Accurate Instantaneous Field of View
RAR	–	Real Aperture Radar
RAM	–	Random Access Memory
RBV	–	Return Beam Vidicon
RC telescope	–	Ritchey–Chretien telescope
RCS	–	Radar Cross Section
RGB	–	Red Green Blue
RI	–	Refractive Index
ROIC	–	Read Out Integrated Circuit
ROIR	–	Reflective Optical Infrared Region
ROM	–	Read Only Memory
RMSE	–	Root Mean Square Error
SSDA	–	Sequential Similarity Detection Algorithms

S&T	–	Science and Technology
S/N	–	Signal to Noise Ratio
S/W	–	Software
SA	–	Selective Availability
SADA	–	Solar Array Drive Assembly
SAGE	–	Stratospheric Aerosol and Gas Equipment
SAM	–	Spectral Angle Mapper
SAMIR	–	Satellite Microwave Radiometer
SAR	–	Synthetic Aperture Radar
SAT	–	Shift Along Track
SAVI	–	Soil Adjusted Vegetation Index
SCC	–	Spacecraft Control Centre
SCIAMACHY	–	Scanning Imaging Absorption Spectrometer for Atmospheric CartograpHY
SCR	–	Selective Chopper Radiometer
SeaWiFS	–	Sea-viewing Wide Field-of-view Sensor
SIR	–	Shuttle Imaging Radar
SLAR	–	Side Looking Airborne Radar
SLR	–	Side Looking Radar
SMMR	–	Scanning Multi-channel Microwave Radiometer
SNR	–	Signal to Noise Ratio
SOI	–	Survey of India
SOM	–	Space Oblique Mercator
SPM	–	Suspended Particulate Matter
SPOT	–	Satellite Pour l'Observation de la Terre (France) (Satellite for observation of Earth)
SR	–	Saturation Radiance
SRTM	–	Shuttle Radar Topography Mission
SSS	–	Sea Surface Salinity
SST	–	Sea Surface Temperature
SWH	–	Significant Wave Height
SWIR	–	Short Wave InfraRed
TAT	–	Turn Around Time
TBD	–	To Be Determined
TDI	–	Time Delay and Integration
TES	–	Tropospheric Emission Spectrometer Technology Experiment Satellite (ISRO)
TGA	–	Total Geographic Area
TIR	–	Thermal InfraRed
TIROS	–	Television InfraRed Observation Satellite
TM	–	Thematic Mapper
TOA	–	Top-Of-Atmosphere
TOAR	–	Top Of Atmosphere Radiance
TOMS	–	Total Ozone Mapping Spectrometer

TPR	–	Total Power Radiometer
TRMM	–	Tropical Rainfall Mapping Mission
TT&C	–	Telemetry, Tracking & Command
TWTA	–	Travelling Wave Tube Amplifier
UARS	–	Upper Atmosphere Research Satellite
UAV	–	Unmanned Aerial Vehicle
UHF	–	Ultra High frequency
UNEP	–	United Nations Environment Programme
UNCCD	–	United Nations Convention to Combat Desertification
USDA	–	US Department of Agriculture
UT	–	Universal Time
UTM	–	Universal Transverse Mercator
UV	–	UltraViolet
VCI	–	Vegetation Condition Index
VHRR	–	Very High Resolution Radiometer
VI	–	Vegetation Index
VNIR	–	Visible to Near Infrared
VTPR	–	Vertical Temperature Profiling Radiometer
WARC	–	World Administrative Radio Conference
WGCV	–	Working Group for Calibration and Validation
WGS84	–	World Geodetic System 1984
WiFS	–	Wide Field Sensor
WIS	–	Wedge Imaging Spectrometer
WRS	–	Worldwide Reference System

References

1. Abel I R and Reynolds B R, Skylab Multispectral Scanner (S-192) – Optical design and operational imagery, *Optical Engineering*, Vol. 13(4), 292–298, 1974.
2. Abel P J, Ellis P, Houghton J T, Peckham J T, Rodgers C D, Smith S D and Williamson E J, Remote Sounding of Atmospheric Temperature from Satellites–(II), The Selective Chopper Radiometer for Nimbus-D, *Proceedings of Royal Society*, Vol. A320, 35–55, 1970.
3. Abkar A A, Sharifi M and Mulder N Likelihood-based image segmentation and classification: A framework for the integration of expert knowledge in image classification procedures, *International Journal of Applied Earth Observation and Geoinformation*, Vol. 2(2), 101–119, 2000.
4. Adams J B, Sabol D E, Kapos V, Filho R A, Roberts D A, Smith M O and Gillespie A R, Classification of multispectral images based on fractions of endmembers: Application of land-cover change in the Brazilian Amazon, *Remote Sensing of Environment*, Vol. 52, 137–154, 1995.
5. Adams J B, Smith M O and Johnson P E, Spectral mixture modeling: A new analysis of rock and soil types at the Viking Lander I site, *Journal of Geophysical Research*, Vol. 91, 8098–8812, 1986.
6. Ajai et. al., Desertification monitoring and assessment using remote sensing and GIS: A pilot project under TPN-1, UNCCD. *Scientific Report No: SAC/RESIPA/MESG/DMA/2007/01, Space Applications Centre, ISRO*, Ahmedabad, India, 2007.
7. Ajai, Arya A S, Dhinwa P S, Pathan S K and Ganeshraj K, Desertification/land degradation status mapping of India, *Current Science*, Vol. 97(10), 1478–83, 2009.
8. Ajai, Personal communication, Space Applications Centre, Ahmedabad, 2002.
9. Ajai, Sashikumar M N, Kamat D S,Chaturvedi G S, Singh A K and Sinha S K, *Proceedings of the Seminar on Crop Growth Conditions and Remote Sensing*, Indian Agricultural Research Institute, New Delhi, 1-1-1 to 1-1-9, 1984.
10. Alesheikh A A, Helali H and Behroz H A, Web GIS: Technologies and its applications. ISPRS Commission IV, Symposium: Geospatial Theory, Processing and Applications, July 9–12, 2002, Ottawa, Canada. http://www.isprs.org/proceedings/XXXIV/part4/pdfpapers/422.pdf
11. Alparone L, Aiazzi B, Baronti S and Garzelli A, *Remote sensing image fusion*, CRC Press, 2015.
12. Anderson G P, Barth C A, Cayla F and London J, Satellite observations of the vertical ozone distribution in the upper stratosphere, *Ann. Geophysics*, Vol. 25, 239–243, 1969.

13. Anderson J R, Hardy E E, Roach J T and Witmer R E, A landuse landcover classification system for use with remote sensing data, *Geological Professional Paper- 964*, United States Govt. Printing Office, Washington, 1976.

14. Anding D and Kauth R, Estimation of sea-surface temperature from space, *Remote Sensing of Environment*, 217, 1, 1970.

15. Annan A P, 2003, accessed on 23 May 2016. http://www.rohan.sdsu.edu/~geology/jiracek/sage/documents/Sensors%20and%20Software%20GPR%20Manual.pdf

16. Anthes R, Ector A D, Hunt D C, Kuo Y-H, Rocken C, Schreiner W S, Sokolovskiy S V, Syndergaard S, Wee T-K and Zeng Z, The COSMIC/FORMOSAT-3 mission early results, *Bull. Am. Meteorol. Soc.*, Vol. 89, 1–21, 2008.

17. Arnaud M and Leroy M, SPOT 4: A new generation of SPOT satellites, *ISPRS Journal of Photogrammetry and Remote Sensing*, Vol. 46, 205–215, 1991.

18. Arnaud M, New SPOT Generation, Paper (IAF88-117) presented at the 39th International Astronautical Congress, Bangalore, India, 1988.

19. Arya A S, Dhinwa P S, Arya V S and Hooda R S, Desert Ecosystems: Mapping, Monitoring and Assessment Using Satellite Remote Sensing. *ISPRS—International Archives of the Photogrammetry, Remote Sensing and Spatial Information Sciences*, Vol. 3820, 170–174, 2011. https://doi.org/10.5194/isprsarchives-XXXVIII-8-W20-170-2011

20. Asner G and Lobell D, A biogeophysical approach for automated SWIR unmixing of soils and vegetation, *Remote Sensing of Environment*, Vol. 74, 99–112, 2000.

21. Attena E P W, The active microwave instrument, on-board the ERS-1 satellite, *Proceedings of IEEE*, Vol. 79(6), 791–799, 1991.

22. Austin R W, The remote sensing of spectral radiance from below the ocean surface, *in Optical Aspects of Oceanography*, Jerlov N G and Nielsen E S (Eds), Academic Press, 317–344, 1974.

23. Badhwar G D, Carnes J G and Austin W W, Use of LANDSAT derived temporal profiles for corn-soybean feature extraction and classification, *Remote Sensing of Environment*, 12, 57–79, 1982.

24. Badhwar G D, Classification of corn and soybeans using multitemporal thematic mapper data, *Remote Sensing of Environment*, 16, 175–182, 1984.

25. Badhwar G D, Crop emergence date determination from spectral data, *Photogrammetric Engineering & Remote Sensing*, 46, 369–377, 1980.

26. Bahuguna A and Nayak S R, Coral reefs of the Indian coast, Scientific Note, SAC/ RSA/ RSAG/DOD-COS/SN/16/97 Space Applications Centre, Ahmedabad, 56, 1998.

27. Bahuguna A and Nayak S R, Space Applications Centre, Ahmedabad, Personal communication, 2004.

28. Bajesy P and Groves P, Methodology for Hyperspectral Band Selection, *Photogrammetric Engineering and Remote Sensing Journal*, Vol. 70(7), 793–802, 2004.

29. Barbe D F, Imaging devices using the charge-coupled concept, *Proceedings of the IEEE*, Vol. 63(1), 38–67, 1975.

30. Bardossy A and Samaniego L, Fuzzy rule-based classification of remotely sensed imagery, *IEEE Transactions on Geoscience and Remote Sensing*, Vol. 40(2), 362–374, 2002.

31. Barnea D I and Silverman H F, A class of algorithm for fast digital image registration, *IEEE Transactions on Computers*, C-21, 179–186, 1972.

32. Barnes R A, Eplee R E, Patt F S and McClain C R, Changes in the radiometric sensitivity of SeaWiFS determined from lunar and solar-based measurements, *Appl. Opt.*, Vol. 38(21), 4649–4664, 1999.

33. Barnsky M J, Strahler A H, Moris K P and Muller J P, Sampling the surface BRDF:1, Evaluation of current and future sensors, *Remote Sensing Reviews*, Vol. 8, 271–311, 1994.

34. Barron A J M, Cortina J M G, Vega C A, Andina D and Martinez E J I S, Data fusion and neural network combination method for air pollution level monitoring, *7th IEEE International Conference on Industrial Informatics*, Cardiff UK, 522–527, 2009.

35. Barton I J, Satellite-derived sea surface temperatures: Current status, *Journal of Geophysical Research – Oceans*, 100(C5), 8777–8790, 1995.

36. Bastiaanssen W G M, Remote sensing in water resources management: The State of the Art, *International Water Management Institute (IWMI)*, Colombo, Sri Lanka, 1998.

37. Bateson A and Curtiss B, A method for manual endmember selection and spectral unmixing, *Remote Sensing of Environment*, Vol. 55, 229–243, 1996.

38. Bateson C A, Asner G P and Wessman C A, Endmember bundles: a new approach to incorporating endmember variability into spectral mixture analysis, *IEEE Trans. on Geoscience and Remote Sensing*, Vol. 38, 1083–1094, 2000.

39. Bauer P, Radnóti G, Healy S and Cardinali C, GNSS Radio Occultation Constellation Observing System Experiments, *Monthly Weather Review*, Vol. 142(2), 2014.

40. Becker F and Li Z L, Towards a local split window method over land surfaces, *International Jounal of Remote Sensing*, Vol. 3, 369–393, 1990.

41. Bellman R, *Adaptive Control Processes: A Guided Tour*, Princeton University Press, 1961.

42. Bendiktsson J A and Sveinsson J R, Multisource data classification and feature extraction with neural networks, *International Journal of Remote Sensing*, Vol. 18(4), 727–740, 1997.

43. Bernstein R, Image Geometry and Rectification, Chapter 21, in *The Manual of Remote Sensing*, Colwell R N (Ed.), Falls Church, VA.: *The American Society of Photogrammetry and Remote Sensing*, Vol. 1, 887–888, 1983.

44. Bevis M, Businger S, Chiswell S, Herring R, Anthes R A, Rocken C and Ware H R, GPS meteorology: mapping zenith wet delays onto precipitable water, *J. Appl. Meteorol.*, Vol. 33, 379–386, 1994.

45. Bevis M, Businger S, Herring R, Rocken C, Anthes R A and Ware H R, GPS meteorology: remote sensing of atmospheric water vapor using the Global Positioning System, *J. Geophys. Res.*, Vol. 97 (15), 787–15, 801, 1992.

46. Bhavsar P D, Demonstrated applications in India of earth resources survey by remote sensing, *Proceedings of Indian National Science Academy*, Vol. 46A, 275, 1980.

47. Bhavsar P D, Joseph G and Calla O P N, Development of remote sensing sensors at ISRO, *Proc. 2nd Asian Conference on Remote Sensing*, China, 1981.

48. Billingsley F C, Data processing and reprocessing, Chapter 17 in *The Manual of Remote Sensing*, Colwell R N (Ed.), Vol. 1, Falls Church, VA, *American Society of Photogrammetry and Remote Sensing*, 1983.

49. Bischof H, Schneider W and Pinz A J, Multispectral classification of Landsat images using neural networks, *IEEE Transactions on the Geosciences and Remote Sensing*, Vol. 30(3), 482–490, 1992.

50. Blair K, *Wind Waves: Their Generation and Propagation on the Ocean Surface*, Prentice Hall, Prentice-Hall, Inc., Englewood Cliffs, New Jersey, 1965.

51. Blanchard B J, McFarland M J, Schmugge T J and Rhoades E, Estimation of soil moisture with API algorithms and microwave emission, *Water Resources Bulletin*, Vol. 17, 767–774, 1981.

52. Blanchard L E and Weinstein O, Design challenges of the thematic mapper, *IEEE Transactions on Geoscience and Remote Sensing*, GE-18(2), 146–160, 1980.

53. Blaschke T, Burnett C and Pekkarinen A, New contextual approaches using image segmentation for object-based classification, in *Remote Sensing Image Analysis: Including the spatial domain*, De Meer F, de Jong S (Eds), Kluver Academic Publishers, Dordrecht, 2004.

54. Blaschke T, Object based image analysis for remote sensing, *ISPRS Journal of Photgrammetry and Remote Sensing*, Vol. 65, 2–16, 2010.

55. Blum Rick S and Liu Z, Multi-Sensor Image Fusion and Its Applications, *CRC press*, 2005.

56. Boardman J W, Analysis, understanding and visualization of hyperspectral data as convex sets in n-space, *Proceedings of International SPIE symposium on Imaging Spectrometry*, SPIE, Vol. 2480, 23–36, 1995.

57. Boardman J W, Automating spectral unmixing of AVIRIS data using convex geometry concepts, *Summaries of the 4th Annual JPL Airborne Geoscience Workshop*, JPL, Pasadena, CA, 11–14, 1993.

58. Boardman J W, Kruse F A and Green R O, Mapping target signatures via partial unmixing of AVIRIS data, *Proceedings of the 5th JPL Airborne Earth Science Workshop*, Vol. 1, 23–26, 1995.

59. Boissin B and Gardelle J P, Intrinsic and extrinsic geometric quality, in *In its SPOT 1: First In-Flight Results*, 83–91, 1987. (SEE N88-12143 03-43)

60. Bolm RG and Danily M, Radar image processing for rock-type discrimination, *IEEE Transactions on Geoscience Electronics*, GE-20, 343–351, 1982.

61. Born M and Wolf E, *Principles of Optics*, Pergamon Press, Oxford, 1964.

62. Bouman B A M, Crop Modelling and Remote Sensing for Yield Prediction, *Netherlands Journal of Agricultural Science*, Vol. 43, 143–161, 1995.

63. Bowers S A and Hanks R J, Reflection of radiant energy from soils, *Soil Science* 100, 130–138, 1965.

64. Brady N C, *The Nature and Properties of Soils*, 8th Ed., MacMillan, New York, 1974.

65. Brown L G, A survey of image registration techniques, *ACM Comput. Surv.*, Vol. 24, 325–376, 1992.

66. Buchanan F, A journey from Madras through the countries of Mysore, Canara and Malabar. First published 1807, London, Vol. 1, Ch. 2, New Delhi and Madras: *Asian Educational Services*, 1988.

67. Burke Hsiao-hua K, Bowley C J and Barnes J C, Determination of snowpack properties from satellite passive microwave measurements, *Remote Sensing of Environment*, Vol. 15, 1–20, 1984.

68. Burrough P A, Van Gaans P F M and MacMillan R A, High-resolution landform classification using fuzzy k-means, *Fuzzy Sets and Systems*, Vol. 113, 37–52, 2000.

69. Byungyong K and Landgrebe D A, Hierarchical decision tree classifiers in high-dimensional and large class data, *IEEE Transactions on the Geosciences and Remote Sensing*, Vol. 29(4), 518–528, 1991.

70. Cabrera R A, GPR Antenna Resolution, 2007. http://geoscanners.es/appnotes/antres.pdf

71. Campbell I, *Glossary of Geology*, American Geological Institute, Washington DC, 1972.

72. Campbell NA, Robust procedure in multivariate analysis I: Robust covariance estimation, *Applied Statistics*, Vol. 29, 231–237, 1980.

73. Camps A, Torres F, Bara J, Carbella I, Pino M and Martin N M, Evaluation of MIRAS spaceborne instrument performance: snapshot radiometric accuracy and its improvements by means of pixel averaging, *Proceedings of SPIE*, Sensors, Systems and Next Generation Satellites, Vol. 3221, 43–52, 1997.

74. Carper W J, Lillesand T M and Kiefer R W, The use of intensity-hue-saturation transformations for merging SPOT panchromatic and multispectral image data, *Photogrammetric Engineering and Remote Sensing*, Vol. 56(4), 457–467, 1990.

75. Chabrillat S, Land Degradation Indicators: Spectral indices, *Annals of Arid Zone*, Vol. 45(3 and 4), 331–354, 2006.

76. Chakraborty M, Manjunath K R, Panigrahy S, Kundu N and Parihar J S, Rice crop parameter retrieval using multi-temporal, multi-incidence angle Radarsat SAR data, *ISPRS Journal of Photogrammetry and Remote Sensing*, Vol. 59(5), 310–322, 2005.

77. Chakraborty M, Panigrahy S and Sharma S A, Discrimination of rice crop grown under different cultural practices using temporal ERS-1 synthetic aperture radar data, *ISPRS Journal of Photogrammetry and Remote Sensing*, Vol. 52(4), 183–191, 1997.

78. Champion H G and Sheth S K, Revised Survey of Forest types of India, Manager ofPublications, Govt. of India, New Delhi, 1968.

79. Chang C I, An information theoretic-based approach to spectral variability, similarity and discriminability for hyperspectral image analysis, *IEEE Transactions on Information Theory*, Vol. 46(5), 1927–1932, 2000.

80. Chase A F, Chase D Z and Weishampel J F, Lasers in the jungle: Airborne sensors reveal a vast Maya landscape, *Archaeology*, Vol. 63(4), 27–29, 2010. http://www.caracol.org/wp-content/uploads/2016/05/CCW2010lidar.pdf

81. Chauhan P and Nayak S, Shoreline-change mapping from space: A case study on the Indian coast, in *The Proceedings of the International Workshop on International Mapping from Space*, 1996.

82. Chauhan P, Mohan M, Sarangi R K, Kumari B, Nayak S and Matondkar S G P, Surface chlorophyll an estimation in the Arabian Sea using IRS-P4 OCM satellite data, *International Journal of Remote Sensing*, Vol. 06, 1–13, 2002.

83. Chauhan P, Personal communication, Space Applications Centre (ISRO), Ahmedabad, 2002. (chauhanp@rediffmail.com)

84. Chavez P S, Berlin G L and Sowers L B, Statistical method for selecting Landsat MSS ratios, *Journal of Applied Photographic Engineering*, Vol. 8(1), 23–30, 1982.

85. Chavez P S, Guptill S C and Bowell J A, Image processing techniques for thematic mapper data, *Proceedings, ASPRS-ACSM Technical Papers*, Vol. 2, 728–742, 1984.

86. Chavez P S, Sides S C and Anderson J A, Comparison of three different methods to merge multi-resolution and multi-spectral data: TM & SPOT pan, *Photogrammetric Engineering and Remote Sensing*, Vol. 57, 295–303, 1991.

87. Chelton D B, WOCE/NASA Altimeter Algorithm Workshop, *US Woce Technical Report No.2*, US Planning Office for WOCE, College Station, TX, 1988.

88. Chen C M, Comparison of principal component analysis and minimum noise fraction transformation for reducing the dimensionality of hyperspectral imagery, *Geographical Research*, Vol. 33(1), 163–178, 2000.

89. Chen K S, Tzeng Y C, Chen C F and Kao W L, Land-cover classification of multispectral imagery using a dynamic learning neural network, *Photogrammetric Engineering & Remote Sensing*, Vol. 61, 4, 1995.

90. Chevrel M, Courtois M and Weill G, The SPOT satellite remote sensing mission, *Photogrammetric Engineering and Remote Sensing*, Vol. 47, 1163–1171, 1981.

91. Chin R T and Yeh C, Quantitative Evaluation of Some Edge-Preserving Noise-Smoothing Techniques, *Computer Vision, Graphics, and Image Processing*, Vol. 23, 67–91, 1983.

92. Choi J K, Park Y J, Ahn J H, Lim H S, Eom J and Ryu J H, GOCI, the world's first geostationary ocean color observation satellite, for the monitoring of temporal variability in coastal water turbidity, *J. Geophys. Res.*, Vol. 117, 2012.

93. Choudhury I, Chakraborty M and Parihar J S, Estimation of Rice Growth Parameter and Crop Phenology with Conjunctive Use of Radarsat and Envisat. *Proc. 'Envisat Symposium 2007', Montreux, Switzerland*, 23–27 April 2007 (ESA SP-636, July 2007), 2007.

94. Chulhee L and Landgrebe D A, Analysing high dimensional multispectral data, *IEEE Trans. on Geoscience and Remote Sensing*, Vol. 31(4), 792–800, 1993.

95. Cierniewski J, Bidirectional reflectance of bare soil surfaces in the visible and near infrared range, *Remote Sensing Reviews*, Vol. 7, 321–339, 1993.

96. Cimino J B, Elachi C and Settle M, SIR-B, the second shuttle imaging radar experiment, *IEEE Transaction on Geoscience and Remote Sensing* GE, Vol. 24(4), 445, 1986.

97. Cipra J E, Baumgardner M F, Stoner E R and MacDonald R B, Measuring radiance characteristics of soil with a field spectroradiometer, *Proceedings of Soil Science Society of America*, Vol. 35, 1014–1017, 1971.

98. Civico D L, Artificial neural networks for landcover classification and mapping, *International Journal of Geographical Information Systems*, Vol. 7(2), 173–186, 1993.

99. Clark R N and Roush T L, Reflectance spectroscopy: Quantitative analysis techniques for remote sensing applications, *Journal of Geophysical Research*, Vol. 89(B7), 6329–6340, 1984.

100. Clark R N, Gallagher A J and Swayze G A, Material absorption band depth mapping of imaging spectrometer data using the complete band shape least-squares algorithm simultaneously fit to multiple spectral feature from multiple materials, *Proceedings of the 3rd Airborne Visible/Infrared Imaging Spectrometer (AVIRIS) Workshop*, JPL Publication, Vol. 90(54), 176–186, 1990.

101. Clark R N, Swayze G A, Livo K E, Kokaly R F, Sutley S J, Dalton J B, McDougal R R and Gent C A, Imaging spectroscopy: Earth and planetary remote sensing with the USGS Tetracorder and expert systems, *Journal of Geophysical Research*, Vol. 108(E12), 5131, 5–1 to 5–44, 2003. (http://speclab.cr.usgs.gov/PAPERS/tetracorder)

102. Cochran G W, *Sampling Techniques*, Third Edition, John Wiley, New York, 1977.

103. Cogdell J R, Foundations of Electronics, *Pearson Education India*, 1999.

104. Coll C, Caselles V, Sobrino J A and Valor E, On the atmospheric dependence of the split-window equation for land surface temperature, *International Journal of Remote Sensing*, Vol. 15(1), 105–122, 1994.

105. Collin R E, *Antennas and Radiowave Propagation*, McGraw Hill, 1985.

106. Colvocoresses A P, Proposed parameter of Mapsat, *Photogrammetric Engineering and Remote Sensing*, Vol. 45(4), 501–506, 1979.

107. Colwell J E, *Manual of Remote Sensing*, Vol. 2, 1983.

108. Colwell J E, Vegetation canopy reflectance: V.3, *Remote Sensing of Environment*, 175–183, 1974.

109. Condit H R, Application of characteristic vector analysis to the spectral energy distribution of daylight and the spectral reflectance of American soils, *Applied Optics*, Vol. 11(1), 74–86, 1972.

110. Condit H R, The spectral reflectance of American soils, *Photogrammetry Engineering*, Vol. 36, 955–966, 1970.

111. Coulson K L, Bouricius G M and Gray E L, Optical reflection properties of natural surfaces, *Journal of Geophysical Research*, Vol. 70, 4601–4611, 1965.

112. Coulson K L, Effects of reflection properties of natural surfaces in aerial reconnaissance, *Applied Optics*, Vol. 5, 905–917, 1966.

113. Craig M and Atkinson D, A Literature Review of Crop Area Estimation, 2013. http://www.fao.org/fileadmin/templates/ess/documents/meetings_and_workshops/GS_SAC_2013/Improving_methods_for_crops_estimates/Crop_Area_Estimation_Lit_review.pdf

114. Crist E P and Cicone R C, A physically-based transformation of thematic mapper data – The TM tasseled cap, *IEEE transactions on Geoscience and Remote Sensing*, Vol. GE-22(3), 256–263, 1984.

115. Cross A M, Settle J J, Drake N A and Paivinen R T M, Sub-pixel measurement of tropical forest cover using AVHRR data, *International Journal of Remote Sensing*, Vol. 12, 1119–1129, 1991.

116. Curtis P O, Houghton J T, Peskett G D and Rodgers C D, Remote sounding of atmospheric temperature from satellites; V. The pressure modulator radiometer for Nimbus F; *Proceedings of Royal Society*, London, Vol. A337, 135–150, 1974.

117. DAC&FW, Manual For Drought Management,Department of Agriculture, Cooperation & Farmers Welfare Ministry of Agriculture & Farmers Welfare, Government of India, 2016. http://agricoop.nic.in/sites/default/files/Manual%20Drought%202016.pdf

118. Dadhwal V K and Parihar J S, Comparative study of digital MOS-1 MESSR, Landsat MSS and IRS LISS-I data for land cover classification in Sambalpur district, India, 270–276 in *Proceedings of MOS-1 Data Evaluation*, Maeda K and Ogawa S (Eds), HE-90015, NASDA, Japan, 1990.

119. Dadhwal V K and Ray S S, Crop assessment using remote sensing – Part II: Crop condition and yield assessment, *Indian Journal of Agricultural Economics*, Vol. 55(2, Suppl.), 55–67, 2000.

120. Dadhwal V K, Parihar J S, Ruhal D S, Jarwal S D, Medhavy T T, Khera A P and Singh J, Effect of acquisition data and spectral bands on wheat, mustard and gram classification accuracies, *Journal of Indian Society of Remote Sensing*, Vol. 17(4), 19–24, 1989.

121. Dadhwal V K, Parihar, J S, Medhavy T T, Ruhal D S, Jarwal S D and Khera A P, Comparative performance of thematic mapper middle-infrared bands in crop discrimination, *International Journal of Remote Sensing*, Vol. 17(9), 1727–1734, 1996.

122. Dadhwal V K, Remote sensing applications for agriculture – retrospective and perspective, *Proceedings of ISRS National Symposium on Remote Sensing Applications for Natural Resources*, Bangalore, 11–18, 1999.

123. Dadhwal V K, Ruhal D S, Medhavy T T, Jarwal S D, Khera A P, Singh J, Sharma T and Parihar J S, Wheat acreage estimation for Haryana using satellite digital data, *Journal of Indian Society of Remote Sensing*, Vol. 19(1), 1–15, 1991.

124. Dadhwal V K, Singh R P, Dutta S and Parihar J S, Remote sensing based crop inventory: A review of Indian experience, *Tropical Ecology* 43(1), 107–122, 2002.

125. Dadhwal, V.K. & J.S. Parihar, (1988). Comparison of IRS LISS-I and LISS-II digital data with Landsat MSS and IRS LISS-I data for land cover classification in Sambalpur district, India. pp. 77–86. In: *Remote Sensing Applications Using IRS-1A data. Scientific Note, IRS-UP/SAC/AD/ SN/02/88. Space Applications Centre*, Ahmedabad, India.

126. Dakshinamurti C, Krishnamurthy B, Summanwar A S, Shanta P and Pisharoty P R, Remote sensing for coconut wilt, *Proceedings of 6th International Symposium of Remote Sensing and Environment*, Ann Arbor, 25–29, 1971.

127. Daniels D J, *Ground penetrating radar*, John Wiley & Sons, Inc., 2005.

128. Danielsson P E, Getting the median faster, *Computer Graphics and Image Processing*, Vol. 15, 71–78, 1981.

129. David B, Gregory L and Asner P, Cropland distributions from temporal unmixing of MODIS data, *Remote Sensing of Environment*, Vol. 93, 412–422, 2004.

130. David L P, *Introduction to Microwave Remote Sensing*, Centre for Remote Sensing and Geographic Information Sciences, Michigan State University, 1999. http://www.brsi.msu.edu/ trific/products/profcorner.html.

131. Davies J E, Geographical variation in coastal development, Oliver and Boyd, Edinburg, 204, 1972.

132. Davis J C, *Statistics and Data Analysis in Geology*, Wiley, New York (2nd Edition, 1986), 1973.

133. Davis J L, Herring T A, Shapiro I I, Rogers A E E and Elgered G, Geodesy by radio interferometry: effects of atmospheric modeling errors on estimates ofbaseline length. *Radio Sci.*, Vol. 20, 1593–1607, 1985.

134. Davis L S, A Survey of Edge Detection Techniques, *Computer Graphics and Image Processing*, Vol. 4, 248–270, 1975.

135. Dawson M S and Fung A K, Neural Networks and their applications to parameter retrieval and classification, *IEEE GRS-S Newsletter*, 6–14, 1993.

136. Deng G, Guo H D, Wang C L and Nie Y P, Applications of remote sensing technology in archaeology: a review, *Journal of Remote Sensing*, Vol. 14(1), 187–2006, 2010.

137. Dennison P E and Roberts D A, Endmember selection for multiple endmember spectral mixture analysis using endmember average RMSE, *Remote Sensing of Environment*, Vol. 87, 123–135, 2003.

138. Desai P S and George J, Satellite observations for the study of global change, *Indian Journal of Radio and Space Physics*, Vol. 23, 101–124, 1994.

139. Desbois M, Roca R, Eymard L, Viltard N, Viollier M, Srinivasan J and Narayanan S, The megha-tropiques mission, *Proc. SPIE 4899, Atmospheric and Oceanic Processes, Dynamics, and Climate Change*, 172–183, 2003.

140. Deschamps P Y, Herman M and Tanre D, Modelling of the atmospheric effects and its application to remote sensing of ocean colour, *Applied Optics*, Vol. 22, 3751–3758, 1983.

141. Dittman B, Michael G and Firth O, OLI telescope post-alignment optical performance, *Proc. of SPIE*. 7807:780705.1-780705.5, 2010.

142. Dobson M C and Ulaby F T, Active microwave soil moisture research, *IEEE Transaction on Geoscience and Remote Sensing*, Vol. GE-24(1), 23–36, 1986.

143. Dobson M C, Ulaby F T, Hallikainen M T and El-Rayes M A, Microwave dielectric behaviour of wet soil – Part II: dielectric mixing models, *IEEE Transactions on Geoscience and Remote Sensing,* GE-23, 35–46, 1985.

144. Doolittle J A, Noninvasive geophysical methods used in Soil science, *Handbook of Soil Sciences: Properties and Processes*, 2nd Ed., Huang P M, Li Y, Sumner M E, Eds, CRC press, 2012.

145. Doraiswamy P C, Moulin S, Cook P W and Stern A, Crop Yield Assessment from Remote Sensing. *Photogrammetric Engineering & Remote Sensing*, Vol. 69(6), 665–674, 2003.

146. Dorigo W A, Zurita Milla R, de Wit A J W, Brazile J, Singh R and Schaepman M E, A review on reflective remote sensing and data assimilation techniques for enhanced agro ecosystem modeling, *International Journal of Applied Earth Observation and Geoinformation*, Vol. 9(2), 165–193, 2007

147. Doyle E J, A large format camera for shuttle, *Photogrammetric Engineering and Remote Sensing*, Vol. 45(1), 73–78, 1979.

148. Dozier J and Warren S G, Effect of viewing angle on the infrared brightness temperature of snow, *Water Resources Research*, Vol. 18(5), 1424–1434, 1982.

149. Dozier J, Schneider S R and McGinnis D F Jr, Effect of grain size and snowpack water equivalence on visible and near-infrared satellite observation of snow, *Water Resources Research,* Vol. 17, 1213–1221, 1981.

150. Dozier J, Snow reflectance from Landsat-4 Thematic Mapper, *IEEE Tranactions on Geoscience Remote Sensing,* GE-22, 323–328, 1984.

151. Drummond J R, Houghton J T, Peskett G D, Rodgers C D, Wale M J, Whitney J, Williamson E J, The stratospheric and mesospheric sounder on Nimbus 7, *Phil. Trans R. Society*, London, Vol. A296, 219–241, 1980.

152. Du P, Liu S, Xia J and Zhao Y, Information fusion techniques for change detection from multi-temporal remote sensing images, *Information Fusion*, Vol. 14(1), 19–27, 2013.

153. Du Y, Chang C I, Hsuan R, D'Amico F and Jensen J O, A new hyperspectral discrimination measure for spectral similarity, *Proceedings of SPIE*, Vol. 5093, 430–439, 2003.

154. Du Y, Chang C I, Ren H, Chang C C, Jensen J O and D'Amico F M, New hyperspectral discrimination measure for spectral characterization, *Optical Engineering*, Vol. 43(8), 1777–1786, 2004.

155. Dubey R P, Ajwani N and Navalgund R R, Relation of wheat yield with parameters derived from a spectral growth profile, *Journal of Indian Society of Remote Sensing*, Vol. 19(1), 45–58, 1991.

156. Duda R O and Hart P E, *Pattern Classification and Scene Analysis*, New York, John Wiley & Sons, Inc., 1973.

157. Duggin M J and Cunia T, Ground reflectance measurement techniques, *Applied Optics*, Vol. 22, 3771–3777, 1983.

158. Dutta S, Sharma S A, Khera A P, Ajai, Yadav M, Hooda R S, Mothikumar K E and Manchanda M L, Accuracy assessment in cotton acreage estimation using Indian remote sensing satellite data, *ISPRSJournal of Photogrammetry and Remote Sensing*, Vol. 49, 21–26, 1994.

159. Dwivedi R M, Ocean colour as a tool for potential fishing zone identification and forecast. Lecture note PORSEC 2000 pre-conference training, National Institute of Oceanography, Goa, India, 17–22, 2000.

160. Dwivedi R M, Solanki H N and Nayak S R, Exploration of fishery resources through integration of ocean colour with SST: Indian experience, *Indian Journal of Marine Science*, 2005.

161. Dwivedi R M, Space Applications Centre, Personal communication, 2004.

162. Dwivedi R S, Soil resources mapping: A remote sensing perspective, *Remote Sensing Reviews*, Vol. 20, 89–122, 2001.

163. Eastman F H, A high-resolution image sensor, *Journal of the SMPTE 79: 10–15. EOS Instrument Panel Report*, Vol. Iib, NASA, 1970.

164. E-Cognition, User Guide Documentation, 2001.

165. Ehlers M, Klonus S, Johan Åstrand P and Rosso P, Multi-sensor image fusion for pansharpeningin remote sensing, *International Journal of Image and Data Fusion*, Vol. 1(1), 25–45, 2010.

166. Egido A, Caparrini M, Ruffini G, Paloscia S, Guerriero E S L, Pierdicca N and Floury N, Global Navigation Satellite Systems Reflectometry as a Remote Sensing Tool for Agriculture, *Remote Sensing*, Vol. 4(8), 2356–2372, 2012; doi:10.3390/rs4082356.

167. Egido A, GNSS Reflectometry for LandRemote Sensing Applications, PhD thesis dissertation, Universitat Politècnica de Catalunya, Barcelona, Spain, 2013. https://upcommons.upc.edu/bitstream/handle/2117/95070/TAEE1de1.pdf

168. Elachi C, Becknell T, Jordon R L and Wu C, Spaceborne synthetic aperture imaging radars: Applications, techniques and technology, *Proceedings of IEEE*, 1174–1209, 1982a.

169. Elachi C, Brown W E, Cimino J B, Dixon T, Evans D L, Ford J P, Saunders R S, Breed C, Masursky H, McCauley J F, Schaber G, Dellwig L, England A, MacDonald H, Martin-Kaye P and Sabins F, Shuttle Imaging Radar experiment, *Science*, Vol. 218, 996–1003, 1982.

170. Elachi C, Im K E, Li F and Rodriguez E, Global digital topography mapping with a synthetic aperture scanning radar altimeter, *International Journal of Remote Sensing*, Vol. 11(4), 585–601, 1990.

171. El-Mezouar M C, Taleb N, Kpalma K and Ronsin J, An Improved Intensity-Hue-Saturation for A High-Resolution Image Fusion Technique Minimizing Color Distortion, *International Journal on Information and Communication Technologies*, Vol. 3(1), 1–6, 2010.

172. El-Samie, Fathi E Abd, Mohiy M Hadhoud and Said E El-Khamy, *Image Super-Resolution and Applications*, CRC Press, 2013.

173. *ESA SP-1225*, Envisat: ASAR Science and applications, European Space Agency, 1998.

174. *ESA STR-231*, The physics and instrumentation of passive atmospheric sounding by Paul Ingmann, European Space Research and Technology Centre, Noordwijk, The Netherlands, 1991.

175. ESA, CONTRACT No.21096/07/NL/HE-Geo-Oculus: A Mission for Real-Time Monitoring through High-Resolution Imaging from Geostationary Orbit, 2009. Accessed on 14 May 2014. http://emits.sso.esa.int/emits-doc/ESTEC/AO6598-RD2-Geo-Oculus-FinalReport.pdf

176. Estes J E, Hajic E J and Tinney C R, *Manual of Remote Sensing*, Vol. 1, Chapter 24, 1983.

177. Evans D, Pottier C, Fletcher R, Hensley S, Tapley I, Milne A and Barbetti M, A comprehensive archaeological map of the world's largest preindustrial settlement complex at Angkor, Cambodia, *Proceedings of the National Academy of Sciences*, Vol. 104(36), 14277–14282, 2007.

178. Fagan Brian M and Durrani N, In the Beginning: An Introduction to Archaeology, *Pearson Education Inc.*, 2014.

179. Fahnestock J D and Schowengerdt R A, Spatially-variant contrast enhancement using local range modification, *Optical Engineering*, Vol. 22(3), 1983.

180. Fairbridge R W, *Encyclopedia of Geomorphology*. Encyclopedia of Earth Sciences series, Vol. III, Dowden, Hutchinson & RossInc., Stroudsburg, Pennsylvania, 1968.

181. FAO, Crop Yield Forecasting:Methodological and Institutional Aspects. Food and Agriculture Organisation, 2016. http://gsars.org/wp-content/uploads/2016/03/AMIS_CYF-Methodological-and-Institutional-Aspects_0303-web.pdf

182. Farrow J B, Influence of the atmosphere on remote sensing measurements: Microwave and radio wavelengths, *ESA report ESA (ESRO) CR-354*, 1975.

183. Fisher P F and Pathirana S, The evaluation of fuzzy membership of land cover classes in the suburban zone, *Remote Sensing of the Environment*, Vol. 34, 651–663, 1990.

184. Fitzgerald E, Multispectral scanning systems and their potential application to earth-resources surveys, *Spectral Properties of Materials, ESRO CR-232*, Neuilly, France, 231, 1974.

185. Foody G M, Lucas R M, Curran P J and Honzak M, Non-linear mixture modeling without end-members using an artificial neural network, *International Journal of Remote Sensing*, Vol. 18(4), 937–953, 1997.

186. Francois F, Coste P and Kang G, The GOCI instrument on COMS mission – the first geostationary ocean color imager, 2014. Accessed on 24 April, 2014. http://www.ioccg.org/sensors/GOCI-Faure.pdf

187. Franklin S E, Hall R J, Moskal L M, Maudie A J and Lavigene M B, Incorporating texture into classification of forest species composition from airborne multispectral images, *International Journal of Remote Sensing*, Vol. 21(1), 61–79, 2000.

188. Fraser R S and Kaufman Y J, The relative importance of aerosol scattering and absorption in remote sensing, *IEEE Journal of Geoscience and Remote Sensing*, GE-23, 1985.

189. Fraser R S, Bahethi O P and Al-Abbas A D, The effect of the atmosphere on classification of satellite observations to identify surface features, *Remote Sensing of Environment*, Vol. 6, 229, 1977.

190. Frederick J E, Hays P B, Guenther B W and Heath D F, Ozone abundances in the lower mesosphere deduced from backscattered solar radiances, *Journal of Atmospheric Science*, Vol. 34, 1987–1994, 1977.

191. Frei W, Image enhancement by histogram hyperbolisation, *Computer Graphics and Image Processing*, Vol. 6, 286–294, 1977.

192. Friedl M A and Brodley C E, Decision-tree classification of land cover from remotely sensed data, *International Journal of Remote Sensing*, Vol. 61(4), 399–409, 1997.

193. Fried D L, Limiting resolution looking downward through the atmosphere, *Journal of Optics Society*, Vol. 1380, 56, 1966.

194. Friedl M A, Brodley C E and Strahler A H, Maximising land cover classification accuracies produced by decision trees at continental to global scales, *IEEE Transaction on Geosciences and Remote Sensing*, Vol. 37, 969–977, 1999.

195. Frost V S, Styles J A, Shanmugam K S and Holzman J C, A model for radar images and its application to adaptive digital filtering of multiplicative noise, *IEEE Transactions on Pattern Analysis and Machine Intelligence*, PAMI-4, 157–166, 1982.

196. FSI, (2015), http://fsi.nic.in/details.php?pgID=sb_62

197. Fukushima H, Toratani M, Yamamiya S and Mitomi Y, Atmospheric correction algorithms for ADEOS/OCTS ocean colour data: Performance comparison based on ship and buoy measurements, *Advance Space Research*, Vol. 25, 1015–1024, 2000.

198. Gallego F J, Crop Area Estimation in the MARS Project, *Conference on ten years of the MARS Project*, Brussels,Vol. 4, 1999.

199. Gao Y and Mas J F, A comparison of the performance of pixel-based and object-based classifications over images with various spatial resolutions, *Online journal of earth sciences*, Vol. 2(1), 27–35, 2008. http://docsdrive.com/pdfs/medwelljournals/ojesci/2008/27-35.pdf

200. Garg J K, Personal Communication, Space Applications Centre, Ahmedabad, 2004.

201. Garg J K, Singh T S and Murthy T V R, Wetlands of India, *Project Report: RSAM/ SAC/ RESA/PR/01/98*, Space Applications Centre, Ahmedabad, 239, 1998.

202. Garg J K, Structural Components and Land use Pattern Analysis in the Catchment of Nal Sarovar Notified Wetland (Gujarat, India) as an aid for biodiversity conservation using remote sensing techniques, Paper presented in *ISPRS Symposium on Resource and Environment Monitoring, National Remote Sensing Agency (NRSA)*, Hyderabad, 2002.

203. Garguet-Duport B, Girel J, Chassery J M and Patou G, The use of multiresolution analysis and wavelets transform for merging SPOT panchromatic and multispectral image data, *Photogrammetric Engineering and Remote Sensing*, Vol. 62(9), 1057–1066, 1996.

204. Garn E L and Petito F C, Thermal imaging with pyroelectric vidicons, *IEEE Transactions on Electron Devices ED-24*, Vol. 10, 1221–1228, 1977.

205. Garrison J L A, Komjathy V U, Zavorotny and Katzberg S J, Wind speed measurements using forward scattered GPS signals, *IEEE Trans. Geosci. Remote Sensing*, Vol. 40(1), 50–65, 2002.

206. Gates D M and Keegan H J, Schleter J C and Weidner V R, Spectral properties of plants, *Applied Optics*, Vol. 4, 11–20, 1965.

207. Gausman H W, Allen W A, Wiegand C L, Escobar D E and Rodriguez R R, Leaf light reflectance, transmittance, absorptance, and optical and geometrical parameters for eleven plant genera with different leaf mesophyl arrangements, *Proceedings of the 7th International Symposium on Remote Sensing Environment*, University of Michigan, Ann Arbor, Vol. 3, 1599–1625, 1971.

208. Genda H and Okayama H, Estimation of soil moisture and components by measuring the degree of spectral polarisation with a remote sensing simulator, *Applied Optics,* Vol. 17, 3439–3443, 1978.

209. Genderen J L and Lock B F, Testing land use map accuracy, *Photogrametric Engineering and Remote Sensing,* Vol. 43(9), 1135–1137, 1977.

210. Ghosh R, Sridhar V N, Venkatesh H, Mehta A N and Patel K I, Linear polarisation measurements of a wheat canopy, *International Journal of Remote Sensing*, Vol. 14(13), 2501–2508, 1993.

211. Gille J C and House F B, On the inversion of limb radiance measurements 1: temperature and thickness, *Journal of Atmospheric Sciences*, Vol. 29, 1427–1442, 1971.

212. Gille J C, Hailey P L and Russel J M III, Temperature and composition measurements from the LRIR and LIMS experiments on Nimbus 6 and 7, *Phil. Trans R. Society*, London, Vol. A296, 205–218, 1980.

213. Gillespie A R, Kahle A B and Walker R E, Color enhancement of highly correlated images. I: Decorrelation and HSI contrast stretches, *Remote Sensing of Environment*, Vol. 20, 209–235, 1986.

214. Goede A P H, Aarts H J M, van Baren C, Burrows J P, Change K V, Hoekstra R, Holzle E, Pitz W, Schneider W, Smorenburg C, Visser H and de Vries J, SCIAMACHY instrument design, *Advance Space Research*, Vol. II (3), (3)243–(3)246, 1991.

215. Goetz A F H and Boardman J W, Atmospheric corrections: On deriving surface reflectance from hyperspectral imagers, imaging spectrometry III, *Proceedings of SPIE*, Vol. 3118, 14–22, 1997.

216. Goetz A F H and Herring M, The high resolution imaging spectrometer (HIRIS) for EOS. *IEEE Transactions on Geoscience and Remote Sensing*, Vol. 27(2), 136–144, 1989.

217. Gohil B S and Pandey P C, An algorithm for retrieval of oceanic wind vectors from the simulated SASS normalised radar cross-section measurement, *Journal of Geophysical Research*, Vol. 90(C4), 7307–7311, 1985.

218. Gong P, Miller J R, Freemantle J and Chen B, Spectral decomposition of Landsat Thematic Mapper data for urban land-cover mapping, *Proceedings of the 14th Canadian Symposium on Remote Sensing*, 458–461, 1991.

219. Gonzalez R C, Woods R E, Digital Image Processing, 3rd Ed., *Pearson Prentice Hall*, 2008.

220. Gonzalez-Alonso F and Cuevas J M, Remote sensing and agricultural statistics: crop area estimation through regression estimators and confusion matrices, *International Journal of remote Sensing*, Vol. 14, 1215–1219, 1993.

221. Gordon H R and Clark D K, Clear water radiance of the atmospheric correction of CZCS imaging, *Applied Optics*, Vol. 20, 4175, 1981.

222. Gordon H R and McCluney N R, Estimation of the depth of sunlight penetration in the sea for Remote Sensing, *Applied Optics*, Vol. 14, 413–416, 1975.

223. Gordon H R and Morel A, Remote Assessment of Ocean Colour for Interpretation of Satellite Visible Imagery - A Review, Springer Verlog publishers, 1983.

224. Gordon H R and Wang M, Retrieval of water leaving radiance and aerosol optical thickness over the oceans with SeaWiFS: A preliminary algorithm, *Applied Optics*, Vol. 33, 443–452, 1994.

225. Gordon H R, Atmospheric correction of ocean colour imagery in the earth observing system era, *Journal of Geophysical Research*, Vol. 102, 17081–17106, 1997.

226. Gordon H R, Clark D K, Brown J W, Brown O B, Evans R H and Broenkan W W, Phytoplankton pigment concentrations in the Middle Atlantic bright comparison of sharp determination and CZCS estimates, *Applied Optics*, Vol. 22(1), 20–36, 1983.

227. Gordon H R, Removal of atmospheric effects from satellite imagery of the ocean, *Applied Optics,* Vol. 17(10), 1631, 1978.

228. Gower J F R and Borstad G A, Mapping of phytoplankton by solar-stimulated fluorescence using an imaging spectrometer, *International Journal of Remote Sensing*, Vol. 11, 313–320, 1990.

229. Grana M and Gallego M J, Associative morphological memories for spectral unmixing, *Proceedings of European Symposium on Artificial Neural Networks Bruges (Belgium)*, d-side publications, 481–186, 2003.

230. Granahan J C and Sweet J N, An evaluation of atmospheric correction techniques using the spectral similarity scale, *IEEE International Geoscience and Remote Sensing Symposium*, Vol. 5, 2022–2024, 2001.

231. Granger J L, Shuttle Imaging Radar – A/B Sensors, *Spaceborne Imaging Radar Symposium*, Pasedena, CA, Jet Propulsion Lab, 83–11, 1983.

232. Grantham W L, Bracalente E M, Jones W L and Johnson J W, The SEASAT-A Satellite Scatterometer, *IEEE Journal of Oceanic Engineering*, OE-2, 200–206, 1977.

233. Gross H N and Schott J, Application of spatial resolution enhancement and spectral mixture analysis to hyperspectral images, *Proc. SPIE*, Vol. 2821, 30–41, 1996. http://gsars.org/wp-content/uploads/2017/09/GS-REMOTE-SENSING-HANDBOOK-FINAL-04.pdf

234. Guerova G, Jones J, Douša J, Dick G, Haan S D, Pottiaux E and Bender M, Review of the state of the art and future prospects of the ground-based GNSS meteorology in Europe, *Atmospheric Measurement Techniques*, Vol. 9(11), 5385–5406, 2016.

235. Gugan D J and Dowman I J, Topographic mapping from SPOT imagery, *Photogrametric Engineering and Remote Sensing*, Vol. 54(10), 1409, 1988.

236. Gunson M R, Farmer C B, Norton R H, Zander R, Rinsland C P, Shaw J H and Gao B C, Measurements of CH4, N2O, CO, H2O and O3 in the Middle Atmosphere by the Atmospheric trace molecule spectroscopy experiment on spacelab 3, *Journal of Geophysical Research*, Vol. 95(D9), 13867–13882, 1990.

237. Guntupalli R and Allen R, Evaluation of InGaAs camera for scientific near infrared imaging applications, *Proc. SPIE*. 6294:629401.1-629401.7, 2006.

238. Gupta E, Das S, Rajani M B, Archaeological exploration in Srirangapatna and its environ through Remote Sensing Analysis, to be published in *Journal of Indian Society of Remote Sensing*, 2017.

239. Guyon I, Gunn S, Nikravesh M, Lofti and Ed Z, *Feature Extraction: Foundations and Applications*, Springer, 2006.

240. Haboudane D, Bonn F, Royer A, Sommer S and Mehl W, Land degradation and erosion risk mapping by fusion of spectrally-based information and digital geomorphometric attributes, *International Journal of Remote Sensing*, Vol. 23, 3795–3820, 2002.

241. Haldar D, Patnaik C and Chakraborty M, Jute Crop Discrimination and Biophysical Parameter Monitoring Using Multi-Parametric SAR Data in West Bengal, India, *Open Access Library Journal*, Vol. 1, 1–10, 2014. doi: 10.4236/oalib.1100817.

242. Hanel R A, Schlachman B, Clark F D, Prokesh C H, Taylor J B, Wilson W M and Chaney L, The Nimbus-3 Michelson interferometer, *Applied Optics*, Vol. 9, 1767–1774, 1970.

243. Hard R M and Brooner W, Landuse Map Accuracy Criteria, *PERS*, Vol. 42, 671–677, 1976.

244. Harry J M, *Ground Penetrating Radar Theory and Applications*, Elsevier Science, 2009.

245. Hartl Ph. and Wu X, SAR interferometry: Experiences with various phase unwrapping methods, *Proceedings of Second ERS-1 Symposium*, Hamburg, Germany, 727–732, 1993.

246. Hay M A, Sampling designs to test land-use map accuracy, *Photogrammetric Engineering and Remote Sensing*, Vol. 45(4), 529–533, 1979.

247. Hayden R A, C M, Hubert C F, McClain E P and Seaman R S, *Quantitative Meteorological Data from Satellites, WMO-TN 166*, Geneva, WMO No. 531, 32, 1979.

248. Hays P B and Roble R G, Stellar spectra and atmospheric composition, *Journal of Atmospheric Sciences*, Vol. 25, 1141–1153, 1968.

249. Healy S B and Eyre J R, Retrieving temperature, water vapor and surface pressure information from refractive index profiles derived by radio occultation: A simulation study, *Q J R Meteorol. Soc.*, Vol. 126, 1661–1684, 2000.

250. Heath D F, Krueger A J, Roeder H A and Henderson B D, The solar backscatter ultraviolet and total ozone mapping spectrometer (SBUV/TOMS) for Nimbus G, *Optical Engineering*, Vol. 14, 323–331, 1975.

251. Henini M and Razeghi M .*Handbook of Infrared Detection Technologies*, Elsevier, 2002. http://web.pdx.edu/~emch/ip2/RADAR.pdf

252. Hepner G F, Logan T, Ritter N and Bryant N, Artificial neural network classification using a minimal training set: comparison to conventional supervised classification, *Photogrammetric Engineering and Remote Sensing*, Vol. 56, 469–473, 1990.

253. Hermann P D and Khazenie N, Classification of multi-spectral remote sensing data using a back-propagation neural network, *IEEE Transaction on the Geosciences and Remote Sensing*, 1992.

254. Heywood I, Cornelius S and Carver S, *An Introduction to GIS*, Addison Wesley Longman Ltd., England, 1998.

255. Hinkley E D, (Ed.), Laser monitoring of the atmosphere, *Topics in Applied Physics*, Vol. 14, Springer-Verlag Berlin Heidelberg, New York, 1976.

256. Hoffer R M and Johannsen C J, Ecological potential in spectral signature analysis, in *Remote Sensing in Ecology*, Univ. of Georgia Press, Athens, Georgia, 1–16, 1969.

257. Hofmann-Wellenhof B, Lichtenegger H and Collins J, *GPS. Theory and practice*, 5th Ed., Springer Wien New York, Vol. 384, 2001.

258. Hollinger J P and Mennella R A, Oil spills measurements of their distributions and volumes by multifrequency microwave radiometry, *Science*, Vol. 181, 54–56, 1973.

259. Homayouni S and Roux M, Hyperspectral image analysis for material mapping using spectral matching, *Proceedings of XX ISPRS Congress, Commission-7*, Istanbul, Vol. XXX, 1682–1750, 2004. (www.isprs.org/istanbul2004/index.html)

260. Hong G, Zhang Y and Mercer B, A wavelet and his integration method to fuse high resolution SAR with moderate resolution multispectral images, *Photogrammetric Engineering & Remote Sensing*, Vol. 75(10), 1213–1223, 2009.

261. Hord R M and Brooner W, Land-use map accuracy criteria, *Photogrammetric Engineering and Remote Sensing*, Vol. 42, 671–677, 1975.

262. Houghton J T, Absorption and emission by carbon dioxide in the mesosphere, *Quarterly Journal of Royal Meteorological Society*, Vol. 95, 1–20, 1969.

263. Houghton J T, Taylor F W and Rodgers C D, *Remote Sounding of Atmospheres*, Cambridge University Press, Cambridge, 1984.

264. Hovanessian S A, *Introduction to Synthetic Array and Imaging Radars*, Artech House Inc., MA, 1980.

265. Hudson R D, *Infrared System Engineering*, Wiley, New York, 1969.

266. Huete A R and Escadafal R, Assessment of biophysical soil properties through spectral decomposition techniques, *Remote Sensing of Environment*, Vol. 35, 149–159, 1991.

267. Huete A R and Jackson R D, Soil and atmosphere influences on the spectra of partial canopies, *Remote Sensing of Environment*, Vol. 25, 89–105, 1988.

268. Huete A R, A soil adjusted vegetation index (SAVI), *Remote Sensing of Environment*, Vol. 25, 295–309, 1988.

269. Huete A R, Jackson R D and Post D F, Spectral response of a plant canopy with different soil backgrounds, *Remote Sensing of Environment*, Vol. 17, 37–53, 1985.

270. Huete A R, Post D F and Jackson R D, Soil spectral effects on 4-space vegetation discrimination, *Remote Sensing of Environment*, Vol. 15, 155–165, 1984.

271. Hughes G F, On the mean accuracy of statistical pattern recognizers, *IEEE Transactions on Information Theory*, Vol. 14(1), 55–63, 1968.

272. Hunt G R, Salisbury J W and Lenhoff C J, Visible and near-infrared spectra of minerals and rocks, IV. Sulphides and sulphates, *Modern Geology*, Vol. 3, 1–14, 1971.

273. Idso S B, Jackson R D, Reginato R J, Kimball B A and Nakayama F S, The dependence of bare soil albedo on soil water content, *Journal of Applied Meteorology*, Vol. 14, 109–113, 1975.

274. Irons R J, Ranson K J, Williams D L, Irish R R and Huegel F G, An off-nadir-pointing imaging spectroradiometer for terrestrial ecosystem studies, *IEEE Transactions on Geoscience and Remote Sensing*, Vol. 29(1), 66–74, 1991.

275. Isaacs R G, *Review of 183 GHz Moisture Profile Retrieval Studies*, Air Force Geophysics Laboratory, Massachusetts, TR-87-0127, 52, 1987.

276. Iyengar V S, Nagrani C M, Dave R K, Aradhye B V, Nagachenchaiah K and Kiran Kumar A S, Meteorological imaging instruments on-board INSAT-2E, *Current Science*, Vol. 76, 1436–1443, 1996.

277. Iyer M, Nagendra H and Rajani M B, Using satellite imagery and historical maps to investigate the original contours of Lalbagh Botanical Garden, *Current Science*, Vol. 102(3), 507–509, 2012. http://eprints.nias.res.in/296/1/2012-rajani-cs.pdf

278. Jackson P, *Introduction to Expert Systems*, Addison-Weily Publishers, England, 1986.

279. Jackson R D, Spectral indices in n-space, *Remote Sensing of Environment*, Vol. 13, 409–421, 1983.

280. Jackson T J and Schmugge T J, Passive microwave remote sensing system for soil moisture: some supporting research, *IEEE Transactions on Geoscience and Remote Sensing*, Vol. 27(2), 1989.

281. Jackson T J, Profile soil moisture from surface measurements, *Journal of Irrigation Drainage Division*, Vol. IR-2, ASCE, 81–92, 1980.

282. Jackson T J, Schmugge T J and Wang J R, Passive microwave sensing of soil moisture under vegetation canopies, *Water Resources Research*, Vol. 18(4), 1137–1142, 1982.

283. Jacobson K, Workshop on Mapping and Space held under ISPRS, *Proceedings*, Hanover, Germany, 1999.

284. Jadhav R N, Encroachments in Sanjay Gandhi National Park, Photonirvachak, *Journal of Indian Society of Remote Sensing*, Vol. 23, 87–88, 1995.

285. Jagalingam P and Hegde A V, A Review of Quality Metrics for Fused Image, *Aquatic Procedia*, Vol. 4, 133–142, 2015.

286. Jain A K, Duin R P W and Mao J, Statistical pattern recognition: A review, *IEEE Transactions on Pattern Analysis and Machine Intelligence*, Vol. 22(1), 4–37, 2000.

287. Janssen M A, Ed., *Atmospheric Remote Sensing by Microwave Radiometry*, New York, Wiley, 1993.

288. Jarrett M L and Charlton J E, Verification of the AMSU (B) design, *Proceedings of SPIE*, Vol. 1935, 136–147, 1993.

289. Jeganathan C, Bisht G, Sinha E, Raju P L N and Roy P S, Comparative study of object oriented classification approach with the conventional method for interpreting high resolution images, *Asian journal of Geoinformatics*, Vol. 3(2), 65–70, 2002.

290. Jennings S B, Brown N D and Sheil D, Assessing forest canopies and understorey illumination: canopy closure, canopy cover and other measures, *Forestry*, Vol. 1, 59–74, 1999.

291. Jensen J R, *Introductory Digital Image Processing – A Remote Sensing Perspective*, Prentice-Hall, Englewood Cliffs, New Jersey, 1986.

292. Jerlov N G, *Optical Oceanography*, Elsevier Publishing Company, 1968.

293. Jimenez L O and Landgrebe D A, Hyperspectral data analysis and supervised feature reduction via projection pursuit, *IEEE Transactions Geoscience and Remote Sensing*, Vol. 37(6), 2653–2664, 1999.

294. Jol H M (Ed.), *Ground penetrating radar theory and applications*, Elsevier, 2008.

295. Jordan E L, Huneycutt B L and Werner M, The SIR-C/X-SAR Synthetic Aperture Radar System, *Proceedings of IEEE*, Vol. 79(6), 827–838, 1991.

296. Jordon R L, Huneycutt B L and Werner M, The SIR-C/X-SAR Syhthetic Aperture Radar System, *IEEE Transactions on Geoscience and Remote Sensing*, Vol. 33(4), 829–839, 1995.

297. Jordon R L, The *Seasat*-A SAR system, *IEEE Journal of Oceanic Engineering*, OE-5(2), 154–164, 1980.

298. Jordon R L, The SEASAT-A Synthetic Aperture Radar System, *IEEE Transactions on Geoscience and Remote Sensing*, Vol. 33(4), 1995.

299. Joseph G and Kamat D S, A five channel MSS for aircraft platform, *Proceedings of 12th International Symposium on Remote Sensing*, Manila, 1219, 1978.

300. Joseph G, Building Earth Observation Cameras, *CRC Press*, 2015. http://dx.doi.org/10.1201/b18022

301. Joseph G, How well do we understand Earth observation electro-optical sensor parameters?, *ISPRS Journal of Photogrammetry and Remote Sensing*, Vol. 55(1), 9–12, 2000.

302. Joseph G, Imaging sensors for remote sensing, *Remote Sensing Reviews*, Vol. 13, 257–342, 1996.

303. Joseph G, India's Journey Towards Excellence in Building Earth Observation Cameras, Notion Press, 2016.

304. Joseph G, Iyengar V S, Rattan R, Nagachenchaiah K, Kirankumar A S, Aradhye B V, Gupta K K, Samudraiah D R M, Subrahmanyam D and Kothari S K, Camera for Indian Remote Sensing, IRS-1C, *Journal of Spacecraft Tech.*, Vol. 5(2), 38–48, 1995.

305. Joseph G, Iyengar V S, Rattan R, Nagachenchaiah K, Kirankumar A S, Aradhye B V, Kaduskar V N, Dave R K and Nagrani C M, Very-High resolution radiometers for INSAT-2, *Current Science*, Vol. 66(1), 42–56, 1994.

306. Joseph G, Payload onboard BHASKARA satellite, *Proceedings of Indo-Soviet Symposium on Space Research*, Bangalore, 4.01, 1982.

307. Joseph G, Remote sensing using balloons, *Space (ISRO publication)*, Vol. 4(1), 26–28, 1977.

308. Jouan J, Reulet J F and Costes G, SPOTHRVIR: A significant improvement of high-resolution visible SPOT camera to IR wavelengths, *IAF-89*, 1989.

309. Just D, Adam N, Schwbisch M and Balmer R, Comparison of Phase Unwrapping Algorithms for SAR Interferograms, *Proceedings of IGARSS '95*, Florence, Italy, 767–769, 1995.

310. Justice C, Fusco L and Mehl W, A preliminary analysis of LANDSAT-4 thematic mapper radiometric performance, *Proceedings of the LANDSAT-4 Science Characterisation Early Results Symposium*, NASA Goddard Space Flight Centre, Greenbelt, Maryland, 309–320, 1983.

311. Kahle A B, *Surface Thermal Properties in Remote Sensing in Geology*, Siegal B S and Gillespie A R, (Ed.), 1980.

312. Kalubarme M H, Mahey R K, Dhaliwal S S, Sidhu S S, Rajwant Singh, Mahajan A and Sharma P K, Agromet-spectral Wheat Yield Modelling in Punjab, *Proceedings of National Symposium on Remote Sensing of Environment*, Ludhiana, 11–17, 1995.

313. Kalubarme M H, Potdar M B, Manjunath K R, Mahey R K and Sidhu S S, Spectral Wheat Yield Modelling based on Growth Profile Parameters derived from NOAA-11 AVHRR Data, *Scientific Note: RSAM/SAC/CAPE-II/SN/69/97*, Space Applications Centre, ISRO, Ahmedabad, 1997.

314. Kamat D S, Gopalan A K S, Ajai, Shashikumar M, Sinha S, Chaturvedi G and Singh A, Assessment of water-stress effects on crops, *International Journal of Remote Sensing*, Vol. 6(3–4), 577–589, 1985.

315. Kamykowski D, A preliminary biophysical model of relationship between temperature and plant nutrients in the upper ocean, *Journal of Deep Sea Research*, Vol. 34, 1067–1079, 1987.

316. Kaplan L D, Inference of atmospheric structure from remote radiation measurement, *Journal of Optical Society of America*, Vol. 49, 1004, 1959.

317. Karathanassi V, Kolokousis P and Ioannidou S, A comparison study on fusion methods using evaluation indicators, *International Journal of Remote Sensing*, Vol. 28(9), 2309–2341, 2007.

318. Karnatak H C, Concept and Applications of Web GIS and Geo-Web services—Technology and Applications, *SPIE-Asia-Pacific Remote Sensing Symposium, Pre-Symposium Tutorial*, India, 2016. https://nrsc.gov.in/sites/all/pdf/SPIE%20APRS%20Tutorial_Geowebservices_HCK.pdf

319. Kasturirangan K, Joseph G, Kalyanraman S, Thyagarajan K, Chandrasekhar M G, Raju D V, Raghunathan S, Gopalan A K S, Venkatachari K V and Shivakumar S K, IRS Mission, *Current Science*, Vol. 61(3&4), 25, 136–151, 1991.

320. Katsuhisa F and Ishikawa J, Ed., Anti-personnel Landmine Detection for Humanitarian Demining, *Springer*, 2009.

321. Katzberg S J, Torres O, Grant M S and Masters D, Utilizing Calibrated GPS Reflected Signals to Estimate Soil Reflectivity and Dielectric Constant: Results from SMEX02, *Remote Sensing of Environment*, Vol. 100(1), 17–28, 2006. https://ntrs.nasa.gov/archive/nasa/casi.ntrs.nasa.gov/20080015510.pdf

322. Kaufman V J, Tanre D, Gordon H R, Nakajima T, Lenoble J, Franin R, Grassl H, Herman B M, King M D and Teillet P M, Passive remote sensing of tropospheric aerosol and

atmospheric correction for the aerosol effect, *Journal of Geophysical Research*, Vol. 102(No.D14), 16815–16830, 1997.

323. Kaufman Y J and Fraser R S, Atmospheric effect on classification of finite fields, *Remote Sensing of Environment*, Vol. 15, 95–118, 1984.

324. Kaufman Y J and Fraser R S, Different atmospheric effects in remote sensing of uniform and non-uniform surfaces, *Advance Space Research*, Vol. 2(5), 147–155, 1983.

325. Kaufman Y J and Joseph J H, Determination of surface albedos and aerosol extinction characteristics from satellite imagery, *Geophysical Research*, Vol. 87, 1287, 1982.

326. Kaufman Y J and Sendra C, Algorithm for automatic atmospheric correction to visible and near IR satellite imagery, *International Journal of Remote Sensing*, Vol. 9, 1357–1381, 1988.

327. Kaufman Y J, Aerosol optical thickness and atmospheric path radiance, *Journal of Geophysical Research*, Vol. 98(No. D2), 2677–2692, 1993.

328. Kaufman Y J, Atmospheric effect on spatial resolution of surface imagery, *Applied Optics*, Vol. 23(22), 3400, 1984.

329. Kaufman Y J, Atmospheric effect on spectral signature – measurements and corrections, *IEEE Transactions on Geoscience and Remote Sensing*, Vol. 26, 441–450, 1988.

330. Kaufman Y J, The atmospheric effect on the separability of field classes measured from satellites, *Remote Sensing of Environment*, Vol. 18, 21–34, 1985.

331. Kauth R J and Thomas G S, The tasseled cap – a graphic description of the spectral–temporal development of agricultural crops as seen by Landsat, *Proceedings of the Symposium on Machine Processing of Remotely Sensed Data*, West Lafayette, Indiana, 41–51, 1976.

332. Kemp D D, The Environment Dictionary, London: Routledge, 1998.

333. Kienast B S and Boettinger J L, Applying the optimum index factor to multiple data types in soil survey, Digital Soil Mapping, Vol. 2, *The series Progress in Soil Science*, *Springer Netherlands*, 385–398, 2010.

334. Kimothi M M and Jadhav R N, Forest fire in central Himalayas: an extant, direction and spread using IRS LISS-1 data, *International Journal of Remote Sensing*, Vol. 19, 2261–2274, 1998.

335. King C A M, *Beaches and Coasts*, II Ed., University of Nottingham, Edward Arnold (Publishers) Ltd., London, 1972.

336. Kirdiashev K P, Chukhlantsev A A and Shutko A M, Microwave radiation of the earth's surface in the presence of a vegetation cover, *Radiotekh Electron*, Vol. 24, 256–264, 1979.

337. Kleman J and Fagerlund E, Reflectance properties of barley for different agronomical treatments, *Proceedings of 3rd International Colloquium on Spectral Signatures of Objects in Remote Sensing*, Les Arcs, France, 491–494, 1985.

338. Klonus S and Ehlers M, Image fusion using the Ehlers spectral characteristics preserving algorithm, *GIScience and Remote Sensing*, Vol. 44(2), 93–116, 2007.

339. Klonus S and Ehlers M, Performance of evaluation methods in image fusion, *12th International Conference on Information Fusion*, Seattle, WA, USA, 2009. https://pdfs.semanticscholar.org/a0a2/3baf4db80fe1c53c37d60c299e07536c4e68.pdf accessed on 30thSeptember 2016.

340. Knipling E B, Physical and physiological basis for the reflectance of visible and near-infrared radiation from vegetation, *Remote Sensing of Environment*, Vol. 1, 155–159, 1970.

341. Kogan F N, Droughts of the late 1980s in the United States as derived from NOAA polar-orbiting satellitedata, *Bull. Am. Meteorol. Soc.*, Vol. 76, 655–668, 1995.

342. Komjathy A, Armatys M, Masters D, Axelrad P, Zavorotny V and Katzberg S, Retrieval of ocean surface wind speed and wind direction using reflected GPS signals, *J. Atmos. Ocean Technol.*, Vol. 21(3), 515–526, 2004.

343. Kondratyev K Y and Pokrovsky O M, A factor analysis approach to optimal selection of spectral intervals for multipurpose experiments in remote sensing of the environment and earth resources, *Remote Sensing of Environment*, Vol. 8(1), 3–10, 1979.

344. Kosmas C, Ferrara A, Briasouli H and Imeson A, Methodology for mapping Environmentally Sensitive Areas (ESAs) to Desertification, in *The Medalus project Mediterranean desertification and land use*, Kosmas C, Kirkby M. and Geeson N (Eds), Manual on key indicators of desertification and mapping environmentally sensitive areas to desertification, European Union, Vol. 18882, 31–47, 1999. https://www.kcl.ac.uk/projects/desertlinks/downloads/publicdownloads/ESA%20Manual.pdf

345. Krishnamurthy J, Mani A, Jayaraman V and Manivel M, Groundwater resources development in hard rock terrain–An approach using remote sensing and GIS techniques, *International Journal of Applied Earth Observation and Geoinformation*, Vol. 2(3–4), 204–215, 2000.

346. Kristof S J and Zachary A L, Mapping soil types from multispectral scanner data, *Proceedings of 7th International Symposium on Remote Sensing of Environment*, Vol. III, 2095–2108, 1971.

347. Kruse F A and Lefkoff A B, Knowledge-based geologic mapping with imaging spectrometers, *Remote Sensing Reviews, special issue on NASA Innovative Research Program (IRP) results*, Vol. 8, 3–28, 1993.

348. Kulkarni A V and Bahuguna I M, Correspondence, Glacial retreat in the Baspa Basin, Himalayas, monitored with satellite stereo data, *Journal of Glaciol*, Vol. 48(160), 171–172, 2002.

349. Kulkarni A V and Rathore B P, Snow cover monitoring in Baspa basin using IRS WiFS data, *Mausam*, Vol. 54(1), 335–340, 2003.

350. Kulkarni A V, Mass balance of Himalayan glaciers using AAR and ELA methods, Journal of Glaciol, Vol. 38(128), 101–104, 1992.

351. Kulkarni A V, Mathur P, Rathore B P, Alex S, Thakur N and Manoj Kumar, Effect of global warming on snow ablation pattern in the Himalayas, *Current Science*, Vol. 83(2), 120–123, 2002a.

352. Kulkarni A V, Philip G, Thakur V C, Sood R K, Randhawa S S and Ram Chandra, Glacial inventory of the Sutlej Basin using remote sensing technique, *Himalayan Geology*, Vol. 20(2), 45–52, 1999.

353. Kulkarni A V, Rathore B P and Alex S, Monitoring of glacial mass balance in the Baspa basin using Accumulation Area Ratio method, *Current Science*, Vol. 86(1), 101–106, 2004.

354. Kulkarni A V, Srinivasulu J, Manjul S S and Mathur P, Field based spectral reflectance to develop NDSI method for snow cover monitoring, *Journal of Indian Society of Remote Sensing* Vol. 30(1 & 2), 73–80, 2002b.

355. Kumar G R H and Singh D, Quality assessment of fused images of MODIS and PALSAR, *Progress in Electromagnetic Research B.*, Vol. 24, 191–221, 2010.

356. Kumar K, Indian payload capabilities for space missions, *The International ASTROD Symposium*, Bangalore, India, 2013). http://www.rri.res.in/ASTROD/ASTROD5-Wed/ Kirankumar_Indian-payload.pdf (accessed on 22 June 2014).

357. Kumar R and Silva L, Light ray tracing through a leaf cross section, *Applied Optics*, Vol. 12(12), 2950–2954, 1973.

358. Kursinki E R, Hajj G A, Schofield J T, Linfield R P and Hardy K R, Observing earth's atmosphere with radio occultation measurements using the global positioning system, *J. Geophys. Res.*, Vol. 102(D19), 23429–23465, 1997.

359. Lakshmi B, Chandrasekhara Reddy C and Kishore S V S R K, Archiving and Managing Remote Sensing Data using State of the Art Storage Technologies, *The International Archives of Photogrammetry, Remote Sensing and Spatial Information Sciences*, Vol. 40(8), 1153, 2014.

360. Landgrebe D A, Hyperspectral image data analysis as a high dimensional signal processing problem, *IEEE Signal Processing Magazine*, Vol. 19, 17–28, 2002.

361. Lansing J C and Cline R W, The four and five band multi-spectral scanners for Landsat, *Optical Engineering*, Vol. 14(4), 312–322, 1975.

362. Lark R M, Geostatistical description of texture on an aerialphotograph for discriminating classes of land cover, *International Journal of Remote Sensing*, Vol. 17, 2115–2133, 1996.

363. Lasker R, Pelaez J and Laurs R M, The use of satellite infrared imagery for describing ocean processes in relation to spawning of the northern anchovy, *Journal of Remote Sensing of Environment*, Vol. 11, 439–453, 1981.

364. Lauer D T and Todd W J, Land cover mapping with merged Landsat RBV and MSS stereoscopic images, *Proceedings of the ASP Fall Technical Conference, American Society for Photogrammetry, San Francisco, California*, Vol. 680–689, 1981.

365. Laurs R M, Fiedler P C and Montgomery D R, Albacore tuna catch distribution relative to environmental features observed from satellites, *Journal of Deep Sea Research*, Vol. 31, 1085–1099, 1984.

366. Le Vine D M, Griffis A J, Swift C T and Jackson T J, ESTAR: A synthetic aperture microwave radiometer for remote sensing applications, *Proceedings of IEEE*, Vol. 82, 1787–1801, 1994.

367. Lee C and Landgrebe D A, Feature-extraction based on decision boundaries, *IEEE Trans. on Geoscience and Remote Sensing*, Vol. 15(4), 388–400, 1993.

368. Lee J B, Woodyatt A S and Berman M, Enhancement of high spectral resolution remote sensing data by a noise adjusted principal components transform, *IEEE Trans. on Geoscience and Remote Sensing*, Vol. 28(3), 295–304, 1990.

369. Lee J S, Refined filtering of image noise using local statistics, *Computer Graphics and Image Processing*, Vol. 15, 380–389, 1981.

370. Lees B G and Ritman K, Decision-tree and rule induction approach to integration of remotely sensed and GIS data in mapping vegetation in disturbed or hilly environments, *Environmental Management*, Vol. 15, 823–831, 1991.

371. Leprieur C, Carrere V and Gu X F, Atmospheric corrections and ground reflectance recovery for Airborne Visible/Infrared Imaging Spectrometer (AVIRIS) data: MAC Europe 91, *Photogrammetric Engineering and Remote Sensing*, Vol. 16, 1233–1238, 1995.

372. Lewis W M et. al., *Wetlands – Characteristics and Boundaries*, National Academy Press, Washington DC, 328, 1995.

373. Li F and Goldstein R, Studies of multi-baseline spaceborne interferometric, synthetic aperture radar, *IEEE Transactions on Geoscience and Remote Sensing*, GE-28, 88–97, 1990.

374. Li F and Johnson W T K, Ambiguities in spaceborne synthetic aperture radar systems, *IEEE Transactions on Aerospace and Electronic Systems*, Vol. AES-19(3), 389–397, 1983.

375. Li H, Manjunath B S and Mitra S K, An approach to multi-sensor image registration, *IEEE Transactions on Image Processing*, Vol. 4(3), 320–334, 1995.

376. Li L, Ustin S L, Orueta A P, Jacquemoud S and Whiting M L, Remote sensing based assessment of biophysical indicators for land degradation and desertification, Chapter 2, in *Recent Advances in Remote Sensing and Geoinformation Processing for Land Degradation Assessment*, Roeder A and Hill J (Eds), CRC Press, 2009.

377. Light D L, Characteristics of remote sensors for mapping and earth science applications, *Photogrametric Engineering and Remote Sensing*, Vol. 56, 1613–1623, 1990.

378. Lillesand T M and Kiefer R W, *Remote Sensing and Image Interpretation*, John Wiley and Sons, 1979.

379. Lindahl A, Burmester W, Malone K, et. al., Summary of the Operational Land Imager Focal Plane Array for the Landsat Data Continuity Mission, *Proc. of SPIE*, 8155, 81550Y.1–81550Y.14, 2011.

380. Liou K N, *An Introduction to Atmospheric Radiation*, Academic Press, New York, 392, 1980.

381. Liu and Lathrop Jr., Urban change detection based on an artificial neural network, *International Journal of Remote Sensing*, Vol. 23, 2513–2518, 2002.

382. Liu J G, Smoothing Filter-based Intensity Modulation: a spectral preserve image fusion technique for improving spatial details, *International Journal of Remote Sensing*, Vol. 21(N.18), 3461–3472, 2000.

383. Liu W T and Kogan F N, Monitoring regional drought using the Vegetation Condition Index, *International Journal of Remote Sensing*, Vol. 17, 2761–2782, 1996. http://www.tandfonline.com/doi/abs/10.1080/01431169608949106

384. Lu D and Weng Q, A survey of image classification methods and techniques for improving classification performance, *International Journal of Remote Sensing*, Vol. 28(5), 823–870, 2007.

385. Lu D, Mausel P, Brondizio E and Moran E, Change detection techniques, *International Journal of Remote Sensing*, Vol. 25(12), 2365–2401, 2004.

386. Lu D, Moran E and Batistella M, Linear mixture model applied to Amazonian vegetation classification, *Remote Sensing of Environment*, Vol. 87, 456–469, 2003.

387. Lucas R, Rowlands A, Niemann O and Merton R N, Advanced image processing techniques for remotely sensed hyperspectral data, *Hyperspectral Sensors and Applications*, Springer-Verlag, 11–49, 2004.

388. Luciano S, Bellon O R P, Boye K L, *Robust Range Image Registration Using Genetic Algorithms and the Surface Interpenetration Measure*, Series in machine perception and artificial intelligence, Vol 60, World Scientific publisher, 2005.

389. Lutz H and Armandillo, *Laser Sounding from Space*, Ed. Instrument Tech. Divn., ESTEC, Battrick B, ESA Publications Division, ESTEC, *ESA SP-1108*, 1989.

390. Macdonald R B, A summary of the history of the development of automated remote sensing for agricultural applications, *IEEE Transactions on Geoscience & Remote Sensing*, Vol. GE-22, 473–481, 1984.

391. Macleod R D and Congalton R G, A quantitative comparison of change detection algorithms for monitoring eelgrass from remotely sensed data, *Photogrammetric Engineering and Remote Sensing*, Vol. 64, 207–216, 1998.

392. Mahammad Sazid S K, Personal communication, Space Applications Centre, Ahmedabad, 2002. (sazid@ipdpg.gov.in)

393. Malthus T J, Andrieu B, Clark J A, Danson F M, Jaggard K W, Madeira A C and Stevenson M D, *Candidate High Spectral Resolution Derivative Indices for the Prediction of Crop Cover*, ESA SP-319 (1), 205–208, 1991.

394. Manjunath K R and Potdar M B, Wheat growth profile: satellite monitoring and crop yield modeling, *Journal of The Indian Society of Remote Sensing*, Vol. 32(1), 91–102, 2004.

395. Markham B L and Townshend J R G, Land-cover classification accuracy as a function of sensor spatial resolution, in *Proceedings of 15th International Symposium on Remote Sensing of Environment*, Environmental Research Institute at Michigan, Ann Arbor, USA, 1075–1090, 1981.

396. Marsh, Switzer and Kowalik, Resolving the percentage of component terrains within single resolution elements, *Photogrammetric Engineering and Remote Sensing*, Vol. 46, 1079–1086. 1980.

397. Martonchik J V, Determination of aerosol optical depth and land surface directional reflectances using multi-angle imagery, *Journal of Geophysical Research*, Vol. 102(D14), 17015–17022, 1997.

398. Massonnet D, Satellite radar interferometry, *Scientific American*, Vol. 276(2), 32–39, 1997.

399. Mather P M, *Computational Methods of Multivariate Analysis in Physical Geography*, Wiley, Chichester, 1976.

400. Mather P M, *Computer Processing of Remotely Sensed Imagery – An introduction*, 2nd Ed., John Wiley, NY, 1999.

401. Mathew Kurien, Personal communication, Space Applications Centre, Ahmedabad, 2002.

402. Maul G A and Qualset R H, Computer enhancement of ERTS-1 images for ocean radiances, *Remote Sensing of Environment*, Vol. 3, 237–253, 1974.

403. Maul G A, Williams F, Roffer M and Sausa F M, Remotely sensed oceanographic patterns and variability of blue fin tuna catch in the gulf of Mexico, *Journal of Oceanographica Acta*, Vol. 7, 469–479, 1984.

404. Maurer T, How to pan-sharpen images using the gram-schmidt pan-sharpen method – A recipe, *International Archives of the Photogrammetry, Remote Sensing and Spatial Information Sciences, Vol. XL-1/W1*, ISPRS Hannover Workshop, Hannover, Germany, 2013. http://www.int-arch-photogramm-remote-sens-spatial-inf-sci.net/XL-1-W1/239/2013/isprsarchives-XL-1-W1-239-2013.pdf

405. Mazer A S, Martin M et. al., Image processing software for imaging spectrometry data analysis, *Remote Sensing of Environment*, Vol. 24(1), 201–210, 1988.

406. McClain E P, Pichel W G and Waltson C C, Comparative performance of AVHRR-based multichannel sea surface temperatures, *Journal of Geophysical Research*, Vol. C6, 11587–11601, 1985.

407. McCluney W R, *Introduction to Radiometry and Photometry*, Artech House, 1994.

408. McDonald A R, (Ed.), *Corona - The First NRO Reconnaissance Eye in the Space*, ASPRS, Maryland, USA, 1997.

409. McDonnell M J, Box-filtering techniques, *Computer Graphics and Image Processing*, Vol. 17(1), 65–70, 1981.

410. McGoogan J T, Miller L S, Brown G S and Hayne G S, The S-193 radar altimeter experiment, *Proceedings of IEEE*, Vol. 62, 793–803, 1974.

411. McMillin L M and Crosby D S, Theory and Validation of the multiple window sea-surface temperature technique, *Journal of Geophysical Research,* Vol. 89, 3655–3661, 1984.

412. McMillin L M, Estimation of sea-surface temperature from two infrared window mea- surement, with different absorption, *Journal of Geophysical Research*, Vol. 80, 5113–5117, 1975.

413. Medhavy T T, Sharma T, Dubey R P, Hooda R S, Mohitkumar K E, Yadav M, Manchanda M L, Ruhal D S, Khera A P and Jarwal S D, Crop classification accuracy as influenced by training strategy, data transformations and spatial resolution of data, *Journal of Indian Society of Remote Sensing*, Vol. 21, 21–28, 1993.

414. Meer Van Der F and Bakker W, Cross correlogram spectral matching (CCSM): Application to surface mineralogical mapping using AVIRIS data from Cuprite, Nevada, *Remote Sensing of Environment*, Vol. 61, 371–382, 1997.

415. Meer Van Der F, Geophysical inversion of imaging spectrometer data for geologic modeling, *International Journal of Remote Sensing*, Vol. 21, 387–393, 2000.

416. Meer Van Der F, Spectral curve shape matching with a continuum removed CCSM algorithm, *International Journal of Remote Sensing*, Vol. 21(16), 3179–3185, 2000.

417. Melgani F, Al Hashemy B A R and Taha S M R, An explicit fuzzy supervised classification method for multi-spectral remote sensing images, *IEEE Transactions on Geoscience and Remote Sensing*, Vol. 38(1), 287–295, 2000.

418. Menze B H , Ur J A and Sherratt A G, Detection of ancient settlement mounds: archaeological survey based on the SRTM terrain model, *Photogrammetric Engineering and Remote Sensing*, Vol. 72, 321–327, 2006.

419. Michael J A, (Ed.), *Atmospheric Remote Sensing by Microwave Radiometry*, John Wiley & Sons, Inc., 1993.

420. Midan J P, The SPOT-HRV instrument-an overview of design and performance, *Earth-oriented Applications of Space Technology*, Vol. 6(2), 163–172, 1986.

421. Milton E J, Principles of field spectroscopy, *Remote Sensing Year Book 1988–1989*, 79–99, 1989.

422. Misra T, Jha A M, Putervu D, Jogeswara Rao, Dave D B and Rana S S, Ground calibration of multifrequency scanning microwave radiometer (MSMR), *IEEE Transactions on Geosciences and Remote Sensing*, Vol. 40(2), 504–508, 2002.

423. Misra T, Jha A M, Putrevu D, Jogeswar Rao, Dave D B and Rana S S, Ground calibration of multi-frequency scanning microwave radiometer (MSMR), *IEEE Transactions on Geoscience and Remote Sensing*, Vol. 40(20), 504–508, 2002.

424. Misra T, Rana S S, Desai N M, Dave D B, Rajeevjyoti, Arora R K, Rao C V N, Bakori B V, Neelakantan R and Vachchani J G, Synthetic Aperture Radar payload on-board RISAT-1: configuration, technology and performance, *Current Science,* Vol. 104(4), 446, 2013. http://www.currentscience.ac.in/cs/Volumes/104/04/0446.pdf

425. Mitchell B H, *Image fusion: theories, techniques and applications*, Springer Science & Business Media, 2010.

426. Mobley C D, *Light and Water: Radiative Transfer in Natural Waters*, Academic Press, 1994.

427. Mohan S and Patel P, Personal communication, Space Applications Centre (ISRO), Ahmedabad, 2002.

428. Mohan S, Mehta N S, Mehta R L, Patel P, Patel I D, Patel M R and Patel R B, Monitoring of paddy crop at 5.0 GHz, Scientific Note SAR/RCA/RSAG/SIRC/SN/01/92, Space Application Centre (ISRO), Ahmedabad 380 053, India, 31, 1992.

429. Mohan S, Radar remote sensing for soil moisture estimation, *Proceedings of Workshop on Remote Sensing and GIS Applications in Water Resources Engineering*, Central Board of Irrigation & Power, Bangalore, 1997.

430. Moigne J L, Netanyahu N S, Eastman R D, *Image Registration for Remote Sensing*, Cambridge University Press, 2011.

431. Moik J G, Digital processing of remotely sensed images, NASA Scientific and Technical Information Branch, *NASA SP-431*, Washington, DC, 77–126, 1980.

432. Mollberg H B, Performance characteristics for the orbiter camera payload system's large format camera (LFC), *SPIE Electro-Optical Instrumentation for Resources Evaluation*, Vol. 278, 66–72, 1981.

433. Moore G K, Satellite surveillance of physical water quality characteristics, *Proceedings of 12th International Symposium on Remote Sensing of Environment*, ERIM, Ann Arbor, Vol. 1, 445–462, 1978.

434. Moore R K and Fung A K, Radar determination of winds at sea, *Proceedings of IEEE*, Vol. 67(11), 1504–1521, 1979.

435. Moorthi S Manthira and Garg A, Personal communication, 2016.

436. Morain S A and Budge A M (Eds), Post-Launch Calibration of Satellite Sensors: *Proceedings of the International Workshop on Radiometric and Geometric Calibration, Mississippi, USA (ISPRS Book Series)*,.2004.

437. Moran M S, Inoue Y and Barnes E M, Opportunities and limitations for image-based remote sensing in precision crop management, *Remote Sensing of Environment*, Vol. 61, 319–346, 1997.

438. Morel A and Precur L, Analysis of variations in ocean colour, *Limnology and Oceanography*, Vol. 22, 709–722, 1977.

439. Morfitt R, Barsi J, Levy R, Markham B, et. al., Landsat-8 Operational Land Imager (OLI) Radiometric Performance On-Orbit, Remote Sens., Vol. 7, 2208–2237, 2015, doi:10.3390/rs70202208.

440. Morfitt R, Markham B L, Micijevic E et. al., Landsat-8 Operational Land Imager (OLI) Radiometric Performance On-Orbit, *Remote Sens.*, Vol. 7, 2208–2237, 2015.

441. Mukherjee S, Role of Satellite Sensors in Groundwater Exploration, *Sensors*, Vol. 8(3), 2006–2016, 2008, doi:10.3390/s8032006.

442. Mulders M A, *Remote Sensing in Soil Science*, Elsevier, Amsterdam, 1987.

443. Mullen A S, No more secrets? Policy implications of commercial remote sensing satellites. 1999. http://www.ceip.org/programs/transparency/RemoteSensingConf/Mullen-Transcript. htm.

444. Mura F, Dionisio C and Oricchio D, Future Remote Sensing Systems, *Proceedings of the Conference on Future Trends in Remote Sensing*, Gudmandsen P, (Ed.), 17–24, 1998.

445. Murthy C S, Chari S T, Raju P V and Jonna S, Improved ground sampling and crop yield estimation using satellite data, *International Journal of Remote Sensing*, Vol. 17(5), 945–956, 1996.

446. Murthy C S, Jonna S, Raju P V, Thiruvengadachari S and Hakeem K A, Crop yield prediction in command areas using satellite data, in *Proceedings of the 15th Asian Conference on Remote Sensing*, Bangalore, India, 14.1–14.6, 1994.

447. Myers V I and Allen W A, Electrooptical remote sensing methods as nondestructive testing and measuring techniques in agriculture, *Applied Optics*, Vol. 7, 1819–1838, 1968.

448. Myers V I, Soil, water, and plant relations, in *Remote sensing with special reference to agriculture and forestry*, National Academy of Sciences, Washington, DC, 1970.

449. Naderi F M, Freilich M H and Long D G, Spaceborne radar measurement of wind velocity over the ocean – an overview of the NSCAT Scatterometer system, *Proceedings of IEEE*, Vol. 79, 850–866, 1991.

450. Naidu V P S and Roa J R, Pixel-level image fusion using wavelets and principal component analysis, *Defence Science Journal*, Vol. 58(3), 338–352, 2008.

451. Nalini N S and Rajani M B, Stone fortress of Chitledroog: visualizing old landscape of Chitradurga by integrating spatial information from multiple sources, *Current Science*, Vol. 103(4), 381–387, 2012.

452. Narain A, Dwivedi R M, Solanki H U, Beena Kumari, Chaturvedi N, James P S B R, Subbaraju G, Sudarsan D and Sivaprakasam T E, The use of NOAA-AVHRR data in fisheries exploration in the Indian EEZ, *Proceedings of Seminar on Remote Sensing for Marine Fisheries Studies*, Beijing, China, ESCAP/UNDP, 226–232, 1990.

453. NASA (1987a), '*Earth Observation System*', *Instrument Panel Report* – HIRIS, Vol. II(c).

454. NASA (1987b), '*SAR - Earth Observation System*', *Instrument Panel Report*, Vol. II(f).

455. NASA (1987c), Large area crop inventory experiment (LACIE), *Interim Accuracy Assessment Plan, LACIE-00628*, JSC-13733.

456. NASA (1994), Design Studies of Large Aperture, High resolution, Earth Science microwave radiometers compatible with small launch vehicles – *NASA Technical Report*, 3469.

457. NASA (2003), http://eospso.nasa.gov/sites/default/files/publications/data_products_1.pdf

458. NASA (2006), Earth's Living Ocean: The Unseen World. An advanced plan for NASA's Ocean Biology and Biogeochemistry Research. http://oceancolor.gsfc.nasa.gov/DOCS/OBB_Report_5.12.2008.pdf (accessed on 14 May 2014).

459. NASA, Special Publication #335, Advanced scanners and imaging systems for earth observation, Working Group Report, 1973.

460. *NASA-LANDSAT Users' Handbook*, 1972.

461. Nayak S et. al., Coastal Environment, Scientific Note, Space Applications Centre, Ahmedabad, RSAM/SAC/COM/SN/11/92, 1992.

462. Nayak S et. al., Manual for mapping of coastal wetlands/land forms and shoreline changes using satellite data, Technical Note, Space Applications Centre, Ahmedabad, IRS-UP/SAC/MCE/SN/32/91, 63, 1991.

463. Nayak S R and Bahuguna A, Application of RS data to monitor mangroves and other coastal vegetation of India, *Indian Jour. Marine Sciences*, Vol. 30(4), 195–213, 2001.

464. Nayak S R and Sahai B, Coastal Geomorphology of the Gulf of Khambat, *Proceedings of the symposium on Quaternary episodes of India, Neotectonism, Eustasy and Paleoclimates,* Dept. of Geology, MSU, Baroda, 87–96, 1984.

465. Nayak S R and Sahai B, Coastal morphology: A case study of the Gulf of Khambat (Cambay), *International Journal of Remote Sensing*, Vol. 6(3 & 4), 559–567, 1985.

466. Nayak S R, Bahuguna A, Deshmukh B, Shah D G, Rao R S, Dhargalkar V K, Jagtap T G, Venkataraman K, Sounderajan R, Singh H S, Pandey C N, Patel B H and Prasanna Y, Eco-morphological Zonation of Selected Coral Reefs of India Using Remotely Sensed Data, *Scientific Note*, Space Applications Centre, Ahmedabad, SAC/RESIPA/MWRG/ MSCED/ SN/ 16/2003, 109, 2003.

467. Nayak S R, Bahuguna A, Shah D G, Dhargalkar V K, Jagtap T G, Rout D K, Behera G, Bhattacharya S, Bandopadhyay T, Raman A V, Sounderajan R, Singh H S, Pandey C N and Patel B H Community Zonation of Selected Mangrove Habitats of India Using Satellite Data, *Scientific Note*, Space Applications Centre, Ahmedabad, SAC/RESA/ MWRG/ MSCED/SN/ 17/2003, 93, 2003.

468. Nayak S R, Bahuguna A, Shaikh M G, Chauhan H B, Rao R S, Arya A S, Aggarwal J P, Srivastava B N, Patel A, Vaidya P H, Dwivedi P, Untawale A G, Jagtap T G, Chinna Raj, Sankha N, Dayal R M, Devendranath, More T Y, Dhera D B, Patil A V, Mahadar H S, Ananda Rao T, Sherieff A N, Suresh P V, Nair J K, Shankar G, Nalinakumar S, Guruswamy V, Franklin T, Kandaswamy V, Ramalingam M, Sanjeevi S, Vaidyanathan R, Ramesh R, Das N K, Samal R C and Kumar P, Coastal Environment, *Scientific Note*, Space Applications Centre, Ahmedabad, RSAM/SAC/COM/SN/11/92, 114, 1992.

469. Nayak S, Bahuguna A, Chauhan P, Chauhan H B and Rao R S, Remote sensing applications for coastal environmental management in India, *Maeer's MIT Pune Journal*, Special issue on Coastal Environmental Management, 1997.

470. Nemoto Y, Nishino H, Ono M, Mizutamari H, Nishikawa K and Tanaka K, Japanese Earth Resources Satellite-1 Synthetic Aperture Radar, *Proceedings of IEEE,* Vol. 79(6), 800–809, 1991.

471. Nerry F, Labed J and Stoll M P, Spectral properties of land surfaces in the thermal infrared 1. Laboratory measurement of absolute spectral emissivity signatures, *Journal of Geophysical Research*, Vol. 95(B5), 7027–7044, 1990.

472. Newton R W and Rouse J W, Jr, Microwave radiometre measurements of soil moisture content, *IEEE Transactions on Antenna Propagation,* Vol. AP-28, 680–686, 1980.

473. Newton R W, Black Q R, Makanvand S, Blanchard A J and Randall B, Soil moisture information and thermal microwave emission, *IEEE Transactions on Geoscience and Remote Sensing*, Vol. GE-20(3), 275–281, 1982.

474. Nicholas S M and Locke S M, Jr, *The Heat Capacity Mapping Mission (HCMM) - Anthology, NASA-SP-465*, 1982.

475. Nicodemus F E, Richmond J C, Hsia J J, Ginsberg I W and Limperis T, Geometrical considerations and nomenclature for reflectance, *NBS Monog. (U.S.)*, Vol. 160, 1–52, 1977.

476. Nieuwenhuis G J A and Mucher C A, Satellite remote sensing and crop growth monitoring, *Future Trends in Remote Sensing*, Gudmandsen, (Ed.), Balkema, Rotterdam, 251–262, 1998.

477. Nixon M, Feature Extraction & Image Processing, *Academic Press*, 2008.

478. Nixon O, Wu L, Ledgerwood M, Nam J, Jonathan and Huras, 2.5 µm Pixel Linear CCD, International Image Sensors Workshop, DALSA Inc. 605 McMurray Road, Waterloo, Canada, 2007.

479. Njoku E G, Barnett T P, Laurs R M and Vastano A C, Advances in satellite sea surface temperature measurement and oceanographic applications, *Journal of Geophysical Research*, Vol. 90(C6), 11573–11586, 1985.

480. Njoku E G, Staccey J M and Barath F T, The scanning multichannel microwave radiometer (SMMR): Instrument description and performance, *IEEE Journal of Oceanic Engineering*, Vol. OE-5(2), 100–115, 1980.

481. Norwood V T, Balance between resolution and signal-to-noise ratio in scanner design for earth resources systems, *Proceedings of SPIE "Scanners and Imagery Systems for Earth Observation"*, Vol. 51, 37–42, 1974.

482. NRSA, *IRS-1C Data User's Handbook*, National Remote Sensing Agency, Hyderabad, 1995.

483. NRSC (2011) http://www.euromap.de/download/R2_data_user_handbook.pdf (accessed on 23 January 2017).

484. NRSC, http://www.nrsc.gov.in/RISAT-1(accessed on 17 January 2017).

485. O'Brien H W and Munis R W, Red and Near-infrared spectral reflectance of snow, *Research Report No. 332, U.S. Army Cold Regions Research and Engineering Lab.*, Hanover, New Hamshpire, 1975.

486. O'Connella J, Connolly J B, Vermotec E F and Holden N M, Radiometric normalization for change detection in peatlands: a modified temporal invariant cluster approach, *International Journal of Remote Sensing*, Vol. 34(8), 2905–2924, 2013.

487. O'Neill P E and Jackson T J, Observed effects of soil organic matter content on the microwave emissivity of soils, *Remote Sensing of Environment*, Vol. 31, 175–182, 1990.

488. O'Reilly J E, Maritorena, Mitchell B G, Siegal D A, Carder K L, Graver S A, Kahru M and McClain C R, Ocean colour chlorophyll algorithms for SeaWiFS, *Journal of Geophysical Research*, Vol. 103, 24937–24953, 1998.

489. Oberheuser J H, Optical Concept Generation for the Synchronous Earth Observatory Satellite, *Opt. Eng.*, Vol. 14(4), 295–304, 1975.

490. Olson C E, Elements of photographic interpretation common to several sensors, *Photogrammetic Engineering*, Vol. 26(4), 651–656, 1960.

491. Orlando P and Villa B D, Remote Sensing applications in archaeology. *Archeologia e Calcolatori*, Vol. 22, 147–168, 2011. https://core.ac.uk/download/pdf/33151603.pdf

492. Otazu X, González-Audícana M, Fors O and Núnez J, Introduction of Sensor Spectral Response Into Image Fusion Methods. Application to Wavelet-Based Methods, *IEEE Transactions on Geoscience and Remote Sensing*, Vol. 43(10), 2376–2385, 2005.

493. Oza M P, Selection of band combination for IRS data, *Journal of the Indian Society of Remote Sensing*, Vol. 17(2), 1–9, 1989.

494. Oza M P, Space Applications Centre, 2016, Personal communication.

495. Painter T H, Roberts D A, Green R O and Dozier J, The effects of grain size on spectral mixture analysis of snow-covered area from AVIRIS data, *Remote Sensing of Environment*, Vol. 65, 320–332, 1998.

496. Pal M and Mather M P, An assessment of the effectiveness of decision-tree methods for land cover classification, *Remote Sensing of Environment*, Vol. 86, 554–565, 2003.

497. Pal N R and Pal S K A review on image segmentation techniques, *Pattern Recognition*, Vol. 26(9), 1277–1294, 1993. http://www.isical.ac.in/~sankar/paper/PR_93_NRP_SKP. PDF

498. Palmer J M, Effective bandwidths for Landsat-4 and Landsat-d﹥ multispectral scanner and thematic mapper subsystems, *IEEE Transactions on Geoscience and Remote Sensing*, Vol. 22, 336–338, 1984.

499. Palmer J M, Radiometric bandwidth normalization using root mean square methods, *Proc. SPIE*, Vol. 256, 1980.

500. Palmer J M, The measurement of transmission, absorption, emission and reflection, Chapter 25, *Handbook of Optics*, Vol. II, Bass M, (Ed.), McGraw Hill, 1985.

501. Palmer P I and Barnett J J, Application of an optimal estimation method to GPS/MET bending angle observations, *J. Geophys. Res.*, Vol. 106(D15), 17147–17160, 2001.

502. Pande S, Maji A K, Johansen C and Bantilan F T, Jr, (Eds), GIS application in cropping system analysis – Case studies in Asia: *Proceedings of the International Workshop on Harmonization of Databases for GIS Analysis of Cropping Systems in the Asia Region*, 1997, ICRISAT, Patancheru, India, 98, 2000.

503. Pandya M R, Murali K R and Kirankumar A S, Quantification and comparison of spectral characteristics of sensors on board Resourcesat-1 and Resourcesat-2 satellites, *Remote Sensing Letters*, Vol. 4(3), 306–314, 2013.

504. Panigrahy S, Chakraborty M, Manjunath K R, Kundu N and Parihar J S, Evaluation of RADARSAT ScanSAR synthetic aperture radar data for rice crop inventory and monitoring, *Journal of the Indian Society of Remote Sensing*, Vol. 28, 59, 2000.

505. Panigrahy S, Chakraborty M, Sharma S A, Kundu N, Ghose S C and Pal M, Early estimation of rice area using temporal ERS-1 synthetic aperture radar data – a case study for Howrah and Hooghly districts of West Bengal, India, *International Journal of Remote Sensing*, Vol. 18, 1827–1833, 1997.

506. Panigrahy S, Manjunath K R, Chakraborty M, Kundu N and Parihar J S, Evaluation of RADARSAT Standard Beam data for identification of potato and rice crops in India, ISPRS *Journal of Photogrammetry & Remote Sensing*, Vol. 54, 254–262, 1999.

507. Panigrahy S, Parihar J S and Patel N K, Kharif rice acreage estimation in Orissa using NOAA AVHRR data, *Journal of Indian Society of Remote Sensing*, Vol. 20(1), 35–42, 1992.

508. Paola J D and Schowengerdt R A, A detailed comparison of backpropagation neural networks and maximum likelihood classifiers for urban land use classification, *IEEE Transactions on Geoscience and Remote Sensing*, Vol. 33(4), 981–996, 1995.

509. Paola J D and Schowengerdt R A, A review and analysis of back propagation neural networks for classification of remotely-sensed multi-spectral imagery, *International Journal of Remote Sensing*, Vol. 16, 3033–3058, 1995a.

510. Parashar S, Langham E, McNally J and Ahmed S, RADARSAT mission requirements and concept, *Canadian Journal of Remote Sensing*, Vol. 19(4), 1993.

511. Parihar J S and Oza M P, FASAL: an integrated approach for crop assessment and production forecasting, *Proceedings of the Asia-Pacific Remote Sensing Symposium*, International Society for Optics and Photonics, 641101–641113, 2006.

512. Patel N and Kaushal B, Classification of features selected through Optimum Index Factor (OIF) for improving classification accuracy, *Journal of Forestry Research*, Vol. 22(1), 99–105, 2011.

513. Patel N R, Parida B R, Venus V, Saha S K and Dadhwal V K, Analysis of agricultural drought using vegetation temperature condition index (VTCI) from Terra/MODIS satellite data, *Environmental monitoring and assessment*, Vol. 184(12), 7153–7163, 2012.

514. Paterson W S B, *The Physics of Glaciers*, Butterworth-Heinemann, 26–53, 1998.

515. Pathan S K, Dhinwa P S, Sastry S V G and Rao M, Urban growth trend analysis using GIS techniques – A case study of the Bombay Metropolitan Region, *International Journal of Remote Sensing*, Vol. 14(17), 3169–3179, 1993.

516. Pathan S K, Shukla V K, Patel R G and Mehta K S, Urban land use mapping – A case study of Ahmedabad city and its environs, *Journal of Indian Society of Remote Sensing*, Vol. 19(2), 95–112, 1991.

517. Paul K W, Mcglauchlin L D and Mcquistan T B, *Elements of Infrared Technology*, John Wiley and Sons Inc., NY, 1963.

518. Pavaluri M K, MSc Thesis, University of Missouri, Columbia, 2003. http://www.missouri. edu/~mkpa8f/mpthesis.pdf.

519. Peaks W H and Oliver T L, The response of terrestrial surfaces at microwave frequencies, *Ohio State University Technical Report*, 2440–7, Columbus, Ohio, 1971.

520. Peli T and Malah D, A study of edge detection algorithms, *Computer Graphics and Image Processing*, Vol. 20, 1–21, 1982.

521. Pinet P C, Shevchenko V V, Chevrel S D, Daydou Y and Rosemberg C, Local and regional lunar regolith characteristics at Reiner Gamma Formation: Optical and spectroscopic properties from Clementine and Earth-based data, *Journal of Geophysical Research-Planets*, Vol. 105, 9457–9475, 2000.

522. Plaza A, Martinez P, Perez R and Plaza J, Spatial/spectral endmember extraction by multidimensional morphological operations, *IEEE Transactions on Geoscience and Remote Sensing*, Vol. 40(9), 2025–2041, 2002.

523. Pohl C and Genderen j L van, Multi-sensor image fusion in remote sensing: concepts, methods and applications, *International Journal of Remote Sensing*, Vol. 19(5), 823–854, 1998.

524. Porcello L J, Jordon R L et. al., The Apollo Lunar Sounder Radar System, *Proceedings of IEEE*, 769–783, 1974.

525. Potdar M B, Sorghum yield modelling based on crop growth parameters determined from visible and near-IR channel NOAA-AVHRR data, *International Journal of Remote Sensing*, Vol. 14(5), 585–905, 1993.

526. Prati C, Rocca F and Monti G A, SAR interferrometry experiments with ERS-1, *Proceedings of First ERS-1 Symposium* – Space at the Service of Our Environment, Cannes, France, ESA-SP-359, 1993.

527. Price J C, On the analysis of thermal infrared imagery: The limited utility of apparent thermal inertia, *Remote Sensing of Environment*, Vol. 18, 59–73, 1985.

528. Price J C, On the information content of soil reflectance spectra, *Remote Sensing of Environment*, Vol. 33, 113–121, 1990.

529. Radhakrishnan K, Director, INCOIS, Personal communication, 2004.

530. Rajani M B and Kasturirangan K, 2014, Multispectral remote sensing data analysis and application for detecting moats around medieval settlements in South India, *Journal of the Indian Society of Remote Sensing*, Springer, Published online 03 January 2014. doi: 10.1007/s12524-013-0346-4.

531. Rajani M B and Kasturirangan K, Sea-Level changes and its impact on coastal Archaeological monuments: Seven Pagodas of Mahabalipuram, *Journal of the Indian Society of Remote Sensing*, Springer, Published online 17 April 2012. doi: 10.1007/s12524-012-0210-y

532. Rajani M B and Rajawat A S, Potential of satellite based sensors for studying distribution of archaeological site along palaeo channels: Harappan sites a case study, *Journal of archaeological sciences, Elsevier*, Vol. 38(9), 2010–2016, 2011. doi:10.1016/j.jas.2010.08.008

533. Rajani M B, 2017, Personal communication.

534. Rajani M B, Bangalore from Above: An Archaeological Review, *Current Science*,Vol. 93(10), 1352–53, 2007.

535. Rajani M B, Bhattacharya S and Rajawat A S, Synergistic Application of Optical and Radar Data for Archaeological Exploration in the Talakadu Region, Karnataka, *Journal of the Indian Society of Remote Sensing*, Springer, 519–527, 2011. doi: 10.1007/s12524-011-0102-6

536. Rajani M B, Patra S K and Verma M, Space observation for generating 3D perspective views and its implication to the study of the archaeological site of Badami in India, *Journal of Cultural Heritage*, Elsevier, Vol. 10(1), e20–e26, 2009. doi: 10.1016/j.culher.2009.08.003

537. Rajani M B, Rajawat A S, Krishna Murthy M S, Kamini J and Srinivas Rao, Demonstration of the synergy between multi-sensor satellite data, GIS and ground truth to explore the archaeological site in Talakadu region in South India, *Journal of Geomatics, Indian Society of Geomatics*, Vol. 6(1), 2012.

538. Rajani M B, The Expanse of Archaeological Remains at Nalanda: A Study Using Remote Sensing and GIS, *Archives of Asian Art*, Vol. 66(1), 1–23, 2016.

539. Raju G and Calla O P N, Sea surface emission characteristics as viewed by the spin-scanned Satellite Microwave Radiometer (SAMIR) onboard Bhaskara, *IEEE Transactions of Geosciences & Remote Sensing*, Vol. GE-23(6), 933–940, 1985.

540. Ramamoorthi A S, Forecasting snowmelt runoff of Himalayan Rivers using NOAA AVHRR Imageries since 1980, *International Association of Hydrological Sciences publication*, Vol. 160, 341–348, 1986.

541. Ramamoorthi A S, Large scale effects of seasonal snow cover, *International Association of Hydrological Sciences publication*, Vol. 166, 187–198, 1987.

542. Raney R K, Luscombe A P, Langham E J and Ahmed S, RADARSAT (SAR Imaging), *Proceedings of IEEE*, Vol. 79(2), 839–849, 1991.

543. Ranganath B K, Roy P S, Dutt C B S and Divakar P G, *Use of Modern Technologies and Information Systems for Sustainable Forest Management: Status Report*, ISRO, Department of Space, 2000.

544. Ranson K J, Vanderbilt V C, Biehl L L, Robinson B F and Bauer M E, Soybean canopy reflectances as a function of view and illumination geometry, *Proceedings of 15th International Symposium on Remote Sensing of Environment*, Ann Arbor, MI, 1982.

545. Rao D P, Gautam N C, Nagaraja R and Mohan P R, IRS-1C applications in land use mapping and planning, *Current Science*, 575–581, 1996.

546. Rast M, Hook S J, Elvidge C D and Alley R E, An evolution of techniques for the extraction of mineral absorption features from high spectral resolution remote sensing data, *Photogrammetric Engineering and Remote Sensing*, Vol. 57(10), 1303–1309, 1991.

547. Rawcliffe R D and Elliot D D, Latitudinal distribution of ozone at high altitudes deduced from a satellite measurement of the earth's radiance at 2840A., *Journal of Geophysical Research.*, Vol. 71, 5077–5089, 1966.

548. Ray S S and Neetu, Crop area estimation with Remote Sensing, in *Handbook on Remote Sensing for Agricultural Statistics*, Delincé J (Ed.), Chapter 5, 2017.

549. Ray S S and Neetu, Crop Area Estimation, in *Handbook on Remote Sensing for Agricultural Statistics,* Delince J (Ed.), Food and Agriculture Organisation, 2017. http://gsars. org/wp-content/uploads/2017/09/GS-REMOTE-SENSING-HANDBOOK-FINAL-04. pdf

550. Ray S S and Pokharna S S and Ajai, Cotton yield estimation using agrometeorological model and satellite derived spectral profile, *International Journal of Remote Sensing*, Vol. 20(14), 2693–2702, 1999.

551. Ray S S, Neetu, Mamatha S and Gupta S, Use of Remote Sensing in Crop Forecasting and Assessment of Impact of Natural Disasters: Operational Approaches in India, *FAO Expert Meeting on Crop Monitoring for Improved Food Security, Vientiane, Lao PDR*, Srivastava M (Ed.), 111–122, 2015. http://www.fao.org/3/a-i4273e.pdf

552. Ray S S, Panigrahy S and Parihar J S, Precision farming in Indian context, *GIS@ Development*, Vol. 5(11), 29, 2001.

553. Ray S S, Sesha Sai M V R and Chattopadhyay N, Agricultural Drought Assessment: Operational Approaches in India with Special Emphasis on 2012, in *High-Impact Weather Events over the SAARC Region*, Ray K, Mohapatra M, Bandyopadhyay B K and Rathore L S (Eds), Springer, 349–364, 2014.

554. Reddy C S, Jha C S, Diwakar P G and Dadhwal V K, Nationwide classification of forest types of India using remote sensing and GIS Environ. Monitor. Assess., 2015. doi: 10.1007/ s10661-015-4990-8; http://link.springer.com/article/10.1007/s10661-015-4990-8

555. Rees W G, *Physical Principles of Remote Sensing*, Cambridge University Press, 1990.

556. Reigler G R, Drake J F, Liu SC and Circerone R J, Stellar occulation measurements of atmospheric ozone and chlorine from OAO 2, *Journal of Geophysical Research*, Vol. 81, 4997–5001, 1976.

557. Remondi B W, Performing centimeter-level surveys in seconds with GPS carrier phase: initial results, *Proceedings of the Fourth International Geodetic Symposium on Satellite Positioning*, Austin, Texas, 1229–1249, 1986.

558. Reuter D, Thermal Infrared Sensor TIRS Design and Status, *Landsat Science Team Meeting*, 2009. http://landsat.usgs.gov/documents/7_Reuter_TIRS_Status.pdf (accessed on 14 May 2014).

559. Reynolds J M, *An introduction to applied environmental geophysics*, John Wiley & Sons, New York, 1997.

560. Riano D, Chuvieco E, Ustin S, Zomer R, Dennison P, Roberts D and Salas J, Assessment of vegetation regeneration after fire through multi-temporal analysis of AVIRIS images in the Santa Monica Mountains, *Remote Sensing of Environment*, Vol. 79, 60–71, 2002.

561. Richards J A and Jia X, *Remote Sensing Digital Image Analysis: An Introduction*, Springer, 2006.

562. Richardson A J and Wiegand C L, Distinguishing vegetation from soil background information, *Photogrammetric Engineering and Remote Sensing*, Vol. 43(12), 1541–1552, 1977.

563. Riegler G R, Drake J F, Liu S C and Cicerone R J, Stellar occultation measurements of atmospheric ozone and chlorine from OAO 3, *Journal of Geophysical Research*, Vol. 81(28), 4997–5001, 1976.

564. Ritter N D and Hepner G F, Application of an artificial neural network to land-cover classification of Thematic Mapper imagery, *Computers and Geosciences*, Vol. 16, 873–880, 1990.

565. Roberts D A, Gardner M, Church R, Ustin S and Scheer G, Mapping chaparral in the Santa Monica mountains using multiple endmember spectral mixture models, *Remote Sensing of Environment*, Vol. 65, 267–279, 1998.

566. Robinson A, Sale R and Morrison J, *Elements of Cartography*, John Wiley and Sons, NY, 1978.

567. Robinson I S, *Satellite Oceanography*, Ellis Harwood Limited, 1980.

568. Rodgers C D, Retrieval of atmospheric temperature composition from remote measurements of thermal radiation, *Review of Geophysical Space Physics*, Vol. 14, 609–624, 1976.

569. Rodriguez E and Marin J, Theory and design of interferometric synthetic aperture radars, *Proceedings of Institute of Electronic Engineering*, Vol. 139(2), 147–159, 1992.

570. Rogan J, Franklin J and Roberts D A, A comparison of methods for monitoring multi-temporal vegetation change using Thematic Mapper imagery, *Remote Sensing of Environment*, Vol. 80, 143–156, 2002.

571. Rondeaux G and Herman M, Polarisation of light reflected by crop canopies, *Remote Sensing of Environment*, Vol. 38, 63–75, 1991.

572. Roy P S, Divakar P G and Bhan S K, Assessing classification performance in tropical forests using multi-spectral Landsat TM data, *Proceedings of National Symposium on Remote Sensing applications for Resource Management with Special Emphasis on NE Region*, Guwahati, Vol. 25–27, 394–401, 1993.

573. Roy P S, Ranganath B K, Divakar P G, Vohra T P S, Bhan S K, Singh I J and Pandyan V C, Tropical forest type mapping and monitoring using remote sensing, *International Journal of Remote Sensing*, Vol. 12(11), 2205–2225, 1991.

574. Rulinda C M, Dilo A, Bijker W and Stein A, Characterising and quantifying vegetative drought in East Africa using fuzzy modelling and NDVI data, *Journal of arid environments*, Vol. 78, 169–178, 2012.

575. Ryherd S and Woodcock C E, Combining spectral and texture data in the segmentation of remotely sensed images, *Photogrammetric Engineering and Remote Sensing*, Vol. 62(2), 181–194, 1996.

576. Saaty T L, *The Analytic Hierarchy Process*, McGraw Hill, New York, 1980.

577. Sabins F F, *Remote Sensing Principle and Interpretation*, 2nd Edition, Freeman & Co., 1987.

578. SAC, Desertification and Land Degradation Atlas of India, 2016. http://www.sac.gov.in/SACSITE/Desertification_Atlas_2016_SAC_ISRO.pdf

579. Safavian S R and Landgrebe D, A survey of decision-tree classifier methodology, *IEEE Transactions on Systems, Man and Cybernetics*, Vol. 21(3), 660–674, 1991.

580. Sahai B, Bhattacharya A, Hegde V S, IRS 1A Applications for ground water targeting, *Current Science*, Vol. 61, 1991.

581. Salomonson V V, Barnes W L, Maymon P W, Montgomery H E and Ostrow H, MODIS: Advanced facility instrument for studies of the Earth as a system, *IEEE Transactions on Geoscience and Remote Sensing*, Vol. 27(2), 145–153, 1989.

582. Sato M, GPR and Its Application to Environmental Study, 2001. http://cobalt.cneas.tohoku.ac.jp/users/sato/GPR%20Principle.pdf, accessed on 26 May 2016.

583. Scheers, 2001. http://www.sic.rma.ac.be/~scheers/Papers/chapter3.pdf

584. Schmugge T J, Effect of soil texture on the microwave emission from soils, *IEEE Transactions on Geosciences and Remote Sensing*, Vol. GE-18, 353–361, 1980.

585. Schmugge T J, Remote sensing of soil moisture: recent advances, *IEEE Transactions of Geosciences and Remote Sensing*, Vol. GE-21, 336–344, 1983.

586. Schmuggee T J, Becker F and Zhao-Liang L, Spectral emissivity variations observed in airborne surface temperature measurements, *Remote Sensing of Environment*, Vol. 35, 95–104, 1991.

587. Schowengerdt R A, *Techniques for Image Processing and Classification in Remote Sensing*, Academic Press, 1983.

588. Schroeder T, Cohen W, Song C, Canty M and Yang Z, Radiometric Correction of Multi-Temporal Landsat Data for Characterization of Early Successional Forest Patterns in Western Oregon, *Remote Sensing of Environment*, Vol. 103, 16–26, 2006.

589. Schwilch G, Bachmann F and Liniger H P, Appraising and selecting conservation measures to mitigate desertification and land degradation based on stakeholder participation and global best practices, *Land Degradation and Development*, Vol. 20(3), 308–326, 2009. doi: 10.1002/ldr.920

590. Seigal B S, (Ed.), *Remote Sensing in Geology*, John Wiley and Sons, New York, 1980.

591. Selvam, Environmental classification of mangrove wetlands of India, *Current Science*, Vol. 84(6.25), 757–764, 2003.

592. Settle J J and Drake N A, Linear mixing and the estimation of ground cover proportions, *International Journal of Remote Sensing*, Vol. 14(6), 1159–1177, 1993.

593. Shackelford A K and Davis C H, A combined fuzzy pixel-based and object-based approach for classification of high-resolution multi-spectral data over urban areas, *IEEE Transactions on Geoscience and Remote Sensing*, Vol. 41(10), 2354–2364, 2003a.

594. Shackelford A K and Davis C H, A hierarchical fuzzy classification approach for high-resolution multi-spectral data over urban areas, *IEEE Transactions on Geoscience and Remote Sensing*, Vol. 41(9), 1920–1932, 2003.

595. Sharma S A and Parihar J S, Sampling design for global scale mapping and monitoring of agriculture, *ISPRS Archives XXXVIII-8/W3 Workshop Proceedings*: Impact of Climate Change on Agriculture, 2009. http://www.isprs.org/proceedings/XXXVIII/8-W3/B5/2-82.pdf

596. Sharma S A, Bhatt H P and Ajai, Oilseed crop discrimination, selection of optimum bands and role of middle IR photogrammetry and Remote Sensing, *Photogrammetry and Remote Sensing*, Vol. 50(5), 25–30, 1995.

597. Sharman M J, The agriculture project of the joint research centre: Operational use of remote sensing for agricultural statistics, *Proceedings of International Symposium on Operationalisation of Remote Sensing*, ITC Enschede, The Netherlands, 46–57, 1993.

598. Shen S S, Summary of types of data fusion methods utilized in workshop papers, Multi-source Data Integration in Remote Sensing, *Proceedings of Workshop,Maryland, USA, NASA Conference Publication 3099* (Greenbelt, MD:NASA), 145–149, 1990.

599. Shippert P, Why use hyperspectral imagery? *Photogrammetric Engineering and Remote Sensing*, 377–380, 2004.

600. Shuanggen J, Cardellach E and Xie F, *GNSS Remote Sensing: Theory, Methods and Applications*, Springer, 2014.

601. Singh P and Dash S S, Plant Discoveries 2013– New Genera, Species and New Records, Botanical Survey of India, Kolkata, 2014.

602. Singh R P, Dadhwal V K, Singh K P and Navalgund R R, Study on sensor's spatial, radiometric and temporal resolution requirements for crop monitoring, *Proceedings of Symposium on Advances in Electronics (ELECTRO-2001)*, BHU Varanasi, India, 213–218, 2001.

603. Singh R P, Sridhar V N, Dadhwal V K, Jaishankar R, Neelkanthan M, Srivastava A K, Bairagi G D, Sharma N K, Raza S A, Sharma R, Yadav M, Joshi F K and Purohit N L, Village level crop inventory using remote sensing and field survey data, *Journal of Indian Soc. of Remote Sensing*, Vol. 31(1), 93–98, 2005.

604. Singh R, Goyal R C, Saha S K and Chhikara R S, Use of satellite spectral data in crop yield estimation surveys, *International Journal of Remote Sensing*, Vol. 14, 2583–2592, 1992.

605. Singh R, Semwal D P, Rai A and Chhikara R S, Small area estimation of crop yield using remote sensing satellite data, *International Journal of Remote Sensing*, Vol. 23(1), 49–56, 2002.

606. Slater P N, Biggar S F, Thome K J, Gellman D I and Spyak P R, Vicarious radiometric calibrations of EOS sensors, *J. Atmospheric and Oceanic Technology*, Vol. 13, 349–359, 1996.

607. Slater P N, Multiband cameras, *Photogrammetric Engineering*, Vol. 38, 543–555, 1972.

608. Slater P N, *Remote Sensing: Optics and Optical systems*, Addison-Wesley Publishing Company, 1980.

609. Small C, Multitemporal analysis of urban reflectance, *Remote Sensing of Environment*, Vol. 81, 427–442, 2002.

610. Smit M W and Davis W A, A new algorithm for edge detection, *Computer Graphics and Image Processing*, Vol. 4, 55–62, 1975.

611. Smith E and Weintraub S, The constants in the equation for atmospheric refractive index at radio frequencies, *Proceedings of the IRE*, Vol. 41, 1035–1037, 1953.

612. Smith M O, Johnson P E and Adams J B, Quantitative determination of mineral types and abundances from reflectance spectra using principal components analysis, *Journal of Geophysical Research*, Vol. 90, C797-804, 1985.

613. Smith W L, Howell H B and Woolf H M, The use of interferometric radiance measurements for sounding the atmosphere, *Journal of the Atmospheric Sciences*, Vol. 36, 566–676, 1979.

614. Smith W, *Modern Optical Engineering: The Design of Optical Systems*, McGraw-Hill, New York, 1966.

615. Sobrino J A, Li Z L, Stoll M P and Becker F, Multi-channel and multi-angle algorithms for estimating sea and land surface temperature with ATSR data, *International Journal of Remote Sensing*, Vol. 17, 2089–2114, 1996.

616. Sobrino J, Coll C and Caselles V, Atmospheric correction for land surface temperature using NOAA-11 AVHRR channels 4 and 5, *Remote sensing of environment*, Vol. 38(1), 19–34, 1991.

617. Sokolovskiy S, Rocken C and Lowry A R, Use of GPS for estimation of bending angles of radio waves at low elevations, *Radio Science*, Vol. 36(3), 473–482, 2001.

618. Solanki H U, Dwivedi R M, Nayak S R, Somvanshi V S, Gulati D K and Pattnayak S K, Fishery forecast using OCM chlorophyll concentration and AVHRR SST: validation results off Gujarat coast, India, *International Journal of Remote Sensing*, Vol. 24(18), 3691–3699, 2003.

619. Solimene R, Cuccaro A, Dell'Aversano A, Catapano I and Soldovieri F, Ground Clutter Removal in GPR Surveys, IEEE *Journal of Selected Topics in Applied Earth Observations and Remote Sensing*, Vol. 7(3), 792–798, 2014.

620. Sridhar V N, Dadhwal V K, Chaudhari K N, Sharma R, Bairagi C D and Sharma A K, Wheat production forecasting for a predominantly unirrigated region in Madhya Pradesh (India), *International Journal of Remote Sensing*, Vol. 15(6), 1307–1316, 1994.

621. Srinivasulu J and Kulkarni A V, A Satellite based Spectral Reflectance Model for Snow and Glacier Studies in the Himalayan terrain, *Proc. of the Indian Acad. Sci. (Earth and Planet. Sci.)* Vol. 113(1), 117–128, 2004.

622. Stanley H R, The Geos-3 Project, *Journal of Geophysical Research*, Vol. 84(B8), 3779–3783, 1979.

623. Stathaki T, *Image fusion: algorithms and applications*, 2011.

624. Steila D, *The Geography of Soils*, Prentice-Hall, Englewood Cliffs, New Jersey, 1976.

625. Stephen H S, *Mapping the Next Millennium; the Discovery of New Geographies*, Random House, NY, 1992.

626. Stiles W H and Ulaby F T, The active and passive microwave response to snow parameters, Part I: Wetness, *Journal of Geophysical Research*, Vol. 85, 1037–1044, 1980.

627. Stiles W H, Ulaby F T, Fung A K and Aslam A, Radar spectral observations of snow, *IEEE International Geosciences and Remote Sensing Symposium (IGARS'81) Digest*, Washington DC, 654–668, 1981.

628. Stoner E R and Baumgardner M F, Characteristic variations in reflectance of surface soils, *Soil Science Society of America Journal*, Vol. 45, 1161–1165, 1981.

629. Story M and Congalton R G, Accuracy assessment: A User's perspective, *Photogrammetric Engineering and Remote Sensing*, Vol. 52(3), 397–399, 1986.

630. Strahler A H, The use of prior probabilities in maximum likelihood classification of remotely sensed data, *Remote Sensing of Environment*, Vol. 10, 135–163, 1980.

631. Sudarsan D, John M E and Somvanshi V S, Marine fishery resources potential in the Indian Exclusive Economic Zone: An update, *Bulletin Fishery Survey of India*, Vol. 20, 1990.

632. Sugumaran R, Pavaluri M and Zerr D, The use of high-resolution imagery for identification of urban climax forest species using traditional and rule-based classification approach, *IEEE Transactions on Geoscience and Remote Sensing*, Vol. 41(9), 2003.

633. Susskind J, Rosenfield J and Reuter D, An accurate radiative transfer model for use in the direct physical inversion of HIRS-2 and MSU temperature sounding data, *Journal of Geophysical Research*, Vol. 88, 8550–8568, 1983.

634. Swain P H and Davis S M, *Remote Sensing: The Quantitative Approach*, McGraw-Hill, 1978.

635. Swamy L N, Srirangapattana Fort through the ages origin, development and the fall of the Fort, in *Tipu Sultan theTtiger of Mysore*, Gopal R (Ed.), Mysore: Directorate of Archaeology and Museums, 2010.

636. Swift C T, LeVine D M and Ruf C S, Aperture synthesis concepts in microwave remote sensing of the earth, *IEEE Transactions on Microwave Theory Tech.*, Vol. 39, 1931–1935, 1991.

637. Takashima T and Masuda K, Emissivities of quartz and Sahara dust powders in the infrared region (7–17 micrometres), *Remote Sensing of Environment*, Vol. 23, 51–63, 1987.

638. Tatani K, Enomoto Y, Yamamoto A, Goto T, Abe H and Hirayama T, High-Sensitivity 2.5 μm Pixel CMOS Image Sensor Realized Using Cu Interconnect Layers, *SPIE-IS&T/*, Vol. 6068, 2006.

639. Taylor F W, Rodgers C D, Whitney J G, Werrett S T, Barnett J J, Peskett G D, Venters P, Ballard J, Palmer C W P, Knight R J, Morris P, Nightingale T and Dudhia A, Remote sensing of atmospheric structure and composition by pressure modulator radiometry from Space: The ISAMS experiment on UARS, *Journal of Geophysical Research*, Vol. 98(D6), 10799–10814, 1993.

640. Thenkabail P S, Lyon G J and Huete A, Advances in hyperspectral remote sensing of vegetation and agricultural crops, in *Hyperspectral remote sensing of vegetation*, Thenkabail P S, Lyon G J,and Huete A (Eds), CRC Press, Taylor and Francis Group, 2011.

641. Thomas C and Wald L, Assessment of the quality of fused products, Oluic., *24th EARSeL, Symposium* on New Strategies for European Remote Sensing, Dubrovnik, Croatia, 2004, Millpress, 317–325, 2005. https://hal.archives-ouvertes.fr/file/index/docid/395061/filename/2004_earsel_thomas.pdf

642. Thomas J R, Contributing author, Soil, water and plant relations: in *Remote Sensing National Academy of Sciences*, Washington DC, 264–267, 1970.

643. Thurman H V, *Introductory Oceanography*, Charles E Merrill Publishing Co., A Bell and Howell Co., Columbus, Ohio, 1975.

644. Toet A, Image fusion by a ratio of low-pass pyramid, *Pattern Recognition Letters*, 245–253, 1989.

645. Tompkins S, Mustard J F, Pieters C M and Forsyth D W, Optimization of endmembers for spectral mixture analysis, *Remote Sensing of Environment*, Vol. 59, 472–489, 1997.

646. Tsagaris V and Anastassopoulos V, Multispectral image fusion for improved RGB representation based on perceptual attributes, *International Journal of Remote Sensing*, Vol. 26(15), 3241–3254, 2005.

647. Tu T M, Su S C, Shyu H C and Huang P S, A new look at IHS-like image fusion methods, *Information Fusion*, Vol. 2(3), 177–186, 2001.

648. Tucker C J and Miller L D, *Soil spectra contributions to grass canopy spectral reflectance,* *Photogrammetric Engineering & Remote Sensing,* Vol. 43(6), 721–726, 1977.

649. Tucker C J, Holden B N, Elgin G H, McMurtrey J E, III Remote sensing of total dry matter accumulation in winter wheat, *Remote Sensing of Environment.,* Vol. 11, 267–277, 1980.

650. Turner E R, Malila W A, Nalepka R F and Thomson E J, Influence of the atmosphere on remotely sensed data, *Proceedings of Society of Photo-Optical Instrumentation Engineers: Scanners and Imagery Systems for Earth Observation,* Vol. 51, 101, 1974.

651. Ulaby F T and Stiles W H, The active and passive microwave response to snow parameters, Part II: Water equivalent of dry snow, *Journal of Geophysical Research,* Vol. 85, 1045–1049, 1980.

652. Ulaby F T, Batlivala P P and Dobson M C, Microwave backscatter dependence on surface roughness, soil moisture and soil texture, Part I: Bare soil, *IEEE Transactions on. Geoscience Electronics,* Vol. GE-16, 286–295, 1978.

653. Ulaby F T, More R K and Fung A K, From theory to applications, Vol. III, *Remote Sensing - A series of Advanced Level Textbooks and Reference Works,* Artech House, Inc., Norwood, MA, 1986.

654. Ulaby F T, More R K and Fung A K, Microwave remote sensing fundamentals and radiometry, Vol. I, *Remote Sensing - A series of Advanced Level Textbooks and Reference Works,* Artech House, Inc., Norwood, MA, 1981.

655. Ulaby F T, More R K and Fung A K, *Microwave Remote Sensing: Active and Passive,* Vol. I, Addison-Wesley Pub. Co. Inc., Masachusetts, USA, 1981.

656. Ulaby F T, More R K and Fung A K, Radar remote sensing and surface scattering and emission theory, Vol. II, *Remote Sensing - A series of Advanced Level Textbooks and Reference Works,* Artech House, Inc., Norwood, MA, 1982.

657. UN A/AC 105/260,Committee on the peaceful uses of outer Space-Report on effective resolution element and related concepts, 2005. http://www.fas.org/irp/imint/docs/resunga.htm (last accessed 8 February 2014)

658. Valencia E, Camps A, Rodriguez-Alvarez N, Ramos-Perez I, Bosch-Lluis X and Park H, Improving the accuracy of sea surface salinity retrieval using GNSS-R data to correct the sea state effect, *Radio Sci.,* Vol. 46, 2011. doi:10.1029/2011RS004688 http://onlinelibrary.wiley.com/doi/10.1029/2011RS004688/epdf

659. Van Genderen J L and Lock B F, Testing land-use map accuracy, *Photogrammetric Engineering and Remote Sensing,* Vol. 43, 1135–1137, 1977.

660. Vanderbilt V C, Grant L and Daughtry G S T, Polarisation of light scattered by vegetation, *Proceedings of IEEE,* Vol. 73(6), 1012–1024, 1985.

661. Vrabel J, Multispectral imagery band sharpening study, *Photogrammetric Engineering and Remote Sensing,* Vol. 62(9), 1075–1083, 1996.

662. Wakabayashi H, Osawa Y and Hamazaki T, A SAR system on ALOS, *International Photogrammetry and Remote Sensing,* Vol. 31, Part B1, 193–196, 1996.

663. Wald L, Data fusion - Definitions and architectures - Fusion of images of different spatial resolutions, École de Mines de Paris, 2002.

664. Walton C C, Pichel W G and Sapper J F, The development and operational application of non-linear algorithms for the measurement of sea surface temperatures with the NOAA polar-orbiting environmental satellites, *Journal of Geophysical Research,* Vol. 103(C12), 27999–28012, 1998.

665. Wang D C C, Vagnucci A H and Li C C, Digital image enhancement: A survey, *Computer Vision, Graphics, and Image Processing*, Vol. 24, 363–381, 1983.

666. Wang F, Improving remote sensing image analysis through fuzzy information representation, *Photographic Engineering and Remote Sensing*, Vol. 56(8), 1163–1169, 1992.

667. Wang J R and Schmugge T J, An empirical model for the complex dielectric permittivity of soils as a function of water content, *IEEE Transactions on Geosciences and Remote Sensing*, Vol. GE 18, 288–295, 1980.

668. Wang J R, The effect of vegetation on soil moisture sensing observed from orbiting microwave radiometres, *Remote Sensing of Environment*, Vol. 11, 141–151, 1985.

669. Wang Z and Bovic A C, A universal image quality index, *IEEE Signal Processing Letters*, Vol. 9, 81–84, 2002.

670. Wang Z, Ziou D, Armenakis C, Li D and Li Q, A Comparative Analysis of Image Fusion Methods, *IEEE Transactions of Geoscience and Remote Sensing*, Vol. 43(6), 1391–1402, 2005.

671. Wark D Q, HillaryD T, Anderson S P and Fischer J C, Nimbus satellite infrared spectrometer experiments, *IEEE Transactions on Geosciences Electron*, Vol. GE-8, 264, 1970.

672. Warner T A and Shank M, An evaluation of the potential for fuzzy classification of multi-spectral data using artificial neural networks, *Photogrammetric Engineering & Remote Sensing*, Vol. 63, 11, 1997.

673. Warren S G and Wiscombe W J, A model for the spectral albedo of snow, II. Snow containing atmospheric aerosols, *Journal of Atmospheric Sciences*, Vol. 37, 2734–2745, 1980.

674. Warren S G, Optical properties of snow, *Review of Geophysics & Space Physics*, Vol. 20, 67–89, 1982.

675. Watson K, Geologic applications of thermal infrared images, *Proceedings of the IEEE*, Vol. 63, 128–137, 1975.

676. Way J and Smith E A, The evolution of synthetic aperture radar systems and their progression to the EOS SAR, *IEEE transactions on geoscience and remote sensing*, Vol. 29(6), 962–985, 1991.

677. Weimer P K, Sadasiv G, Meyer J E Jr, Meray-HorvathL and Pike W S, A Self-scanned Solid-state Image Sensor, *Proceedings of the IEEE*, Vol. 55(9), 1599–1602, 1967.

678. Welch R and Marko W, Cartographic potential of a spacecraft line – array camera system: Stereosat, *Photogrammetric Engineering and Remote Sensing*, Vol. 8, 1173–1185, 1981.

679. Werner C L, Techniques and application of SAR interferometry for ERS-1: Topographic mapping change detection and slope measurement, *Proceedings of First ERS-1 Symposium – Space at the Service of Our Environment*, Cannes, France, 1992.

680. Wiegand C L and Richardson A J, Comparison among a new soil index and other two and four vegetation indices, *Proceedings of the 48th Annual meeting, American Society of Photogrammetry*, 211–227, 1982.

681. Wilheit T T, Jr, A review of applications of microwave radiometry to oceanography, *Boundary Layer Meteorology*, Vol. 13, 277–293, 1978.

682. Wilheit T, Chang A T C and Milman A S, Atmospheric corrections to passive microwave observations of the ocean, *Boundary-layer meteorology*, Vol. 18(1), 65–77, 1980. www.mdpi.com/2072-4292/7/2/2208/remotesensing-07-02208.pdf

683. Wiscombe W J and Warren S G, A model for the spectral albedo of snow, I. Pure snow, *Journal of Atmospheric Sciences*, Vol. 37, 2712–2733, 1980.

684. Woodham R J and Lee T R, Photometric method for radiometric correction of multi-spectral scanner data, *Canadian Journal of Remote Sensing*, Vol. IX, 132–161, 1985.

685. Woolley J T, Reflectance and transmittance of light by leaves, *Plant Physiology*, Vol. 47, 656–662, 1971.

686. Wu B, Meng J, Li Q, Yan N, Du X and Zhang M, Remote sensing-based global crop monitoring: experiences with China's CropWatch system, *International Journal of Digital Earth*, Vol. 7(2), 113–137, 2014.

687. Wu C, Graf J, Freilich M, Long D, Spencer M, Tsai W, Lisman D and Winn C, The sea winds scatterometer instrument. *International Geoscience and Remote Sensing Symposium*, Vol. 3, Pasadena, CA, Stein T I, (Ed.), IEEE, Pisacataway, NJ, 1511–1515, 1994.

688. Wu D, Qu J J and XianjunHao, Agricultural drought monitoring usingMODIS-based drought indices over the USA Corn Belt, *International Journal of Remote Sensing*, Vol. 36(21), 5403–5425, 2015.

689. Xingwei S and Baide X, Quick reporting state of fishery and sea on the east China sea and the Yellow Sea with NOAA, *Proceeding Symposium, IGARSS'88*, Edinburg, Scotland, 1405–1408, 1988.

690. Yakhdani M F and Azizi A, *Quality assessment of image fusion techniques for multisensor high resolution satellite images (case study: IRS-P5 and IRS-P6 satellite images)*, 205–209, 2010.

691. Yamanaka I, *The fisheries forecasting system in Japan for coastal pelagic fish* (No. 301), Food and Agriculture Organization, 1988.

692. Yelf J R, Application of Ground Penetrating Radar to Civil and Geotechnical Engineering, *Electromagnetic Phenomena*, Vol. 7(1), 18, 2007.

693. Yesou H, Besnus Y and Rolet J, Extraction of spectral information from Landsat TM data and merger with SPOT panchromatic imagery - a contribution to the study of geological structures, *ISPRS Journal of Photogrammetry and Remote Sensing*, Vol. 48, 23–36, 1993.

694. Yin Q and Guo P, Multispectral remote sensing image classification with multiple features, *Proceedings of the Sixth International Conference on Machine Learning and Cybernetics*, Hong Kong, 2007.

695. Yocky D A, Multi-resolution wavelet decomposition image merger of Landsat Thematic Mapper and SPOT panchromatic data, *Photogrammetric Engineering and Remote Sensing*, Vol. 62(9), 1067–1074, 1996.

696. Yoshida T and Omatu S, Neural network approach to landcover mapping, *IEEE Transactions on the Geosciences and Remote Sensing*, Vol. 32, 1103–1109, 1994.

697. Young P J, Scanning System Tradeoffs for Remote Optical Sensing from Geosynchronous Orbit, *Opt. Eng.*, Vol. 14(4), 289–294, 1975.

698. Zavorotny V, Masters D, Gasiewski A, Bartram B, Katzberg S, Axelrad P and Zamora R, Seasonal Polarimetric Measurements of Soil Moisture Using Tower-Based GPS Bistatic Radar, 2003. http://www.esrl.noaa.gov/psd/psd3/multi/remote/pdf/GPS-BAO_Tower_Experiment.pdf

699. Zebker H A and Goldstein RM, Topographic mapping from interferometric synthetic aperture radar observations, *Journal of Geophysical Research*, Vol. 91, 4993–4999, 1986.

700. Zebker H A and Vellesenor J, Deceleration in Interferometric radar echoes, *IEEE Transactions on Geoscience and Remote Sensing*, Vol. 30, 950–959, 1992.

701. Zebker H A, Madsen S N, Martin J, Wheeler K B and Miller T, The TOPSAR Interferometric radar topographic mapping instrument, *IEEE Transactions on Geoscience and Remote Sensing*, Vol. 30, 933–940, 1992.

702. Zhang J and Foody G M, Fuzzy classification of suburban land cover from remotely sensed imagery, *International Journal of Remote Sensing*, 1998, Vol. 19(14), 2721, 1998.

703. Zhang L, Shen H, Gong W and Zhang H, Adjustable model-based fusion method for multispectral and panchromatic images, *IEEE Trans. Syst. Man Cybern. Part B Cybern.*, Vol. 42(6), 1693–1704, 2012.

704. Zhang Y, Understanding image fusion. *Photogrammetric engineering and remote sensing*, Vol. 70(6), 657–661, 2004. http://scenesharp.com/wp-content/uploads/2016/11/Pub_2_Highlight_Article.pdf

705. Zhu X X and Bamler R, Application to Pan-Sharpening, *IEEE Trans. Geosci. Remote Sens.*, Vol. 51, 2827–2836, 2013.

706. Zieger A R, Hancock D W, Hayne G S and Purdy C L, NASA radar altimeter for the TOPEX/Poseidon project, *Proceedings of IEEE*, Vol. 79, 816–818, 1991.

707. Zitová B and Flusser J, Image registration methods: a survey, *Image and Vision Computing*, Vol. 21 (11), 977–1000, 2003.

708. Zoran L F, Quality Evaluation of Multiresolution Remote Sensing Image Fusion, *UPB Sci. Bull.*, Ser. C, Vol. 71, 38–52, 2009. http://www.scientificbulletin.pub.ro/rev_docs_arhiva/full6691.pdf

Index

A

aberrations, 149
absolute accuracy, 142
absorption, 491
accuracy assessment, 399
across-track stereoscopy, 221
active pixel sensor (APS), 194
adjacency effect, 224, 497
aerosol scattering, 501, 502
aerosols, 491
agriculture, 396
Airy pattern, 131
albedo, 55
altimeter, 245
Angstrom exponent, 503
angular motion compensation, 155
antenna gain, 229
antenna, 227
aperture stop, 147
apochromat, 149
apogee, 285
apparent optical property, 88
apparent reflectance, 535
applications, 20, 141, 227, 305, 343, 362, 395, 439, 449, 549
archaeology, 447
argument of perigee, 288
artificial intelligence, 378, 546
artificial neural network, 381
ascending node, 288
astigmatism, 149
astronautical velocity, 286
asynchronous mode, 210, 212
atmospheric refraction, 546

atmospheric sounding, 506
atmospheric windows, 2, 45
attenuation length, 39
attenuation, 39, 495
attribute data, 457
AWiFS, 407, 443
azimuth resolution, 253

B

backscatter LIDAR, 514
backscattering coefficient, 124
base map, 363
beam attenuation coefficient, 88
beam width, 230
bending angle, 546
Bhuvan, 469
Bidirectional Reflectance Distribution
    Function (BRDF), 56, 144
bistatic radar, 243
blackbody, 41
bolometers, 177
boundary pixels , 137, 385
Brewster's angle, 36
brightness temperature, 504
Brovey transform, 349

C

Cassegrain telescope, 148, 172, 230
catadioptic, 171
category error, 392
central perspective, 162
Charge Coupled Device (CCD), 191
chlorophyll, 94

chromatic aberrations, 149
circle of least confusion, 149
classification accuracy, 389
classification stage, 374
classification, 10
coarse acquisition code, 303
Coastal Regulation Zone, 432
coastal zone management, 430
coastal zone, 430
coherence length, 500
coherence time T_C, 500
coherent radiation, 32
colour coding, 337
coma, 150
commission error, 391
compactness, 388
conformality, 522
confusion matrix, 391, 436
conic projection, 527
contrast enhancement, 334
contrast modulation, 132
contrast ratio, 132
contrast transfer function, 132
control points, 369
coral reefs, 431
Correlated Double Sampling (CDS), 192
correlation matrix, 366
crop production, 396
cubic convolution interpolation, 320
curse of dimensionality, 533
curvature of the field, 150
cylindrical projection, 525

D

data analysis, 356
data formats, 307
data model, 458
data products, 322
data registration, 369
decibel, 39, 111, 229, 519
decision tree classifier, 380
depression angle, 251
descending node, 288

desertification, 441
Dicke radiometer, 238
dielectric constant, 31
differential absorption LIDAR (DIAL), 514
differential GPS, 305
diffraction, 37, 130
diffuse attenuation coefficient, 88
diffuse reflection, 53
digital classification, 365
Digital Elevation Model (DEM), 223
digital products, 329
digital terrain model, 223
dimensionality, 533
dispersion, 34, 171
distortion, 150, 225, 263, 307, 522
Doppler effect, 37, 256
Doppler shift, 547
downwelling diffused attenuation
    coefficient, 88
drought assessment, 404
dry temperature, 548
dwell time, 168

E

earth system science, 453
eccentricity, 289
effective instantaneous field of view, 136
electromagnetic radiation, 1, 27, 129, 227,
    491, 548
electromagnetic spectrum, 2, 28, 158, 309
emissivity, 42
end-members, 539
enhanced thematic mapper, 185
entrance pupil, 148
equatorial orbit, 290
equidistance, 523
equivalence, 523
escape velocity, 287
exit pupil, 148
expert systems, 377
extinction coefficient, 39, 495
extinction cross section, 492
extinction, 39, 492

F

False Colour Composite (FCC), 10, 357
false colour film, 159
far range, 251
FASAL, 400
feature identification, 369
feature matching, 370
feature space, 5
field of view, 59, 135, 189, 200, 496
figure of merit, 136
fisheries, 437
fixed pattern noise (FPN), 194
fluorescence, 65, 91
f-number, 148
focal length, 147, 200, 318
focal plane, 147
focal point, 147
foreshortening, 265
forest canopy density, 407
forestry application, 406
forestry, 406, 464
formation-flying, 22
forward motion compensation, 155
frequency domain, 276
fuzzy classification, 384

G

geocoded products, 326
geoid, 124
geometric errors, 225, 315
geopotential height, 547
georeferencing, 317
geostationary orbit, 292
geosynchronous orbit, 291
GeoTIFF, 333
GIS, 456
glacier, 416
global positioning system (GPS), 547
GNSS meteorology, 545
GNSS radio occultation, 545
GNSS reflectometry, 545
GNSS, 301, 544
GPS, 301

grey body, 43
ground control points, 318
ground penetrating radar, 275
ground range resolution, 253
ground range, 251
ground sample distance, 136
ground track, 290
Ground Truth (GT), 361, 399
ground water, 415
growth profile, 76

H

hemispherical emissivity, 43
high pass filter, 339
high tide line, 435
histogram, 5, 314, 334
horn antenna, 230, 231
Hughes phenomenon, 533
humidity profile, 548
hybrid scanners, 218
hydrometeor, 491
hyper-spectral imager, 214

I

IHS based fusion, 345
IHS colour model, 347
image analysis, 356, 388, 533
image fusion, 343
image motion compensation, 155
image plane scanning, 169
image quality, 223
image transforms, 341
imaging radiometer, 60
IMGEOS, 311
impact parameter, 547
incidence angle, 251
inherent optical properties, 88
instantaneous field of view, 135
instantaneous geometric field of view, 135
interferometric SAR, 260
irradiance, 38, 50, 87, 175
IRS-LISS camera, 198

K

Kepler's Law, 285
Keplerian elements, 287

L

Lambert conformal conic, 527
Lambert's cosine law, 54
Lambertian reflector, 53
land cover classification, 360
land cover/land use mapping, 411
land use, 360
lay over, 264
leaf area index, 71
LEO, 545
LIDAR, 448, 514
limb sounding, 510
line pair, 132, 152, 201
linear stretch, 336
LISS sensor, 198
look angle, 251
look up table, 325
low pass filter, 338
low tide line, 435

M

mangroves, 431
map projection, 326
map scale, 135
mapping function, 369
marine fisheries, 437
Maximum Likelihood Classifier (MXL), 376, 551
mean per pixel deviation, 354
membership function, 385
MEOSS, 222
METEOSAT, 144, 186, 299
microwave emission, 106
microwave, 8, 30, 103, 227, 550
Mie scattering, 88
minimum distance to mean classifier, 374
Modulation Transfer Function (MTF), 132, 151
molecular absorption, 492

mudflats, 431
multichannel SST, 504
Multi-spectral Scanners (MSS), 166
multi-variate decision tree, 381

N

near range, 251
Noise Equivalent Power (NEP), 176
normalised difference snow index, 419
normalised difference vegetation index, 75

O

object based classification, 385
object plane scanning, 169
ocean colour, 91
ocean, 86
omission error, 391
on-orbit performance, 225
Operational Land Imager (OLI), 205
optical axis, 146
optical depth, 496
optical thickness, 496
Optical Transfer Function (OTF), 151
optimum index factor, 367
opto-mechanical scanner, 172
orbit, 285
orbital elements, 287
orbital plane, 290
orthophoto, 164
orthorectification, 164

P

paintbrush mode, 214
PAN sharpening, 354
panchromatic camera, 19, 200
panchromatic film, 158, 176
paraboloid antenna, 230
parallax, 220
parallelopiped classifier, 374
passive sensor, 6, 129, 227
path radiance, 3, 93, 496
pattern, 358

penetration depth, 38, 90, 114
per-field classification, 388
perigee, 285
permeability, 31
permittivity, 31
phase function, 494
phased arrays, 232
photoconductive detectors, 180
photodiode, 176, 205
photoemissive detectors, 178
photogrammetry, 223
photometer, 60
photometry, 47
photon, 40, 63, 175
photoproduct, 327
photovoltaic detectors, 181
phytoplankton, 86
picture element, 166
pixel, 166
Planck's equation, 42, 104, 234
Planck's law, 40, 104, 234
Point Spread Function (PSF), 151
polar orbit, 290
polarisation, 30, 77
polyconic projection, 527
potential fishing zones, 438
precise code, 303
precision farming, 403
pre-processing, 312
principal axis, 147
principal component based fusion, 350
principal component transforms, 342
principal plane, 147, 229
principal point, 147
pulsed radar, 276
pushbroom cameras, 189, 196
pushbroom scanning, 154
pyroelectric detectors, 177

Q

quantum detectors, 178

R

radar cross section, 244, 276
radar scattering coefficient, 244
radar, 8, 111, 243, 550
radiance, 8, 50, 65, 92, 129, 204, 421,
    496
radians, 47
radiant energy, 40
radiant flux, 50, 208
radiant intensity, 49
radiation pattern, 229, 270
radiometer, 60
radiometric errors, 143, 224, 312
radiometric quality, 142
radiometric resolution, 142
radiometrically accurate IFOV, 136
radiometry, 47
Raman backscatter LIDAR, 515
Ramsar Convention, 425
range distortion, 263
range resolution, 253, 281
raster model, 458
Rayleigh criterion, 103
Rayleigh scattering, 87
RCS, 244
readout integrated circuit (ROIC), 194
real aperture radar, 249
referencing scheme, 321
reflectance factor, 55
reflectance, 35
refraction, 34, 125
refractive index, 34
relief displacement, 162, 264
resampling, 319, 372
resolution
    radiometric, 7
    spatial, 7
    spectral, 7
    temporal, 7
resolving power, 131
RESOURCESAT, 202
responsivity, 175

restrahlen lines, 37
retrograde orbits, 288
return beam vidicon, 164
RISAT, 267

S

SAR, 3, 245
satellite systems, 297
scale, 135, 147, 361, 411, 507
scan efficiency, 168
scatter plot, 5
scattering coefficient , 39, 111, 244, 492
scattering length, 39
scattering, 491, 493
scatterometer, 270
scene noise, 138
Secchi disk, 90
semiconductor detectors, 179
sensor, 1, 92, 146, 202, 243, 407, 516
side lobe, 235
side looking radar, 249
siderial day, 291
signature, 3, 64
significant wave height, 126
single-scattering albedo, 39
size parameters, 493
slant range resolution, 253
slant range, 251
SLAR, 3, 245
slotted antenna, 231
smoothness, 388
Snell's law, 35, 53
snow cover, 416
snow, 94
soft copy photogrammetry (SCP), 223
soil moisture, 79, 106, 118, 545
soil taxonomy, 80
soil, 77
solar day, 291
solid angle, 47
space oblique mercator projection, 528
spacecraft, 187, 218, 265
spaghetti model, 461
spatial data, 457

spatial filtering, 338
spatial resolution, 130, 251
spatial transformation, 371
specific detectivity, 177
specification matrix, 145
speckle, 262
spectral angle mapper, 535
spectral feature fitting, 536
spectral resolution, 138
spectral response, 175
spectral signature, 64, 342, 428
spectral unmixing, 539
spectrometer, 60
spectroradiometer, 60
specular reflection, 53
spherical aberration, 149
Stefan–Boltzman constant, 42
step and stare mode, 210, 212
steradian, 48
stereo pairs, 219, 358
stereo products, 326
striping, 314
stripmap imaging, 267
sub-satellite point, 168, 219, 287
sunsynchronous orbit, 292
supervised classification, 372
sustainable development, 12
swath, 145, 185, 251
synchronous mode, 212
synthetic aperture radiometer, 242
synthetic aperture, 255

T

tangent height, 547
telemetry, 308
temporal resolution, 144
temporal signature, 75, 115
texture, 357
thematic map, 366
thematic mapper, 184
thermal capacity, 101
thermal conductivity, 101
thermal detector, 177
thermal infrared, 100

thermal radiation, 40
thermocouple, 177
time constant, 177
Time Delay and Integration (TDI), 210
time domain GPR, 276
tone, 357
topological models, 461
total internal reflection, 34
total power radiometer, 237
training stage, 373
transmittance, 35
transport shift register, 191
tropospheric delay, 549
true anomaly, 289
turbulence, 500
turn around time, 400

U

UAV, 285
Ultra-Wave Band (UWB) GPR, 277
uni-variate decision tree, 381
unsupervised classification, 372
upwelling, 87
urban sprawl, 412

V

vector model, 460
vegetation condition, 405
vegetation indices, 74

vegetation, 65
VHRR, 144, 170, 438
vicarious calibration, 226
visual interpretation, 357, 363
visual range, 496
volume scattering, 112, 127

W

wastelands, 412
water resources, 414
wave front, 32
waveguide, 230
webGIS, 468
wedge imaging spectrometer, 217
weighting function, 507
wetland management, 424
wetland, 360, 424
whiskbroom scanning, 154
wide field sensor, 202
Wien's displacement law, 42
wind speed, 93, 126, 271, 549

Y

yield forecasting, 400

Z

zenith hydrostatic delay, 549
zenith wet delay, 549